D1468445

SYNTHETIC PEPTIDES

SYNTHETIC PEPTIDES

VOLUME I

George R. Pettit

Professor of Chemistry
Arizona State University
Tempe, Arizona

 VAN NOSTRAND REINHOLD COMPANY

New York / Cincinnati / Toronto / London / Melbourne

Van Nostrand Reinhold Company Regional Offices:
New York   Cincinnati   Chicago   Millbrae   Dallas

Van Nostrand Reinhold Company Foreign Offices:
London   Toronto   Melbourne

Copyright © 1970 by Litton Educational Publishing, Inc.

Library of Congress Catalog Card Number: 74-132182

Manufactured in the United States of America

Published by Van Nostrand Reinhold Company
450 West 33rd Street, New York, N.Y. 10001

Published simultaneously in Canada by
Van Nostrand Reinhold Ltd.

15 14 13 12 11 10 9 8 7 6 5 4 3 2 1

To Jean

Preface

Living organisms are critically dependent upon peptides and proteins for maintaining chemical regulation and structural integrity. These amino acid derivatives in conjunction with the nucleic acids, carbohydrates and, for example, steroids, represent very important units of life. Thoughtful members of mankind have continued to marvel at the result. Also, the prospect of being able to synthesize a living organism has fired the imaginations of layman and chemist alike. Such an objective, combined with the immediate need of subduing many fatal or otherwise incapacitating medical problems, requires further sophistication in synthetic approaches to proteins. Fortunately, from a modest beginning approximately 150 years ago, the structural and synthetic organic chemistry of peptides has been increasing at a rapid and reassuring rate.

Major events in the development of peptide chemistry begin perhaps with the isolation of glycine from a gelatin hydrolysate in 1820. Some 18 years passed before the presence of nitrogen was established in this gelatin "sugar." Another 30 years transpired before it became possible to begin interpreting the structures of amino acids. Nearly 90 years elapsed before E. Fisher, with characteristic masterful insight, developed the acid chloride procedure for peptide bond formation. At the time, Fisher's synthesis of a 19-unit peptide was a remarkable achievement and served to markedly stimulate interest in peptide chemistry. Introduction of Curtius' azide technique allowed further progress. One of the next milestones, achieved by M. Bergmann and L. Zervas in the 1930's, involved the application of the carbobenzoxy group for protection. During the 1950's, recognition of and rapid adoption of the mixed anhydride, carbodiimide and active ester techniques by, for example, R. A. Boissonnas,

T. H. Wieland, G. W. Anderson, J. C. Sheehan, R. Schwyzer, and M. Bodanszky greatly accelerated progress. Meanwhile, synthetic approaches to natural peptides were under study and V. du Vigneaud's synthesis of oxytocin represented the first major breakthrough. The intervening period has witnessed a rapid succession of peptide hormones, such as ACTH (by Schwyzer and colleagues), yield to the newer synthetic methods. The comprehensive studies of K. Hofmann and C. H. Li in this area are also noteworthy. Advances in peptide chemistry during the 1960's has been explosive. Further refinement of peptide bond forming procedures, new reagents (such as R. B. Woodward's reagent K), methods (Merrifield's solid phase approach), and synthetic approaches to insulin have markedly contributed. The foregoing events hold promise of yet greater strides in the next few years and spectacular developments in the next decade or two.

Prior to 1961, no extensive review of peptide synthesis and methods was available. When our group began a study directed at steroidal peptide synthesis, the need for such a secondary literature source became all too apparent. At about that time (1959), a decision was made to attempt preparation of such a review. The original plan was to prepare a discussion of peptide synthetic methods accompanied by a tabular survey of amino acid derivatives and peptides. Fortunately, the excellent three volume coverage of amino acid chemistry by Greenstein and Wintz (published in 1961) nicely completed the task to about 1959. Three years later, publication of the Schröder and Lübke treatment of peptide synthetic methods satisfied contemporary needs in that area. The Bodanszky and Ondetti review of "Peptide Synthesis" in 1966 was also helpful. With much relief, attention was then focused entirely on preparing a summary of synthetic peptides which would, in part, supplement the Greenstein and Schröder contributions. Accordingly, the current literature survey begun in 1960 was continued through each of the past 10 years. Over this period (1960–January 1970) the major organic and biochemical journals were scanned for peptide syntheses. Over eight hundred such papers were selected for detailed abstracting. Approximately ten-thousand experiments were read and 8,000 were selected and summarized in the tables which comprise this volume. The tables should allow ready review of information useful in peptide synthesis (and purification) to theoretical problems concerned with optical rotation. The examples of peptide bond formation, resultant yields and solvent systems for both reaction and purification should be of special utility.

Doubtlessly, some important papers were inadvertently missed and errors have crept into the tables during preparation. On both counts, my apologies are extended to those affected by these oversights. However, one hopes the information herein correlated will prove useful to both the beginning and practicing peptide chemist and, in an indirect manner, assist in advancing progress during the next decade and beyond.

While each paper was read and evaluated and pertinent data from each experiment was selected by the writer, the very nature of this undertaking created a number of accessory burdens. In the early stages some of these were capably shouldered by Messrs. W. Robbins and W. Thurlow. These contributions were followed by those of P. A. Whitehouse and, during the past two years, by the cheerful, tireless and expert assistance of Miss Gail Dubie and Mrs. Christine H. Duplissa. In the final stages of the manuscript preparation, the valuable assistance of Mrs. Marie D. Baughman and Miss Mary Ann Heiselmann is also gratefully acknowledged. In addition, the writer is greatly indebted to the many excellent chemists whose contributions appear in this work and to a number of inspiring teachers, particularly Professors Carl Djerassi and Gardner Stacy.

Future supplements to the present work and a similar experimentally based review of nucleotide chemistry are presently being undertaken.

GEORGE R. PETTIT

Tempe, Arizona
August, 1970

Contents

Part 1

Amino Acid Derivatives and Dipeptides

Introduction and Glossary

When setting out to synthesize a peptide, as in any synthetic problem, one should have available all necessary past knowledge. In many problems, past experience combined with a relatively fast literature survey provides sufficient information. With peptides, the repetitious and indeed monotonous (but very important) sequencing makes too much reliance on memory of dubious value and literature searching difficult. The matter is easily illustrated by considering the 21 common protein amino acids plus, say, another three widespread in nature. Some years ago, in our laboratory, W. Thurlow computed on the basis of 24 amino acids that the number of possible dipeptides would be 576; tripeptides, 13,824 and tetrapeptides, 331,776. The number of pentapeptides immediately increases to 7.9626×10^6. The same 24 amino acid combinations for a decapeptide would be 6.3403×10^{13} and for a 24 unit peptide 1.3337×10^{33}. Obviously, when considering protecting groups and other simple derivatives, the number of possibilities for each amino acid is infinite. Thus, even at this very early stage in synthetic peptide chemistry, some type of easy access directory seemed necessary. The present work was undertaken, as noted in the preface, to help fill the current void for such information. Hopefully, this volume will allow rapid selection of suitable amino acid derivatives, peptide bond-forming methods and solvent systems for initial approach to specific peptide synthetic problems.

Results of reviewing the literature from 1960 through July 1968 are incorporated in the tables. In the introduction to each table, appropriate literature references available from July 1968 through January 5, 1970 have been included. Recent references of a more general nature are briefly reviewed here.

Newer advances in peptide chemistry include removal of carbobenzoxy protecting groups from methionine containing peptides;[453] conversion of S-trt-cystine-peptides to cystine derivatives[73a] employing iodine in methanol;[295a] use of 4-picolyl[81a] and 4-methylthiophenyl[281a] esters of amino acids; synthesis of peptides with triphenylphosphine and copper salts;[427] application of 1-ethoxycarbonyl-2-ethoxy-dihydroquinoline as a peptide bond forming reagent (did not lead to detectable racemization);[31] and photochemical transformation of glycine-peptides with isobutylene to leucine-peptides.[105] Further studies of racemization[171] in peptide syntheses have led to a discussion of racemization with S-bzl-cysteine derivatives;[347] detection of racemization in the case of p-methylsulfonylphenyl active esters in the presence of excess strong base;[281] amino acid analytical techniques for evaluation of racemization in peptide synthesis;[272] and further studies of the Woodward reagent K with respect to azlactone formation.[713] The WRK method does not give significant amounts of azlactone if employed as recommended by Woodward and colleagues. Some variations have been described which could lead to appreciable azlactone and, thereby, racemization instead of nearly exclusive enol ester formation. An interesting reaction involving DCCI and N-hydroxysuccinimide in tetrahydrofuran has also been discussed.[184] A number of the preceding new references include amino acid derivatives and synthetic peptides.

Before referring to the tables, a brief scan of the glossary should be helpful. In virtually all cases nomenclature was changed from that appearing in the original journal paper. The substantial effort involved in this unification was considered necessary for purposes of consistency, readability and brevity. In general, the nomenclature follows current IUPAC-IUB commission recommendations[270a] while other abbreviations are obvious and/or delineated in the following glossary. The glossary also contains abbreviations used for protecting groups, peptide bond-forming reagents, and solvents. In these cases the abbreviations are either those in current use or suggested by the present author.

The glossary applicable to each table now follows:

Amino Acids

Alanine	Ala
β-Alanine	β-Ala
α-Aminobutyric acid	Abu
ϵ-Aminocaproic acid	ϵAcp
Arginine	Arg
Asparagine	Asn
Aspartic acid	Asp
Citrullene	Cit
Cysteine	Cys
Cystine	Cystine
α, γ-Diaminobutyric acid	Dbu
Glutamic acid	Glu
Glutamine	Gln
Glycine	Gly
Histidine	His

Hydroxyproline	Hyp
Isoleucine	Ile
Leucine	Leu
Lysine	Lys
Methionine	Met
N-Methylisoleucine	MeIle
N-Methylvaline	MeVal
Norleucine	Nle
Norvaline	Nva
Ornithine	Orn
Phenylalanine	Phe
Proline	Pro
Sarcosine	Sar
Serine	Ser
Threonine	Thr
Tryptophan	Trp
Tyrosine	Tyr
Valine	Val

Urethan Type Protecting Groups

Adamentyloxycarbonyl	Adoc–
t-Amyloxycarbonyl	Aoc–
Benzhydryloxycarbonyl	Bzhoc–
Benzyloxycarbonyl	Z–
p-Bromobenzyloxycarbonyl	Z(Br)–
t-Butyloxycarbonyl	Boc–
Cholesteryloxycarbonyl	Coc–
Cyclohexyloxycarbonyl	Hoc–
Cyclopentyloxycarbonyl	Poc–
p-Methoxyphenylazobenzyloxycarbonyl	Mz–
p-Methoxybenzyloxycarbonyl	Z(OMe)–
p-Nitrobenzyloxycarbonyl	Z(NO$_2$)–
p-Phenylazobenzyloxycarbonyl	Pz–

Other N-and O-Protecting Groups

Acetyl	Ac–
Benzoyl	Bz–
Benzyl	Bzl–
Benzylthiomethyl	Btm–
Dinitrophenyl	Dnp–
Formyl	For–
o-Nitrophenylsulfenyl	Nps–
Pentamethylbenzyl	Pmb–
Perchlorophenyl	Pcp–
Phthalyl	Pht–
Tetrahydropyranyl	Thp–
Tosyl	Tos–
Trifluoracetyl	Tfa–
Trityl	Trt–
Tritylsulfenyl	Trs–

S-*Protecting Groups*

Ethylaminocarbonyl	–Eac
Phenylaminocarbonyl	–Pac

Carboxyl-Protecting Groups

Benzyloxy (benzyl ester)	–OBzl
o-Cyanobenzyl	–OCH(Ph)CN
Cyanomethoxy	–OCH$_2$CN
Diphenylmethoxy (benzhydryl ester)	–OBzh
Ethoxy (ethyl ester)	–OEt
Methoxy (methyl ester)	–OMe
p-Nitrobenzyloxy	–ONBzl
p-Nitrobenzylthio	–SNBzl
p-Nitrophenoxy (p-nitrophenyl ester)	–ONp
p-Nitrophenylthio	–SNp
Phenylazophenyl	–OPAP
Phenylthio (phenyl thiolester)	–SPh
N-Succinimide ester	–OSu
Tertiary butoxy (t-butyl ester)	–OBu^t
2, 4, 5-trichlorophenyl	–OTcp

Solvents

Ac	Acetic acid
Acn	Acetonitrile
Ac$_2$O	Acetic acid anhydride
Alc	Ethyl alcohol
An	Acetone
Aq	Water
Be	Benzene
Bu	Butyl alcohol
Ch-Alc	2-chloroethanol
Chf	Chloroform
Cte	Carbon tetrachloride
Cy	Cyclohexane
Di	Dioxane
Diglyme	Diethyleneglycol dimethyl ether
DiP	Diethyl phosphonate
Dipr Eth	Diisopropyl ether
DMA	Dimethylacetamide
DMF	Dimethylformamide
DMSO	Dimethylsulfoxide
EtAc	Ethyl acetate
EtCl	Ethylene chloride
Eth	Ethyl ether
EtO-alc	2-ethoxyethanol
F	Formamide
Fm	Formic acid
Glyme	1, 2-dimethoxyethane
HCl	Hydrochloric acid

He	Hexane
Hep	Heptane
HMPA	Hexamethylphosphotriamide
i-Bu	Isobutyl alcohol
i-Pr	Isopropyl alcohol
i-PrAc	isopropyl acetate
Mcy	Methyl cyclohexane
Me	Methyl alcohol
MeCl	Dichloromethane
MeO Alc	2-methoxyethanol
NaOH	Sodium hydroxide
NMe	Nitromethane
Pe	Petroleum ether or ligroin
Pen	Pentane
Pr	Propyl alcohol
PrEth	di-*n*-propyl ether
Py	Pyridine
t-Bu	*t*-Butanol
TEA	Triethylamine
TFA	Trifluoroacetic Acid
THF	Tetrahydrofuran
THP	Tetrahydropyran
Tol	Toluene

Peptide Bond Forming Reagents

A	Azide
AC	Acid chloride
ACN	Acyl cyamide
BSC	Benzenesulfonyl chloride
C	Cyanamide
CBHA	*p*-chlorobenzohydroxamic acid ester
CDBI	N, N′-carbonyldibenzimidazole
CDI	N, N′-carbonyldiimidazole
CD-1, 2, 4-T	1, 1′-carbonyldi-1,2,4-triazole
CMCI	1-cyclohexyl-3-(N-2-morpholinoethyl)carbodiimide
CTCI	1-cyclohexyl-3-(3′-trimethylamino-propyl) carbodiimide iodide
DCCI	Dicyclohexylcarbodiimide
DCCI-NHS	Dicyclohexylcarbodiimide and N-hydroxy-succinimide
DMchf	N, N-dimethylchloroformiminium chloride
2, 4-DNPO	2, 4-dinitrophenyl ester
EA	Ethoxyacetylene
EDCI	1-ethyl-3-(3-dimethylaminopropyl)carbodiimide hydrochloride
HA	Hydroxamic acid ester
MA	Mixed anhydride (e.g. with pivaloyl chloride, diethyl chlorophosphite, or diphenylphosphoryl chloride)
MCA	Mixed carbonic anhydride
NHP	N-hydroxyphthalimide ester
NHS	N-hydroxysuccinimide ester
O	Oxazolone
OCH$_2$CN	Cyanomethyl ester

ONP	*p*-nitrophenyl ester
OPAP	Phenylazophenyl ester
OPCP	Perchlorophenyl ester
OPh	Phenyl ester
OTCP	2, 4, 5-trichlorophenyl ester
P	Phosphorazo
PHA	Pivalohydroxamic acid ester
SmA	Symmetrical anhydride
SPh	Phenythio ester
2, 4, 6-TBP	2, 4, 6-tribromophenyl ester
TEP	Tetraethyl pyrophosphite
TOSC	*p*-toluenesulfonyl chloride
WRK	Woodward's Reagent K

1

Amino Acid
Derivatives

The utility of a peptide synthesis is greatly dependent upon judicious choice of protecting groups. Of the 100 or so naturally occurring amino acids, 33 of those most frequently studied have been included in Parts 1 through 3 and approximately 1700 of their simple derivatives have been included in Table 1. Use of Table 1 in conjunction with reviews prior to 1960 should allow ready selection and preparation of appropriately protected amino acids.

At an early stage in the preparation of this text, it was assumed that the α-aminobutyric acid-containing peptides would not be numerous. For this reason a substance such as Z-aminoisobutyryl-ala, a dipeptide, was listed in Table 1 as a simple alanine derivative. Later, it became clear that frequency of α-aminobutyric acid peptides would have justified their being included in the count. The same decision was reached with taurine and, for example, tauryl-gly appears as a derivative of glycine in Table 1. Otherwise, amino acids listed in the glossary are each counted one unit of the peptides reviewed. Note, also, in Table 1 that glycine includes phenylglycine, α-phenylalanine appears with phenylalanine and the same applies to cycloserine with serine and isovaline with valine.

All substances containing hydroxy-proline and/or glycollic or hydroxyisovaleric acid residues are found in the depsipeptide chapter of Part 3. Steroid, purine and pyrimidine derivatives of amino acids have been placed in the steroidal peptide and nucleopeptide sections of Part 3.

Many entries in Table 1 represent compounds prepared prior to 1960 and a check of the leading reference given may lead to other methods of preparation and physical constants. In most instances the lack of, for example, a melting point entry would signify some problem in purification or unavailability of the data. Some of the derivatives in Table 1 are liquids and a boiling point has been so designated and listed in the melting point column. All of the tables allow some interesting comparisons of physical data provided by investigators who were apparently unaware of one another's contribution. The summation of data also represents a somewhat critical evaluation, as observations of questionable value were not included.

The most important references not available in time to enter in detail in Table 1 are now summarized. A new and convenient synthesis of t-butyloxycarbonyl derivatives of amino acids using an active carbonate ester derived from t-butyl alcohol and pentachlorophenol has been recommended.[151,152] For the same purpose, the fluorocarbonate prepared from t-butyl alcohol and the monofluoro derivative of phosgene has also been suggested.[542a] A useful procedure for preparing and applying 2,4,6-trimethylbenzyl esters[618] has been reported. New examples of arginine peptide syntheses employing unblocked arginine have appeared.[676a] Improved syntheses of S-trt-cysteine,[777a] β-Obzl-boc-asp[486a] and N^{im}-bzl-Z-his[672] are now available.

TABLE 1 Amino Acid Derivatives

Compound	Method	Solvent	% Yield	Solvent Crystallization	M.P. (°C)	$[\alpha]_D$	Solvent Rotation	Ref.
Alanine								
Ac-Ala-bis(2-chloro-et-alkyl) Amide					85–86			366
Ac-D-di-et-Ala				Aq	175–177	−13	Ac-Aq	128
Ac-DL-di-et-Ala				Aq	197–198			128
N-Ac-N-for-α-me-Ala Anhydride				Aq	198–200.5			365
Ac-α-me-Ala				Chf-Pe	269–272 (dec)			365
Actinocinyl-bis[DL–Ala-OMe]								77
Ala-³H								320
Ala-OBzl Benzenesulfonate				Alc-Eth	111.5–113.5	+7.5	Py	601
Ala-OBzl Toluenesulfonate				Alc-Eth	116–118	−6.0	Me	165
Ala p-Bromophenacyl Ester Hydrobromide				Alc-Eth	180.5–182	−11	DMF	360
β-Ala-N-di(2-chloro-et)-aminophenylamide Hydrochloride				Alc-Eth	210–211 (dec)			516
α-Ala-p-N-Bis(2-chloro-et)-aminophenylamide Dihydrochloride				Me-Alc-Eth	188–189			516
1-DL-Ala-2, 2-bis(2-chloro-et) Hydrazine Hydrobromide				Alc	124–126			523
Ala-OCH(Ph)CN Hydrobromide				Alc-Eth	133–134	−2.1	Aq	633
6-O-(β-Ala-)-D-Glucose Oxalate				AQ-Eth	77–78	+32	Aq	115
Ala-OEt Hydrochloride					76–78			399
D-Ala-OEt Hydrochloride				Chf-Eth	151.5–152.5	−3.3	Aq	330
Ala-2, 4, 6-tri-me-OBzl Hydrochloride						−9.5	Aq	631
DL-Ala-OMe					110.5–111	+5.8	Me	173
					108			169
								761a
Ala-OMe Hydrochloride				Me-Eth	109–111	+6.5	Me	767

11

Table 1 Amino Acid Derivatives (continued)

Compound	Method	Solvent	% Yield	Solvent Crystallization	M.P.(°C)	$[\alpha]_D$	Solvent Rotation	Ref.
D-Ala-OMe Hydrochloride				Me-Eth	109–111	−6.5	Me	767
Ala-ONBzl Benzenesulfonate				Aq	158–160	+7.1	Py	601
Ala-ONBzl Hydrobromide				Me-Eth	177–178.5	−3.0	DMF	601
				Alc-Eth	175–177	−5.7	Me	468
Ala-ONBzl p-Toluenesulphonate				i-Pr	156–158	−4	Me	406
Ala-phenacyl Ester Hydrobromide				Me-EtAc	174–175	+1.5	Me	616
Ala-diphenyl-OMe Hydrochloride				Chf-EtAc	178	−14	DMF	616
β-Ala-SePh Hydrobromide					156–158			719
DL-Ala-SePh Hydrobromide					126–127			719
Ala-SePh Hydrobromide					158–160			719
Bz-Ala-bis(2-chloroethyl)Amide					96–97			366
N-Bz-DL-Ala-OMe				Cy	82			233
N-(β-Bz-et)-α-Ala				Aq	216–217			107
2-1-OBzl-2-acetamido-4,6-OBzl-idene-2-deoxy-3-O-D-glucopyranosyl-ac-Ala-OBzl				Alc	172–173			86
Z-Ala					86–87			399
					97–99			584
Z-DL-Ala Amide				Eth-Hep	86	−15	HoAc	360
Z-Ala-bzl Amide				EtAc-Cy	141–142	+8.7	DMF	55
Z-DL-Ala-DL-Abu					169–171			633, 23
N-[(Z)-β-Ala] Butyrolactam				EtAc	94–95			11
N-[(Z)-β-Ala] Caprolactam				Eth	60–61			11
1-(N-Z-DL-Ala)-2, 2-bis(2-chloro-et) Hydrazine				Alc	119–120			523
Z-Ala OCH(Ph)CN				EtAc-Cy	90.5–91	−13	DMF	633
N-(N$^\alpha$-Z-β-Ala)-N, N'-dicyclohexylurea								651
6-O-(N-Z-β-Ala)-D-Glucose				EtAc-Me	127–128	+52 (5 min) / 31 (20 hr, constant)	Ag	115

12

Compound	Cryst. solvent	mp (°C)	[α]	Solvent	Ref
N-[N-(Z)-Ala]-β-D-glucosylamine	Me-EtAc	227-229	−10	Me	116
Z-DL-Ala Hydroxamic Acid	Chf	127			233
Z-DL-Ala-OMe	Aq-Alc	46			233
Z-Ala-ONBzl	EtAc-Pe	98-99	−16	Me	468
Z-Ala-ONp	Alc	78-79			399
Z-β-Ala-ONp	An-Pe	92-94			397
Z-Ala Phenacyl Ester		89			651
Z-Ala-SePh	Alc	154-155	−26	Chf	616
Z-β-Ala-SePh		101-102	−13	DMF	273
N-[(Z)-β-Ala] Valerolactam		68.5-69.5			273
Z-aminoisobutyryl-Ala	Eth	60-61			11
Z-aminoisobutyryl-DL-Ala		139.5-140.5	+5	Di	429
Z-aminoisobutyryl-Ala Hydrazide		105.6-107			429
Z-aminoisobutyryl-Ala-OMe		68.6-69.6	−7.3	Me	173
Z-aminoisobutyryl-DL-Ala-OMe		101.4-102	−5.5	Di	429
Z-aminoisobutyryl-DL-Ala Oxazolone		119-121			429
Z-aminoisobutyryl-Ala Oxazolone		110-112	−52	Di	429
Z-dehydro-Ala		108-109			429
Z-DL-α-et-Ala	Be-Pe	88-89			609
Z-D-di-et-Ala	EtAc-Pe	75-77	+0.8	Ac-Aq	284
Z-di-et-Ala	EtAc	74-76	−1.1	Ac-Aq	128
Z-di-et-Ala Boc-hydrazide	EtAc-Pe	124-126			128
Z-α-me-Ala	Eth-Pe	72.5-74.5			128
2-(1'-Z-α-me-Ala-amino-1'-me)et-4, 4-di-me-oxazolone	Be	124-125	0	Alc	365
Z-α-me-Ala-OBu^t	Pe	60-61			284
Z-α-me-Ala-OCH_2CN	Eth	45-48.5			284
Z-α-me-Ala Cyclohexylamide	Be-Pe	124-127			365
Z-α-me-Ala Pivalic Acid Mixed Anhydride	Tol-Pe	81-83			365

Table 1 Amino Acid Derivatives (continued)

Compound	Method	Solvent	% Yield	Solvent Crystallization	M.P.(°C)	$[\alpha]_D$	Solvent Rotation	Ref.
Z(OMe)-Ala				EtAc-Pe	82-83	-12	Ac	338
Z-(NO$_2$)-Ala-^{14}C								692
Z-(2, 4-NO$_2$)-Ala-OBzl				Pe	83-84	-53	EtAc	156
Z-(2, 4-NO$_2$)-DL-Ala-OEt				EtAc-Pe	80-81			156
Z-(NO$_2$)-Ala-ONBzl				Be-Pen	132.5-135	-1.3	Chf	601
Boc-Ala-OBzl				EtAc-He	140-141			356a
Boc-Ala-OSu				i-Pr	143-144			7
Boc-β-Ala-ONp				EtAc-Pe	59-61			520
N-Carboxy-3-({2-[3-phenyldithio)Proprion-amido] Et}Dithio)-N-bzl-Ala-OMe				EtAc-He	74.5-75			222
Dichloroac-Ala-bis(2-chloro-et) Amide					117.5-119			366
β-Chloro-Z-Ala					88	+27	Me	708
Cyclohexy-Ala					b.p. 160-180 (1.1 mm)			322
N-OEt-carbonyl-β-Ala-OBzl								205
Di-et-Ala				Me-Eth		+36	5N HCl	128
D-di-et-Ala				Me-Eth		-34	5N HCl	128
DL-β, β-di-et-Ala				Me-Eth	240-243			128
D-di-et-Ala-OMe Hydrochloride				Me-Eth	159-160	-37	Me	128
For-α-me-Ala				Aq	145-147			365
For-α-me-Ala-cyclohexylamide				Aq-Me	142-145			365
N-imidazoyl-Ala-OEt					73-74			155
N-(isopropoxymethylene)-α-me-Ala-OMe					b.p. 57.4 mm			365
N-isopropyl-Ala-OMe Hydrobromide					150-151.7			533
Lipoyl-Ala				Me-Eth	119-120			109
DL-Lipoyl-β-Ala-ammonium Salt					122-123			109
α-Me-Ala-OBu^t					b.p. 160-			284

14

Compound	Solvent	M.P.	$[\alpha]$	Solvent	Ref.
Me-3-(N-Z-Ala)-2-oxo-oxazolidine-4-carboxylate	Be-Pe	163	−126	Me	296
N-(5,5-di-me-cyclohex-2-en-1-on-3-yl)-DL-Ala	Aq-Alc	102.5–103.5			196
4,4-Di-me-2-(1'-me-1'-tos-α-me-Ala-amino)-et-oxazolone	Be-Pe	214–215			365
N-[bis(ONBzl)-phosphoryl]-Ala	Alc	148–149			99
N-[bis(ONBzl)-phosphoryl]-Ala-OMe		60–62			99
DNP-Ala		88–89			390
DNP-Ala Amide		230–231	+103	Alc-Aq	390
DNP-Ala Anilide		203–204	+128	An	390
DNP-Ala Chloride					390
DNP-Ala p-Toluidide		213–214	−96; +103	Alc-Aq; An	390
N-O-Nps-Ala	Alc	128–130	−101	DMF	774
N-O-Nps-Ala DCHA Salt	Alc-Pe	176–178	−56	DMF	774
2-Oxo-oxazolidine-4-carbonyl-Ala		188–191 (dec)	−28	Aq	296
Pht-Ala		153–156			114
Pht-Ala Chloride					516
Pht-β-Ala Chloride					516
Pht-Ala-adenine					131
N-Pht-α-Ala-p-di(2-chloro-et)-amino-phenylamide	Be	147–147.5			516
N-Pht-β-Ala-p-N-di(2-chloro-et)-amino-phenylamide	An	175.5–176.5			516
Pht-Ala Isobutyl Carbonic Anhydride					8
N-Pht-DL-Ala-OMe	Aq-Me	67			233
Pht-tauryl-DL-Ala	Aq	300 (dec)			614
Pht-tauryl-DL-Ala-OEt		143–144			614
Pivaloyl-α-me-Ala-OMe	Eth	92–93			365

Table 1 Amino Acid Derivatives (continued)

Compound	Method	Solvent	% Yield	Solvent Crystallization	M.P.(°C)	$[\alpha]_D$	Solvent Rotation	Ref.
β-(Pyrazolyl-I)-Ala					243	-72	Aq	232
β'-(Pyrazolyl-I)-Ala					247–248	-42	Aq	232
β'-(Pyrazolyl-I)-Ala OMe					112–114	+6.1	Aq	232
β-(Pyrazolyl-I)-Ala Amide					173–174	-8.5	Aq	232
					91–92	+4.8	Aq	232
					158–160	+7.5	Aq	232
N-Tos-N-OEt-me-DL-Ala				Alc-Aq	58–59			419
Tos-α-me-Ala				Aq-Me	151–152			365
Tos-α, N-di-me-Ala				Aq-Me	142.5–145			365
Tos-α, N-di-me-Ala Chloride				Pe	79–80			365
Tos-α-me-Ala Chloride				Be	120–121			365
Tfa-DL-α-et-Ala					120–122 sublimed at 140°/0.1 mm			284
Tfa-α-et-Ala				Eth-Pe	121–123	+9.9	Alc	284
Tfa-α-me-Ala					170.5–172 sublimed at 140°/14 mm			365
N-Trt-β-Ala				Di	175–176			516
N-Trt-α-Ala				Tol	170–172			516
N-Trt-β-Ala-N-bis-(2-chloro-et)-amino-phenylamide				Be	170–172			516
N-Trt-α-Ala-OEt				Pe	132.5–133.5			516
N-Trt-β-Ala-OMe				Alc	100–101			516
N-Trt-α-Ala-OMe					86–86.5			516
N-Trt-Ala-O-diphenyl-me				Me	101			616

16

Arginine

Compound	Solvent	M.p. (°C)	[α]	Solvent	Page
N-α-Aoc-N^G-nitro-Arg	EtAc	139–141 (dec)	−28	Py	248
Arg					495
Arg Hydrochloride		220–223	+22	6N HCl	212
D-Arg Hydrochloride		115–121	−21	HCl	354
N-Arg-5-OMe-Tryptamine Acetate		193			740
N-α-Z-Arg 1-Naphthylamide	Alc	175–180	−16	Aq	484
Arg Phosphate	An				104
Arg Phosphate Barium Salt	Aq-Alc				104
Arg Phosphate Copper (II) Salt					104
N-α-Bz-DL-Arg Anilide	Alc	252			484
N-α-Bz-DL-Arg p-Anisylide	DMF-Eth	150–152			484
N-α-Bz-DL-Arg 3,4-Dichloroanilide	Alc-Eth	212			484
N-α-Z-Arg-OBzl Benzenesulfonate Salt	Alc-An / Pe	137			104
N^α.N^δ.N^ω-Tris-Z-Arg-ONp	EtAc	137–138	+16	Chf	727
Di-Z-Boc^α-Arg-OH	Alc	134–135	−7.2	Chf	727
	Me-Aq	141–142 (dec)			183
N-(N^α-Z-N^G-nitro-Arg)-5-OMe Tryptamine		114–116	−11	Me	740
N^G-Nitro-Z-Arg		132–134	−3.5	Me	165
N^G-Nitro-Z-D-Arg		134–136	+2.5	Me	742
N^G-Nitro-Z-Arg Amide	Aq-Alc	220–221	+4.9 ± 1	DMF	461
N^G-Nitro-Z-Arg-OPcp	THF	109–111.5			343
N^G-Nitro-Z-Arg-ONBzl		122			70
N^G-Tos-Z-Arg	EtAc	86–89	−0.5	Me	495
N^G-Tos-Z-Arg DCHA Salt	Me-Eth	86–88	−1.3	DMF	472
N^G-Tos-Z-Arg Anhydride	An-EtAc	152–154	−1.7	Me	495
		156–157			544

Table 1 Amino Acid Derivatives (continued)

Compound	Method	Solvent	% Yield	Solvent Crystallization	M.P.(°C)	$[\alpha]_D$	Solvent Rotation	Ref.
N^G-Tos-Z-D-Arg					80–90	+1.5	Me	769
N^G-Tos-Z-Arg-δ-aminovaleric Acid OMe					40–45	–1.7	Me	454
N^G-Tos-Z-Arg Cyclohexylamine Salt				Me-Eth	152–154	–6.1	Me	495
N^G-Nitro-N^α-boc-Arg						+23	HCl	732
N^G-Nitro-N^α-boc-Arg Z-hydrazide				Alc-Aq	157–158	–20	Me	727
Tos^--N^α-boc-Arg				EtAc	99–100			495
N^G-Tos-N^α-boc-Arg				EtAc	99–100	–3.3		495
N^G-Nitro-carbethoxy-Arg-OMe				Aq	130–131			165
N^G-Nitro-N-carbothiophenyl-Arg				Me	143	–10	An	212
N-(α-Carboxyphen-et-carbamoyl) Arg					125			218
β-Carboxypropionyl-Arg 2-Naphthylamide				Bu-Eth				484
β-Carboxypropionyl-Arg 2-Naphthylamide Hydrochloride				Bu-Eth				484
N^α-Guanyl-Arg								104
Homo-Arg-phosphonate Copper Salt								104
Homo-Arg-phosphoric Acid								104
γ-Hydroxy-homo-Arg-lactone Dihydrochloride				Alc-Aq	214–215 (dec)	+33	6.0N HCl	153
Iso-Arg Picrate				Me-Be	191 (dec)			104
N^G-Nitro-Arg				Aq	255 (dec)	+24	2N HCl	212
				Alc-Aq		+2.8	Me	165
				Aq	252 (dec)	+24	2N HCl	478
N^G-Nitro-D-Arg				Aq	253–254	–22	2N HCl	165
N^G-Nitro-Arg Amide Hydrobromide				Aq-Alc	237–239	+13	Aq	461
N^G-Nitro-Arg-OBzl Hydrochloride				Me-Eth	128			674
N^G-Nitro-Arg-OBzl								135
N^G-Nitro-Arg-OBzl Ditosylate				Me-Eth	132–134	+11	Py	518
N^G-Nitro-Arg-OBzl Toluenesulfonate						–1.4	Me	461
N^G-Nitro-Arg Z-hydrazide Hydrochloride				Alc-Eth	100	+24	Me	727

Compound	Cryst. solvent	M.p. (°C)	[α]	Solvent	Ref.
NG-Nitro-Arg-OMe Hydrochloride	Me-Eth	157–158	+14	Me	165
NG-Nitro-D-Arg-OMe Hydrochloride	Me-Eth	152–156	−14	Me	354
NG-Nitro-Arg-ONBzl	Et	154–156	−12	Di	165
NG-Nitro-Arg-OPNbz		119–121			605
NG-Nitro-Z-Arg	Alc-Aq	175			70
NG-[Bis-NBzl-phospho]-Nα-Z-Arg-OBzl		135–136	−2	Me	478
N-Nps-Arg					104
N-Nps-Arg-OMe Hydrochloride					479
Phospho-Arg					479
Succinyl-1-bis(NG-Nitro-Arg)	Pr-Eth	141–142	−0.4	DMF	401
Succinyl-1-bis(NG-Nitro-Arg-OMe)	Pr-Alc-Eth	106–107	+2.4	Me	43
NG-Tos-Arg	Aq	146–150	+5 / −5	DMF / Me	43 / 495 / 544 / 495
NG-Tos-Arg-OBzl	EtAc-Pe	74–75			495
Trt-NG-nitro-Arg	Me-Eth	145–152	+3.3	DMF	503
Asparagine					
N-Ac-D-Asn-2, 3, 3-d₂	Me	159–159.5	+3.4	1N HCl	58
N-Ac-DL-Asn-2, 3, 3-d₃	Alc-Aq	176–177.5			58
Aoc-Asn	Alc-EtAc	151.5–152.5	−8.2	Alc	248
Asn-2, 3, 3-d₃	Alc-Eth		+29	1N HCl	58
D-Asn			−14	0.1N HCl	379
DL-Asn-2, 3, 3-d₃	Alc-Eth				58
Asn Amide		136–138	+13		436
DL-Asn n-Butyl Amide		226			779
Asn N-2-Carbethoxyethylamide		188			779
		175			779
Asn-O-2, 4, 6-trime-bzl Hydrochloride	Me-EtAc	194.5–195.5	−3.6	Aq	626

Table 1 Amino Acid Derivatives (continued)

Compound	Method	Solvent	% Yield	Solvent Crystallization	M.P.(°C)	$[\alpha]_D$	Solvent Rotation	Ref.
Asn Naphthalene-2-sulphonate					230			661
Asn-ONBzl Hydrobromide					172–175	+7.7	DMF	669
Asn-O-diphenyl-me Hydrochloride				Me-Eth	159–160	+1.4	DMF	616
N-(β-Bz-et) Asn				Aq	200–201 (dec)			107
N-Bzl-D-α-Asn				Alc	167	+24	Aq	379
N-Bzl-N-cyclohexyl-α-DL-Asn-β-OBzl				Alc-Aq	80			779
Z-Asn					184–186			584
Z-Asn Amide					208–214	+14		436
Z-Asn-OBu^t				Mcy	107–108.5	−12	Alc	81
Z-Asn-OBu^t				EtAc-Pe	105–106	−14	Alc	510
Z-Asn-ONBzl				Me-Ag	167–169	−12	DMF	669
					167–168			309
Z-Asn-ONp					153–154	−34	DMF	720
					150–151	−33	DMF	550
Z-D-Asn-ONp					151–153	+32	DMF	550
				DMF-Aq	164–166	+30	DMF	684
					155–156	+31	DMF	529
					155–156	+31	DMF	529
Z-N$^\beta$-bu^t-Asn-OBu^t				Dipr-Eth	139–140	−8	DMF	81
Z-iso-Asn				Fm-Aq	164	−25	DMF	561
Z-OMe-Asn				Alc-Eth	158–159	−5.3	Me	561
						−4.5	DMF	561
Z-OMe-Asn-ONp				Alc	161–162	−30	DMF	561
Z-OMe-iso-Asn				Me-Eth-Pe	144–146	−25	DMF	561
Boc-Asn				Alc-Aq	181–182	−7.8	DMF	561
					178–179 (dec)	−7	DMF	46
Boc-Asn-ONp				EtAc	161–162.5 (dec)	−44	DMF	46

Compound	M.p. (°C)	Solvent	[α]	Solvent	Ref.
Boc-iso-Asn	157–158	Alc	–45	DMF	561
N-Cyclohexyl-DL-α-Asn	153–155	Alc-Eth-Pe	–31	DMF	561
N-n-hexyl-Asn	247	Aq			779
Iso-Asn	223	Alc or Aq			779
N-Isobutyl-Asn	156–156.5	Aq-Alc	+14	0.1N HCl	497
N-α-Naphthyl-Asn	242	Alc or Aq			779
	227	Alc or Aq			779
Nps-Asn	165–166	Me	–119	DMF	774
Nps-Asn DCHA Salt	185–186	Me	–86	DMF	774
Nps-Asn-2, 4, 6-tri-me-OBzl	173–174	Chf-Cy	–31	DMF	626
Nps-Asn-ONp	145.5–146.5	DMF-Alc	–111	DMF	626
N-Phenyl-Asn	152–154	Me	–116	DMF	271
Pht-Asn	252	Alc or Aq	–80	Alc	779
Pht-Asn-ONp	185–186	Alc	–117	DMF	561
Tos-Asn	150–151	Alc	–10	DMF	561
Tos-iso-Asn	186.5–187	Alc-Aq	–13	DMF	497
N-p-tolyl-Asn	155–156	Alc or Aq			779
Aspartic Acid					
N-Ac-Asp-OBzl	158–159	EtAc-Pe			589
N-Ac-Asp-β-OEt	112–114	EtAc-Pe			39
N-Aoc-Asp-β-OBzl	58–60	Aq	+2.7	Aq	248
DL-Asp-2, 3, 3-d₃					58
DL-Asp-d₇					58
DL-Asp-d₇ Deuteriochloride					58
Asp-β-OBzl	212	Glyme-Alc	+28	1N HCl	775
Asp-OBzl	221	Aq	+24	1N HCl	213
Asp-α-OBzl-β-OBuᵗ Hydrochloride	109–110	EtAc-Pe	–8.7	Me	561
D-Asp-di-OBzl Toluenesulfonate	156–158	Alc-Et	–7.4	Chf	165
Asp-β-OBuᵗ	194–195	Alc-Aq-An			510
Asp-α-OBuᵗ-β-OBzl Hydrochloride	115–117	EtAc			510

Table 1 Amino Acid Derivatives (continued)

Compound	Method	Solvent	% Yield	Solvent Crystallization	M.P.(°C)	[α] D	Solvent Rotation	Ref.
Asp-di-OBu^t Hydrochloride					152–154			660
Asp-α-OEt-β-OBu^t					158–160			658
Asp-α-OEt-β-OBu^t Hydrochloride				Alc-Eth or Alc-EtAc	170.5–171	+16	Alc	729
Asp-α-OEt-β-OBu^t Toluenesulfonate				Alc-Eth	103–103.5	+12	Alc	729
DL-Asp-2, 3, 3-d$_3$-β-OMe				Me	195–196.5			58
Asp-α-ONBzl				Aq	172–173	−15	1N HCl	561
Asp-β-ONBzl					180–182	+6.4	Ac	361
					180–182	+11	Ac	361
Asp-di-ONBzl				Me	162–163	−8.4	Py	561
Asp-β-OBu^t				Me-Eth	189–190 (dec)	+8.5	AcOH	572
Asp-β-OBu^t N-Carboxyanhydride				Me-Eth	197	+7.5	Ac-Aq	561
				EtAc-Pe	138–140 (dec)	−35	EtAc	510
Asp-α-OMe-β-OBu^t Hydrochloride				Me-Eth	167	+25	Alc	729
Asp-ONBzl Hydrobromide					175–178	−3.0	Aq	141
Asp-α-ONp-OBzl Hydrobromide				An-Eth	135–137	+38	Alc	775
Asp-di-O-phenacyl Hydrobromide				Me-Eth	150–151	+10	Me	616
Asp-O-diphenyl-me Naphthalene-2-sulfonate				i-Pr	143–144	+4.8	DMF	661
N-(β-Bz-et) Asp				Aq	169–170			107
N-Bz-DL-Asp-β-OBzl				Aq-Alc	148			33
N-Bz-DL-Asp-di-OBzl				Eth	72–74			33
N-Bz-Asp-OBzl				Aq-Me	88	−11	Me	33
N-Bzl-DL-Asp-β-OBzl				Alc-Aq				779
N-Bzl-Asp-β-OBzl N-Carboxyanhydride				Chf-Eth	92			779
N-Bzl-D-Asp-Chloroformic Anhydride								379
2-(β-Bzl-N-bz-DL-Asp) Aminoethanol				EtAc-Alc	122			33
2-(β-Bzl-N-bz-DL-Asp) Aminoethanol Acetate								33
Z-Asp					161.5–163	+6.3	Ac	550

Compound	Recryst. solvent	mp (°C)	[α]	Solvent	Ref.
Z-D-Asp		161–162	−5.8	Ac	550
Z-D-Asp-OBzl		62–63			111
Z-Asp-β-OBzl	Be	107–108; 106–108	+12	Ac	111; 118
Z-Asp-di-OBzl	EtAc-Pe	105–106	−15	Alc	213
Z-Asp-α-OBzl	Eth-Pe	61–63; 82–85	−9.6	Ac	118; 213
Z-DL-Asp-β-OBzl	Pe-EtAc	84–85			383
Z-D-Asp-β-OBzl	EtAc-Pe	103–105	+1.5	Di-Ag	383
Z-Asp-β-OBzl Amide		90–92			111
Z-Asp-α-OBzl-β-OBu^t		101			39
Z-Asp-α-OBzl DCHA Salt		45–47.5	+6.0	Alc	572
Z-Asp-β-OBzl Dimethylamide		118–119	−39	Di	383
Z-Asp-β-OBzl Ethanolamide Amide		Oil			39
Z-Asp-β-OBzl Methylamide		104			39
Z-Asp-β-OBu^t	Eth-Pe	47.5–48.5	−11	Py	39; 572
Z-Asp-β-OBu^t DCHA Salt		Oil			561; 199
	An-Eth	Oil	+7.7	Ac-Aq	658
Z-Asp-α-OEt		126–127			561
	Aq	123–124; 126–128; 125–126.5	+5.5	Ac-Aq	658; 510
	Eth	78–79; 83–84	−16	Alc	572; 658
Z-Asp-α-OEt-β-OBu^t	Alc-Eth-Pe	Oil	+8.2	Alc	383
Z-Asp-α-OEt DCHA Salt	Me	157–158			658
Z-Asp-α-hydrazide-β-OBu^t	Me	161	−17	DMF	383
Z-Asp-α-hydrazide-β-OMe	Me	129–130	−3.6	DMF	729
Z-Asp-O-β-isopropyl Piperazine Salt		149–151			561; 520
Z-Asp-α-OMe-β-OBu^t	Eth-Pe	33–34	−13	Alc	729

Table 1 Amino Acid Derivatives (continued)

Compound	Method	Solvent	% Yield	Solvent Crystallization	M.P.(°C)	$[\alpha]_D$	Solvent Rotation	Ref.
Z-Asp-α-OMe DCHA Salt				Alc-Pe	159-160	+4.9 / +5.3	Alc	729
Z-Asp-ONBzl					169-173 / 166-168	-15	DMF	141 / 315
Z-Asp-α-ONBzl				EtAc-Pe	124-125	-17	Ac-Aq	561
Z-Asp-α-ONBzl-β-OBu^t				EtAc-Pe	93-94	-16	Me	561
Z-Asp-α-ONBzl DCHA Salt				Eth / Alc	155-156 / 153-154	-11 / -11	Alc-Aq / Alc-Aq	561
Z-Asp-α-ONp-β-OBzl				EtAc-Pe	76	-30 / -16	Me / DMF	190
Z-Asp-α-ONp-β-OBu^t				Alc	75-76	+12	Chf	775
Z-Asp-di-O Phenacyl				Alc	86.5-87.5 / 105-107	+1.5 / +1.5	Chf / Chf	260 / 616
Z-DL-Asp-α-SePh-β-OBzl				Alc	124.5-125.5			719
Z-Asp-O-2, 4, 5-tcp				Alc	225 (dec)	-30	DMF	254
Z-D-Asp-α-2, 4, 5-tcp-β-OBzl				Alc	90-92			111
Z-Asp-α-OSu-β-OBu^t					151.5-152.5	-19	Di	730
Z-3-me-DL-Asp				Cy	67-68			181
Z-3-me-DL-Asp DCHA Salt				EtAc	126-128			181
Z-3-me-DL-Asp-α-OSu-β-OBzl					Oil			181
Z-(OMe)-Asp Anhydride				An-Pe	136-137	-38	Ac	561
Z-(OMe)-Asp Anhydride DCHA Salt				Alc	150-151	-7.9	DMF	561
Z-(OMe)-Asp-α-OBzl				EtAc-Pe	105-106	-15	Me	561
Z-(OMe)-Asp-α-OBzl-β-OBu^t				Eth-Pe	70.5-71	-17	Me	561
Z-(OMe)-Asp-α-OBzl DCHA Salt				Alc	150-151			561
Z-(OMe)-Asp-β-OBu^t DCHA Salt								561
Z-(OMe)-Asp-α-ONBzl				EtAc-Pe	118-119	-16	Me	561

Z-(OMe)-Asp-α-ONBzl DCHA Salt	Alc	153-154	-12	Ac	561
Boc-Asp	Pe	160-161	-6.2	Me	561
Boc-Asp Anhydride	An-Pe	118-119	-38	Ac	561
Boc-Asp-β-OBzl	Alc	133-134	-21	Me	356
Boc-Asp-α-OBzl-β-OBu^t	Pe	102-103	-21	DMF	561
Boc-Asp-β-OBu^t	Aq-Alc	54-55	+16	Me	561
Boc-Asp-β-OBu^t DCHA Salt	Alc-Pe	63-64			561
Boc-Asp-OBu^t DCHA Salt	Alc-Eth-Pe	144-145	+10	Me	729
Boc-Asp DCHA Salt	Aq	139.5-142			561
Boc-Asp-α-OEt DCHA Salt	Me-Eth	176-177			561
Boc-Asp-α-hydrazide-β-OBu^t	Ac-Pe	136-137	-8.1	DMF	729
Boc-Asp-α-ONBzl	Alc	161.5			561
Boc-Asp-α-ONBzl DCHA Salt	An-Pe	135-136	-8.5	Me	561
Boc-Asp-α-OSu-β-OBzl		166-167	-11	DMF	356
N-For-Asp-β-OBzl		103-104	-20	Di	213
Lithium Copper Asp		123-125	+28	Alc	362
N-[Bis(NBzl)-phosphoryl]-Asp-di-OBzl	Me	101			99
N-Pht-Asp-α-OBzl	EtAc-Pe	111-112	-45	Me	561
	Alc-Pe	111.5-112	-42	Alc	729
N-Pht-Asp-α-OBzl-β-OBu^t	Eth-Pe	74-75	-34	Me	561
	Pe	73.5-75	-32	Alc	729
N-Pht-Asp-α-OBzl DCHA Salt	EtAc	147-148	-26	Me	561
		152-153	-26	Me	561
N-Pht-Asp-OBu^t	EtAc	152-153	-50	Me	561
	Eth-Pe	112-113	±0.5	Alc	729
Pht-Asp-OBu^t DCHA Salt	Eth-Pe	114-115	-22	Me	561
N-Pht-Asp-α-ONBzl	EtAc	197-198	-62	Me	561
N-Pht-Asp-α-ONBzl DCHA Salt	EtAc-Pe	148-149	-38	Me	561
N-Pht-Asp-α-ONp-β-OBu^t	Alc-Eth	152-153	-86	Me	561
N-Tos-Asp Anhydride	EtAc-Pe	118-119			561
	EtCl	149			531
N-Tos-Asp-α-bzl-amide	Alc-Aq	193	-30	Me	419

Table 1 Amino Acid Derivatives (continued)

Compound	Method	Solvent	% Yield	Solvent Crystallization	M.P.(°C)	[α]D	Solvent Rotation	Ref.
N-Tfa-Asp-α-OBzl				Be-Pe	116–117	−45	Alc	729
N-Tfa-Asp-α-OBzl-β-OBu^t				Pe	52–54	−32	Alc	729
N-Tfa-Asp-β-OBu^t DCHA Salt				Alc-Pe	143.5–145	+17	Alc	729
Citrullene								
Z-Cit				Alc	115–117			61
Z-Cit-OMe				EtAc	155–157			456
Z-Cit-ONBzl				Alc-Ac	163–165			61
Cysteine								
N-Ac-S-bz-Cys-ONp				Pr-He	115.5–116.5			82
N-Ac-A-bzl-DL-Cys				Pr-He	113–114			82
N-Ac-S-bzl-Cys				Alc	143.5–145.5			82
N-Ac-Cys Bis(2-chloro-et) Amide				Me	81–82			366
N,N'-Di-ac-Cystine Me-amide				EtAc	128–129 (dec)			187
N,N'-Di-ac-Cystine-OMe				Aq	>230 (dec)			187
Bis[2-amino-2-carboxy-et]-diseleno-Cystine								144
S-2-Amino-et-Cys				Aq-Alc	194–195 (dec)	−7.0	N-HCl	250
S-2-Amino-et-homo-Cys				Me	216–217 (dec)	+2.5	N-HCl	250
N-OBzh-carbonyl-S-trt-Cys-di-et-ammonium Salt				Chf-Eth-He	167.5–169 (dec)	+19	Chf	229
S-Bzh-Cys					206–207 (dec)	+15	0.1N Alc-HCl	221
N-Bzh-oxycarbonyl-S-trt-Cys-di-et-ammonium Salt					165–166			222

Compound	Solvent	M.p.	[α]	Solvent	Ref.
S-Bz-Cys	Aq	145–146	−27	N HCl	777
N,S-Di-bz-Cys-OMe	Me	165–166	+56	Chf	777
S-Bz-Cys-OMe Hydrochloride		155.5–157	−4.2	Me	777
S-Bz-Cys-ONp Hydrobromide	Ac-Eth				82
S-Bz-Cys-Ophenacyl Hydrobromide	Me-Alc	118–119	−232	DMF	616
S-Bz-DL-homo-Cys-OBz-p-toluene Sulphonate	Me	177–179		Me	95
N,N-Bis-bz-Cystine-di-OMe		178–178.5			777
N,N'-Di-bz-Cystine-OMe					187
S-Bzl-N-Z-Cys-ONp		93–94	−43	DMF	46
Bzl-N-Z-se-bzl-seleno-Cys	Alc-EtAc	64–65	−39	DMF	668
S-Bzl-N-boc-Cys-ONp	Alc-Pe	95–96	−37	DMF	46
S-Bzl-Cys-ONBzl Benzenesulfonate	Aq-Alc	170–171	−20	DMF	561
S-Bzl-Cys-SePh Hydrobromide		170–172			719
S-Bzl-DL-Cys-SePh Hydrobromide					719
S-Bzl-DL-homo-Cys-OBzl Toluene-sulphonate	Me-Eth	118–119			97
S-Bzl-N-(imidazolecarbonyl)-Cys-OEt		59–62	−81	EtAc	155
S-Bzl-seleno-Cys		191–192	+35		145
S-Bzl-seleno-Cys-OEt Hydrochloride		153–154			145
S-Bzl-DL-seleno-Cys-OEt Hydrochloride		135–136			145
S-Bzl-DL-seleno-Cys-OMe Hydrochloride		139			145
S-Bzl-seleno-Cys-OMe Hydrochloride		147–148	+6.8		145
N-Z-S-ac-Cys	Be	115–116	−52	Alc	777
N-(Z-11-amino-undecyl)-S-bzl-Cys-OBzl		103	−24	An	515
N-Z-S-bzh-Cys-ONp		96–97	−19	EtAc	228
Z-S-bz-Cys	Me-Aq	135 and 137	−36	Alc	777
Z-S-bz-Cys-ONp	Alc	128	−55	DMF	776
Z-S-bz-Cys-Ophenacyl		105–106	−109	DMF	616
Z-S-bz-Cys-SePh		93–94	+45	Alc	719
Z-S-bzl-D-Cys	EtAc-Cy	78.5–79	−26	Alc	251
Z-S-bzl-Cys-OBzl	Cy	85–86	−35	DMF	619
Z-S-bzl-Cys-2,4,6-tri-me-OBzl		92–93	+44	DMF	630
Z-S-bzl-Cys-ONp					251

Table 1 Amino Acid Derivatives (continued)

Compound	Method	Solvent	% Yield	Solvent Crystallization	M.P. (°C)	[α] D	Solvent Rotation	Ref.
N-Z-S-bzl-DL-homo-Cys-SePh					87–88			719
Z-S-bzl-seleno-Cys					104–105	–46		145
Z-S-bzl-DL-seleno-Cys					80–81			145
Z-S-bzl-seleno-Cys-ONp					94	–34		145
N-Z-S-btm-Cys				EtAc-He	68–70			231
N-Z-S-btm-Cys-ONp				Alc	107.5–108	–44	DMF	103
				Alc	105.5–106			231
N,S-Di-Z-Cys								777
Z-Cys					163–165	–134	DMF	584
N,S-Di-Z-Cys					121–123	–91	Ac	610
S-Z-Cys-OBzl					106–107			610
Di-Z-Cys-bismelphalan-OEt								36
N,S-Di-Z-Cys-OMe				EtAc-Pe	60–61	–68	DMF	777
S-Z-Cys-OMe Hydrochloride				Me-EtAc	146–147	–14	Me	777
N-Z-Cys Di-me-sulfonium Bromide				Alc-Eth	Oil			609
N-S-Di-Z-Cys-ONp				Alc	93–94	–50	DMF	777
S-Z-Cys-ONp Hydrobromide				Alc-EtAc	148–149	–6.2	Me	777
Mono-Z-Cystine						–120	NaOH-Aq	230
						–111	5N HCl	231
N,N'-Di-Z-Cystine Amide				Me	192–193			187
N,N'-Di-Z-Cystine Me-amide				Me-An	210–211			187
N,N'-Di-Z-Cystine-OMe				Me	59–60			187
Mono-Z-Cystine-bis-OMe Hydrochloride				Me-Eth	155–156			230
N,N'-Z-Cystine-ONp					100			187
N,N'-Bis-Z-diseleno-Cystine					Oil			144
N-Z-S-me-Cys								609
N-Z-4,4'-di-OMe-diphenyl-me-Cys Cyclohexyl-amine Salt				Alc	141–145	–6.5	Me	200
N-Z-S-4,4'-di-OMe-diphenyl-me-Cys-ONp				Alc	126–127.5	–15	DMF	200

Compound	Solvent	mp (°C)	[α]	Solvent	Ref
N-Z-S-NBzl-Cys	Alc-Eth	Oil			304
N-Z-S-NBzl-Cys Cyclohexylamine Salt	Alc	129–130			304
Z-S-NBzl-Cys-ONp	Alc	105–107			309
N-Z-S-bzh-Cys-ONp		96–98	−33	DMF	223
N-Z-S-phenylurathan-Cys		121	−25	Ac	188
			−63	DMF	
N-Z-se-bzl-seleno-Cys-OBzl	Alc-EtAc	64–65	−39	DMF	668
N-Z-se-bzl-seleno-Cys Hydrazide	EtAc-Pe	137–139	−20	DMF	668
N-Z-se-bzl-seleno-Cys-OMe	EtAc-Pe	73–74	−40	DMF	668
N-Z-se-bzl-seleno-Cys-ONBzl	EtAc-Alc	89–90.5	−34	DMF	668
N-Z-se-bzl-DL-seleno-Cys-ONp	EtAc-Pe	98–99			687
N-Z-se-bzl-seleno-Cys-O-diphenyl-Me	Alc	66–67	−48	DMF	668
N-Z-S-(2-Thp)-Cys					231
N-Z-S-(2-Thp)-Cys Benzylamine Salt	Eth	105–107			231
S-Btm-Cys	Aq	200			304
		193–194 (dec)			231
S-Btm-Cys-OMe Hydrochloride	Me-Eth	152.5–154			231
S-Btm-Cys-ONp Hydrobromide	Alc-Eth	141–143	−13	DMF	103
S-(p-Bromophenacyl)-Cys		119–120 (dec)			167
S-Bu^t-Cys-OBu^tHHydrochloride Salt	i-Pr-Eth-Alc	173			81
Boc-S-bzl-Cys		65–66	−44	Ac	46
		85–86			
N-Boc-S-4,4'-di-OMe-diphenyl-me-Cys Cyclohexylamine Salt	Alc	157–159	+16	DMF	200
N-Boc-S-4,4'-di-OMe-diphenyl-me-Cys-Onp	Alc	111–112.5	−21	DMF	200
Boc-se-bzl-seleno-Cys-ONBzl		99–102	−18	DMF	668
S-(2-Carbo-OMe-me-thio)-N-Z-Cys					225
S-Carboxy-me-Cys					654
N-Dichloro-ac-Cys-bis(2-chloro-et) Amide		82.5–84			366
N,N'-Bis(chloro-ac)-Cystine Di-et-amide					187

Table 1 Amino Acid Derivatives (continued)

Compound	Method	Solvent	% Yield	Solvent Crystallization	M.P. (°C)	[α]D	Solvent Rotation	Ref.
S-2-Chloro-et-DL-homo-Cys Hydrochloride					137			97
S-Cys-OBu^t				Aq-An	203–204			81
Cys Copper (I) Complex								654
N, S-Di-Dnp-Cys				Ac-Aq	157–158			609
S-Dnp-Cys-OMe Hydrochloride				DMF-Eth	176 (dec)			609
N-[(2.4-Dnp)-oxycarbonyl] -S-bzl-Cys-OBzl				Pe	87–88	−43	EtAc	156
Et-S-NBzl-Cys Hydrochloride					161–163			231
N-For-S-bz-Cys				An	165	−40	Alc	777
N-For-S-Z-Cys				Aq	141–142			304
				EtAc	140–141	−431	DMF	777
N-For-S-Btm-Cys				Aq	138			304
N-For-S-trt-Cys-di-et-ammonium Salt					162–165			222
S-2-Hydroxy-et-DL-homo-Cys				Aq-An	230 (dec)			97
N-(2-Hydroxy-l-naphthylidene)-S-trt-Cys				Alc-Me	154.5–155	−23	Alc	228
S-(N-me-2-amino-et)-Cys-di-hydrochloride				Alc	170–171 (dec)	−6.4	N HCl	250
Di-me-N, N′-bis-bz-Cystine				Me	179–180	−241	DMF	224
S-Me-Cys-OMe Hydrochloride				Acn	150–151	+27	DMF	33
				Me-Eth	135			609
S-4, 4′-Di-OMe-diphenyl-me-Cys				Aq-DMF	211	+10	1N-NaOH	200
S-3, 3′, 4, 4′-Tetra-OMe-diphenyl-me-Cys				Aq-DMF	208–210 (dec)	+10	DMF	200
Me-S-(2-Thp)-Cys Hydrochloride					Oil			193
S-(N-Me-2-toluene-p-sulphonamido-et)-Cys				Aq	184–188	+2.6	N HCl	250
N-Me-N-tos-S-bzl-Cys Hydrazide				Alc	141–142			295
N-Me-N-tos-S-bzl-Cys DCHA Salt				Be-Pe	132–133			295
N-Me-N-tos-S-bzl-Cys-OMe				Aq-Alc	87–88			295
N-Bzl-N-Z-se-bzl-seleno-Cys				Et-Ac-Alc	89–90.5	−34	DMF	668
N-Nps-S-bz-Cys-ONp				Alc	101–102	−51	DMF	775

30

Compound	Crystn. solvent	M.p.	$[\alpha]_D$	Solvent	Ref.
Nps-S-bzl-Cys DCHA Salt		168–169	−43	DMF	774
S-Nps-Cys		168 (dec)	−72	Me	479
N,S-Di-Nps-Cys-OMe		198	−42	DMF	775
N-Nps-S-trt-Cys	Me	146	−46	Chf	774
N-Nps-S-trt-Cys-O-phenacyl	Aq-Acn	115			661
S-Di-bzh-Cys		210 (dec)			200
S-Phenylurathan-Cys			−91 −36	Ac HCl	188
N-Pht-S-trt-Cys Di-et-ammonium Salt	EtAc-Eth	161–164	−22	Chf	229
N-Salicylidene-S-trt-Cys	MeCl-Eth	141 (dec)	−5.5	THF	228
N-Salicylidene-S-trt-Cys DCHA Salt		150–151 (dec)	−41	THF	228
Se-bzl-seleno-Cys	Aq	175–178 175–178 (dec)	+36 +36	NaOH-Aq NaOH-Aq	668 668
Se-bzl-seleno-Cys-ONBzl Hydrobromide	i-Pr-DMF-Eth	183–184 (dec)	+35	NaOH-Aq	687
Diseleno-Cystine-di-OMe Dihydrochloride		154–155	−11	Alc	668
S-(2-Toluene-p-sulphonamido-et)-Cys	Aq	192–193 (dec)			144
S-(2-Toluene-p-sulphonamido-et)-homo-Cys	Aq	198–200	+12	N HCl	250
N-(Tos-6-aminohexoyl)-S-bzl-Cys-OBzl		135–147	−21	Alc	250
Tos-S-bzl-D-Cys		125–126	−10	Alc	515
N-Tos-S-bzl-Cys Chloride	Chf-Pe	111–112 114–116	+14	Chf	292 42
N-Tos-S-bzl-Cys-OEt	Chf-Pe-Alc-Aq	72–73	+35	Alc	292
N,N′-Di-p-tos-Cystine Bis-bzl-amide	i-Pr	204			42
S-Trt-Z-Cys Diethylamine Salt	An	168–170			419
S-Trt-Z-Cys-OMe		Oil	+118	Di	230 230
S-Trt-Cys	DMF-Aq	183.5 (dec)	+114	0.04N Alc HCl	221
S-Trt-Cys		167–168	+108	0.04 Alc HCl	228

Table 1 Amino Acid Derivatives (continued)

Compound	Method	Solvent	% Yield	Solvent Crystallization	M.P.(°C)	$[\alpha]_D$	Solvent Rotation	Ref.
S,N-Di-trt-Cys-OBzh				Eth-Me	124-124.5	-51	An	219
S-Trt-Cys-OBzh Hydrochloride					80			219
S-Trt-Cys-OBzh Oxalate				An-Pe-Eth	192-194			219
N,S-Di-trt-Cys Di-et-ammonium Salt								222
S-Trt-Cys-O-phenacyl Hydrochloride				EtAc-Eth	68			661
Glutamine								
N-Ac-DL-Gln-2, 3, 3, 4, 4-d$_5$				Alc	180.5-181.5			58
N-Ac-D-Gln-2, 3, 3, 4, 4-d$_5$				Alc	193-195	+12	Aq	58
N-Ac-Gln-α-OMe-γ-bzl					148-148.5			603
Aoc-Gln				EtAc-Eth	115.5-116.5	-19	DMF	248
Z-Gln					130-131			163
Z-Gln-γ-OBzl				THF	182-183	-5.7	DMF	603
Z-Gln-OBzl				Me	137			384
Z-Gln-ONBzl				EtAc	129-130	-7.5	Ac	694
Z-Gln-γ-OBu^t				Alc-Eth	138-142	-7.3	DMF	669
Z-Gln-α-OMe-γ-OBzl				Pe	80-82	-9	Alc	534
Z-Gln-α-ONp-γ-OBu^t				Di	235-235.5			603
Z-Gln-O-phenacyl					55-58	-24	An	542
Z-iso-Gln				Alc	151-152	-18	DMF	661
				Aq	174.5-175	-6.0	Me	497
				Ac-Pe	171-173	-4.6	Me	163
Z-iso-Gln-OBzl				Me	126-127			384
Z-iso-Gln-OMe				Alc	119-120	-6.9	Me	384
N$^\alpha$-Z-N$^\gamma$-xanthyl-Gln-ONp				Alc-DMF	196-198	-8.6	DMF	400
Boc-Gln					116-119	-16	DMF	46
Boc-Gln-ONp				Alc	154-155	-35	DMF	46

Gln	Aq-Alc	176-180	+6.4	Aq	661
	Alc	183-184	+5.8	Aq	163
Gln-2, 3, 4, 4-d$_5$			+31	1N HCl	626
Gln-α-OBzl		218-220	+29	N HCl	58
					603
Gln 2, 4, 6-Tri-me-OBzl Hydrochloride	Me-EtAc	172.5-174	-2.8	Aq	626
Gln-ONBzl Hydrobromide	i-Pr-Pe	163-165	+5.6	DMF	669
Gln-ONp Toluenesulphonate	Aq	164.5-166	+9.0	DMF	628
Gln-O-bzh Hydrochloride	Me-EtAc	169	-7.5	DMF	661
Iso-Gln	Aq-Alc	186-186.5	+21	Aq	497
					163
N-ONp-Gln		165	-74	DMF	774
Nps-Gln-2, 4, 6-tri-OMe-bzl	Chf-Cy	143.5-145.5	-5.2	DMF	626
Pht-Gln	Aq	161-163	-34	Alc	562
Pht-Gln-ONp	Alc-Pe	86.5-88	-87	Me	562
Pht-iso-Gln	EtAc-Pe				562
Tos-Gln-α-OBu^t	Me-Alc	120-122	+13	Me	660
N-Trt-Gln-OBzl	Me-Eth	148-148.5			775
N$^\alpha$-Xanthyl-Gln-OMe Acetate					603
Glutamic Acid					
N-Ac-2-carbethoxy-Glu-3, 3, 4, 4-d$_4$-di-OEt	Aq-Alc	64-64.5			58
N-Ac-D-Glu-2, 3, 3, 4, 4-d$_5$	Aq-Alc	188.5-190			58
N-Ac-Glu-2, 3, 3, 4, 4-d$_5$		178-180			58
N-Ac-Dl-Glu-2, 3, 3, 4, 4-d$_5$-γ-OMe	Di-He	111.5-112.5			58
N-Ac-Glu-α-OMe-γ-bzh		148-148.5			603
N-Aoc-Gly-γ-OBzl DCHA Salt	EtAc-Pe	120.5-122	+11	Alc	248
Z-γ-OBu^t-Glu-Abu-OBu^t		Oil			658
Z-D-Glu	EtAc	118-120	+7.6	Ac	330
		93-95			449
Z-Glu Anhydride	Chf-Eth	91-92	+43	Ac	330
					332

Table 1 Amino Acid Derivatives (continued)

Compound	Method	Solvent	% Yield	Solvent Crystallization	M.P.(°C)	$[\alpha]_D$	Solvent Rotation	Ref.
Z-Glu Anhydride				Chf-Eth	86-88	-39	Ac	163
					91-92	-15	THF	24
Z-Glu-α-[4-cl-ph-azo]-Oph-γ-OBzl				EtAc-He	122.5-123	-5.7	DMF	603
Z-Glu-γ-OBzh				Thf	182-183	+1.8	Ac	163
Z-Glu-γ-OBzl-Amide				EtAc	130-132			163
Z-Glu-γ-OBzl-Amide DCHA Salt				EtAc	141-142			384
Z-Glu-OBzl				Pe	77	-23	KHCO$_3$-Aq	384
				Eth-Pe	96-97	-10	Ac	384
				Cte	69-71	-24	KHCO$_3$-Aq	694
Z-Glu-α-OBzl				Me-Aq	96.5-98.5	-11	Ac	423
Z-Glu-γ-OBzl					94-96	-22	KHCO$_3$-Aq	674
					75-76			213
Z-Glu-α-OBzl-DL-abu-ONp				EtAc-He	94-96	-18	THF	382
Z-Glu-α-OBzl-γ-4-[4-cl-ph-azo]-OPh				EtAc-Pe	134-134.5			24
Z-Glu-α-OBzl-γ-OBu^t				EtAc-Pe	46-48			575
					49-51.5	-20	Me	423
Z-Glu-α-OBzl-α-OBu^t				EtAc-Pe	48-49	+12	Alc	562
Z-Glu-γ-OBzl DCHA Salt				Alc-Eth	143-145	+7.9	Me	384
Z-Glu-α-OBzl-γ-DCHA Salt				Me-i-Pr-Eth	144-146	-13	Me	694
				Me-i-Pr-Eth	163-164			694
Z-Glu-mono-OBzl Mixture								384
Z-Glu-α-OBzl-γ-OPht-me				Alc	91-93	-14	DMF	705
Z-Glu-α-OBzl-γ-SPh				EtAc-Pe	85-86	-2.3	THF	694
Z-Glu-α-OBu^t					Oil	-16	Me	562
								660

Compound	Recryst. solvent	m.p.	$[\alpha]_D$	Solvent	Ref.
Z-Glu-α-OBu^t DCHA Salt	Alc-Eth	149			660
Z-Glu-α-OBu^t DCHA Salt	Alc-Eth	139–141			434
Z-Glu-γ-OBu^t DCHA Salt	Aq	139			658
Z-Glu-α-OBu^t-γ-hydrazide	EtAc-Pe	140–141			575
Z-Glu-α-OBu^t-γ-OMe		111			660
Z-Glu-α-OBu^t-α-OPcp	Me	Oil			660
Z-Glu-γ-OBu^t-α-OPht-me	i-Bu-Pe	122–124			343
Z-Glu-O [4-(4-chloro-phenylazo)-phenyl] Mixture		72	−13	DMF	434, 24
N-[γ-(Z-Glu)]-N,N′-dicyclohexyl Urea					165
Z-Glu-γ-OEt	EtAc-Pe	150–151			674
Z-Glu-α-OEt					225
Z-Glu-α-OEt-γ-OBu^t		Oil			575, 658
Z-Glu-α-OEt DCHA Salt	Aq	155–157			225
Z-Glu-α-OEt-γ-ONBzl		75–76	−11	DMF	635
Z-Glu-α-OEt-γ-ONBzl Hydrobromide	Aq	139–140	+5.3	Aq	635
Z-Glu-γ-hydrazide		180–181	−14	HCl	163
Z-Glu-OMe					449
Z-D-Glu-γ-OMe		65–70	+15	1N KHCO$_3$	175
Z-Glu-γ-OMe		76	−16	1N KHCO$_3$	175
Z-Glu-γ-OMe		68–70	−14	NaHCO$_3$-Aq	384
Z-Glu-α-OMe-γ-OBzl	Di	235–235.5	−24	An	603
Z-Glu-α-ONp-α-OBu^t	Alc	55–58	−33	DMF	542
Z-Glu-α-ONp-γ-OMe	Alc	108	−27	DMF	175
Z-Glu-α-Ophenacyl	An-Aq	74–75	−31	Me	637
Z-Glu-α-Ophenacyl DCHA Salt	Alc	69–79	−16	Me	661
Z-Glu-γ-Ophenacyl DCHA Salt	An	149–151	+7.0	Me	661
Z-Glu-α-Odiphenyl-me DCHA Salt	Alc	141–142	−19	Me	661
Z-Glu-α-Odiphenyl-me-γ-Ophenacyl	Me	176–177	−22	DMF	661
		124.5–125.5			661

Table 1   Amino Acid Derivatives (continued)

Compound	Method	Solvent	% Yield	Solvent Crystallization	M.P. (°C)	[α] D	Solvent Rotation	Ref.
Z-Glu-α-OPht-me DCHA Salt				i-Pr	150–153			434
Z-Glu-α-SePh-γ-OCH₃				Alc	104.5–105	−31	Alc	719
Z-Glu-α-OTcp-γ-OBu^t				Cy	108–109			423
Z(OMe)-Glu				EtAc-Pe	110–111	−5.5	Ac	695
Z(OMe)-Glu Anhydride					87–88			694
Z(OMe)-Glu-α-OBzl				Alc-Aq	70–71	−9.0	Ac	694
								695
Z(OMe)-Glu-α-OBzl-γ DCHA Salt				Me-Aq	163–164	−12	Me	694
Z-(OMe)-Glu-γ-OBzl-α DCHA Salt				Me-i-Pr	146–147	+4.2	Me	694
Z(OMe)-Glu Diammonium Salt				Alc	176–177			695
Z(OMe)-pyro-Glu					143–144	−10	Me	562
Z(OMe)-pyro-Glu DCHA Salt					170–171	−24	Ac-Aq	562
Z(NO₂)-pyro-Glu					167–168	−45	Ac	562
Z(NO₂)-pyro-Glu DCHA Salt					202–203	−28	Ac	562
Z-D-pyro-Glu				EtAc-Pe	137–138	+44	Ac	330
Z-pyro-Glu				EtAc-Pe	134–135	−29	Me	163
Z-pyro-Glu Amide				Aq	157–158	+1.4	Alc	163
Z-pyro-Glu-OBzl				EtAc	106–107	−41	Alc	163
Z-pyro-Glu Boc-hydrazide				EtAc	130–131	−14	DMF	330
Z-pyro-Glu Chloride				Be-Pe	70–72	−31	THF	163
Z-pyro-Glu DCHA Salt				Chf-Eth	195–196	−17	Chf	163
					199–200			
Z-pyro-Glu Hydrazide				Alc-Aq	188–190	−23	Ac-Aq	330
Z-pyro-Glu-ONBzl				EtAc	108–109	−27	Ac-Aq	163
Z-pyro-Glu-ONp				EtAc	141–142	−52	THF	551
				EtAc	140–141	−50	THF	163
Z-pyro-Glu-Op				EtAc	141–143	−50	THF	330
				EtAc-Pe	106–107	−51	THF	163
Z-pyro-Glu-Trt-hydrazide				Chf-Pe	186–188	+4.7	DMF	330

Compound	Solvent (recrystn.)	m.p. (°C)	$[\alpha]_D$	Solvent	Ref.
Z-SePh-Glu-OBzl		92–93	−16	Alc	719
Boc-Glu		110–112	−16	Me	562
Boc-Glu Anhydride		115–116	−47	Ac	562
Boc-Glu-α-OBzl		123–125	−37	THF	90
Boc-Glu-γ-OBzl		138–139	+11	Me	562
		Oil		Me	90
Boc-Glu-γ-OBzl DCHA Salt		92–93	−29	Me	562
Boc-Glu-α-OBu^t-γ-OBzl		172	−19	Me	562
Boc-Glu-γ-OBu^t		73–74	−25	Me	562
Boc-Glu-γ-OBu^t DCHA Salt		101–102	−10	Me	562
Boc-Glu-α-OCH$_2$-CN-γ-OBu^t		140–141	+10	Me	562
Boc-Glu-α-OMe		89–90	−30	Me	562
		Oil			9
Boc-Glu-α-OMe-γ-OBzl		63–64	−22	Me	562
Boc-Glu-γ-OMe DCHA Salt	EtAc	155–157	+10	Me	9
Boc-Glu-γ-ONBzl		167–168	−13	Me	562
Boc-Glu-α-ONp-γ-OBzl		171–172	−10	Me	562
Boc-pyro-Glu	EtAc	120–121			370
		182–184	−1.8	Chf	90
Boc-pyro-Glu DCHA Salt		115–116	−35	Ac	562
Boc-pyro-Glu-α-ONp		183–184	−16	Ac	562
N-For-Glu-γ-OBzl		143–145	−25	EtAc	90
For-Glu-ONBzl	Alc	130–131	+17	Alc	213
N-For-pyro-Glu	Alc	152–153	−19	DMF	669
		180	−1.1	Alc	163
DL-Glu		189–190.5			6
Glu-2,3,4,4-d_5					6
DL-Glu-2,3,3,4,4-d_5					6
N-(DL-γ-Glu)-2-aminoethanol	Aq-Alc	193–194			149
N-(DL-γ-Glu)-n-bu-amine	Aq-Alc	213–214			149
N-(DL-γ-Glu)-aniline	Aq-Alc	208–209			149
Glu-γ-OBzl		174	+21	Ac	674
					213
					362

Table 1 Amino Acid Derivatives (continued)

Compound	Method	Solvent	% Yield	Solvent Crystallization	M.P.(°C)	[α] D	Solvent Rotation	Ref.
Glu-di-OBzl Benzenesulfonate				Me-Eth	115-117	+18	Py	601
Glu-α-OBzl-γ-OBu^t Hydrochloride					122-123	+14	Me	562
Glu-di-OBzl Hydrochloride				Me-Eth	100-102			601
Glu-α-OBzl-γ-ONp Hydrobromide				Ac-Eth	123.5	+29	Alc	383
					128-131	+6	Alc	
Glu-α-OBzl-γ-ONp Hydroiodide				Ac-Eth	132-134	+6.3	Ac	383
				Alc-Eth	140-142 (dec)	+9.6	Alc	383
Glu-γ-OBu^t					186-187	+10	Aq	562
						+18	Ac	
					182	+9.8	Aq	775
					168-169			658
Glu-γ-OBu^t N-Carboxyanhydride				EtAc-Pe-Eth	95-96	-19	EtAc	510
Glu-γ-OBu^t Hydrochloride					180	+22	Aq	775
DL-Glu-d$_9$ Deuteriochloride								58
Glu-α-2, 6-dichloro-4-ONp-γ-OEt Hydrobromide				Alc-EtAc	148-148.5 (dec)	+9.0	DMF	623
Glu-α-Odiphenyl-OMe					165	-5.0	Me	661
Glu-α-OBzh-γ-Ophenacyl Hydrochloride				Me-EtAc	137	-27	Me	661
Glu-γ-OEt				Alc	174-176	+12	Aq	674
				EtAc-Pe	96-97	-14	Me	58
Glu-di-OEt				Alc-An	167-168			43
N-(DL-γ-Glu)-di-et-amine								149
Glu-α-OEt-γ-OBu^t				Aq	131-133	+18	Alc	225
Glu-α-OEt-γ-OBu^t Oxalate				Me-Eth	109-110	+22	Alc	225
Glu-di-OEt Hydrochloride				Aq-Me	165-166			175
N-(DL-γ-Glu)-N-me-aniline					173.5-174.5	+13	Aq	149
								58
Glu-γ-OMe				Aq-Me	175-176	+31	5N HC1	175

Compound	Recrystn.	M.p.	[α]	Solvent	Page
DL-Glu-2,3,3,4,4-d$_5$-γ-OMe		169.5-172	-32	5N HCl	58
D-Glu-γ-OMe		175-176	+30	Aq	175
Glu-α-OMe-γ-ONp Hydrobromide		172-173	+90	Aq	384
Glu-α-OMe-γ-SPh		183-185	+18	Ac	384
Glu-γ-1-Onaphthylmethyl		180-181	+15	Py	361
Glu-di-ONBzl Benzenesulfonate	Alc	152-153			561
Glu-α-ONp-γ-OBzl Hydrobromide	CHF-Eth	120	-2.3	DMF	774
Glu-α-ONp-γ-et Hydrobromide	Alc-Eth	162-163	+23	Alc	637
Glu-α-ONp-γ-OMe Hydrobromide	Me-Eth	179	+23	Me	175
Glu-α-Ophenacyl Hydrobromide	EtAc-Alc	163-164	+18	Me	661
Glu-γ-Ophenacyl Hydrochloride	Me-EtAc	166	+31	Me	661
Glu-α-Ophenacyl-γ-Odiphenyl-OMe Hydrochloride	Me-Eth	150-151	+13	Ac	661
Glu-γ-OPht-me	Aq	174			705
Glu-γ-OPht-me α, N-Carboxy Anhydride	EtAc-Pe	134			705
Glu-α-SePh-γ-OMe Hydrobromide		174-175	+86	1N HCl	719
Glu-α-SPh Hydrobromide		172-174			384
Glu-γ-SPh Hydrobromide		149-152			384
B-[Bis(NBzl)-phosphoryl]-Glu-di-OBzl	Alc	84			99
N-[Bis(NBzl)-phosphoryl]-Glu-di-OEt	Alc	94			99
N-O-Nps-Glu-γ-OBzl DCHA Salt		168	-34	Chf	774
N-Nps-Glu-α-diphenyl-OMe- DCHA Salt	Alc	180-181	-33	Me	661
N-Nps-Glu-α-Odiphenyl-me-γ-Ophenacyl	i-Pr	133-133.5	-33	DMF	661
N-Nps-Glu-α-Np-γ-Bzl		77-78	-121	DMF	774
N-Nps-Glu-γ-Ophenacyl DCHA Salt	Alc	180-181	-17	DMF	661
N-Nps-Glu-α-Ophenacyl DCHA Salt	EtAc	148-149	-57	Me	661
N, N-Pht-(DL-γ-Glu)-aniline	Alc-Cy	177-178			149
N, N-Pht-(DL-γ-Glu)-di-et-amine	Aq-Alc	135-136			149
N, N-Pht-(DL-γ-Glu)-N-me-aniline	Aq-Alc	185-186			149
Pht-lauryl-Glu	Aq	above 300 (dec)			614
Pht-lauryl-DL-Glu-di-OEt	Alc-Aq	75-77			614
Pyro-Glu	EtAc-Alc-Pe	156-157	+7.7	Me	163

39

Table 1 Amino Acid Derivatives (continued)

Compound	Method	Solvent	% Yield	Solvent Crystallization	M.P.(°C)	[α]D	Solvent Rotation	Ref
Pyro-Glu N-Buᵗ-amide				Alc-Aq	184.5-185.5			81
Pyro-Glu DCHA Salt				Alc-Pe	185-187	-13	Aq	163
Pyro-Glu-OTcp				Me-Pe	158-159	+18	DMF	9
Sodium Copper Glu								362
Succinyl-bis (Glu)				Me-Eth	108-109	-2.8	Alc	43
Succinyl-bis (Glu-di-OBzl)				Cte-Pe	57-58	-10	Alc	43
Succinyl-bis (Glu-di-OEt)				EtAc-Pe	185-190	-24	Alc	43
N-Tos-Glu-γ-bzl DCHA Salt				DMF		+35	Chf	434
N-Tos-Glu-α-OBzl-γ-OPht-me								434
N-Tos-Glu-α-OBuᵗ				Me	121	+32	Chf	660
N-Tos-Glu-α-OBuᵗ-γ-hydrazide				Me	104	+42	Chf	660
N-Tos-Glu-Di-ONBzl				EtAc	118	-9.0	DMF	434
N-Tos-Glu γ-ONBzl DCHA Salt				Alc	189.5-191	+89	Chf	434
N-Tos-Glu γ-OPht				Alc	110-112	-0.7	DMF	434
N-Tos-Glu-α-OPht-γ-OBzl					194-195			434
N-Tos-Glu γ-OPht-me DCHA Salt				Alc	136-137	-6.0	DMF	434
N-Tos-Glu-γ-α-Pht-ONBzl-me				EtAc-Pe	130-131	-28	EtAc	163
Tos-pyro-Glu				Me	109			660
Tos-pyro-Glu-OBuᵗ					214-215	-24	Chf	163
Tos-pyro-Glu DCHA Salt				Chf-Pe	66-67	-42	THF	163
N-Tfa-Glu Anhydride								
Glycine								
Ac-D-cyclohexyl-Gly				Aq-Ac	210-211	-32	Ac	128
Ac-DL-cyclohexyl-Gly				Aq	196-197			128
Ac-D-cyclopentyl-Gly				Aq	184-186	+2	Ac	128
Ac-DL-cyclopentyl-Gly				Aq	170-172	+6	Alc	128

Compound	Solvent	M.p. (°C)	$[\alpha]$		Ref.
Actinocinyl-bis[Gly-OMe]	Alc-Pe	291–293			77
N-OBzhoc-Gly-ONp	Eth-Pe	96–97			219
N-Bzhoc-Gly		114.5–115			219
S-Bzhoc-Gly	Aq	161–163			421
N, N-Bis(β-bz-et)Gly		189.5–191.5			107
Bz-Gly					631
Bz-Gly Azlactone		89–90			119
Bz-Gly-bzl Amide		163–164			119
N-Bz-Gly Anilide	Alc	213–214			623
Bz-Gly 2, 6-Dichloro-4-ONp	Alc	144–144.5			182
Bz-Gly-OCH (Ph) CN	EtAc-Cy	88.5–89			623
N-Bz-Gly-OCH₂CN	EtAc-Cy	100–101			633
Bz-Gly-Odicyclohexylurea	EtAc	156–160			636
Bzl-N-Z-N-(carboxy-me)-Gly-OSu		Oil			119
S-Bzl-carbonyl-Gly Phenylhydrazide					181
N-Bzl-Gly-bis (2-chloro-et) Amide		100–102			421
Z-aminoisobutyryl-DL-phenyl-Gly		158–159.5			366
Z-aminoisobutyryl-D-phenyl-Gly		175.5–176.5			429
Z-aminoisobutyryl-D-phenyl-Gly-OMe	Eth	122–123	−85	Di	429
Z-aminoisobutyryl-DL-phenyl-Gly-OMe		127.5–128.5			429
Z-buᵗ-Gly Amide		149	+4.4	DMF	275
Z-DL-ethionyl-Gly-OEt	EtAc-Pe	74			97
Z-Gly		73–75			584
		119–120			119
		119–120			634
Z-Gly-Abu	Aq	155–158.5			125
Z-Gly-Abu-OEt	EtAc	80.5–83			125
Z-Gly Amide		135–136			700
		138–139			

Table 1 Amino Acid Derivatives (continued)

Compound	Method	Solvent	% Yield	Solvent Crystallization	M.P. (°C)	[α]D	Solvent Rotation	Ref.
Z-Gly-α-aminoisobutyric Acid					135–136			55
								615
Z-Gly-α-aminoisobutyric-OEt				Aq	155–158.5			125
Z-Gly-anhydride				EtAc-Pe	80.5–83			125
					118–119			615
								119
Z-Gly Anilide				Chf	145–146.5			388
Z-Gly Bzl Amide				Me-Aq	145–147			99
Z-Gly-OBzl				An-Aq	119–120			712
1-(N-Z-Gly)-2, 5-di-bzl-3,6-dioxopiperazine				Cy	72–73			619
Bis[Z-Gly]-carbohydrazide				EtAc-Pe	175–176			177
O(N-Z-Gly) p-Chlorobenzohydroxamic Acid					208–209			157
1(N-Z-Gly)-2, 2-bis(2-chloro-et) Hydrazine				EtAc-Pe	173–174			178
Z-Gly-2,6-dichloro-4-ONp				Alc-Cy	126–127			523
					139.5–140.5			623
Z-Gly-Odicyclohexylurea					144–145			119
Z-Gly-OCH (Ph) CN				EtAc-Cy	73–74			633
Z-Gly-OCH₂CN				Eth	57–58			636
Z-Gly-et-Orthoester					38–40			773
N-[N-(Z)Gly]-D-glucosylamine				Alc	178–179	+1.6	Me	116
Bis[di-Z-Gly] Hydrazide				Ac-Aq	211–212			711
N-(Z-Gly)-imidazole				THF-Eth	119–120			465
Z-Gly Me-amide								55
Z-Gly-p-me-OBzl				Cy	86.5–87.5			624
Z-Gly-p-MeO-OBzl				EtAc-Cy	55.5–56			619
				EtAc-Pe	60			695
Z-Gly-O-tri-me-silyl								54
Z-Gly-ONp				Alc	128			32

Compound	Solvent	m.p./b.p.	[α]	Solvent	Ref.
3-(N-Z-Gly)-2-oxo-oxazolinine-4-carbonyl-Ala-OMe	EtAc-Pe	172.5–173	−113	Me	296
Z-Gly-OPmb	Cy	113.5–115			624
Z-Gly-Ophenacyl	i-Pr	103			616
Z-Gly Piperidide		109–110			700
Z-Gly-SePh		70.5–71			719
Z-Gly Semicarbazide	Aq	188–190			444
Z-Gly-OSu	MeCl-Pe	113–114			7
Z-Gly-thiocresyl Ester	EtAc-Pe	93–94			703
Z-Gly-thiophenyl Ester	EtAc-He	71–73			59
N-(Z-hydrozinothiocarbonyl)-Gly-OEt		141–143			155
Z(NO₂)-allyl-Gly	Be	81–83	+4.5	DMF	612
Z(NO₂)-Gly Amide	Di	198–199			469
Z(NO₂)-Gly-ONp	EtAc-Pe	138			305
Z(NO₂)-OMe	Me	121			469
Boc-Gly	EtAc-Pen	89–90			475
Boc-Gly DCHA Salt	Alc-Pe	168–169			46
Boc-Gly-OSu					356
N, N-Di-n-bu-Gly-OEt		b.p. 136–137 C/35 mm			519
β-Carboxypropionyl-Gly-OEt	Chf-Eth	96–97			43
Chloroac-DL-cyclopentyl-Gly	Aq	140–142			128
N-Di-chloro-ac-Gly-bis (2-chloro-et) Amide		62.5–63.5			366
7-Chloro-1-descarboxy-actinocinyl-Gly-OMe	Chf-Pe	256–259			77
N-[Bis (2-chloro-et) amino-bz] Gly					150
N-[Bis(2-chloro-et) amino-bz] Gly-OEt					150
1, 1-Bis (2-chloro-et)-2-Gly-hydrazine Picrolonate		183–184 (dec)			523
[Co (trien) Gly-N, N-di-et-amide Cl] (ClO₄)₂					96
[Co (trien) (Gly-OEt) Cl] (ClO₄)₂					96
[Co (trien) Gly-OEt-Cl] Cl₂					96
[Co (trien) Gly-N-isopropyl Amide Cl] (ClO₄)₂					96
[Co (trien) Gly-N-me-amide Cl] (ClO₄)₂					96

Table 1 Amino Acid Derivatives (continued)

Compound	Method	Solvent	% Yield	Solvent Crystallization	M.P.(°C)	[α]D	Solvent Rotation	Ref.
[Co (trien) Gly-N, N-di-me-amide Cl] (ClO4)2								96
[Co (Trien) Gly-OMe] (ClO4)3								96
Cyclohexyl-Gly						+35	5N HCl	128
D-Cyclohexyl-Gly						-217	1N HCl	128
D-Cyclohexyl-Gly-OMe				Me-Eth	190-191			128
L-Cyclohexyl-Gly-OMe				Me-Eth	188-189	+33	Me	128
Cyclopentyl-Gly				Aq-Alc		+17	5N HCl	128
D-Cyclopentyl-Gly				Aq-Alc		-17	5N HCl	128
Cyclopentyl-Gly-OMe Hydrochloride				Me-Eth	177-179	+31	Me	128
Dnp-Gly					230-231			391
					261-262			390
Dnp-Gly Anilide					129-130			390
Dnp-Gly Chloride					263-264			391
Dnp-Gly p-Toluidide				Pe	85-86			156
N-[(2,4-Dinitro-ph)-oxycarbonyl]-Gly-OEt					Oil			99
N-Diphenylphosphoryl-Gly-OBzl				Aq-An	195 (dec)			97
DL-Ethionyl-Gly					b.p. 96-98 C/28 mm			519
N, N-Di-et-Gly-O-n-pr								630
For-Gly-2,4,6-tri-me-OBzl				EtAc-Cy	125.5-126.5			36
N-For-melphalanyl-Gly-OEt								182
Gly Anilide Hydrochloride					200-203			219
Gly-OBzh Oxalate				Me	155-155.5			229
Gly-OBzh Toluenesulfonate				MeCl-Eth	138-141			213
Gly-OBzl								564
Gly Bzl-amide- Hydrobromide				Alc	184-186			458
Gly Z-hydrazide Trifluoroacetate				Eth-He	174-175			360
Gly-O-p-bromophenacyl Hydrobromide					195.5-			

Compound	Solvent	M.p. (°C)	[α]_D	Ref.
Gly-OBu^t		197.5 (dec)		96
		b.p. 56–59 (15 mm)		564
Gly-OBu^t Hydrochloride		137–140		6, 370
Gly-OBu^t Phosphite				564
Gly-2,6-dichloro-4-ONp Hydrobromide	Alc-EtAc	216–218		623
Gly-OCH (Ph) CN Hydrobromide	Alc-Eth	163.5–165		633
Gly-DL-ethionine	Aq-An	195 (dec)		97
Gly-OEt		b.p. 30 (1 mm)		173
N-Gly-D-glucosylamine Hydrogen Oxalate	Aq	190–191 (dec)	−14	6, 116
Gly-N-isopropylamide Hydrochloride	EtAc-Pe	98		96
Gly N-Me-amide Hydrochloride	EtAc-Pe	108–109		96
Gly-p-me-OBzl Hydrochloride	Me-EtAc	158.5–159.5		624
Gly-2,4,6-tri-me-OBzl Hydrochloride	Me-EtAc	175–176		631
Gly-N,N-di-me-di-et-amide Hydrochloride				96
Gly-N,N-di-me Hydrochloride				96
Gly-ONBzl	Eth	51–53		269
Gly-ONBzl Benzenesulfonate	Alc	191–192		561
Gly-ONBzl Hydrobromide		194.5–197		734
Gly-OPmb Hydrochloride	Me-EtAc	226–228		624
Gly-Ophenacyl Hydrobromide	i-Pr	171–172		616
Gly-O-β-phenethyl Hydrochloride	Me-Eth	140–141		661
Gly-OBzh Hydrochloride		134–135		616
Gly-semicarbazide Hydrochloride	Aq-Alc	183–185		444
Gly-SePh Hydrobromide		176		719
Gly-OTrt Hydrochloride	Thf-DMF	133–134		616
DL-Dihydrolipoly-Gly	EtAc	63–64		109

Table 1 Amino Acid Derivatives (continued)

Compound	Method	Solvent	% Yield	Solvent Crystallization	M.P.(°C)	[α] D	Solvent Rotation	Ref
N-(2-Hydroxy-2-phenyl-et)-Gly				DMF	204			40
N-(2-Hydroxy-1-phenyl-et)-Gly Hydrochloride				Alc-An	152			40
N-(2-Hydroxy-2-phenyl-et)-Gly Lactone				EtAc	118–120			40
N-Imidazole-carbonyl-Gly-OEt					107–108			155
N-((Imidazolethylcarbonyl)-Gly-OEt					94–96			155
2-Iodo-OEt-carbonyl-Gly								182
2-Iodo-OEt-carbonyl-Gly Anilide				Alc	173–174			182
DL-Lipoyl-Gly Bzh-ammonium Salt				Me-Eth	130–131			109
N-(5,5-Di-me-cyclohex-2-en-1-on-3-yl)-Gly				Aq	224–225			196
				Aq	224			197
N-(5,5-Di-me-2-cyclohexen-1-on-3-yl)-Gly Amide				Aq	204			197
N-i5,5-Di-me-2-cyclohexen-1-on-3-yl)-Gly-OBzl				Be	132			197
N-(5,5-Di-me-2-cyclohexen-1-on-3-yl)-Gly Hydrobromide				Alc-Eth	189			197
N-(5,5-Di-me-2-cyclohexen-1-on-3-yl)-Gly Hydrochloride				Alc-Eth	192			197
N-4,4′-Di-OMe-diphenyl-me-Gly				Aq-An	192–194			200
N-4,4′-Di-OMe-diphenyl-me-Gly Hydrazide				EtAc-Eth	113–114			200
N-4,4′-Di-OMe-diphenyl-me-Gly Hydrochloride								200
N-4,4′-Di-OMe-2,2′-di-me-diphenyl-me-Gly-OMe				Pe	62–64			200
N-4,4′-Di-OMe-2,2′-di-me-diphenyl-me-Gly				Alc	160			200
Nps-Gly DCHA Salt					190–191			774
Nps-Gly-OEt					81–83			774
DL-Phenyl-Gly					b.p. 96–98 (0.1 mm)			429
DL-Phenyl-Gly-OMe						+61		173
Nγ-Pht-Dbu-Gly Amide				Alc	188–190		Ac	771

46

Compound	M.p. (°C)	[α]	Solvent	Cryst. solvent	Ref.
Pht-Gly Acid Chloride	131–131.5			An-Pe	516
N-Pht-Gly-OBzh	74–75			Be-Pe	219
Pht-Gly Bromide	93–96			Alc	285
Pht-Gly-OBu^t					564
N-Pht-Gly-p-N-di(β-chloro-et)-aminophenyl-amide	226–227 (dec)			An	516
Pht-Gly Cyanide	140–143 (dec)			Be	285
N-Pht-Gly-OCH$_2$CN	136–137			Alc	636
Pht-Gly-OPmb	171–172.5			EtAc	630
Pht-Gly-Ophenacyl	149–150			Alc	591
Pht-Gly-SePh	101				719
Pht-Gly-OSu	182–183			i-Pr	7
Pht-Tauryl-Gly	300 (dec)			Aq	614
Pht-Tauryl-Gly-OEt	121–122			Me	614
N-2-Quinoxalinecarbonyl-Gly	215 (sub) / 226 (dec)			Aq	340
N-2-Quinoxalinecarbonyl-Gly-OEt	89–91			Be-Hep	340
N-2-Quinoxalinecarbonyl-Gly-Hydrazide	215 (dec)			Alc	43
Succinyl (Gly-OEt, DL-Phe-OEt)	101–102			EtAc-Pe	43
Succinyl (Gly-OEt, Phe-OMe)	92–93	+12	Me	THF-Eth	43
Succinyl (Gly, DL-Phe)	191–193				187
Succinyl (Gly, Phe)	149–150	+23	Alc		187
Bis(thio-ac-Gly-OEt)	107				419
Bis(4-thiobutyryl-Gly-OEt)					771
N-Tos-N-OEt-me-Gly	92–93			Be-Pe	771
N^{ε}-Tos-N^{γ}-Pht-α,γ-diaminobutyryl-Gly Amide	244	+11	DMF	Aq-Ac	229
N^{α}-Tos-N^{γ}-Pht-α,γ-diaminobutyryl-Gly-OEt	166–167	+25	Ac	Aq-Alc	616
N-Trt-Gly-OBzh	137–139			An-Me	774
N-Trt-Gly-Odiphenyl-me	139–140			EtAc	624
Trt-Gly-ONp	153–154				
Trt-Gly-OPmb	167–168.5			EtAc-Alc	

Table 1 Amino Acid Derivatives (continued)

Compound	Method	Solvent	% Yield	Solvent Crystallization	M.P. (°C)	[α] D	Solvent Rotation	Ref
Trt-Gly-OSu				i-Pr	145.5-146.5			7
Trt-Gly-OTrt				EtAc	175-176			616
N-Trs-Gly				Alc	149-151			774
N-Trs-Gly-OMe					95-97			774
Histidine								
Di-Adoc-His				Cy-Pe	134-144 (dec)			195
Bis-Adoc-His-OSu				Dcm-Pe	164.5-167.5			736
Di-Z-His				EtAc-Eth	90.5-92 (dec)	+29	EtAc	261
Z-D-His Hydrazide					172-173	+36	HCl	742
Z-His-OMe Dihydrobromide					167-167.5			264
Di-Z-His-OMe Hydrochloride				Me	121.5-122.5 (dec)	-20	Me	261
Di-Z-His Methanol Solvate					105-107	+13	Me-An	261
Boc-His Hydrazide					145-146	-24	Py	734
Boc-His-OMe					124-125	-13	Py	734
N$^\alpha$-For-bzl-His					190-192	+47	Aq	669
His Hydrobromide Hydrate								261
His-OMe Dihydrochloride					200-201	+10	Aq	550
D-His-OMe Dihydrochloride					199-202	-11	Aq	550
DL-His-ONBzl Dibenzenesulfonate				Alc	215-217			601
His-ONBzl Dibenzenesulfonate				Alc-Eth	92-95	-4.9	Py	601
His-ONBzl Di-p-toluenesulfonate				Me-i-Pr	217-219	+6	Me	406
N^{im}-Z-His-OMe Dihydrobromide					167-167.5 (dec)			261

Compound	Recryst. Solvent	m.p.	[α]	Solvent	Ref.
N-Nps-His					479
N-Nps-His-OMe					479
Isoleucine					
Z-Ile	Tol-Pe	44–46	+6.5		277, 517
3-(Z-Ile)-amino-1-tos-2-pyrrolidone	Di-Me-Aq	216–219	−8.8		486
N-Z-Ile 1-Boc-2-hydrazide	Chf-Pe	168–170	−17	DMF	258
N^β-[Z-Ile]-N^α-boc-hydrazino Acetic Acid	EtAc-Pe	100–102	−2.7	DMF	443
N^β-[Z-Ile]-N^α-boc-hydrazinoacetic-OEt	He	95–96	−1.5	DMF	443
N^β-[Z-Ile]-hydrazino Acetic Acid	NMe	181–183	−27		443
Z-Ile-N^γ-tos-Dbu Acid Hydrazide	Alc	170	−38		486
Z-Ile-N^γ-tos-Dbu-N^γ-pelargonyl-Dbu-OMe		175–178			486
Boc-Ile	An-Aq	57–59	+2	Ac	46
N^β-[Boc-Ile]-N^α-boc-hydrazino Acetic Acid	EtAc-Cy-He	136–137	−17	DMF	443
Boc-Ile DCHA Salt	Eth-He	121–122	−14	DMF	443
D-Allo-Ile	EtAc-Pe	127–128	+6	DMF	46
Ile-N^γ-Z-Dbu-OMe Hydrochloride	Me-Eth	205–207	+0.2		514
Ile-boc-hydrazide	Eth-Pe	97–100	+24	Ac	485
Ile-OMe Hydrochloride		100–101	+16		258
Ile-ONp Hydrobromide	THF-Alc	194	−10	Alc	569
Ile-N^γ-tos-α,γ-Dbu-N^γ Pelargonyl-α,γ-Dbu-OMe	Me-Eth	151–153			276
N-Me-Ile		133–135	+44	5N HCl	486
Me-Nps-Ile-N^γ-Z-Dbu-OMe	Me	174–176	−49		77
Me-poc-Ile-N^γ-tos-Dbu-N^γ-pelargonyl-Dbu-OMe		90–93	−29		485
N-Nps-Ile		145–147	−102	DMF	486
Nps-Ile-N^γ-boc-Dbu-OMe	Aq-Me	188–189	−57		774
N-Nps-Ile DCHA Salt		125–127	−53	Me	485
N^β-[Nps-Ile]-hydrazinoacetic-OEt		125–135	−27		774
Poc-Ile-N^γ-tos-Dbu-N^γ-pelargonyl-Dbu					443
3-(Poc-Ile)-amino-1-tos-2-pyrrolidone	Di-Me-Aq	231–234	−9.7		486

Table 1 Amino Acid Derivatives (continued)

Compound	Method	Solvent	% Yield	Solvent Crystallization	M.P. (°C)	[α]$_D$	Solvent Rotation	Ref
1-Z-3-(Poc-Ile-tos-Dbu)-amino-2-pyrrolidone				Di-Eth	185–189	–46		486
Poc-Ile-N$^\gamma$-tos-Dbu Azide					110 (dec)			486
Poc-Ile-N$^\gamma$-tos-Dbu-N$^\gamma$-Z-Dbu					125–135	–31		486
Poc-Ile-N$^\gamma$-tos-Dbu-Dbu				Eth	185 (dec)	–28		486
					195			
Pco-Ile-N$^\gamma$-tos-Dbu Hydrazide					183–185 (dec)	–30		486
Leucine								
Ac-Leu				Aq	170–171	–22	Me	700
N-Ac-Leu-bis (2-chloroalkyl) Amide					133–135	+6.1	N-KOH	366
Bz-Leu				Chf-Pe	106	–6.9	Alc	709
Bz-Leu-OCH$_2$CN				EtAc-Pe	83–83.5	–39	Alc	52
Bz-Leu DCHA Salt				Me-Eth	145–146	+14	Alc	709
Bz-Leu-OMe				EtAc-Pe	104	–22	Alc	709
N-Bz-Leu-ONp					82.5–83.5	–41	Alc	52
					95–96			
Bzl-β-(N-Z-Leu)-propionate				An	164–165	–19		205
N-Bzl-N-me-nor-Leu				Aq	199–200	–3.5	NaOH-Aq	424
N-Bzl-nor-Leu				Alc	193–194		NaOH-Aq	424
4, 6-Benzylidene-3-O-(N-Z-DL-nor-Leu)-Glucose								115
Z-Abu-DL-Abu-DL-Leu-OEt				Be-He	175			23
Z-DL-Abu-DL-nor-Leu					76–78			23
Z(Br)-DL-Leu				EtAc-Pe	122–123	–12		692
Z-Leu Amide				Alc-Aq	124–125			700
Z-Leu Isoamylamide				i-Pr-Eth	94	–18	Alc	700
Z-Leu-OPcp				Me	125–126.5			343

Compound		mp			Ref.
Z-Leu-O-phenacyl	Eth-Pe	54–55	−25	Chf	616
Z-Leu Semicarbazide	NMe	145–146	−11	DMF	444
Z-Leu-SePh		64.5–65.5			719
Z-Leu-O-2,4,6-tribromophenyl		Oil			586
Z-Leu-OTcp	Pe	62–64	−53	EtAc	323
N^{α}-Z-N^{ϵ}-tri-me-amino-nor-Leu		64–65	−29	Me	199
Z-(NO$_2$)-D-Leu	Me-Eth	157–158	+11	Be	207
Z-(NO$_2$)-Leu Hydrazide		Oil			596
6-O-(N-Z-DL-nor-Leu)-D-glucose	Alc	133–134	+42	Me	430
N^{α}-Z-N^{γ}-tos-Dbu-N^{γ}-tos-Dbu-Leu Hydrazide	Me-Eth	159–161	−18		115
N^{α}-Z-N^{γ}-tos-Dbu-N^{γ}-tos-Dbu-Leu-OMe	Me-Eth	122–126			486
	EtAc	154–157			486
N^{α}-Z-N^{γ}-tos-Dbu-N^{γ}-tos-D-Leu Hydrazide	Me-Eth	189–190	−11		486
N-[Bis(p-bromo-bzl)-phosphoryl]-Leu	Alc-Aq	81			99
N-[Bis(p-bromo-bzl)-phosphoryl]-Leu-OMe		Oil			99
Bu^t-Z-D-Leu-α-hydroxycaproate	He	68–69	−5	Be	464
Bu^t-D-Leu-α-hydroxyisocaproate		b.p. 110–113 (0.5 mm)	−32	Be	464
Boc-D-Leu		84	+25	Ac	301
Boc-Leu		86–87	−24	Ac	301
Boc-Leu-ONp	Me-Aq	94–95	−48	DMF	46
Boc-nor-Leu	Alc-Pe	Oil	−11	Ac	46
N-(p-[Bis(2-chloro-et)-amino]benzylidene)-DL-Leu-OEt	Alc	46–47		Ac	393
N-(p-[Bis(2-chloro-et)-amino]bzl)-Dl-Leu-OEt Oxalate Salt	Alc	147–148			608
Et 1-(Z-Leu-amido)-cyclopentane-carboxylate	Aq-Alc	75–78	−22	Alc	608
Et 1-(Leu-amido)-cyclopentanecarboxylate Hydrochloride					97
For-Leu	Alc-Eth	129–130	−5	Alc	97 / 584

Table 1 Amino Acid Derivatives (continued)

Compound	Method	Solvent	% Yield	Solvent Crystallization	M.P. (°C)	[α]D	Solvent Rotation	Ref
Nγ-[For-D-Leu]-Nα-caprylyl-Dbu-OMe Acid					95			133
N-(2-Hydroxy-1-naphthylidene)-Leu					162 (dec)	-84	Alc	228
N[Bis(p-iodo-bzl)-phosphoryl]-Leu-OMe				Cy-Pe	48			99
Leu						+12	5N HCl	228
DL-Leu								421
Leu-OBzl				Alc-Eth	167-168	+4.4	DMF	165
D-Leu-OBzl Toluenesulfonate					155-156	-0.5	Alc	446
Leu-Z-hydrazide Trifluoroacetate				Eth-He	181-183	-23	DMF	458
Leu Boc-hydrazide					114-116	+21	Me	720
Nγ-D-Leu-Nα-caprylyl-Dbu					Oil			133
Leu-ONBzl Benzenesulfonate				Alc	213-215	+16	Py	561
Leu-ONBzl Toluenesulfonate				Me	202	+10	Alc	15
Leu-O-phenacyl Hydrobromide				Me-Eth		+15	Me	616
β-Leu-O-propionic Acid				Me-Eth	188, 215 (dec)	+6.0	5N HCl	205
Leu Semicarbazide Acetate Salt				Alc-Eth	108-110 (dec)			444
Leu Semicarbazide Hydrochloride Salt				i-Pr-Eth	154-157 (dec)			444
Leu-SePh Hydrobromide					156-158			719
ε-Tri-me-amino-nor-Leu Monohydrochloride				Alc-Eth	232	+14	6N HCl	207
N-Me-nor-Leu				Aq-Alc	200	+22	Aq	424
N-Me-nor-Leu-OMe Hydrochloride				EtAc	100-101.5	+17	DMF	424
N-[Bis(p-nitro-bzl)-phosphoryl]-Leu					Oil			99
N-[Bis(p-nitro-bzl)-phosphoryl]-Leu-OMe				Eth-Pe				99
N-O-Nps-Leu					102-106	-99	DMF	774
Nβ-[Nps-Leu]-Nα-Z-hydrazinoacetic Acid								443
DCHA Salt					165-166	-18	DMF	443
Nβ-[Nps-Leu]-Nα-boc-hydrazinoacetic-OEt				EtAc-He	147-148	-19	DMF	443

52

Compound	Solvent	M.P. (°C)	[α]	Solvent	Ref.
N-O-Nps-Leu DCHA Salt	EtAc-He	182–183	−76	DMF	774
N$^\beta$-[Nps-Leu]-hydrazinoacetic-OEt		110–112	−29	DMF	443
6-O-(DL-nor-Leu)-D-glucose Oxalate Salt		138–138.5	+36	Aq	115
Pht-Leu Boc-hydrazide	Be-Pe	86–88	−14	Me	720
N-Pht-Leu-ONp		102–103	−86	DMF	48
Pht-DL-Leu-SePh					719
N-Trt-Leu Di-et-ammonium Salt		153	+2.1	Me	48
Lysine					
N$^\epsilon$-Ac-N$^\alpha$-Z-Lys Amide	Acn	179			32
N$^\epsilon$-Ac-N$^\alpha$-Z-Lys DCHA Salt	Acn	132–133			32
N$^\epsilon$-Ac-N$^\alpha$-boc-Lys-ONp		96–98	−24	Alc	393
N$^\epsilon$-Ac-Lys					32
N$^\alpha$-Ac-Lys	Aq-Alc	247–248 (dec)	−6.7	6N HCl	359
	Alc-Eth	243			207
N$^\epsilon$-Ac-Lys Hydrochloride		206–208			32
N$^\epsilon$-Benzylidene-Lys		205–207			53
					100
N$^\epsilon$-Z-N$^\alpha$-Ac-Lys	Aq	85 (dec)	+3.8	Alc	207
N$^\epsilon$-Z-N$^\alpha$-Ac-Lys Amide	Alc-Aq	159–160			109
N$^\epsilon$-Z-N$^\alpha$-Adoc-Lys	Eth-Cy	56–60			195
N$^\epsilon$-Z-boc-Lys					571
N$^\epsilon$-Z-N$^\alpha$-boc-Lys-ONp	Alc-Pe	70–77	0.0	Ac	646
N$^\epsilon$-Z-N$^\alpha$-For-Lys		94–95			239
N$^\epsilon$-Z-N$^\alpha$-For-Lys DCHA Salt					333
N$^\epsilon$-Z-N$^\alpha$-Guanyl-Lys		179–180	−2.9	DMSO	104
N,Nʹ-Di-Z-γ-hydroxy-Lys-lactone		116–118			153
N$^\alpha$-Z-Lys		232–233			53
N$^\alpha$-Z-Lys	Aq	230–233	−10	0.2N HCl	100
N-Z-Lys		278–280			363
					100
	Ac-Aq	235	+14	2N HCl	353

Table 1 Amino Acid Derivatives (continued)

Compound	Method	Solvent	% Yield	Solvent Crystallization	M.P.(°C)	$[\alpha]_D$	Solvent Rotation	Ref
N^α-Z-Lys-OBz Benzenesulfonate				Alc-Eth	256–258	+15	HCl	207
N^ϵ-Z-Lys-OBzl Toluenesulfonate				Alc-Eth-Pe	96–98		DMF	53
N^ϵ-Z-Lys-N-carboxy-anhydride				EtAc-He	110–112	−5.4		1
N^α-Z-Lys Lactam				Me	101–101.5			132
N^α-Z-Lys-OMe Hydrochloride					228–230			538
					Oil			100
N^ϵ-Z(NO$_2$)-Lys					239–240			363
				Aq	240–241 (dec)	+14	HCl	601
N^ϵ-Z(NO$_2$)-Lys-ONBzl Benzenesulfonate				Aq	168–169	+3.7	DMF	601
N^ϵ-Z-N^α-Nps-Lys DCHA Salt					184–187	−29	DMF	774
N^ϵ-(6,8-Di-bzl-thiooctanoyl)-Lys								109
N^ϵ-(6,8-Di-bzl-thiooctanoyl)-Lys-OBu^t					Oil			109
N^ϵ-p-Bromobenzenesulphonyl-Lys					264–265			363
N^ϵ-Boc-N^α-ac-Lys Hydrazide					123–125	−20	Alc	393
N^ϵ-Boc-N^α-Z-Lys				Alc-Eth-Pe	63.5–64.5	−5.9	Me	724
					Oil	−2.4	An	576
								775
								576
N^ϵ-Boc-N^α-Z-Lys OBu^t				EtAc-Eth-Pe	153–154	+5.0	Me	724
N^ϵ-Boc-N^α-Z-Lys DCHA Salt				An-Eth	150–153			775
N^ϵ-Boc-N^α-Z-Lys-OMe					62–63	−10	An	100
					Oil	−10	An	100
								576
N^ϵ-Boc-N^α-Z-Lys-ONp				EtAc-Eth-Pe	88–90	−16	An	400
N^ϵ-Boc-N^α-Z-Lys-OSu				An-Eth	88–91	−14	An	576
N^α-Boc-Lys				EtAc-i-Pr-Eth	94.5–95.5	−14	Di	461
N^ϵ-Boc-Lys				Alc	200–201			571
				Aq	237–255	+4.7	2N NH$_4$OH	576

Compound	Solvent	mp	[α]	N HCl	
N^ε-Boc-Lys-OBu^t Hydrochloride	Aq	238	+14		775
N^ε-Boc-Lys Copper Complex		220–255	+12	Me	576
N^ε-Boc-Lys-OMe	Me–Eth	139–140	+19	Me	724
N^ε-Boc-Lys-OMe Acetate	Me–Eth	230	+15	Me	576
N^ε-Boc-Lys-OMe Hydrochloride	Eth–Pe	Oil			100
N^ε-Boc-N^α-pz-Lys	Eth–Pe	78–79	–1.0	Me	576
N^ε-Boc-N^α-pz-Lys-OMe	Eth–Pe	158–159	–5.5	An	576
		105–106			576
		88–92			576
		96–104			
N^ε-Carboxy-N^α-{7-[3-(phenyldithio)-proprionamido]-4,5-dithiaheptanamido}-N^ε-bzl-Lys-OBzl	EtAc–He	81.5–82.5	–26	Chf	222
N^ε-Bis(2-chloro-et)-N^α-bz-DL-Lys-OEt		Oil			678
1,1-Bis(2-chloro-et)-2-(N^α,ε-di-Z-Lys)Hydrazine		134–135			523
N^ε-Bis(2-chloro-et)-DL-Lys					678
1,1-Bis(2-chloro-et)-2-Lys-hydrazine Hydrobromide Picrolonate	Me	158–159			523
N^ε-For-N^α-Z-Lys Amide	Alc–Eth	178–179			239
N^α-For-Lys	Aq–Alc	185–186			239
N^ε-For-Lys		214–215			239
Di-For-Lys Amide	Alc	228 (dec)			363
N^ε-For-Lys-OMe Hydrochloride		120–123			239
N^α,ε-Diguanyl-Lys		201 (dec)			239
N^α-Guanyl-Lys Picrate		228–230 (dec)			104
N^ε-Dihydrolipoyl-Lys					104
N^ε-Dihydrolipoyl-N^α-ac-Lys Bzh-ammonium Salt		123.5–125			109
N^ε-Bis(2-hydroxy-et)-N^α-bz-DL-Lys		Oil			678
N^ε-Bis(2-hydroxy-et)-N^α-bz-DL-Lys-OEt		Oil			678

Table 1 Amino Acid Derivatives (continued)

Compound	Method	Solvent	% Yield	Solvent Crystallization	M.P.(°C)	[α]D	Solvent Rotation	Ref
N$^\epsilon$-Bis(2-hydroxy-et)-N$^\alpha$-bz-DL-Lys Reineckate				Be	86-88			678
N$^\epsilon$-Bis(2-hydroxy-et)-DL-Lys Reineckate					193 (dec)			678
γ-Hydroxy-Lys Lactone Dihydrochloride				Alc	229-230 (dec)	+20	HCl	153
N$^\epsilon$-Isopropyl-Lys-OMe Dihydrobromide				Me-Eth	156.5-157.5			533
N$^{\alpha,\epsilon}$-Diisopropyl-Lys-OMe Dihydrobromide				Eth-Me	186.5-188.5			533
N$^\epsilon$-Lipoyl-N$^\alpha$-ac-Lys Amide					169-170			109
N$^\epsilon$-Lipoyl-N$^\alpha$-ac-Lys-bzh-ammonium Salt					136.5-137.5			109
Lys Monohydrochloride					255-257	+27	5N HCl	747
N$^\epsilon$-Mz-Lys Hydrochloride				Me-Eth	242-243			580
N$^\epsilon$-Mz-Lys-OMe Hydrochloride					241			580
N$^\epsilon$-Pht-N$^\alpha$-boc-Lys								571
N$^\epsilon$-Pht-Lys								571
Threo-N$^\epsilon$-Z-Lys-OBzl					93-94	-15		197a
Threo-γ-hydroxy-Lys								153
N$^\epsilon$-Tos-N$^\alpha$-Z-Lys				EtAc-Pe	102-103	-13	NaHCO$_3$-Aq	765
						-14	NaHCO$_3$-Aq	240
N$^\epsilon$-Tos-N$^\alpha$-Z-D-Lys					89-93	+13	NaHCO$_3$-Aq	769
N$^\epsilon$-Tos-N$^\alpha$-Z-Lys-ONp				Alc	109-110	-16	DMF	62
N$^\epsilon$-Tos-N$^\alpha$-Z-Lys N-(β-Tos-amino)-et Amide				EtAc-Pe	153-155			767
N$^\epsilon$-Tos-N$^\alpha$-boc-Lys-ONp				EtAc-Pe	113-114	-22	DMF	373
N$^\epsilon$-Tos-N$^\alpha$-for-Lys					237-238			333
N$^\epsilon$-Tos-Lys				Aq	234-237	+14	2N HCl	765
								130

Compound		Solvent	M.p. (°C)	[α]	Solvent	Ref.
Nᵉ-Tos-D-Lys			(dec) 238 (dec)			363
Nᵅ,ᵉ-Di-tos-DL-Lys						353
Nᵅ,ᵉ-Di-tos-Lys Bzl-amide						769
Nᵉ-Tos-Lys-OBzl Hydrochloride		Alc	235–238	−13	2N HCl	419
Nᵉ-Tos-Lys-OBuᵗ		Be	125–130		Me	419
Nᵉ-Tos-Lys Copper Complex		Me-Eth	143–144	−10		130
			172–174			510
			241–243 (dec)			414
Nᵉ-Tos-Lys-OEt Hydrochloride		Alc-Eth	136–137.5	−10	Ac	130
Nᵉ-Tos-Lys Hydrazide		Alc	136–137			240
Nᵉ-Tos-Lys-OMe Hydrochloride		Me-Eth	135–137	+14	1N HCl	560
Nᵉ-Tos-Lys-ONBzl Benezenesulfonate		Aq	170–172	+3.2	DMF	601
Nᵉ-Trt-Lys-OMe Dihydrobromide		Me-An	138–140			53
Nᵉ-Trt-Lys-OMe Dihydrochloride		Me-An	155–157			53
Methionine						
Adoc-Met DCHA Salt		Eth	133–135			195
Z-Br)-DL-Met	ONP	EtAc-He	129–130			692
Z-hyp-D-Met	DMF		118–120	−22	DMF	440a
N-Z-Met-carbamyl-me-sulfonium Acetate						358
N-Z-Met-carbamyl-me-sulfonium Nitrate						358
Z-Met-ONBzl		Eth-Pe	63–65	−15 / +2.5	An / Chf	269
Z-Met-OPcp			112.5–113.5	−31	DMF	101
Z-DL-S-oxide-Met						268
Z-DL-S-oxide-Met Hydrazide						268
Z-DL-S-oxide-Met-OMe						268
Z-DL-S-oxide-Met-OMe Hydrochloride						268
Z-DL-Met-SePh						719
S-Bzl-thio-carbamyl-Met Phenylhydrazide						421
N-Boc-DL-S-oxide-Met-0-2,4,5-trichlorophenyl		EtAc	90.5–92			424

Table 1 Amino Acid Derivatives (continued)

Compound	Method	Solvent	% Yield	Solvent Crystallization	M.P. (°C)	$[\alpha]_D$	Solvent Rotation	Ref
Met Amide					50–51	−2.0	Alc	89
DL-Met-OEt					b.p. 110–113 (1.7–2.0 mm)			222
Met-ONBzl				Acn	149–151	+4.1	Me	269
Met Sulfonium Bromide Hydrobromide				Me	122–125			268
N-Nps-Met DCHA Salt				An-Aq	196–197	−34	Me	774
DL-S-Oxide-Met								268
N-Pht-Met				Pe-Be	125–126	−78	DMF	48
N-Pht-Met-ONp					99	−90	DMF	48
Tfa-Met Boc-hydrazide					75			720
Tfa-Met Hydrazide					159–161			720
Ornithine								
N^δ-Z-N^α-Z(OMe)-Orn				EtAc-Pe	73–75	−2.3	DMF	337
N^δ-Z-N^α-Z(OMe)-Orn-ONp				Alc	123–124	−14	DMF	337
N^δ-Z-N^α-boc-D-Orn					Oil			301
N^δ-Z-N^α-boc-Orn DCHA Salt					128–129	+7.8	Alc	565
N^δ-Z-N^α-boc-Orn-OMe					70–71	−13	Me	565
N^δ-Z-N^α-boc-D-Orn-ONp				EtAc-Eth-Pe	108			301
N^δ-(Z)-N^α-Carboxy-Orn Cyclic Anhydride				Be	89			112
N^δ-Z-N^α-for-Orn				EtAc-Pe	72–77	+3.0	DMF	333
N^δ-Z-N^α-guanyl-Orn				Alc-Eth	174			104
N^δ-Z-Orn					254–255			363
N^α,N^δ-Di-Z-D-Orn				EtAc-Pe	113–115	+4.7	Alc	207
N^δ-Z-D-Orn					255	−21	6N HCl	301
Z-Orn					209–210	−8.4	5N HCl	565
D-Z-Orn Amide					168			378
N^δ-Z-Orn-OBzl Hydrochloride				Me-Eth	161	+3.1	Me	385
N^δ-Z-D-Orn-OEt p-Toluenesulfonate								301
Di-Z-Orn-OMe				Chf-Pe	71–72	−8.9	DMF	378

Compound	m.p./b.p.	Recryst. solvent	$[\alpha]$	Solvent	Ref.
N^α,N^δ-Di-Z-D-Orn-ONp	118–120	EtAc-Pe	+5.1	Me	207
N^δ-Boc-N^α-Z-Orn	Oil		+7.9	Alc	400
N^δ-Boc-N^α-Z-Orn DCHA Salt	128–129				400
N^δ-Boc-N^α-Z-Orn-ONp	101–102	An-Eth-Pe	–17	An	400
N^δ-Boc-Orn Ac Salt	234–235		+13	Ac	400
N^δ-Boc-Orn-OMe Hydrochloride	154–155		+15	Me	565
N^δ-For-N^α-Z-Orn	109–111				743
N^δ-For-Orn	212–214		–2.9	Me	743
N^δ-Orn-OBu^t	111–112	EtAc-Pe	+1.5	Aq	332
Orn Copper (II)Complex					385
N^δ-Tos-N^α-Z-Orn					375
N^δ-Tos-N^α-for-Orn	Oil				333
N^δ-Tos-Orn-OBzl Hydrochloride	125–127	Me-Eth			129
N^δ-Tos-Orn-OBzl Phosphate	196–197	Me			129
N^δ-Tos-Orn-OEt Hydrochloride	Oil				129
N^δ-Tos-Orn-OMe Hydrochloride	135–136	Me-Eth	+16	1N HCl	330

Phenylalanine

Compound	m.p./b.p.	Recryst. solvent	$[\alpha]$	Solvent	Ref.
N-(β-Ac-et)-Phe	212 (dec)	Aq			107
N-Ac-Phe-bis(2-chloroalkyl) Amide	119–121				366
Aoc-Phe-ONp	127–127.5	EtAc-Pe	–14	Alc	518
N-(β-Bz-et)-β-Phe	188–190 (dec)	Aq			107
N-Bz-Phe	70.5–71		0.0	An	119
N-Bz-Phe Azlactone	133–135				119
N-Bz-Phe Bis(2-chloroalkyl) Amide					366
N-Bz-Phe-ONp	84–85.4				119
Z-Aminoisobutyryl-DL-Phe	144.5–145.5				429
Z-Aminoisobutyryl-Phe	60–65	Eth	+34	Di	429
Z-Aminoisobutyryl-Phe-aminoisobutyric-OMe	156–157.5		–42	Chf	429

Table 1 Amino Acid Derivatives (continued)

Compound	Method	Solvent	% Yield	Solvent Crystallization	M.P.(°C)	$[\alpha]_D$	Solvent Rotation	Ref.
Z-Aminoisobutyryl-DL-Phe-aminoisobutyric-OMe					170–171.5			173
					169.5–			429
					170.5			
Z-Aminoisobutyryl-DL-Phe Hydrazide				Chf	162.5–			429
					163.5			
Z-Aminoisobutyryl-Phe Hydrazide					51–56	−34	Chf	429
Z-Aminoisobutyryl-DL-Phe-OMe					102.5–			429
					103.5			
Z-Aminoisobutyryl-Phe-OMe				EtAc-He	95–96	+26	Di	429
Z-Aminoisobutyryl-Phe Oxazolone				Eth-He	97.4–98.8	−131	Di	429
Z-(Br)-DL-Phe				EtAc-He	147			692
Z(OMe)-D-Phe				EtAc-Pe	81–83	−5.7	Alc	301
Z(OMe)-Phe-O-vinyl					Oil	−12		52
Z-N-me-Phe				EtAc-Pe	69.5–70.5	−70	EtAc	176
Z(NO$_2$)-Phe				Alc	149.5–			600
					151.5			
Z-Phe-[^{14}C]								671
Z-D-Phe					84–86.5	−6.0	Me	742
Z-DL-α-Phe				Be-Pe	104–106			284
Z-Phe Amide					161–162			111
				EtAc	164–165	−6.8	Me	323
Z-D-Phe Amide					162–163			111
Z-Phe Anhydride				Acn	139–140	+19	MeCl	727
Z-Phe-2,4,6-tribromophenyl				Alc	134			586
Z-Phe-OBu^t				i-Pr-Eth	81–82			6
Z-DL-α-Phe-OBu^t				Eth-Pe	54–55			284
Z-DL-Phe Bu^t-amide				EtAc	151.5–			81
					152.5			
Z-Phe Boc-hydrazide					81–84			728

Compound		m.p.	[α]		Ref.
N-(Z-DL-α-Phe)-N,N′-bis(cyclohexyl)urea	EtAc-Pe	123–123.5			284
Z-DL-Phe DCHA Salt	Aq-Me	175–176			284
Z-Phe Dicyclohexylurea		122–123			81
Z-Phe-ONp					176
N-Z-Phe-O-phenacyl	Alc	100	−7.5	Chf	616
Z-Phe-o-pivalohydroxamic Acid	EtAc-Pe	104–106			491
Z-Phe-o-pyridyl-(3)					659
Z-Phe-SePh	EtAc-Pe	112–113	−70	DMF	719
N-Z-Phe-SPh	Me-An-Eth	117–118	−77	DMF	52
Z-Phe-N^α-tos-Dbu Hydrobromide		167–168			683
Z-Phe-N^α-tos-Dbu-OMe	EtAc	138–139			683
Z-Phe-N^γ-tos-Dbu-OMe	EtAc	138–139			683
Z-m-trifluoro-me-Phe		106–107	−2	Me	441
Z-m-trifluoro-me-Phe-ONp		106–107	−30	Me	441
N^α-Boc-Phe	EtAc-He	88–88.5	+47	Chf	475
Boc-Phe-OSu	EtAc	152–153	−20	Di	718
N-(α-Carboxyphenethylcarbanoyl)-Phe	EtAc-He	188–188.5	+67	Alc	218
β-Carboxy-propionyl-Phe-OEt	EtAc-Pe	83–84	+17	Me	43
β-Carboxy-propionyl-DL-Phe-OEt	EtAc-Pe	103–104			43
N-Chloro-ac-et-D-Phe	Be	133–134	−70	Alc	778
N-Chloro-ac-p-et-DL-Phe	Be	114–116			778
N-Chloro-ac-p-me-D-Phe	Be	115–140			778
N-Chloro-ac-p-me-DL-Phe	Aq	136–138			778
N-Trichloro-ac-Phe Bis (2-chloro-et)-amide		118			366
N-Dichloro-ac-Phe Bis(2-chloro-et)-amide		147–148			366
α-Chloropropionyl-DL-Phe-OMe					355
α-Chloropropionyl-Phe-OMe					355
p-Et-Phe	Hcl	189–191	−7.1	5N HCl	778
p-Et-DL-Phe					778
p-Et-D-Phe Hydrochloride	Me-Eth	229–232	+26	Aq	778
p-Et-Phe-OMe Hydrochloride	Alc-Eth	178–180			778
p-Fluoro-Phe-OEt Hydrochloride		180–181			295
N-(Imidazolecarbonyl)-Phe-OEt		130–132			155

Table 1 Amino Acid Derivatives (continued)

Compound	Method	Solvent	% Yield	Solvent Crystallization	M.P.(°C)	$[\alpha]_D$	Solvent Rotation	Ref.
Mz-Phe					Oil			695
Mz-Phe-DCHA Salt					157–159			695
N-(5,5-Di-me-2-cyclohexen-1-on-3-yl)-DL-Phe Hydrazide				Be	77			197
N-3,3',4,4'-Tetra-OMe-diphenyl-me-Phe				Aq-An	190 (dec)	−22	DMF	200
N-4,4'-Di-OMe-diphenyl-me-Phe				NMe	198 (dec)	+2.3	1N NaOH	200
N-4,4-Di-OMe-diphenyl-me-Phe-OMe				Eth-Pe	70–72	−14	Me	200
N-4,4'-Di-OMe-2,2'-di-me-diphenyl-me-Phe								200
p-OMe-Phe-OMe Hydrochloride				Me-Eth	188.5–190 (dec)	+74	Py	357
Me-DL-Phe					226–229 (dec)			778
Me-Phe Hydrochloride					204–209	−18	Aq	778
p-Me-D-Phe Hydrochloride					204–205			778
N-Me-Phe Hydrochloride						+49	0.1N NaOH	176
p-Me-Phe-OMe Hydrochloride				Me-Eth	189–190	+42	Me	778
N-Me-Phe-ONp Hydrobromide					200–201	+39	DMF	176
DL-p-Tri-me-silyl-Phe-OMe Hydrochloride				Alc-Eth	193			146
N-[Bis(NBzl)-phosphoryl]-Phe				Alc	127–128			99
N-[Bis(NBzl)-phosphoryl]-Phe-OMe				Alc	111			99
N-Nps-Phe				EtAc-Pe	134–135	−47	DMF	774
N-Nps-Phe-OMe					93–95	−32		774
N-Nps-Phe-ONp					116–118	−115		774
Phe Amide					91–92			111
Phe Amide Acetate					116–117	+17	Aq	111
D-Phe Amide Acetate					116–117	−18	Aq	111
Phe-OBzl Benzenesulfonate					165–166	+19	Py	530
						+19	Py	601

62

Compound	Solvent	M.p. / B.p. (°C)	$[\alpha]_D$	Solvent	Ref.
Phe-OBzl Benzenesulfonate Hydrochloride	EtAc-Pe	203–205	–23	0.25N HCl	601
Phe-OBzl Hydrochloride	Pe	46–47			610
DL-α-Phe-OBu^t			–21		284
D-Phe-OBu^t			+24		550
Phe-OBu^t	Me-i-Pr-Eth	156–158	+3.1	Aq	550
Phe-OBu^t Phosphite	Be-Pe	162–163	+20	Alc	6
DL-α-Phe-OBu^t Picrate		115–116	+3.5	Alc	284
Phe Boc-hydrazide					728
Phe-2,6-dichloro-4-ONp Hydrobromide	Alc-Eth	146–147 (dec)			623
Phe Tetra-et-ammonium Salt					703
DL-Phe-OMe		b. p. 80 (0.5 mm)			173
DL-α-Phe-OMe		b. p. 138–142 (15 mm)			284
Phe-ONBzl Benzenesulfonate	Aq	190–191	+11	DMF	601
Phe-ONBzl Toluenesulfonate	i-Pr	180–182	+1.1	Me	406
Phe-O-phenacyl Hydrobromide	Me-Eth	158	+115	DMF	616
Phe-SPh Hydrobromide	Alc-Eth	148–150			52
Phe-SePh Hydrobromide		155–156			719
Phe Sodium Salt					703
Phe-N^γ-tos-Dbu-OMe Hydrobromide	Me-An-Eth	167–168 (dec)	+1	Aq	683
Phe-O-vinyl Hydrochloride		159–161			52
Pz-DL-α-Phe	Ac-Pe	145–146			284
Pz-DL-α-Phe-pivalic Acid Mixed Anhydride	Eth	62–64			284
N-Diphenylphosphoryl-Phe-OBzl	Eth-Pe	90			99
Pht-Phe		185	–213		719
Pivaloyl-Phe-OMe	Eth-He	90.5–91	+37	Alc	429
Succinyl-bis-(Phe)		209–210	+22	Di	43
Succinyl-bis(DL-Phe-OEt)		146–147		DMF	43
Succinyl(DL-Phe-OEt, Glu-Di-OEt)	Tol-Pe	83–84	+8	Alc	43

Table 1 Amino Acid Derivatives (continued)

Compound	Method	Solvent	% Yield	Solvent Crystallization	M.P.(°C)	[α] D	Solvent Rotation	Ref.
Succinyl(DL-Phe-OEt, N^G-nitro-Arg-OMe)				Me-Pe	114–116	–1	Me	43
Succinyl(Phe-OEt, N^G-nitro-Arg-OMe)				Me-Pe	124–126	–5	Me	43
Succinyl-bis(phe-OMe)					133–134	–13	Alc	43
Tfa-DL-α-Phe				Eth-Pe	126–128			284
Tfa-DL-α-Phe Anilide				Be-Pe	137–138.5			284
Tfa-DL-α-Phe Cyclohexylamide				Aq-Me	140–142			284
m-Trifluoro-me-Phe					210–211	–14	Aq	441
m-Trifluoro-me-D-Phe					210–212	+14	Aq	441
N-Trt-Phe-ONp					72–82	+7.3		774
N-Trt-Phe-p-ONp					154–156	–67		774
Proline								
N-Bzl-Pro					95–97			119
Z-Aminoisobutyryl-Pro-OMe								429
N^α-Z-N^γ-Z-Dbu-Pro								683
α, γ-Di-Z-Dbu-Pro					Oil			683
α, γ-Di-Z-Dbu-Pro-OMe					Oil			683
N^α-Z-N^γ-Dbu-Pro-OMe								683
Z-D-Pro					76.5–77.5	+60		550
Z-Pro					78–80	–61		550
Z-Pro-OBu^t				Pe-Eth	44–45			6
N-Z-Pro-boc-hydrazide						–83	Me	190
N-Z-Pro 4,4'-Di-OMe-OBzh				EtAc-Pe	83	–53	Chf	616
Z-D-Pro-ONp					94–96	+67	DMF	336
Z-DL-Pro-ONp					71–73			136
N-Z-Pro-Ophenacyl					93–94	–76	DMF	661
N-Z-Pro-OBzh				EtAc-Pe	96–97			616
Boc-Pro					134–135	–60	Ac	46
Boc-Pro-OSu					134–136	–55	Di	46

Compound	Solvent of crystallization	M.p. (°C)	$[\alpha]_D$	Solvent	Ref.
Dansyl-Pro					547
N-Nitro-guanyl-Pro	Aq	198 (dec)	−55	KHCO$_3$-Aq	467
N-Nitro-guanyl-Pro-OBu^t	Aq	157–158	−72	Alc	467
N-Nps-Pro			−127	Me	455
N-Nps-Pro DCHA Salt	Alc	151–154	−43		774
Pro-OBzl Hydrochloride		148–149			494
Pro-O-p-bromophenacyl-hydrobromide		153.5–154 (dec)	−19	Aq	360
Pro-OBu^t		b. p. 57 (1.5 mm)			6
Pro Boc-hydrazide		Oil	−45 / −40	Me / DMF	503
Pro-OMe		119			190
Pro-OMe Hydrochloride	Me-Eth	71	−32 / −35	Me / DMF	190
Pro-Ophenacyl Hydrobromide	DMF	157–158			190
Trt-Pro		117–119			661
Trt-Pro-OBzl	Eth-Pe		−67	Chf	573 / 573
Serine					
OAc-DL-Ser-OEt	Acn-Aq	95–97			33
OAc-N-Z-DL-Ser		123			81
OAc-N-Z-DL-Ser-OBu^t	Alc-Ac	94–96			81
OAc-N-Z-Ser-ONp		96–97			456
OAc-Z-Ser		93			620
O-(2,3,4,6-Tetra-OAc)-β-D-glucopyranosido-N-Z-D-Ser-OMe	Eth-He		−27	Chf	675
O-(2,3,4,6-Tetra-OAc)-β-D-glucopyranosido-N-Z-Ser-OMe	Eth-He		+16	Chf	675
N-Ac-Ser Amide		141			67
OAc-DL-Ser-OMe Hydrochloride	Aq		−135		589

Table 1 Amino Acid Derivatives (continued)

Compound	Method	Solvent	% Yield	Solvent Crystallization	M.P. (°C)	[α]$_D$	Solvent Rotation	Ref.
Bzl-β-(N-Z-OBu^t-DL-OSer)propionate				Eth-Pe	44–45			205
OBzl-N-Z-Ser-ONp				He	45–47			456
OBzl-N-boc-Ser Z-hydrazide					75–77			728
OBzl-boc-Ser					Oil			356
OBzl-N-boc-Ser				Alc-Eth	60–62	+20	Alc	734
OBzl-N-boc-D-Ser DCHA Salt					135.5–136	+24	Me	463
OBzl-boc-Ser-OSu				Eth-Pe				356
OBzl-N-carboxy-Ser Anhydride								67
								655
OBzl-N-carboxy-DL-Ser Anhydride				Eth-Pe	73–74			655
OBzl-N-carboxy-D-Ser Anhydride				EtAc-Pe	129–130	+54	Alc	655
OBzl-N-for-Ser					133–134	+54	Alc	213
OBzl-Ser					219–221 (dec)	+5.0	3N HCl	142
				Aq		+6.0	5N HCl	213
								602
								655
								655
OBzl-D-Ser				Aq		–7.2	N HCl	463
OBzl-DL-Ser								67
								655
OBzl-Ser Z-hydrazide				EtAc-Pe		+8.3	Me	728
N-Z-OBu^t-Ser-OBu^t					68–70.5			49
Z-OBu^t-Ser-ONbzl								723
Z(OMe)-Ser Hydrazide				Me-Eth	177–178	+7.0	DMF	452
Z-Ser				Aq	114–116			118
					119	+5.9	Ac	723
N-Z-DL-Ser Amide				EtAc-Alc				399
								33

Compound	Recryst. solvent	MP (°C)	$[\alpha]$	Solvent	Ref.
Z-Ser Amide	Chf-Pe	132	+14	Alc	201
N-Z-Ser-OBzh	Pe-Eth	127	-13	DMF	668
N-Z-DL-Ser-OBu^t	Pen-Eth	76–77			81
N-Z-DL-Ser-OMe	EtAc-Pe	36–38			205
N-Z-Ser-ONBzl		114–115	-13	DMF	668
	Be	117.5–118.5	-9.8	Alc	602
Z-Ser-ONBzl	EtAc-Pe	115.5–116.6	-11	Me	723
Z-Ser-2,4,di-ONp	Pe	116–117	-32	DMF	399
N-Z-Ser-OPcp	EtAc	191.5–192.5			343
OBu^t-N-Z-DL-Ser	i-Pr-Aq	48–50			81
	i-Pr-Aq	75–77	+18	Me	205
OBu^t-N-Z-Ser	EtAc-He	83.5–85	+22	Alc	556
OBu^t-N-Z-DL-Ser Anhydride	Cte	87–87.5			81
OBu^t-N-Z-Ser-OBu^t	Pen	85–87	+21	Alc	602
OBu^t-N-Z-Ser DCHA Salt		89–91			205
OBu^t-N-Z-DL-Ser Hydrazide		Oil			49
OBu^t-N-Z-Ser Hydrazide	Alc	149–150	+22	Alc	723
OBu^t-N-Z-Ser-OMe	Eth-Pe	113.5–114	+14	Alc	81
OBu^t-N-Z-Ser-ONBzl		112.5–113.5			81
		108–109	+13	DMF	556
		32–33	+3.1 / +4.6	Me / Alc	556
OBu^t-N-Z-Ser-ONp	Alc	69–71	-17	DMF	602
OBu^t-N-Z-Ser-OSu		55–56	-21	Me	730
OBu^t-N-boc-Ser-OMe		Oil			735
OBu^t-Ser		Oil			556
OBu^t-DL-Ser	Aq-An	238–239	-12	Aq	556
		200–205			81

Table 1 Amino Acid Derivatives (continued)

Compound	Method	Solvent	% Yield	Solvent Crystallization	M.P.(°C)	[α]_D	Solvent Rotation	Ref.
OBu^t-Ser-OBu$^{\overline{t}}$					b. p. 70–71 (0.9 mm)	−2.9	Me	81
								556
						−2.7	Alc	49
						−2.7	Alc	81
OBu^t-DL-Ser-OBu^t					b. p. 73 (1.5 mm)			
OBu^t-Ser-OBu^t Hydrochloride				t-Bu-Eth	170	−6	DMF	49
OBu^t-Ser-OMe					b. p. 43 (0.2 mm)			556
OBu^t-Ser-OMe Hydrochloride				i-Pr-Eth	173.5 174.5	+8.8	Alc	735
β-(OBu^t-DL-Ser)-Opropionic Acid				Me-Eth	143–144	−3.0	Ac	205
Boc-Ser					45–47	−7.6	Aq	463
N-Boc-Ser DCHA Salt				EtAc	142–144	+13	Me	463
N-Boc-Ser Hydrazide				EtAc	109–110	−9.0	Me	463
Boc-Ser Hydrazide				EtAc	112–114	−9.4	Me	270
Boc-Ser-OMe					Oil			270
N-Boc-Ser-ONBzl				EtAc-Pe	100–103	−6.8	Chf	668
N-(5-Chlorosalicylidene)-D-cyclo-Ser					166–167			470
N-(5-Chlorosalicylidene)-2-trt-DL-cyclo-Ser				An-Me	81			470
O-Cinnamoyl-N-Z-DL-Ser-OMe					154 (dec)			589
O-Cinnamoyl-DL-Ser-OMe				Me	169–171			589
N,N′-Dicyclohexyl-N-(N″-2-quinoxaline-carbonyl-DL-Ser)-urea								340
O-β-D-Glucopyranosido-N-Z-Ser-OMe								675
O-β-D-Glucopyranosido-N-Z-D-Ser-OMe						−3.3	Me	675
N-Hippuryl-DL-Ser				Acn	174–176			33

N-Hippuryl-DL-Ser Amide	Aq-Alc	176–177			33
N-Hippuryl-Ser-OMe	Aq-Alc	96–98			33
N-Hippuryl-Ser-OMe		112–113	+10	Py	33
O-Hippuryl-DL-Ser-OMe Toluenesulfonate	Chf-Eth	70 (dec)			33
DL-Homo-Ser-lactone Toluenesulphonate	Alc	211–212			424
OMe-N-dichloro-ac-Ser Bis(2-chloro-et) Amide		84–85			366
N-Nps-Ser-OMe	Me	136–138	+45	DMF	775
O-Phosphoryl-Ser-OMe					140
N-2-Quinoxalinecarbonyl-DL-Ser	DMF-Aq	224 (dec)			340
Ser					118
Ser Amide		103	+24	HOAc	201
Ser Amide Hydrochloride	Me-Eth				39
Ser-OBzl Benzenesulfonate	i-Pr-Eth	97–98			335
Ser-OBu^{t}	Me-An	250			723
Ser-ONBzl Benzenesulfonate	Alc	157–158	−17	Aq	561
Ser-ONBzl Toluenesulfonate	i-Pr	158–163	−14	Py	406
O-Tos-N-Z-DL-Ser Amide	Alc	112	−18	Me	33
O-Tos-N-Z-Ser-OBzh		83–84	−15	DMF	668
O-Tos-N-Z-Ser-OBzl	Alc	75.5–77	−7.4	DMF	668
O-Tos-N-Z-Ser-ONBzl	Alc	108–110	−6.5	DMF	668
O-Tos-N-boc-Ser-ONBzl	Alc	115–116	+13	Chf	668
O-Tos-N-hippuryl-DL-Ser Amide	Alc	126–128			33
O-Tos-DL-Ser Amide Hydrobromide	Aq	140–143			33
N-Tos-Ser-Bzl-amide	Alc	136–137	+12	An	419
O-[2,2,2-Trifluoro-1-Z-amino-et]-N-Z(OMe)-Ser	EtAc-Pe	70			701
O-[2,2,2-Trifluoro-1-Z-amino-et]-N-Z(OMe)-Ser-OSu					
O-[2,2,2-Trifluoro-1-Z-amino-et]-N-Z(OMe)-Ser DCHA Salt	Alc-Aq	155			701
O-[2,2,2-Trifluoro-1-Z-amino-et]-N-boc-Ser	Pe	80–85			701
	Me-Eth	55–62			701
2-Trt-DL-cyclo-Ser Hydrochloride		149–152			470
N-Trt-Ser		160			189
N-Trt-Ser-OMe	Be-Pe	157–158	+23	Alc	89
	Be-Pe	145			89

Table 1 Amino Acid Derivatives (continued)

Compound	Method	Solvent	% Yield	Solvent Crystallization	M.P. (°C)	$[\alpha]_D$	Solvent Rotation	Ref.
Threonine								
O-Ac-N-carboxy-Thr-Anhydride				EtAc-Pe	94-95			706
O-Bzl-N-tos-DL-Thr					113			522
Z-OBu^t-Thr-OSu					Oil			735
N$^\gamma$-Z-Dbu-Thr-OMe Hydrochloride				Me-Eth	189-190	+23	Me	485
N-Z(OMe)-Thr				EtAc-Pe	83-84	-3.4	Me	701
Z(OMe)-Thr Hydrazide				Me-Eth-Pe	194-195	+10	DMF	452
N$^\gamma$-Z-N$^\alpha$-Nps-Dbu-Thr-OMe				Me-Eth	153-156	+28	DMF	485
Z-Thr				EtAc-Pe	97-99			761a
Z-Thr-ONBzl				EtAc-Pe	101-102	-5.8	Ac	104
Z-Thr-OMe				EtAc-Pe	114-115	-14	Me	104
OBu^t-Z-Thr						+8.4	DMF	556
					126-126.5	+8.2	DMF	556
					Oil			556
OBu^t-Z-Thr-OBu^t					126-126.5			101
OBu^t-Z-Thr-DCHA Salt						+8.2	DMF	556
OBu^t-Z-Thr Hydrazide				Alc-Eth-Pe	146-147	+9.9	Alc	723
OBu^t-Z-Thr-OMe				Me-Aq	96.5	+9.7	DMF	556
OBu^t-Z-Thr-ONBzl				Pe	55-56.5	+6.3	DMF	556
OBu^t-Z-Thr-2,4-di-ONp				Eth-Pe	87-88	-12	Me	723
OBu^t-Z-Thr-OSu				Me-Cl-Pe	90	-6.3	Di	735
								403
OBu^t-N-boc-Thr Hydrazide					64-73	+5.6	Me	556
OBu^t-N-boc-Thr-OMe					Oil			556
OBu^t-Thr				Me-An	259-260 (dec)	-42	Me	723
OBu^t-Thr-OBu^t					Oil			101
					Oil			49
					b.p. 127 (.25 mm)			81

Compound	M.p./B.p. (°C)	$[\alpha]_D$	Solvent	Recrystn. solvent	Ref.
OBu^t-Thr-OBu^t Phosphite Salt					81
OBu^t-Thr-OBu^t Picrate	74–76			Eth-Pe	49
OBu^t-Thr-OMe	140	−6	DMF	Bu^t-Aq	556
	b.p. 46.5 (0.4 mm)	−0.2	Me		
N$^\alpha$-Caprylyl-N$^\gamma$-Z-Dbu-D-Thr	Oil				133
N$^\alpha$-Caprylyl-N$^\gamma$-Z-Dbu-D-Thr-OMe	Oil				133
N$^\alpha$-Caprylyl-Dbu-D-Thr	140				133
OMe-Z-Thr DCHA Salt	138–139			Me-Pe	91
OMe-Z-Thr-OMe	b.p. 150–170 (0.12 mm)				91
OMe-Thr	213–214	−37	Aq	EtAc	91
OMe-Thr-OMe Hydrobromide	100–110				91
N-Me-Thr	225–232 (dec)	−33	Aq		77
N-Nps-Thr	138–141	−111	DMF	Alc	774
N-Nps-Thr DCHA Salt	181–182	−103	DMF	Aq-Alc	774
O-Phosphoryl-Thr	189 (dec)	−7.9	Aq		140
Thr		−28	Aq		723
DL-Thr-OBzl					655
Thr-OBu^t Phosphite Salt	140–141			Alc-Pe	81
Thr-OMe	70–72				399
O-[2,2,2-Trifluoro-1-Z-amino-et]-Z(OMe)-Thr	113–116			EtAc	701
O-[2,2,2-Trifluoro-1-Z-amino-et]-Z(OMe)-Thr DCHA Salt	151–153			Pe	701

Tryptophan

Compound	M.p. (°C)	$[\alpha]_D$	Solvent	Recrystn. solvent	Ref.
Adoc-D-Trp	152–154	+10	1N HCl	Chf	195
6-Amino-Trp	210–212	+5.0	Me	Aq	170
Z-D-Trp	127–129			EtAc-Pe	742
Z-Trp 2-Hydroxyethylamide	124–125	−4.6	Me	Alc	527
Z-Trp-ONp	105	−4.5	DMF	DMF	707
N$^\alpha$-Boc-Trp	138.5–139.5	+23	Chf	EtAc-Pe	475

71

Table 1 Amino Acid Derivatives (continued)

Compound	Method	Solvent	% Yield	Solvent Crystallization	M.P.(°C)	[α]D	Solvent Rotation	Ref.
Boc-D-Trp-OTcp				Ac	126.6–127.7	+18.6		111
Nα-(γ-Chlorobutyryl)-Trp				Alc-Aq				471
Nα-(γ-Chlorobutyryl)-Trp-OMe				MeCl-He	111.5–112	+42	Di	471
Nα-(γ-Chlorobutyryl)-Trp-OMe				Me-Cl-He	113–113.5			471
7-Bis(2-chloro-et)amino-DL-Trp								170
6-Bis(2-chloro-et)-amino-DL-Trp								170
5-Bis-(2-chloro-et)-amino-DL-Trp								22b
Nα-Me-Trp					275–290 (dec)			471
Nα-Me-Trp-OMe Hydrochloride				Me-Eth	171–172			471
N-Nps-Trp DCHA Salt				THF-Eth	168–169	−20	DMF	774
Octahydro-Trp								322
Nα-(2-Tetrahydrofuranylidene)-Trp-OMe				Me-Cl-He	171–172			471
Trp								320; 321
Trp-OBzl				Aq	222			707
Trp-OBzl Hydrochloride				Aq	222	+4	Me	707
Trp 2-Hydroxyethylamide				Me-Eth	144			527
Trp-OMe Hydrochloride				Me-Eth	213.5–214 (dec)			471
Tyrosine								
1-Ac-2(α-N-ac-Tyr)-hydrazine				Aq-Pr	238			352
N-Ac-Tyr Hydrazide					232–233			352
1-Ac-2-(O,N-di-α-Tyr)-hydrazine				Aq	219–220			352
1-Ac-2-(Tyr)-hydrazine				Acn	144–146			352
1-Ac-2-(D-Tyr)-hydrazine				Pr	143–144	−60	Aq	352
1-Ac-2-(Tyr)-hydrazine β-Naphthalene Sulfonate Salt				Pr	147–149			352

Compound	Recryst. solvent	M.p. (°C)	[α]	Solvent	Ref.
N-(1-Aminocyclopentanecarbonyl)-Tyr-OEt Hydrochloride		128–130			97
N-Aoc-OBzl-Tyr DCHA Salt	EtAc-Pe	113.5–115.5	+43	Alc	248
OBzl-Z-Tyr	EtAc-Cy	112–113			423
OBzl-boc-Tyr DCHA Salt		135 (dec)			46
OBzl-boc-Tyr-ONp	Alc	137–139	−2	DMF	46
OBzl-N-Nps-Tyr	EtAc-Pe	136–139			671
Obzl-N-Nps-Tyr DCHA Salt	Me	182–183 (dec)			625
OBzl-N-Nps-Tyr-ONp	Pr-EtAc	156–157			671
OBzl-Z-Tyr-OTcp	EtAc-Pe	108–110			423
OBzl-Tyr	Aq-Ac	224–226 (dec)			423
3-Bzl-thio-propionyl-Tyr Hydrazide	Aq-Alc	193–194	−6.0	DMF	46
3-Bzl-thio-propionyl-Tyr-OMe	EtAc-Pe	89–90	−3.4	DMF	768
N-(1-Z-Amidocyclopentanecarbonyl)-Tyr-OEt	EtAc-Pe	102	+5	Alc	768
O,N-Di-Z-N-me-Tyr	Eth-Pe	91–94	−50	DMF	97
O,N-Di-Z-N-me-Tyr-ONp	Alc	84–86	−72	DMF	258
Z-Tyr		92–95			258, 723
Di-Z-Tyr Boc-hydrazide		147	−18	Me	190
O,N-Di-Z-Tyr Boc-hydrazide	EtAc-Eth	147	−18	DMF	190
Z-Tyr Boc-hydrazide	Etn-Pe	90–100 (dec)	−18	Me	190
Z-Tyr-OEt	EtAc-Pe	88–91	−19	Me	723
N,O-Di-Z-Tyr-OMe	EtAc-He	110–111	−33	DMF	328
Z-Tyr-OMe	EtAc-Pe	92–93	−32	DMF	328
Z-Tyr-ONBzl	EtAc-Be-Pe	117–119	−11	Me	723
O,N-Di-Z-Tyr-ONp	EtAc-Cy	137–138	−26	DMF	406
OBu^t-Z-Tyr		Oil			556
OBu^t-Z-Tyr-OBu^t		Oil			49

Table 1 Amino Acid Derivatives (continued)

Compound	Method	Solvent	% Yield	Solvent Crystallization	M.P. (°C)	[α]D	Solvent Rotation	Ref.
OBu^t-Z-Tyr DCHA Salt					154–154.5	+24	DMF	556
				Alc	160–161.5	+34	Alc	723
OBu^t-Z-Tyr-OEt						–22	DMF	556
OBu^t-Z-Tyr-OMe				Pe	51–53.5	–29	DMF	328
OBu^t-Z-Tyr-ONBzl				EtAc-Be-Pe	73.5–74.5			723
OBu^t-N-boc-Tyr-OEt					Oil			556
OBu^t-boc-Tyr Hydrazide					121–121.5	+2.7	DMF	556
OBu^t-Tyr-OBu^t				i-Pr-Ac	159–160			81
								49
Obu^t-Tyr-OBu^t Hydrochloride					154–155	+42	DMF	49
OBu^t-Tyr-OEt						+22	DMF	556
Boc-Tyr Hydrazide					191–193	+8.8	DMF	556
Boc-Tyr-OMe					102–104	+5.4	Me	46
Boc-Tyr-ONp					134–138	–5	An	43
β-Carboxypropionyl-OBzl-Tyr-OMe								
OEt-Carbonyl-Z-Tyr				Me	117–119	–5.3	Me	160
OEt-Carbonyl-Z-Tyr-OMe				i-Pr-Eth	95.5–96.5	–14	Me	160
OEt-Carbonyl-Z-Tyr-ONp				i-Pr	111–112	–12	DMF-Ac	160
OEt-Carbonyl-Z-Tyr-OTcp					123	–38	DMF	160
OEt-Carbonyl-boc-Tyr					166	+10	Me	160
OEt-Carbonyl-for-Tyr				Aq-Me	172–173	+49	Me	160
OEt-Carbonyl-Tyr Hydrobromide					215 (dec)	–4.8	Me	160
OEt-Carbonyl-Tyr Hydrochloride					219–220 (dec)	–4.9	Me	160
OEt-Carbonyl-Tyr-OMe Hydrochloride					162–163	+7.1	Me	160
OEt-N-for-Tyr				Aq	166–167			778
OEt-Tyr					236	+11	HCl	778
OEt-Tyr-OMe Hydrochloride				Me-Eth	204–205			778
Hexahydro-Tyr								322

Compound	Solvent	mp	[α]	Solvent	Ref.
O-Isobutyloxycarbonyl-Z-Tyr	Me-Aq	103–105	−3.9	Me	160
O-Isopropyloxycarbonyl-Z-Tyr	i-Pr-Aq	119–121.5	+1.0	Me	160
O-Me-N-ac-Tyr	Aq	146–147			604
N-[β-Me-amino-et]-Tyr Dihydrochloride	Alc	203–204			548
OMe-Carbonyl-Z-Tyr	Me-Aq	112 and 130	−3.0	Me	160
OMe-Tyr	Aq	243–244			604
			−7.0	3N HCl	292
OMe-Tyr-OEt Hydrochloride	Alc	196–198			292
OMe-Tyr-OMe					604
O,N-Di-Me-N-tos-Tyr		138	−26	Alc	258
			−19	DMF	
N-Me-Tyr		292–295 (dec)	+19	HCl	258
N-Me-Tyr-OBu^t	Aq	118–119	+19	3.4N HCl	295
N,N-Di-Me-Tyr-OMe	Be-Pe	128	+39	Ac	258
N-Me-Tyr-OMe	Acn	111–112	+46	Alc	258
N-Me-Tyr-OMe Hydrochloride	EtAc	145–147	+39	Me	258
N-Nps-Tyr DCHA Salt	Me-Eth	173–175			295
Succinyl-bis(OBzl-Tyr-OMe)	Alc	159–161	+41	Me	774
Succinyl-bis(Tyr-OMe)	EtAc-Pe	154–155	+61	THF	43
O-Tos-N-Z-N-me-Tyr	Me-Pe	143–146	+19	Alc	43
O-Tos-N-Z-N-me-Tyr-ONp	Ac	67–68	−44	DMF	258
O-Tos-Z-Tyr-ONp	Be-Pe	101.5–103 (dec)	−60	Ac	258
O-Tos-N-me-Tyr	Alc	265 (dec)	−12	DMF	628
O-Tos-N-Nps-Tyr DCHA Salt		148–148.5	+30	4N HCl	258
	EtAc	144–148	+14	DMF	625
O-Tos-N-Nps-Tyr-ONp	EtAc-Eth	119–121			671
O-Tos-Tyr-OMe Hydrochloride	Pr-EtAc	146–147			671
O-Tos-Tyr-ONp-hydrobromide	Me-Eth	210–211 (dec)			295
	Alc		+34	DMF	628
N-Tos-Tyr		186–187			42

75

Table 1 Amino Acid Derivatives (continued)

Compound	Method	Solvent	% Yield	Solvent Crystallization	M.P.(°C)	$[\alpha]_D$	Solvent Rotation	Ref.
N-Tos-Tyr-OEt					111.5–112.5			42
Tyr						−8.5	3N HCl	292, 322
Tyr-OBzl Bz-sulfonate				Alc-Eth	143–145	−3.8	DMF	165
Tyr-OBu^t				EtAc-Pe	143–145			510
				i-Pr-Eth	142–144			81
				Aq-Me	248–249.5 (dec)	−25	Aq	723
Tyr Boc-hydrazide				Pe-EtAc	167	+1.0	Me	190
						+3.1	DMF	190
						+27	Me	190
Tyr Hydrazide				Aq	267–270	−3.1	DMF	352
Tyr Hydrazide Di-β-naphthalene Sulfonate Salt				Me-Eth-Pe	136–137	+45	Ac	352
Tyr-OMe								569
Tyr-OMe Hydrochloride					184–185	+72	Py	550
D-Tyr-OMe Hydrochloride					185–186	−74	Py	550
Tyr-ONBzl Bz-sulfonate				Me	218–219	+15	Py	561
Valine								
N-Ac-Val Bis(2-chloro-et) Amide				EtAc-He	157–158			366
N-Bzhoc-Val DCHA Salt				EtAc-He	116.5–117.5			225
Z(Br)-DL-Val					Oil			692
Z(OMe)-Val								302
Z(NO$_2$)-Val				EtAc-Pe	60–62	+4.2	Ac	430
Z-D-Val					60–62	+5.0	Me	550, 527

Compound	Solvent	m.p. (°C)	[α]	Solvent	Ref.
Z-Val		57-61	-4.3	Ac	550
N-[N-Z-Val]-1,3,4,6-tetra-ac-β-D-glucosamine	Alc	228-229 (dec)			685
Z-Val Amide	EtAc	206-208	+22	DMF	66
Z-Val Boc-hydrazide	Alc-i-Pr-Eth	145	-45	Me	719
N-[N-Z-Val]-D-glucosamine	Alc	218-221 (dec)	+37	Me	685
6-O-(N-Z-DL-Val)-D-glucose	EtAc	61.5-63	+28	Me	115
Z-Val-2,4,6-tri-me-OBzl		106-107	-2.5	DMF	630
Z-Val-ONBzl		61-62	-4.9	DMF	635
N-Z-Val-Ophenacyl		92-93	-14	Chf	616
Z-DL-Val-SePh		260-263			719
N^4-(Z-Val)-sulfanilamide	Me	156-157			590
Boc-Val Amide		94-100			571
Boc-Val-Z-hydrazide		145-148			715
N-(5-Chlorosalicylidene)-Val					592
For-Val					584
N-(2-Hydroxy-1-naphthal)-Val	Alc	181.5-185 (dec)	-92	Alc	592
Iso-Val-OEt	Aq-Alc	70-72	+8.1	Ac	396
Iso-Val Hydrazide	Alc	138-139	-71	Alc	396
N-(5,5-Di-me-cyclohex-2-en-1-on-3-yl)-DL-Val		217-218			196
N-Me-Val	THF	297-300 (dec)	+32	5N HCl	77
N-Me-Val-OBu^t		Oil	+5.3	Chf	410
N-Me-Val-OBu^t-tos Salt		109-110	+4.8	Aq	410
N-Nps-Val		105	-127	DMF	774
N-Nps-Val DCHA Salt		191-193			774
N-Nps-Val-OMe	Alc	98	-85	Me	774
N-Nps-Val-ONp		75-77	-182	Me	774
Pht-D-Val-OBu^t		79-82	+22	EtAc	564
Pht-DL-Val-SePh		104			719
N-Salicylidene-Val		124-125			228

Table 1 Amino Acid Derivatives (continued)

Compound	Method	Solvent	% Yield	Solvent Crystallization	M.P.(°C)	[α]_D	Solvent Rotation	Ref.
Tos-Val								584
Tfa-Val								584
Val				Aq-Alc	melting above 300	+45	Ac	592
N-[Val]-1,3,4,6-tetra-ac-β-D-glucosamine-acetate					220	-10	Chf	685
Val Amide Acetate Salt								571
Val Amide Tfa Salt								571
Val-OBzl Benzenesulfonate				Me	124-125	+14	Py	601
Val-OBzl Benzenesulfonate Hydrochloride				EtAc	177-180	+9.1	Py	601
Val-OBzl Toluenesulphonate				Alc-Eth	138-139	-3.6	Me	165
DL-Val-OBzl Toluenesulphonate				Alc-Eth	138-140			446
D-Val-OBzl Toluenesulphonate					157-158	+4.8	Alc	446
Val Z-Hydrazide					196-197			715
Val-OBu^t								698
D-Val-OBu^t					b.p. 44-50 (1 mm)	-24		564
Val OBu^t Hydrochloride					140-144	+6.8	Aq	564
D-Val-OBu^t Hydrochloride					144-146	-7.5	Aq	330
Val Boc-hydrazide				i-Pr-Eth-Pe	105-108			719
Val-OBzh Hydrobromide				EtAc	141-142	-24	DMF	616
Val-OBzh Hydrochloride				EtAc	159.5-160	-35	THF	616
N-[Val]-D-glucosamine Hydrochloride						+64	Aq	685
Val-melphalan								36
Val-ONBzl Bz-sulphonate				Me-Eth	155	+15	Py	561
Val-ONBzl Hydrobromide					149-150	+6.6	DMF	635
Val-Ophenacyl Hydrobromide				Me-EtAc		+12	Me	616
N^4-(Val)-sulfanilamide Acetate								590

2

Dipeptides

Evaluation of new peptide bond-forming techniques has primarily been performed with dipeptide formation. Accordingly, Table 2 includes the greatest variety of peptide-forming reagents to be found in this volume. Many such experiments have involved a relatively small number of peptides. The greatest number have been prepared using dicyclohexylcarbodiimide. The mixed carbonic anhydride and p-nitrophenol ester techniques have also received wide use. One of the most extensive studies[440a] of synthetic dipeptides utilized predominantly these three methods. Reference 440a provides a valuable single source of such experimental information. Generally, dicyclohexylcarbodiimide has been used in reactions varying from approximately 4 to 60 hr with a majority in the range of 1 day. Presumably an approximate 6 hr period at room temperature would have been satisfactory in most cases. Direct comparison of peptide reagents and solvents appears in some peptide syntheses noted in Table 2. Such examples include preparation of Z-leu-OBu^t-Tyr-OMe by the p-nitrophenyl ester (82% yield) and N-hydroxysuccinimide (87%) methods (in tetrahydrofuran),[328] synthesis of Z-the-Leu-OMe using DCCI in methanol-dioxane (68% yield) and in ethyl acetate (76%).[487] Further refinements in initial choice of peptide bond-forming reagent and solvent system should be more easily made when a greater number of such comparative experimental results become available.

Inspection of Table 2 should suggest a potentially workable choice of reagent, reaction solvent, and crystallizing solvent for a particular dipeptide synthesis. The choice should be made keeping in mind that individual peptide chemists have favored certain reagents and techniques which have been routinely applied and, if reasonably successful, comparative studies would not have been undertaken. For example, in our laboratory, for small peptides, the mixed carbonic anhydride, water soluble carbodiimide (EDCI) or Woodward's reagent K methods would in many cases be given first consideration.

As in the other tables, sufficient optical rotation data has been included to give an indication of the sign of rotation for related types of dipeptides. Also, with optical values, it is unfortunate that these measurements have been made in such a variety of solvents. With a considerable number of rotations already reported in either dimethylformamide or methanol or chloroform, one of these should be given first choice in future work. Uniformity here will allow more effective use of rotation values. Many of the dipeptides included in Table 2 were prepared prior to 1960 by other methods and only data found in the reference listed has been included. Thus, as with Table 1 and each successive compilation, missing data does not mean such information is unavailable in earlier literature.

In general, the introduction to Table 1 and the glossary should be consulted when using Table 2 and subsequent tabulations. Again, it should be stressed that aminobutyric acid amides are included in the table as simple derivatives of the respective dipeptides. Also, a substance such as N,N'-di-Bzhoc-cystinyl-di-gly-OEt would be found in Table 3 rather than 2.

Recent work, available too late to be given detailed treatment in Table 2, includes: syntheses of penicillin dipeptides;[134] aspartic acid dipeptides;[380] dipeptides containing cyclopentylglycine, β-2-thienyl-ala;[217] and methionine containing peptides.[738] Selective cleavage of Boc-Phe-Gly-OBu^t to Phe-Gly-OBu^t by passing a methanol-water solution of the dipeptide over a column of Zeo-Carb 225 H$^+$ has been reported. The method allows selective hydrolysis of Boc-N in the presence of Boc-O.[180] Palladium catalyzed hydrogenolysis of Z from methionine peptides in methanol containing boron trifluoride etherate has been used to prepare Met-Arg with simultaneous removal of a nitro protecting group.[739]

Table 2 Dipeptides

Compound	Method	Solvent	% Yield	Solvent Crystallization	M.P.(°C)	[α]D	Solvent Rotation	Ref.
Alanine								
Ala-Ala-OEt Hydrobromide								330
DL-Ala-DL-Ala Hydrochloride								389
Ala-Ala-OMe								197a
Z-Ala-Ala-OBu^t	ONP	Py	85		98-102			398
Z-DL-Ala-DL-Ala-OEt				Eth-Pe	126-128	-35	Alc	388
Z-Ala-Ala-OEt				EtAc-Pe	70-71	-46	Alc	399
Z-DL-Ala-Ala-OPAP					75			23
Z-DL-Ala-DL-Ala-OPAP					116			23
Z-β-Ala-β-Ala-OPAP					190-192			23
Z-DL-α-et-Ala-DL-α-et-Ala					170-172			284
Z-DL-α-et-Ala-α-me-Ala-OMe					220-222			284
Z-α-me-Ala-α-me-Ala				Aq-Me	126-128			365
2-(1'-Z-α-me-Ala-α-me-Ala-amine-1'-me)et-4,4-di-me-oxazolone	DCCI	THF	64	EtAc-Pe	76-77			284
Z-α-me-Ala-α-me-Ala-OMe				Aq-Me	161-162.5			284
N-Z-Ala-3-chloro-Ala-OMe				Be-Pe	158-159			296
Boc-Ala-Ala-OBzl			86	EtAc-Pe	107-109			356a
N-(Chloro-ac)-3-phenyl-β-Ala-Ala-OEt				Eth-Pe	109-111			318
For-DL-Ala-DL-Ala				Be	150.5-151.3	+14	Me	389
For-DL-Ala-DL-Ala-OEt				He	73-74			389
N-Me-DL-Ala-DL-Ala				Alc-EtAc	161-163			55
Me-3-(N-Z-Ala-Ala)-2-oxo-oxazolidine-4-carboxylate				EtAc-Pe	95-97			296
4,4-Di-me-2-(1-me-1'-tos-α-me-Ala-α-me-Ala-amino)et-oxazolone				Be	224-225			365
Tos-α,N-di-me-Ala-α-me-Ala				Aq-Me	210.5-212			365

Table 2 Dipeptides (continued)

Compound	Method	Solvent	% Yield	Solvent Crystallization	M.P.(°C)	[α]$_D$	Solvent Rotation	Ref.
Tos-α-me-Ala-α-me-Ala				Me	216–218			365
Tos-α-me-Ala-α-me-Ala-OMe	DCCI	An	83	EtAc	146–147.5			365
Tfa-DL-α-et-Ala-DL-α-et-Ala-OMe	DCCI	MeCl	76	EtAc-Pe	68–70			284
Tfa-DL-α-et-Ala-α-me-Ala-OMe	O	Acn	85		105–107			284
Tfa-α-me-Ala-α-me-Ala-OMe				Be	113.5–115.5			365
Z-D-Ala-N^G-nitro-Arg	MCA	MeCl		An-Eth	120–121	−10	DMF	440a
N-Z-Ala-N^G-nitro-Arg-ONBzl Hemi-ac Solvate	ONP	DMF			69–74	−23	Ac	646
Ala-Asp Amide					184–186	+39		436
Z-Ala-Asp Amide	MCA	MeCl			240–242	−10		436
Z-D-Ala-S-bzl-Cys	ONP		77	Alc	115–117	−3	Me	440a
Z-Ala-S-bzl-Cys-ONp	DCCI	Chf	81		173–174	−44	DMF	628
Me-N-bz-S-(N-Z-Ala)-Cys	DCCI	Chf	48	Me	178–179			224
Me-N-Z-Ala-S-bz-Cys	DCCI	Chf	87	EtAc-Pe	135–135.5	−32	Me	224
Me-N-Z-Ala-Z-Cys	DCCI	Chf	84	EtAc-Pe	95.8–96.2	−37	Me	224
Me-N-Z-S-(N-Z-Ala)-Cys					90–91.5	−42	Me	224
Ala-D-Glu-di-OBzl					Oil			86
Ala-Gly Hydrate	DCCI	Acn	73	Alc	214–215	+11	Aq	603
Z-Ala-D-Glu-di-OBzl					114.5	−3.5	Ac	86
Z-Ala-Glu-ONBzl					192–194			669
H-Ala-Gly				Aq-Alc	230–231.5 (dec)	+50	Aq	631
Ala-Gly-OBzh Hydrochloride	EDCI	MeCl	97	EtAc-Eth-He	53–60	−1.5	Me	227
DL-Ala-Gly Hydrochloride					65–68			389
Ala-Gly-2,4,6-tri-me-OBzl Hydrochloride				Alc-Eth	189.5–191	+8.8	DMF	625
Ala-Gly-OMe Hydrobromide				Me-Eth	162	+7.3	Me	774
Ala-Gly-ONp Hydrochloride				Me-EtAc	159–161	+7.7	Me	227
Ala-Gly-Ophenacyl Hydrochloride				Me-EtAc	170–171	+3.7	Aq	632
					171	−2.5	Me	616

82

Compound	Reagent	Solvent	Yield (%)	Recryst. solvent	M.p. (°C)	[α]	Solvent	Ref.
Aza-Ala-Gly-OEt				EtAc-Eth-He	71–72			154
Bzh-Ala-Gly Hydrochloride	DCCI	Chf	76	An-Pe	53–60	−1.5	Me	227
N-Bzh-Ala-Gly-OEt					114–114.5	−22	Alc	219
N-Bzl-DL-Ala-Gly								55
N-Benzyliden-aza-Ala-Gly-OEt					115–116			154
Z-DL-Ala-aza-Gly Di-me Amide					165–166			154
Z-DL-Ala-aza-Gly-ONp					119–121			157
Z-Ala-Gly	OPCP	DMF	94	Eth	125–128	−16	Alc	553
				Alc	127–132	−17	Alc	619
				Aq	134–135	−17	Alc	700
				EtAc-Pe	127–128	+4.8	DMF	275
Z-Ala-Gly Amide					119–121	+7.5	Me	615
Z-Ala-Gly-OBzl	DCCI	DMF	73		111–112	−15	DMF	360
Z-Ala-Gly-O-p-bromophenacyl	MCA	Acn	78	Alc	152.5–154.5	−7.4		633
Z-Ala-Gly-OCH(Ph)CN				Chf-Cy	132.5–133	−3.4	DMF	168
Z-Ala-Gly-OEt				EtAc-Cy	101–103	0	DMF	623
					88–89.5	−18	DMF	23
Z-β-Ala-Gly-OEt	ONP	DMF	76	Aq-Alc	98–99			305
	ONP	DMF	80	Aq-Alc	98–99			305
N-Z-DL-Ala-Gly Hydroxamic Acid				NMe	140			23
Z-Ala-Gly-OMe	DCCI	Chf	79	EtAc-He	96–97			233
Z-Ala-Gly-ONp	DCCI	Chf	77	Alc	98–99	−25	Me	227
Z-Ala-Gly-Ophenacyl	DCCI	Chf	70	Alc	179	−33	Ac	774
Z-Ala-Gly-SPh				EtAc-Pe	153–155	−7.5	Chf	649
N-[N-Carboxy-3-({2-[3-phenyldithio propianamido]et}-dithio)-N-bzh-Ala]-Gly-OEt					115–117			616
N-(Chloro-ac)Ala-Gly-OEt	DCCI	Chf	81	EtAc	68–70	−6.6	Chf	700
					114–115			222
N-(Chloro-ac)-3-phenyl-β-Ala-Gly-OEt	DCCI	Chf		Alc	138–139			318
								318

Table 2 Dipeptides (continued)

Compound	Method	Solvent	% Yield	Solvent Crystallization	M.P. (°C)	[α]D	Solvent Rotation	Ref.
Z-Cl-Ala-Gly-OEt	DCCI		81		104-105	-3.9	DMF	708
Z-Dehydro-Ala-Gly	DCCI	EtAc-Chf	50	Eth-Pe	83-84			469
Z-Dehydro-Ala-Gly-OEt								469
For-DL-Ala-Gly	DCCI		54	Me-EtAc	123-125			389
For-DL-Ala-Gly-OEt	DCCI	Be	47	EtAc-Pe	88.5-89			389
For-α-me-Ala-Gly-OEt	O	THF	50	EtAc-Pe	102-103.5			365
(±)-2-Iodo-OEt-carbonyl-Ala-Gly-OEt	MCA			EtAc-Pe	102-103			182
N-Me-DL-Ala-Gly								55
Me-Ala-Gly Hydrobromide	DCCI	EtAc	79	EtAc-He	96-97			227
N-Nps-Ala-Gly					144-145	-44	DMF	776
Nps-Ala-Gly				EtAc-Cy	144.5-145.5	-44	DMF	632
Nps-Ala-Gly-OEt				Alc	101-102	-42	DMF	632
Nps-Ala-Gly-2,4,6-tri-me-OBzl				EtAc-Cy	171-172	-34	DMF	625
N-Nps-Ala-Gly-OMe				Me	169-169.5	-34	DMF	631
N-Nps-Ala-Gly-4,4'-di-OMe-diphenyl Ester				EtAc	123-125	-42	DMF	774
Nps-Ala-Gly-ONp	MCA	DMF	68	DMF-Alc	138	-55	THF	616
N-[3-({2-[3-(phenyldithio) propionamido] -et} dithio) -Ala] -Gly-OEt					179.5-180	-64	DMF	632
Tos-α-me-Ala-Gly	AC	An	71	Aq-Me	150-151			222
Tos-α-me-Ala-Gly-OEt	MCA	Tol	24	Aq-Me	149-151			365
Ala-His					260-262 (dec)			386
β-Ala-3-me-His					260-263 (dec)	+32	Aq	114
Pht-Ala-His					221-224 (dec)			386

Compound	Method	Solvent	Yield (%)	Recryst. solv.	[α]	Solv.	mp (°C)	Ref.
Pht-β-Ala-3-me-His							224–225 (dec)	114
Pht-β-Ala-3-me-His-OMe							186–187	114
DL-Ala-DL-Leu							240	389
Ala-Leu					−17	Aq	163	218
Z-Ala-Leu	MCA	THF	84	Alc-Pe	−16	Alc	52	756
Z-Ala-Leu DCHA Salt				Alc-Aq	−39	Alc	55–56	333
Z-Ala-Leu-OEt			91	EtAc-Pe	−55	Alc	158–162	756
Z-Ala-Leu Hydrazide				EtAc-Pe			165–167	333
Z-Ala-Leu-melphalan-OEt	A							36
Z-DL-Ala-DL-nor-Leu-OPAP								36
N-[Bis(p-nitro-bzl)-phosphoryl]-Ala-Leu Anilide				Me			185	36
N-[Bis(p-nitro-bzl)-phosphoryl]-Ala-Leu Hydrazide							202	23
N-[Bis(p-nitro-bzl)-phosphoryl]-Ala-Leu-OMe							134	99
Tos-Ala-Leu	DCCI	MeCl	77	Aq-Me			190–191	99
Z-Ala-D-Met	DCCI	MeCl			+13	DMF	91–93	99
Z-D-Ala-D-Met	MCA	MeCl			+0.5	DMF	112–114	344
N-[N-Carboxy-3-({2-[3-(phenyldithio) propionamido]et}dithio)-N-bzl-Ala]-DL-Met-OEt	DCCI	EtAc	70	EtAc-He			94–95	440a
Pht-lauryl-DL-Ala-DL-Met				Alc-Aq			300 (dec)	440a
Pht-lauryl-DL-Ala-DL-Met-OEt				EtAc-Cy			94–96	222
Ala-N^δ-tos-Orn-OMe Hydrochloride	MCA	THF	83		+6.1	Ac	Oil	614
Z-Ala-N^δ-tos-Orn-OMe	MCA	Thf-Chf	66				90–92	614
Z(OMe)-Ala-N^δ-Z-Orn-OEt				EtAc-Eth	−2.0	DMF	190–193	330
Z(OMe)-Ala-N^δ-Z-Orn Hydrazide				Di-Eth	−1.2	DMF		330
Ala-Phe					+17	1N HCl		338
Ala-Phe 2-Chloroethylamide					+19		187–189	338
Z-Ala-D-Phe	MCA	MeCl			+2	DMF	49–51	218

Table 2 Dipeptides (continued)

Compound	Method	Solvent	% Yield	Solvent Crystallization	M.P.(°C)	$[\alpha]_D$	Solvent Rotation	Ref.
Z-D-Ala-D-Phe	MCA	MeCl			56–60			440a
Z-Ala-Phe 2-Chloroethylamide					181–182	−21		401
Z-Ala-Phe Hydrazide				Alc-Aq	198–199	−19	Ac	553
Z-Ala-Phe-OMe			75		99–100	−9.3	Alc	553
Boc-Ala-Phe Hydrazide					162–163	−22	Ac	395
N-[p-Chloro-bz]-Ala-Phe				EtAc-Pe	170–172	+24	Me	701
N-[p-Chloro-bz]-Ala-Phe-OMe				EtAc-Pe	175	+6.6	Me	701
N-[p-Chloro-bz]-Ala-Phe-OSu				MeCl	180–186	−35	Me	701
β-Chloro-Z-Ala-Phe-OBzl			82		145	−13	DMF	708
N-[Bis(p-nitro-bzl)-phosphoryl]-Ala-Phe-OMe					152			99
Z-Ala-hydroxy-Pro-OMe	MCA		60-80	Me				704
Ala-Pro-OBu^t					79–81	−92	Me	259
Z-Ala-Pro-OBu^t	MCA		79			−90	Me	259
						−93	Ac	
						−58	DMF	
Ala-Ser				Alc	208–210	+11	Aq	218
Z-Ala-O-chlorocarbonyl-Ser-OMe					146.3–146.8	−7.8	Me	296
Z-Ala-O-chlorocarbonyl-Ser-OMe Hydrochloride	MCA			Pe-Be	93.5–94	+20	Be	296
Z-Ala-D-Ser	MCA	MeCl			153–155	−20	Me	440a
Z-Ala-Ser Hydrazide					218–220	+7.2	DMF	555
Z-Ala-Ser-OMe	DCCI	Chf	70	EtAc-Pe	134.5–135.5	−17	Me	296
Boc-D-Ala-2-trt-DL-cyclo-Ser	MCA	EtAc	92	Diglyme-Pe	191–193	+9.4	Chf	470
Boc-DL-Ala-2-trt-DL-cyclo-Ser	MCA	EtAc	60					470
N-[p-Chloro-bz]-Ala-o-[2,2,2-trifluoro-1-Z-amino-et]-Ser-OMe				EtAc-Pe	167			701
N-[p-Chloro-bz]-Ala-Ser-OMe	DCCI-NHS	THF	77	EtAc	167	+15	Me	701
Ala-Thr-OMe Hydrochloride Hydrate				Aq-Me-Alc	50–51			704

Compound	Method	Solvent	Yield (%)	Recryst. solvent	m.p. (°C)	$[\alpha]$	Rot. solvent	Ref.
Z-Ala-Thr-OMe	DCCI	MeCl	75	Alc-EtAc	108			704
Ala-Trp	TEA	MeCl	78	Alc-Eth	105			707
Z-Ala-Trp-OBzl				Alc	198–199 (dec)			707
Boc-β-Ala-Trp Hydrazide								111
Boc-β-Ala-Trp-OMe	DCCI	An	77	EtAc	157–158			111
Ala-Tyr-OEt Hydrochloride Monohydrate				Alc-Eth-Pen	146–147		Aq	228
Z-D-Ala-DL-Tyr	MCA	MeCl	70		50–55	−4	DMF	440a
N-Z-Ala-Tyr-OMe	DCCI	MeCl	46	EtAc	126–128	+9	Ac	98
Et-N-(1-benzoylisopropenyl)-Ala-Tyr	DCCI	Chf		An	198–200			228
Z-Ala-D-Val	MCA	MeCl	53		Oil	−10	Me	440a
Z-D-Ala-D-Val	MCA	MeCl		EtAc-Pe	149–150	+23	Me	440a
Z-Ala-Val	SPh	Ac		EtAc-Pe	121–124	−12	Alc	700
N-Z-phenyl-Ala-Val-OMe	DCCI				110–111			179
Arginine								
Arg-D-Ala					151–152	+16	Me	401
Arg-Ala				Alc	170–171			203
N^G-Nitro-Arg-Ala-OBzl								732
N^G-Nitro-Arg-D-Ala-OBzl								401
N^G-Nitro-Arg-Ala-OMe Hydrobromide					156–157	−3		102
N^G-Nitro-N^α-Z-Arg-D-Ala	DCCI	THP	81	Aq-Alc	184–185	+4	Py	401
N^G-Nitro-N^α-Z-Arg-Ala				Aq-Alc	206–207			203
N^G-Nitro-N^α-Z-Arg-Ala-OBzl					113			203
N^G-Nitro-N^α-Z-Arg-D-Ala-OBzl	DCCI	MeCl	70		143–144	−3	Me	401
N^G-Nitro-N^α-Z-Arg-Ala-OMe		THF		Aq-Alc	157.5–160	−22	Me	102
N^G-Nitro-N^α-boc-Arg-Ala-OBzl	MCA	DMF	78		118.5–120	−26	Me	732
Arg-Arg 2-Naphthylamide Dihydrochloride								484
N^α-Z-Arg-Arg Amide Dihydrochloride	MCA	Py						484
N^α-Z-Arg-Arg Dihydrobromide	DCCI	DMF	81		115–120 (dec)			71
N^α-Z-Arg-Arg 2-naphthylamide Dihydrochloride								484

Table 2 Dipeptides (continued)

Compound	Method	Solvent	% Yield	Solvent Crystallization	M.P. (°C)	$[\alpha]_D$	Solvent Rotation	Ref.
N^α-Z-N^G-tos-Arg-N^G-Tos-Arg-δ-amino Valeric Acid-OMe	WRK	Acn	78		87-91	-6.2	Me	454
β-Carboxyproprionyl-Arg-Arg 2-Naphthylamide Dihydrochloride								484
N^G-Nitro-Arg-N^G-nitro-Arg Amide Hydrobromide				Aq-Alc	153.5-156 (dec)	+14	Aq	461
N^G-Nitro-Arg-N^G-nitro-Arg-OBzl Trifluoro-acetate								461
N^G-Nitro-N^α-Z-Arg-N^G-nitro-Arg Amide	MCA	THF	66.1	DMF	115-115.5	-6.2	Ac-Aq	461
N^G-Nitro-N^α-boc-Arg-N^G-nitro-Arg-OBzl	DCCI	DMF	79.2	Me	115-120	-18		461
N^G-Tos-N^α-Arg-N^G-tos-Arg-OMe	DCCI	Acn	74	An	115-120			371
N^G-Tos-N^α-Z-Arg-N^G-tos-Arg Amide					110-120	+1.1	Me	492
Arg-Asp Acetate Salt				Aq-Me	260 (dec)			44
N^G-Nitro-N^α-Z-Arg-Asp	DCCI	Di-EtCl	48	DMF-Me-Acn	201			44
N^G-Nitro-N^α-Z-Arg-S-bz-Cys-OMe		THF	71		153-154	-16	DMF	165
N^G-Nitro-N^α-Z-Arg-S-bzl-Cys	MCA	DMF	71	Alc			DMF	585
N^G-Nitro-N^α-Z-Arg-S-bzl-Cys-OMe	DCCI	THF	71	Alc-Aq	153.5-154	-37	Me	585
N^G-Nitro-N^α-Z-Arg-S-btm-Cys	MCA	DMF	85		149-150	-34	Me	165
N^G-Nitro-N^α-Z-Arg-S-btm-Cys-OMe	MCA	DMF	82	Me	126.5-127.5	-30	DMF	585
N^G-Nitro-N^α-Z-Arg-S-Bu^t-Cys	DCCI	THF-MeCl	60	Aq-Me	99-101			81
N^G-Nitro-N^α-Z-Arg-S-Bu^t-Cys-OBu^t					140-141			81
Arg-Glu Acetate					168			44
N^G-Nitro-N^α-Z-Arg-Glu				Ac-EtAc	167-170	+38	Aq	44
Arg-Gly Acetate Acetic Acid Solvate								520
N^G-Arg-Gly Amide								259
N^α-Z-Arg-Gly				Me-Aq	141.5-142.5	-7	Ac	585

Compound	Method	Solvent	Yield (%)	Recrystn. solvent	m.p. (°C)	$[\alpha]_D$ (solvent)	Ref.
N^G-Nitro-Arg-Gly-OMe				Me	151	−10 (Me)	536
N^G-Nitro-N^α-Z-Arg-Gly	MCA	DMF	85	Me	105–107	−10 (Ac)	103
N^G-Nitro-N^α-Z-Arg-Gly Amide	DCCI	DMF	73	Me-Pr	149–151	−2.1 (Me)	585
N^G-Nitro-N^α-Z-Arg-Gly Amide Hydrate				Eth-Pe	107–108	−3.6 (Me)	259
N^G-Nitro-N^α-Z-Arg-Gly-OBu^t	DCCI	THF	58	EtAc-Pe	77–78	−3.3 (Me)	103
N^G-Nitro-N^α-Z-Arg-Gly-OEt	MCA	DMF	57	Alc-Aq	118–120	−11 (Me)	103
N^G-Nitro-N^α-Z-Arg-Gly-OMe	MCA	DMF	75	EtAc	117–118	−13 (Me)	403, 165
N^G-Nitro-N^α-Z-Arg-Gly-ONp	DCCI	THF	63	EtAc	75–77	−10 (Me)	519, 165, 585, 103
N^G-Tos-Arg-Gly							308, 65
N^G-Tos-N^α-Z-Arg-Gly-OMe	DCCI	Acn	78	Alc	90–95	−10 (Me)	539
N^G-Tos-N^α-Z-Arg-Gly				Me	98–102	+9.7 (Me)	539
N^G-Tos-N^α-Z-Arg-Gly-OBzl	DCCI	Acn	67	Aq	145–148	−5 (Me)	539
N^G-Tos-N^α-Z-Arg-Gly-OEt	P	Py	61	EtAc-Pe	95–98	−4.5 (Ac)	539, 257
N^G-Tos-N^α-Z-D-Arg-Gly-OEt	DCCI	Chf	99	Eth-Pe	77–79	+6.0 (Alc)	769
Di-Z-N^α-boc-Arg-Leu-OMe	MCA	THF	77	Aq-An	110–111	−16 (Me)	183
N^G-Nitro-N^α-Z-Arg-Leu-OMe	P	Py	62	Me-Eth-Pe	159–160	−22 (DMF)	165, 165, 585
N^α-Arg-N^ϵ-Z-Lys-OMe Hydrochloride					160–161		44
N^G-Tos-Arg-N^ϵ-Lys-OMe	MCA	DMF	62	Me-Eth	131	−7.0 (DMF)	409
N^G-Tos-N^α-Z-Arg-N^G-tos-Lys-OMe	DCCI	DMF	74	Alc-Eth	66–71	+18 (Aq)	409
Arg-Met Acetate					185–186		741
N^G-Nitro-N^α-Z-Arg-Met	DCCI	DMF	65	Aq-Alc	161–162	−13 (Me)	741
N^G-Nitro-N^α-Z-Arg-D-Met	MCA	MeCl	59	Me	133–135	+2 (DMF)	440a
N^G-Nitro-N^α-Z-Arg-Met-OMe	MCA	THF	70	Me	137–138	−25 (Me)	741

Table 2 Dipeptides (continued)

Compound	Method	Solvent	% Yield	Solvent Crystallization	M.P.(°C)	[α]D	Solvent Rotation	Ref.
N^G-Tos-N^α-Z-Arg-Met-OMe	MCA	THF-DMF	95		oil	+1.5	Me	741
N^α-Z-N^G-tos-Arg-Met Monohydrate					117–118	–48	Me	741
N^G-Nitro-N^α-boc-Arg-Met DCHA Salt	MCA	THF-DMF	79	An-Eth		+6.4	Me	741
Arg-Orn Diacetate					103–106			44
N^α-Arg-N^δ-Orn Hydrochloride				Aq	122			44
N^α-Arg-N^δ-Orn-OMe Hydrochloride				MeCl-Eth	93–105			44
Z-N^G-nitro-Arg-D-Phe								440a
N^G-Nitro-N^α-Z-Arg-D-Phe	DCCI	DMF			130–131	+8.2	Me	681
N^G-Nitro-N^α-Z-Arg-Pro-OMe	DCCI	THF	66	Alc	159–160	–53	Me	560
N^G-Nitro-Arg-Pro-OBu^t								503
N^G-Nitro-Arg-Pro-OMe								298
N^G-Nitro-N^α-Z-Arg-Pro					119			70
N^G-Nitro-N^α-Z-Arg-Pro-OBzl	MCA	Di-DMF	56	THF-Pe	124–126	–28	DMF	560
				Me	108–110			456
N^G-Nitro-N^α-Z-Arg-Pro Hydrazide				Me	147–148.5			456
N^G-Nitro-N^α-Z-Arg-Pro-OMe	DCCI	DMF-An			92–95	–48		605
	DCCI or MCA				155–157			70
								298
	MCA	DMF-THF	61	Me	125–128	–48	Me	605
					159–160			574
N^G-Nitro-N^α-Z-Arg-Pro-ONp				Alc-Eth	55–70			456
N^G-Nitro-N^α-trt-Arg-Pro-OBu^t	DCCI	Acn	58	An-Eth	176–178			503
N^G-Tos-Arg-Pro					55–60	–1.8	Me	455
N^G-Tos-N^α-Z-Arg-Pro					103–106	–31	DMF	584
N^G-Tos-N^α-Z-Arg-Pro-OBzl	WRK	Acn	85	Alc	80–82	–39	Me	495

Compound	Method	Solvent	Yield (%)	Recryst. solvent	m.p. (°C)	[α]	Solvent	Ref.
N^G-Tos-N^α-Z-Arg-Pro-OBzl Hydrochloride	WRK	An	85	Alc	80–82			495
N^G-Tos-N^α-Z-Arg-Pro-OBu^t	WRK	Acn	76	EtAc	115–118	−42	Me	372
N^G-Tos-N^α-Z-Arg-Pro-OMe	DCCI	An	72	EtAc	152–153	−38	Me	371
N^G-Tos-N^α-Z-Dnp-Arg-Pro	DCCI	MeCl	82	Alc	110–115			455
N^G-Nitro-N^α-Z-Arg-Sar-OMe				Alc	96–102	−7.3	DMF	752
N^G-Nitro-N^α-Z-Arg-Sar				Alc	119–120	−8.8	DMF	752
N^G-Nitro-N^α-Z-Arg-Sar-ONp				Alc-Eth	78–87	−8.2	DMF	752
Z-Arg-Tyr Hydrochloride Hydrate				Aq-Alc	116–117	+12	Aq	407
Arg-Val Acetate Salt				Alc-Aq	213–215			165
N^G-Nitro-N^α-Z-Arg-Val				Alc-Aq	183–185	−30	Alc	569
N^G-Nitro-N^α-Z-Arg-Val-OBzl	MCA	THF	58	Pe	179–179.5	−23	Di	165, 585
N^G-Nitro-N^α-Z-Arg-Val-OMe	MCA	DMF	66	Me	148–150	−2.3	DMF	165, 585, 569
	DCCI	DMF	85	Pe-Eth				

Asparagine

Compound	Method	Solvent	Yield (%)	Recryst. solvent	m.p. (°C)	[α]	Solvent	Ref.
Z-Asn-D-Ala	ONP	DMF			193–195	−4	DMF	440a
Z-D-Asn-D-Ala	ONP	DMF			220–221	+13	Me	440a
Boc-Asn-Ala-ONp	MA	Chf			212–215	−230	DMF	185
Z-Asn-N^G-nitro-Arg	MCA	MeCl	63	NMe	103–104.5	+8.4	Ac	563
Z-D-Asn-N^G-nitro-D-Arg				Acn	224–225	−9	Ac	440a, 684
Z-D-Asn-N^G-nitro-Arg				Acn	96–100	−9.1	Ac	563, 551
Z-Asn-N^G-nitro-Arg Hydrate	CDI	DMF	71	Aq	104–106	−4.0	Ac	234
Z-Asn-N^G-nitro-Arg-OMe					134–136	+5.0	Ac	466
Z-D-Asn-N^G-nitro-D-Arg-OMe					109–113	−7.0	Ac	563
					180–183	−6.5	Ac	563
					173–174.5			684
Nps-Asn-Asn-2,4,6-tri-me-OBzl	ONP	DMF	76	DMF-Alc	173–175	−26	DMF	626
					178–179			
					230.5–232.5 (dec)			

Table 2 Dipeptides (continued)

Compound	Method	Solvent	% Yield	Solvent Crystallization	M.P.(°C)	$[\alpha]_D$	Solvent Rotation	Ref.
Asn-S-bzl-Cys-OMe Hydrobromide				Me-EtAc-Eth	132-133	-24	Aq	765
Z-D-Asn-S-bzl-Cys		DMF			161-163	-11	Me	440a
Z-Asn-S-btm-Cys-OMe	MA	DMF	62	Me-Aq	149	-31	DMF	103
Z-Asn-S-btm-Cys-ONp	WRK	NMe	72	Aq-Ac	171-172.5	-51	DMF	103
Boc-Asn-S-btm-Cys-ONp	WRK	NMe	60	An	175-176	-50	DMF	103
Asn-Gln				Aq-Alc	217-219 (dec)	+7.3	0.5N HCl	626
Z-Asn-Glu-2,4,6-tri-me-OBzl	ONP		90	Ac-Alc	225-227 (dec)	+11	Ac	626
Z-Asn-Gly-OEt	SPh	Chf	83	Ac-Aq, EtAc-Alc, Aq	186-187, 189-190, 165	-35, -22	Alc, Me	712, 383, 419
N-Tos-Asn-Gly							Me	419
Z-D-Asn-Ile	ONP	DMF			187-188	+16	Me	440a
Z-D-Asn-D-Ile	ONP	DMF			188-189	-4	DMF	440a
Asn-Leu-OBu^t					75-77			641
Z-D-Asn-Leu	ONP	DMF			188-190	+15	Me	440a
Z-D-Asn-D-Leu	ONP	DMF			178-180	+5	DMF	440a
Z-Asn-Leu-OBu^t	ONP	DMF	80	An-Aq	130-131			641
Z-Asn-Leu-OMe					177.5-178.5			712
N$^\alpha$-(Asn)-N$^\epsilon$-dihydrolipoyl-Lys				Aq-Alc	220 (dec)			109
N$^\alpha$-(Z-Asn)-N$^\epsilon$-(6,8-dibenzylthiooctanoyl)-Lys				Me-Aq	143-145			109
N$^\alpha$-(Z-Asn)-N$^\epsilon$-(6,8-dibenzylthiooctanoyl)-Lys-OBu^t	ONP	DMF	36	DMF-Aq	109-110	-10		109
Z-Asn-N$^\epsilon$-boc-Lys Hydrazide					216-217	+4	DMF	552
Z-Asn-D-Met	ONP	DMF			163-165	-5	DMF	440a
Z-D-Asn-Met	ONP	DMF			157-159	+9	DMF	440a
Z-D-Asn-D-Met	ONP	DMF			183-185		DMF	440a
Z-Asn-N$^\delta$-Z-Orn					183-185	+11	Ac	499

Table (rotated on page). Reconstructed as columns: Compound — Coupling method — Reaction solvent — Yield (%) — Recryst. solvent — m.p. (°C) — [α] — Rotation solvent — Ref.

Compound	Method	Solvent	Yield (%)	Recryst.	m.p. (°C)	$[\alpha]$	Solvent	Ref.
Z-Asn-Nδ-Z-Orn-OMe	MA	DMF			173–174	−13	Me	499
Z-D-Asn-Phe	DCCI	DMF	35		189–192	+4	DMF	440a
Z-D-Asn-D-Phe	DCCI	THF-Be			215–218	−8	Me	440a
Z-Asn-Phe-OMe	MCA	DMF	24	Me	195–197	+16	Ac	195
Z-D-Asn-Pro	DCCI	DMF			55–60	−11	DMF	440a
Z-Asn-D-Ser	DCCI	DMF			172–174	+15	DMF	440a
Z-D-Asn-Ser	DCCI	DMF			180–183	−11	DMF	440a
Z-D-Asn-D-Ser	DCCI	DMF	18		199–202	+9.6	DMF	440a
Z-Asn-Ser Amide					220–222	+3	DMF	201
Asn-OBu^t-Thr-OBu^t				Alc-Eth-Pe	149	−3	Aq	48
Asn-Thr				Alc-Aq	200–202 (dec)	+7	DMF	48
Asn-Thr Picrolonate Hydrate					118–119			48
Z-Asn-OBu^t-Thr-OBu^t	ONP	DMF	90	Be-Pe	120–121	−2.2	DMF	48
Z-Asn-Thr	ONP			Di-Aq	207	−8.9	Me	720
Z-Asn-Thr-OMe	ONP	DMF	85	Me	194	+10	DMF	48
Z-D-Asn-D-Trp	DCCI	DMF			223–225	+12	Ac	48
Asn-Tyr-OEt Hydrobromide					oil	−18	DMF	440a
Z-Asn-Tyr			77	Me	206			452
Z-Asn-Tyr Boc-hydrazide	ONP	DMF	24		249–251	−25	DMF	309
Z-Asn-Tyr-OEt	MCA		47	Alc-Aq	175			762
Z-Asn-D-Val	ONP	DMF		DMF-Aq	174–175	+1.9	DMF	309, 440a
Z-D-Asn-Val	DCCI	DMF			195–197	−12	Me	309, 440a
Z-D-Asn-D-Val	DCCI	MeCl			196–198 / 197–199	−2	DMF	452, 440a
Aspartic Acid								
β-OBzl-boc-Asp-Ala-OBzl			75	EtAc-He	66–68			356a
Z-β-OBu^t-Asp-D-Ala-OBu^t					oil	+8	Me	658
Z-D-Asp-N^G-nitro-Arg-OMe	DCCI			Aq	165–168	−3.3	Ac	551
Z-β-OBu^t-Asp-N^G-nitro-Arg	MCA			Pe	74–76	−5.7	DMF	551

Table 2 Dipeptides (continued)

Compound	Method	Solvent	% Yield	Solvent Crystallization	M.P. (°C)	[α]D	Solvent Rotation	Ref.
Z-β-OBu^t-Asp-N^G-nitro-Arg-OMe	MCA	THF	50	EtAc-Pe	61-64.5	-9.7	DMF	551
Z-β-OBzl-Asp-β-OBzl-D-Asp Amide	DCCI	MeCl		Alc	131-132			639
Z-β-OBu^t-Asp-β-OBu^t-Asp-OBu^t				EtAc-Pe	116-118			658
Z-β-OBu^t-Asp-OBu^t-Asp-OEt					oil			658
Z-Asp-Se-bzl-Cys					194-196			145
Z-Asp-Se-bzl-Cys-OMe					181-182			145
Z-β-Asp(α-OBzl)-Glu-α-OBzl-γ-ONp	DCCI	EtAc	50	EtAc-Pe	119-120	-10	Ac	383
Z-β-Asp(α-OBzl)-Glu-γ-OBzl-α-ONp	DCCI	EtAc	96	Alc		-30	Ac	383
α-D-Asp-Gly				Aq		-35	1N HCl	379
α-Asp-Gly					187	+31	1N HCl	379
α-D-Asp-Gly-OEt				Alc	167			379
α-Asp-Gly-OEt					166-167			379
N-Bzl-α-D-Asp-Gly	MCA			Aq-Alc	198	+17	NaHCO$_3$	379
N-Bzl-α-Asp-Gly	MCA			Aq-Alc	197	-17	NaHCO$_3$	379
N-Bzl-α-Asp-Gly-OEt	MCA	Di	51		136	-23	Aq	379
N-Bzl-α-D-Asp-Gly-OEt	MCA	DMF	53	Alc	137	+24	Aq	379
β-Bzl-N-Z-Asp-Gly Amide	MCA		45		126			39
Z-β-Asp(α-OBzl)-Gly-OBzl	ONP	Chf	77.5	EtAc-Pe	123-124	-9.2	DMF	383
Z-α-DL-Asp(β-OBzl)-Gly-OBzl	ONP	Acn	71.5	EtAc-Pe	83			383
Z-α-DL-Asp(β-OBzl)-Gly-OEt	OCH$_2$CN	EtAc	88	Alc	111-112			383
	ONP	Chf	76					383
Z-Asp(β-OBzl)-Gly-ONBzl	DCCI	MeCl	85	Alc	107-108	+4.2	Chf	269
Z-(α and β)-Asp-Gly Amides					oil			39
Z-β-OBu^t-Asp-Gly-OMe					126-128			658
β-OBu^t-Asp-Gly-OBu^t	ONP	DMF	54	EtAc	oil			493
β-OBu^t-Z-Asp-Gly-OBu^t	ONP	Ac						493
β-OBu^t-boc-Asp-Gly Z-hydrazide				Alc-Pe				458
β-OMe-Z-Asp-Gly					122	-17	Alc	700
β-OBzl-Z-Asp-His Amide	DCCI	DMF	53		120-122			545

Compound	Reagent	Solvent	Yield (%)	m.p. (°C)	[α]	Solvent	Ref.
α-Asp-Leu							612
Nα-(α-Asp)-Nε-(6,8-dibenzylthiooctanoyl)-Lys				159–162 (dec)	–5.4	Ac	109
Nα-(β-Asp)-Nε-(6,8-dibenzylthiooctanoyl)-Lys				189–190 (dec)	–9.6	1N HCl	109
Nα-(α-Asp)-Nε-lipoyl-Lys				172–175 (dec)	+20	DMF–1N HCl	109
Nα-(β-Asp)-Nε-lipoyl-Lys Ammonium Salt				178–180 (dec)	+20	DMF	109
Z-β-Asp(α-OBzl)-δ-Orn	MCA	THF	86.7	190			383
D-Asp-Phe Amide				202–203 (dec)	+9.6	1N HCl	111
Asp-Phe Amide				188–189 (dec)	–20	DMF–1N HCl	111
Asp-D-Phe Amide				189–190 (dec)	–2.3	1N HCl	520
D-Asp-D-Phe Amide				200–201 (dec)	–0.9	DMF	111
Asp-Phe-OMe				178–179 (dec)	+0.3	DMF	111
β-Bzl-Asp-Phe Amide Hydrobromide Hydrate				246–247			111
β-OBzl-Z-Asp-D-Phe Amide	ONP	Chf	80	185 (dec)			111
β-OBzl-Z-Asp-Phe Amide	OTCP	DMF	89	162–163			111
β-OBzl-Z-Asp-Phe Amide	MCA	THF	51	–25			111
β-OBzl-Z-Asp-Phe Amide	DCCI	THF	73	171–172			111
β-OBzl-Z-D-Asp-Phe Amide	OTCP	DMF	81	170.5–171			111
β-OBzl-Z-D-Asp-D-Phe Amide	OTCP	DMF	74	165–167	+26	DMF	9
β-OBzl-Z-Asp-Phe-OMe	DCCI	MeCl	90	169–170			111
β-OBzl-Z-Asp-Phe-OMe	OTCP	DMF	96	115–116			111
β-OBut-Asp-Phe Amide				116–117	–15	DMF	111
β-OBut-Z-Asp-Phe Amide	MCA	THF-Chf	51	123–124			111
β-OBut-Z-Asp-Phe-OMe	DCCI	Me	66	158.5–159.5 / 77–78	–26	Me	260

Table 2 Dipeptides (continued)

Compound	Method	Solvent	% Yield	Solvent Crystallization	M.P.(°C)	[α]$_D$	Solvent Rotation	Ref.
Z-β-Asp(α-OBzl)-Phe-OBzl	ONP	Chf	64	EtAc-Pe	136-138	-14	Ac	383
Z-Asp-D-Phe	DCCI	DMF			192-194	-4	DMF	440a
Z-β-OBu^t-Asp-D-Phe-OBu^t					oil			658
β-Isopropyl-Z-Asp-Phe Amide	DCCI	DMF	74.6	Alc-Aq	171-174	-27	DMF	520
N-Ac-Asp-OAc-Ser-OMe					114			589
Asp-Ser Amide					208 (dec)	+15	Aq	201
Asp-Ser-OMe Hydrate			73		178-180			201
β-Bzl-Z-Asp-Ser-OMe	DCCI		55		125-126	0.0	Me	201
β-OBzl-N-ac-Asp-OAc-Ser-OMe	DCCI		75		89			589
β-OBzl-Z-Asp-OAc-DL-Ser-OMe	DCCI				88			589
β-OBzl-Z-Asp-OAc-Ser-OMe					89-90			589
β-OBzl-Z-Asp-Ser Amide	MCA				162	+1.5	Py	39
					157			39
					151			39
β-OBzl-Z-D-Asp-Ser Amide					121-123			39
β-OBzl-Z-Asp-Ser-OMe	DCCI	DMF	73	EtAc-Pe	125-126	0.0	Me	201
Z-Asp-(β-OBzl)-DL-Ser Amide	DCCI		70		148-150	-2.3	Aq-Py	545
Z-Asp-Ser Amide					197-199 (dec)			201
Z-(α and β)-Asp-Ser Amides					190			39
Z-α-Asp-Ser-di-OBzl	DCCI	THF-Acn	82	Me-Aq	129	+6.9	Ac	140
Z-iso-Asp-Ser Amide				Ac-Eth	230	+10	DMF	201
Z-iso-Asp-Ser-OMe Hydrate					192	+13	DMF	201
β-Bu^t-Asp-Ser-OMe					oil			199
β-OBu^t-Z-Asp-Ser-OMe	EDCI	MeCl	80	Me-Aq	57-58.5	-5.4	Me	199
β-OEt-N-ac-Asp-Ser Amide	MCA			EtAc	124-126			39
Iso-Asp-Ser Hydrochloride Hydrate					150-152 (dec)	+6.5	Aq	201
Iso-Asp-Ser-OMe					140-141	+22	Ac	201

Compound	Method	Solvent	Yield %	Recryst.	M.p.	[α]	Solvent	Ref.
β-OMe-Z-Asp-OAc-Ser	ONP	An	87	EtAc-He	141–142			118
β-OMe-Z-Asp-OAc-Ser Amide	DCCI		40		137			589
β-OMe-Z-Asp-O-cinnamoyl-DL-Ser-OMe					oil	+3.3	DMF	589
Asp-OBu^t-Thr-OBu^t	WRK		75		150–152			101
Z-Asp(β-OBzl)-DL-Thr	DCCI	DMF	74.6		150–152			545
Z-Asp-OBu^t-Thr-OBu^t					45–49			101
Z-D-Asp-DL-Tyr	DCCI	DMF			173–175	+4	DMF	440a

Citrullene

Boc-Cit-Gly-OEt	ONP	Py	88		166.5–168			61

Cysteine

S-Bzl-Z-Cys-β-Ala-OEt	DCCI	MeCl	75	Alc	104–105			435
S-Bzl-Z-Cys-Ala-OMe	MCA	Tfa		EtAc-Pe	133			704
S-Bzl-Z-Cys-Ala-OMe Hydrobromide					159–160			704
S-Bzl-Cys-β-Ala-OEt Hydrobromide								435
S-NBzl-Z-Cys-Ala	TEA-DCCI	THF	70	Alc-Aq	157–159			304
S-NBzl-Z-Cys-Ala-OMe	MCA	MeCl		EtAc	173–174			304
S-Bzl-Z-Cys-D-Ala	MCA	Chf			109–111	−25	DMF	440a
Se-Bzl-Z-DL-Cys-Ala-OMe					130			145
S-Bzl-Cys-Asn-2,4,6-tri-me-OBzl Hydrochloride	MCA	Me-EtAc	80		215.5–217	+2.2	DMF	625
S-Bzl-Nps-Cys-Asn-2,4,6-tri-me-OBzl	ONP	Acn	80		174–175	−1.0	DMF	625
S-NBzl-Z-Cys-Asn-ONBzl	MCA	DMF-Aq	47		225–227			309
S-Bzl-Z-Cys-Asp	MCA	Me	72		157–158			41
S-Bzl-Z-Cys-Asp-ONBzl	ONP	DMF	95		177–179	−32	DMF	315
S-Bzl-Z-Cys-ε-Acp-S-bzl-Cys-OBzl	ONP	DMF	69		137–139	−37	Ac	515
S-Bzl-Z-Cys-ε-amino-undecyl-S-bzl-Cys-OBzl	ONP				86–87	−28	Ac	515
S-Bzl-Cys-ε-amino-undecyl-S-bzl-Cys					150			515
Cys-ε-Acp-Cys					183–188 (dec)			515
Se-bzl-Z-Cys-Se-bzl-Cys	MA	THF			139–140			145
Se-bzl-Z-DL-Cys-Se-bzl-Z-DL-Cys	MA	Chf			106			145

97

Table 2 Dipeptides (continued)

Compound	Method	Solvent	% Yield	Solvent Crystallization	M.P.(°C)	$[\alpha]_D$	Solvent Rotation	Ref.
Se-Bzl-Cys-Se-bzl-Cys					122 (dec)			145
S-Trt-Z-Cys-S-bzh-Cys Hydrazide	DCCI	Chf	74		178-179	-8.7	DMF	776
S-Trt-boc-Cys-S-bzh-Cys Hydrazide								776
N,N'-Bis(N-Z-S-diphenyl-me-Cys)-Cystine-OMe	DCCI	DMF	25.7	Alc	155-156	-86	DMF	224
S-Ac-Z-Cys-Gly-OEt					135-136	-48	DMF	708
					135-136	-48	DMF	777
					134-135	-48	DMF	481
S-Ac-Z-Cys-Gly-OMe					125-126	-46	DMF	777
(N-Ac-2,2-di-me-DL-Cys)-Gly-OEt				An	173-174			187
(N,N'-Di-ac-2,2'-di-me-DL-Cys)bis(Gly-OEt)								187
(α,α'-Di-deamino-Cys)bis(Gly-OEt)								187
S-Bzh-N-bzh-Cys-Gly Toluenesulfonate	DCCI	Chf	44	MeCl	152-153			228
S-Bzh-Z-Cys-Gly-OEt	ONP	Chf	67	Alc	117-118			228
S-Bzh-Cys-Gly-OBu^t								220
S-Bzh-Cys-Gly-OEt Hydrochloride	DCCI	Chf	82	An	167-168	-17	DMF	220
S-Bzh-Cys-Gly-ONp Toluenesulfonate	DCCI	Chf	50	EtAc-He	157-159			220
N-Bzhoc-Cys-Gly-OEt				EtAc		-2.5	Chf	222
S-Bzh-N-pht-Cys-Gly	EDCI	MeCl	72		188-190	-108	An	229
S-Bzh-N-pht-Cys-Gly-OBu^t	DCCI		57			-102	An	220
S-Bz-Z-Cys-Gly-OEt				Alc	153.5	-58	DMF	481
					152	-58	DMF	708
					153	-58	DMF	777
S-Bz-Z-Cys-Gly-OEt	ONP	Chf		EtAc-He	96.5-98			82
				EtAc-Pe	154-156			223
					97.5-98.5			350
S-Bz-Z-Cys-Gly-OMe	ONP	DMF	92	Me	154	-59	DMF	777
S-Bz-Z-Cys-Gly-ONp	DCCI	Chf	62	Alc	174-176	-42	DMF	777
S-Bz-Cys-Gly-OMe Hydrochloride	DCCI	Chf	88	Me-EtAc	163-164	+29	Me	777
				Me-EtAc	163	+29	Me	775

Compound	Method	Solvent	Yield (%)	Recryst. solvent	M.p. (°C)	[α]	Solvent	Ref.
S-Bz-Cys-Gly-ONp Hydrobromide				Alc-EtAc	162–163	+20	DMF	777
N-(1-Bz-isopenyl)-S-trt-Cys-Gly-ONp				Pr	103–106	−27	Chf	228
S-Bz-N-Nps-Cys-Gly-OMe				Me	139–140	+18	Chf	775
S-Bzl-N-ac-Cys-Gly-OEt	ONP	Chf		Aq-Alc	115.5–116.5			82
				Aq	116.5–117.5			82
S-Bzl-N-ac-DL-Cys-Gly-OEt					86.5–87.5			82
S-Bzl-Z-Cys-Gly	DCCI		73	EtAc-Pe	198	+74	Aq	382
S-Bzl-Z-Cys-Gly-OBzl	ONP		88	EtAc-Pe	130	−24	Ac	382
S-Bzl-Z-Cys-Gly-OEt	ONP	DMF	86	EtAc-Pe	98–99	−42	DMF	452
					98–99			519
S-Bzl-Z-Cys-Gly-OEt S-oxide	A	DMF		EtAc	99	−39	Di	249
S-Bzl-Z-Cys-Gly Glycolamide Ester	ONP	Acn	85	EtAc-Eth	157–159	−37	DMF	708
	DCCI				145–146			249
	MCA							
S-Bzl-Z-Cys-Gly-OMe				EtAc	104–105	−43	DMF	636
S-Bzl-Cys-Gly				Alc-Eth	164–166			636
S-Bzl-Cys-Gly Amide				Alc-Eth	91–93	+16	Ac	636
S-Bzl-Cys-Gly-OBzl					44.5			166
S-Bzl-Cys-Gly-OEt Hydrobromide					oil			292
S-Bzl-Cys-Gly-OMe-OBzl Toluenesulfonate				Alc-Eth	102.5–104	+6.6	Alc	292
S-Bzl-N-tos-Cys-Gly	DCCI	Chf		Alc-Aq	124–125	−16	Alc	382
S-Bzl-N-tos-Cys-Gly-OBzl	DCCI	DMF	66	Chf-Pe	99–100.5	−10	Chf	452
S-Bzl-N-tos-Cys-Gly-OEt	DCCI	THF	54	Alc	113–114	−28	Alc	674
S-Bzl-N-tos-Cys-Gly-ONp			64	Pe	116–117			619
N-Z-S-bzl-Cys-Gly-OCH₂CN				EtAc-Cy	94.5–95.5	−41	DMF	42
Z-Cys-S-bzl-Gly-OEt					99–100	−32		42
Di-Z-Cys-Gly-OBz	DCCI		90		118–119	−44	DMF	42
								41
								636
								584
								610

Table 2 Dipeptides (continued)

Compound	Method	Solvent	% Yield	Solvent Crystallization	M.P. (°C)	[α] D	Solvent Rotation	Ref.
Z-Cys-Gly-OBzl Hydrobromide					126–128	+12	Me	610
Z-Cys-Gly-OEt					122–123	−16	Alc	610
Di-Z-Cys-Gly-OEt	DCCI		79		167	−139	DMF	188
N,S-Di-Z-Cys-Gly-OMe	ONP	Chf	50	Alc	94	−31	Alc	610
N,S-Di-Z-Cys-Gly-ONBzl	ONP	Chf	73	Alc	103	−51	DMF	777
S-Z-Cys-Gly-ONBzl Hydrobromide				Alc-EtAc	146	−39	DMF	777
N,S-Di-Z-Cys-Gly-ONp	DCCI	Chf	60	EtAc-Alc	141–142	+13	DMF	777
S-Z-Cys-Gly-ONp Hydrobromide				Alc	141	+18	DMF	775
S-Z-N-for-Cys-Gly-OEt				Alc	169–170	−46	DMF	777
S-Z-N-Nps-Cys-Gly-ONBzl				An	132–133	+12	Me	777
Z-S-Pac-Cys-Gly-OEt					126–127	−36	DMF	777
S-Pac-Cys-Gly-OEt Hydrobromide					126–128	−46	Chf	775
					115–116	−43	DMF	188
					198	+12	DMF	188
N,N′-Bis-Z-Cystinyl-mono-Gly-OEt	DCCI	EtAc-Chf	80	EtAc-Eth-Alc	148–150	+3	Ac	225
						+11	Me	
S-Me-Z-Cys-Gly-OEt				EtAc-Pe	86–87	−162	DMF	609
Nps-S-bzl-Cys-Gly				Alc	122–122.5	−9.1	DMF	631
Nps-S-bzl-Cys-Gly-ONp	MCA	DMF	70		163.5–164.5	−35	DMF	619
Se-Bzl-Z-DL-Cys-Gly	DCCI	Chf			145–146			145
Se-Bzl-Z-Cys-Gly-OBzl	MCA	Chf		EtAc-Pe	91–93	−28	Alc	668
Se-Bzl-Z-Cys-Gly-OEt					102–103			145
Se-Bzl-Z-DL-Cys-Gly-OEt					84			145
Se-Bzl-boc-Cys-Gly-OBzl								668
Se-Bzl-Cys-Gly					206–207 (dec)			145

Compound	Reagent	Solvent	Yield (%)	Recrystn.	M.p.	[α]	Solvent	Ref.
Se-Bzl-Cys-Gly-OEt	DCCI	MeCl	40		oil			144
Se-Bzl-Cys-Gly-OEt Hydrobromide	EDCI	EtAc	73		oil			144
S-Trt-N-bzhoc-Cys-Gly-OBu^t	DCCI	MeCl	89		81–82	+3.6	Alc	229
S-Trt-N-bzhoc-Cys-Gly-OEt				Eth-He	137–138	+10	Chf	222
S-Trt-Z-Cys-Gly-OBzh	EDCI	MeCl	87	EtAc-He	140.5–142			227
S-Trt-Z-Cys-Gly-OEt					114–115			225
S-Trt-Cys-Gly-OBzl Hydrochloride								225
N,S-Di-trt-Cys-Gly-OEt								222
N-Trt-Cys-Gly-OEt Hydrochloride								223
S-Trt-Cys-Gly-OEt Hydrochloride	DCCI	MeCl	54.8	Be-He				642
S-Trt-Cys-Gly-ONp Hydrochloride	DCCI	Chf	68					774
S-Trt-N-for-Cys-Gly-OEt	DCCI	MeCl	46		77–79	+39	Alc	228
S-Trt-N-pht-Cys-Gly-OBu^t								222
N,N-Di-Z-Cystine-mono-Gly-OEt								229
S-Bzl-Z-Cys-His Hemihydrate	MCA	THF	50	Me	156–158	−1.3	An	227
S-Bzl-Z-Cys-His Hemihydrate Hydrochloride					156–159			746
Se-Bzl-Z-DL-Cys-His	MCA	Chf			124–125	−26	DMF	746
Se-Bzl-Z-DL-Cys-His-OMe					121			145
S-Bzl-Cys-Leu								145
S-Bzl-Cys-Leu Amide					112			292
S-Bzl-N-tos-Cys-Leu Hydrazide	MCA	THF	77					292
Di-Z-Cys-Leu-OMe								295
S-Bzl-Z-Cys-N$^\epsilon$-Z-Lys Amide					98–100	−36	Me	610
S-Bzl-Z-Cys-N$^\epsilon$-Z-Lys-OMe	MCA	MeCl			178–181	−16	DMF	746
S-Bzl-Cys-Lys Amide Dihydrobromide					106–108	−22	Me	746
Z-S-Bzl-Cys-D-Met					100–103	+11	Me	746
S-Ac-N-Z-Cys-Phe-OBzl					152	−13	Me	440a
S-Bzl-N-Z-Cys-p-OMe-Phe				An-Aq	160–161	−38	DMF	708
S-Bzl-Z-Cys-p-OMe-Phe-OMe				Me	133.5–135	−14	Py	357
S-Bzl-Z-Cys-Phe	DCCI	DMF	69	Alc	158	−29	DMF	357
S-Bzl-Cys-Phe	MCA	THF		Me	229–231	−36	DMF	68
								292

Table 2 Dipeptides (continued)

Compound	Method	Solvent	% Yield	Solvent Crystallization	M.P. (°C)	[α]D	Solvent Rotation	Ref.
S-Bzl-Cys-Phe Amide				Alc-Pe	133–135			292
S-Bzl-N-tos-Cys-p-et-Phe Hydrazide	AC	EtAc	88	Aq-Alc	187–189			778
S-Bzl-N-tos-Cys-p-et-Phe-OMe	AC	EtAc		Aq-Me	115–117	+34	Di	778
S-Bzl-N-tos-Cys-p-fluoro-Phe-OEt					191.5–192.5			295
S-Bzl-N-tos-Cys-p-me-Phe Hydrazide				Aq-DMF				778
S-Bzl-N-tos-Cys-p-me-Phe-OMe	AC	EtAc	80	EtAc	144–146	+26	Di	778
S-Bzl-N-tos-Cys-Phe				Aq-Alc	125–126			292
S-Bzl-N-tos-Cys-Phe Amide				Alc	180–182			292
S-Bzl-N-tos-Cys-Phe-OBzl	AC / DCCI	EtAc	69 / 60	EtAc-Pe	88–89.5	+17	Chf	42
S-Bzl-N-tos-Cys-Phe Hydrazide	AC	EtAc	85	DMF-Aq	202–204	-7.5	DMF	294
S-Bzl-N-tos-Cys-Phe-OMe	AC	EtAc		Aq-Alc	107	-44	DMF	292
N-Z-Cys-Phe	DCCI		82		148–150	-6.5	Me	610
Di-Z-Cys-Phe-OBzl					147–148	-11	Alc	610
S-Z-Cys-Phe-OBzl Hydrobromide					141			610
N-Z-Cys-Phe-OMe					98			610
S-Btm-Cys-Pro-OMe Toluenesulfonate	DCCI	MeCl	75	Me-Dipr-Eth	123–124	-87	Me	103
S-Bz-Cys-Ser-OMe Hydrobromide	DCCI	DMF	73	Me-EtAc	172	+7	Me	776
Bz-N-for-Cys-Ser-OMe	MCA	Chf		Me	168	-13	DMF	776
Se-bzl-Z-DL-Cys-DL-Ser					145			145
Se-bzl-Z-DL-Cys-DL-Ser-OMe					110			145
Se-bzl-DL-Cys-OAc-DL-Ser					207–208 (dec)			145
S-Trt-Cys-Ser-OMe Hydrochloride	DCCI	EtAc	59		108–111 (dec)	+38	Me	228
	DCCI		85					776
S-Bz-Z-Cys-OMe-Tyr	ONP	THF			156–158			604
S-Bzl-N-ac-Cys-Tyr-OMe				EtAc-He	141.5–142.5			82

Compound	Coupling	Solvent	Yield (%)	Recryst. solvent	M.p. (°C)	[α]	Solvent	Ref.
S-Bzl-Z-Cys-OMe-Tyr-OMe	DCCI	THF	75	EtAc-Aq	128–130	–82	Ac	604
S-Bzl-Z-Cys-N-me-Tyr	DCCI	Acn	78			–83	DMF	258
S-Bzl-Z-Cys-N-me-Tyr-OBu^t						–81	Me	258
S-Bzl-Z-Cys-N-me-Tyr-OMe	DCCI	THF	89	Alc	171.5–172	–104	Me	258
S-Bzl-Z-Cys-O-tos-Tyr-ONp					196–198	–34	DMF	628
S-Bzl-Z-Cys-Tyr						+5	1N NaOH	51
S-Bzl-Z-Cys-Tyr-OEt	DCCI / ONP	Acn / DMF	92	i-Pr-Pe	104–105	–15 / +23	Py / Chf	295 / 452
S-Bzl-Cys-Tyr-OMe	DCCI	DMF	88.5	Me	85–90			51
S-Bzl-Cys-OMe-Tyr				i-Pr-Pe	210–212			292
S-Bzl-D-Cys-Tyr					115–117			292
S-Bzl-Cys-Tyr-OEt Hydrobromide								292
S-Bzl-N-me-N-tos-Cys-OBzl-Tyr-OMe				Alc-Eth	180–181			452
S-Bzl-N-me-N-tos-Cys-Tyr Hydrazide	AC	Chf	79	i-Pr-Pe	71–74			295
S-Bzl-N-tos-Cys-OBzl-Tyr-ONp				i-Pr-Pe	92–95			295
S-Bzl-N-tos-Cys-OEt-Tyr Hydrazide				EtAc-Pe	166–167			295
S-Bzl-N-tos-Cys-OEt-Tyr-OMe				Alc-Aq	178–179			671
S-Bzl-N-tos-Cys-O-tos-Tyr-ONp				Be	122–123			778
S-Bzl-N-tos-Cys-Tyr-OEt	DCCI / MA	THF	84	EtAc-Pe	128–131	–12	Di	778
S-Bzl-N-tos-Cys-Tyr-OMe	DCCI	THF	65	EtAc-Pe	117–118	+4.5	Alc	671
Z-S-bzl-Cys-Tyr-ONp			60	Me-Aq	139–140	+7.8	Alc	765
Di-Z-Cys-Tyr Amide					135–135.5	–36	Ac	414
Cys-Tyr Amide				Alc	226–228			628
S-4,4'-Di-OMe-diphenyl-me-N-Z-Cys-Tyr	DCCI	DMF	91.5	Me-Eth / EtAc-Pe / Eth-He	259–261 / 149–150 / 81–83 (dec)			710 / 710 / 200
Se-bzl-Z-Cys-Tyr	DCCI	DMF			202–204	–8.2	Me	145
Se-Bzl-Z-Cys-Tyr-OMe	MCA	Chf			84–85	–12	Me	145

Table 2 Dipeptides (continued)

Compound	Method	Solvent	% Yield	Solvent Crystallization	M.P. (°C)	$[\alpha]_D$	Solvent Rotation	Ref.
Se-bzl-Cys-Tyr					196–198 (dec)			145
Tos-S-bzl-Cys-N-me-Tyr Hydrazide				i-Pr-Pe	65–68			295
Z-S-bzl-Cys-D-Val	MCA	MeCl			50–55	−34	DMF	440a
Glutamine								
Z-Gln-D-Ala	ONP	DMF			180–181	−1	DMF	440a
Z-DL-Gln-D-Ala	MCA	MeCl			135–140	+5.6	DMF	440a
Z-Gln-Ala Amide				Me	246–247	−11	Ac	163
Z-iso-Gln-γ-Ala-OEt	MCA	THF-DMF		Alc-Eth	161–162	−7.0	DMF	163
Z-Gln-N^G-nitro-Arg-OMe	DCCI	DMF	52	Aq	166–167.5			165
Z-iso-Gln-N^G-nitro-Arg-OMe	MCA	Chf-DMF	40	Aq	155–156	−2.0	DMF	165
	DCCI	THF-DMF	28	Alc-Aq	152–154	+5.7	DMF	165
Z-Gln-Asn Hydrazide	MCA	DMF	71	HMPA	183–184			289
Z-Gln-Asn-OMe	ONP	DMF	91	Aq	224–226	−3.4	DMF	289
Z-Gln-Asn-2,4,6-tri-me-OBzl				Ac-Alc	225–227	−1.3	DMF	626
Z-iso-Gln-Asn	NHS	THF	63	DMF-Acn	187–190	+6.2	Ac	7
Gln-Asn				Aq-Alc	203–204 (dec)	+19	Aq	626
Gln-Asn-β-OBu^t-α-OMe Hydrochloride	MCA	DMF	54	Acn	122–125	+20 / +20	5N HCl / Me	726
Nps-Gln-Asn				DMF-Ac	150–151.2	−13	DMF	626
Nps-Gln-Asn-2,4,6-tri-me-OBzl				DMF-EtAc	211.5–212.5 (dec)	−13	DMF	626
Z-DL-Gln-D-Asp	ONP	DMF	88		142–144	+4	DMF	440a
Z-Gln-Asp-ONBzl	ONP	DMF			212–215	−9.6	DMF	141

Compound	Reagent	Solvent	Yield (%)	Recryst. solvent	M.p. (°C)	[α]	Solvent	Ref.
Z-Gln-β-OBu^t-Asp	DCCI		79.4		160	+3.7	Ac	715
Z-Gln-β-OBu^t-Asp-OMe					154–156	−5.4	Aq	715
Gln-Asp-ONBzl Hydrobromide					120–125	+25	Ac	141
Gln-β-OBu^t-Asp					180–181			715
Tfa-Gln-β-OBu^t-Asp					170			715
Z-Gln-S-bzl-Cys	MCA	THF	71	Me	201–202	−16	DMF	746
Z-Gln-S-bzl-Cys-OMe	DCCI	DMF	79	Ac	202–203	−25	DMF	746
Z-γ-iso-Gln-S-bzl-Cys-OMe					144–146	−22	DMF	163
Z-Gln-Gln-ONp	ONP	DMF	60	Ac-An	180–181.5	−33	DMF	626
Z-Gln-Gly-OEt					169–171	−7.2	DMF	584
Z-Gln-Gly-OMe	DCCI / MCA	DMF	81	Me	140–145	−2	DMF	47
Z-Gln-Gly-ONBzl					174.5–175.5	−16	Alc	736
Gln-Gly-OEt					200.5–201	−9.5	Aq-Ac	734
Gln-Gly-OMe Hydrochloride				Alc	110–113	+16	Me	47
Gln-Gly-ONBzl Hydrobromide				Alc	173–174	+15	Aq-Ac	736
Z-Gln-His					196–197			734
Z-Gln-His-OMe	CDI / ONP	DMF	88	DMF	170–173			297
N^α-Z-N^γ-xanthyl-Gln-His-OMe	ONP	Py	42	EtAc-He	242–244	−2.0	DMF	297
Boc-Gln-N^{im}-bzl-His-OBzl	ONP	Py	71	Py-Alc-Eth	119–121			400
Boc-Gln-His-OMe				Di	161–162	−5.8	Alc	356a
Mz-Gln-His	DCCI	DMF		Alc	214–215			400
Mz-Gln-His-OMe	OPAP	EtAc		THF-Pe	167–169			297
Z-Gln-Leu-OEt	ONP	DMF	80	Me	141–142	−7.4	THF	297
Z-Gln-Leu-OMe	MCA	THF	75	Me	164			24
Z-Gln-D-Phe				EtAc-Pe	164			311
Z-Gln-Phe-OBu^t	DCCI	DMF		EtAc-Eth-Pe	193–195	−0.8	DMF	440a
Z-Gln-Phe-OBu^t DCHA Salt	OPh	THF	78	EtAc-Pe	114–115			332
N-Z-Gln-Pro					131–133			332
Boc-Gln-Pro					55–58	−45	Alc	89
Z-Gln-D-Ser	MCA	MeCl			174–176	−68	Alc	90
					160–161	−3	DMF	440a

Table 2 Dipeptides (continued)

Compound	Method	Solvent	% Yield	Solvent Crystallization	M.P.(°C)	$[\alpha]_D$	Solvent Rotation	Ref.
Z-Gln-Tyr-OEt	ONP	DMF	70		197-199	+1.8	DMF	451
Z-Gln-Tyr-OMe					197.5–198.5			712
Gln-Tyr-OEt Hydrobromide								451
Z-Gln-D-Val	MCA	MeCl			206-207	-2	DMF	440a
Z-Gln-Val				Aq-An	193-194	+1.4	Ac	330
Z-Gln-Val DCHA Salt				Alc-Eth	165-167			330
Z-Gln-D-Val-OBu^t				EtAc-Eth	120-122	+4.6	Ac	330
Z-Gln-Val-OMe								712
Glutamic Acid								
γ-OBzl-Z-Glu-Ala-OMe	DCCI	THF	56	EtAc-Pe	102-105	-7.5	DMF	22
Z-γ-OBzl-Glu-Ala-OBzl					oil			331
Z-α-OBu^t-Glu-β-Ala	DCCI	MeCl	63	Alc	96			346
Z-α-OBu^t-D-Glu-β-Ala-OTcp				Me-Eth	122	+5.4	Me	346
Z-α-OBu^t-D-Glu-β-Ala DCHA Salt	OPCP	MeCl	82	EtAc-Pe	51	+1.4	MeCl	346
Z-α-OBu^t-Glu-β-Ala-OMe				EtAc-Pe	50-51	-1.3	MeCl	346
Z-α-OBu^t-D-Glu-β-Ala-OMe					102-104	-13	DMF	411
N-Z-γ-OBu^t-Glu-Ala-OMe			89		56-57			346
Z-α-OBu^t-D-Glu-β-Ala-ONp	DCCI	MeCl	74	Me	151	+14	Chf	346
Z-α-OBu^t-Glu-β-Ala-OPCP				EtAc-Pe	150-151	-14	Chf	346
Z-α-OBu^t-Glu-β-Alc-OPCP				EtAc-Pe	177-178			332
Z-Glu-Ala				EtAc	180-181	-17	Ac	330
				EtAc	151-152	-26	Ac	330
Z-Glu-Ala-OBzl				EtAc	150-151			332
Z-Glu-Ala-OBzl DCHA Salt					148-149			332
Z-Glu-Ala-OEt				EtAc	143-144	-25	EtAc	330
Z-Glu-(α-Ala-hydrazide)-γ-hydrazide				Alc	207-209	-19	Alc	330

Compound	Reagent	Solvent	Yield (%)	Recryst. solvent	m.p. (°C)	$[\alpha]$	Solvent	No.
Z-Glu-(α-Ala-OMe)-γ-hydrazide					156–157	−19	EtAc	330
Z-Glu-β-(3-pyrazoyl)-Ala Amide	ONP	DMF			207–208	−14	Ac	232
Z-Glu-β-(1-pyrazoyl)-Ala Amide	ONP	DMF			241–242	−25	Alc-Aq	232
Z-pyro-Glu-Ala				Aq-Alc	214–215	−57	Ac	163
Z-pyro-Glu-D-Ala-OBzl	DCCI	THF	70	Alc	145–147	−7.8	Ac	330
Z-pyro-Glu-Ala-OBzl	DCCI	THF	71	EtAc-Pe	129–130	−64	Ac	163
Z-pyro-Glu-Ala DCHA Salt				Alc-Eth	188–189			163
Z-pyro-Glu-Ala-OEt	DCCI	THF	71	Alc	161–162	−33	DMF	534
γ-OBu^t-Z-Glu-Ala-OMe	OSU	DMF	70		99–101	−12	DMF	346
α-OBu^t-Glu-β-Ala-OPCP				Me-Eth	159–160			346
α-OBu^t-D-Glu-β-Ala-OPCP Hydrochloride					160			330
Glu-Ala				Alc	190–191	+12	Aq	232
Glu-β-(1-pyrazoyl)-Ala Amide						+13	Ac-Aq	232
Glu-β-(3-pyrazoyl)-Ala Amide						+36	Ac-Aq	163
Pyro-Glu-Ala				Me-Eth	212–213	−64	Ac	551
Z-γ-OBu^t-Glu-N^G-nitro-Arg				EtAc-Pe	74–76	−1.8	DMF	674
Z-γ-OBzl-Glu-N^G-nitro-Arg-OBzl	DCCI	Py	56	Alc-Aq	87–88			551
Z-γ-OBu^t-Glu-N^G-nitro-Arg-OMe	MCA	Chf	86	EtAc-Pe	62–64	−5.0	Me	674
Z-γ-OEt-N^G-nitro-Arg-OMe	MCA	THF	76	EtAc-Pe	58			333
Z-α-OEt-γ-Glu-N^G-nitro-Arg-OMe	DCCI	DMF	94	Pe	72–75			165
Z-α-OEt-Glu-N^G—nitro-Arg-OMe	DCCI	DMF	94					165
Z-Glu-N^G-nitro-Arg-OMe	DCCI	DMF	52		74–78	−13	Me	674
γ-OEt-Glu-Arg-OMe Dihydrochloride				THF	164–165	−15	Alc	
Z-Glu-Asn				EtAc-Pe	163–165			330
Z-γ-Glu-Asn DCHA Salt				Alc-Eth	260			660
Z-Glu-Asn-di-OEt				EtAc-Pe	114–115	+5.3	Ac	330
Z-Glu-Asn-di-OEt DCHA Salt				THF-Eth	140–141			330
Z-pyro-Glu-Asn-di-OBzl				Alc	119–120	−1.9	Ac	163
γ-OMe-Z-Glu-Asn-di-OEt				EtAc-Pe	86–87			333
γ-OBzl-Z-Glu-Asp-di-OBzl					132	−24	Ac	377
Z-γ-OBu^t-Glu-β-OBu^t-Asp-OBu^t	MCA	DMF	84	Me	129		Ac	658

107

Table 2 Dipeptides (continued)

Compound	Method	Solvent	% Yield	Solvent Crystallization	M.P.(°C)	$[\alpha]_D$	Solvent Rotation	Ref.
Z-Glu-β-OEt-Asp-OEt	DCCI			EtAc-Pe	119–120			332
Z-Glu-β-OEt-Asp-OEt DCHA Salt	MCA	THF	81	Alc-Eth	158–159	−23	Ac	332
Z-pyro-Glu-Asp-di-OEt	MCA	THF	62	EtAc-Pe	105–106	−26	Ac	330
	MCA	Tol	88		106–108			330
α-OBu^t-Z-γ-Glu-Asp-di-OBu^t					Oil			660
α-OBu^t-γ-Glu-Asp-di-OBu^t Hydrochloride					57–61			660
Z-γ-OBu^t-Glu-S-bzl-Cys-OBu^t				Eth-Pe	84–86			658
Z-Glu-S-bzl-Cys				Alc	178–179	−37	Ac	330
					Oil			449
Z-Glu-S-bzl-Cys-OEt	WRK		56		195–196	−40	Ac	669
Z-Glu-S-bzl-Cys Hydrazide					220 (dec)			669
Z-Glu-S-bzl-Cys-OMe				Me	133–135	−36	Ac	330
α-OBu^t-Z-γ-Glu-S-bzl-Cys-OMe	A		55	EtAc-Pe	60–61			660
α-OBu^t-tos-γ-Glu-S-bzl-Cys-OMe	A		57	EtAc-Pe	69–70			660
α-OEt-Z-γ-Glu-Se-bzl-Cys-OMe								144
For-Glu-S-bzl-Cys-OBzl	WRK	Acn	65		185–187			669
Glu-S-me-Cys					107–109			449
γ-OMe-Z-Glu-S-bzl-Cys-OMe								449
Tos-pyro-Glu-S-bzl-Cys-OEt	MCA	Chf	43.8	Eth	145–146			41
Z-γ-Glu-Gln-α,α'-di-OBzl	MCA	Di	58	Me-Aq	139–142	−5.4	Ac	694
Z-γ-Glu-Gln-tri-OBzl	DCCI		76	Me-Aq	134–137	−5.1	Ac	694
Z-(OMe)-γ-Glu-Gln-α,α'-di-OBzl	MCA	Di	46.2	EtAc-Pe-Me-Aq	133–135	−5.1	Ac	694
OMe-Z-γ-Glu-Gln-tri-OBzl	DCCI		64	Me	124–126	−3.7	Me	694
γ-Bzl-N-nps-Glu-Glu-OBzl	ONP	THF	35	EtAc	139–140	−20	DMF	775
Zα-(γ-bzl-Glu)-α-(γ-bzl-Glu)mephalan-OEt	DCCI	Chf						656
Z-γ-OBu^t-Glu-γ-OBu-Glu-OBu^t					90			658
Z-Glu-Glu				EtAc-Eth	167–169	−10	Alc	330
Z-Glu-di-OBzl	MCA				92			377
Z-pyro-Glu-Glu-di-OBzl	MCA		71	EtAc-Pe	112–113	−19	DMF	163

Compound	Reagent	Solv.	Yield (%)	Recryst. solv.	M.p. (°C)	[α]	Solv.	Ref.
Z-pyro-Glu-Glu-di-OEt			46	Alc	97–98	−34	Ac	163
γ-OEt-Z-Glu-γ-OEt-Glu					129.5–131.5	−3.9	DMF	635
γ-OEt-Z-Glu-γ-OMe-Glu			54		113–114	−4.5	DMF	635
Glu-Glu					178			377
γ-OMe-Z-Glu-γ-OEt-Glu			41		132.5–133.5			635
γ-OMe-Z-Glu-γ-OEt-Glu-ONBzl	ONP	EtAc	59		95–96	−10	DMF	635
	DCCI	EtAc	92					
γ-OMe-Z-Glu-Glu-di-OEt	OCH₂CN	EtAc	67	EtAc-Pe	79–80	−11	Ac	384
	SPh		31		79–81	−4.8	DMF	
	ONP		83		81–82			
γ-OMe-Z-Glu-γ-OMe-Glu			34	EtAc-Pe	112.5–113.5			635
γ-OMe-Z-Glu-γ-OMe-α-ONp-Glu	MCA	DMF	45	Chf-Alc	161	−32	DMF	175
γ-OMe-Glu-Glu-di-OEt	MCA	Chf	69	Alc	86	−5.1	Di	175
Pyro-Glu-Glu				Me-Eth-Pe	180–181	−32	Ac	163
Pyro-Glu-Glu-di-OEt	ONP	Acn	68	EtAc	128–129	−34	Ac	163
	SPh	Ac	51					
γ-OBzl-Z-Glu-DL-Abu-Gly-OBzl	MCA		68	Alc-Aq	149–151			382
α-OBzl-Z-Glu-Gly	DCCI	THF	72		114–116	−5.5	Ac	694
γ-OBzl-Z-Glu-Gly-OBzl				EtAc-Pe	115–117			331
α-OBzl-Z-γ-Glu-Gly-OBzl	ONP	Acn	92.5	EtAc-Pe	110, 114–116	−15	DMF	384
α-OBzl-Z-Glu-Gly-OEt	OPAP	THF	83	THF-n-He	122	−4.7	THF	24
γ-OBzl-Z-Glu-Gly-glycolamide Ester	DCCI	Chf	60	EtAc-Eth	121–122	−9.7	DMF	636
γ-OBzl-N-for-Glu-Gly-OEt				An-Pe	100–102	−13	Chf	422
γ-OBzl-Glu-Gly-OBzl Hydrobromide				Alc-Eth	105–107			754
Z-γ-OBuᵗ-Glu-Gly-OBuᵗ				EtAc-Pe	87–107			658
Z-Glu-Gly				Aq	82			559
Z-γ-Glu-Gly				EtAc-Eth	172–174			332
Z-Glu-Gly-OBzl				Eth-Pe	152–153			660
					158			754
					133			

Table 2 Dipeptides (continued)

Compound	Method	Solvent	% Yield	Solvent Crystallization	M.P.(°C)	[α]$_D$	Solvent Rotation	Ref.
Z-Glu-Gly-OBu^t	OPh	THF	84	EtAc-Pe	106-107			332
Z-Glu-Gly-OBu^t DCHA Salt				Eth-Pe	158-159			332
Z-Glu-Gly DCHA Salt				Alc-Eth	145-148			332
Z-Glu-Gly-OEt	MCA	DMF-THF		EtAc-Alc	158-161			559
N-Z-pyro-Glu-Gly-OBzl	DCCI	MeCl	75	Alc	116-118	-22	DMF	423
	ONP	DMF	81	Alc	116-118			
Z-pyro-Glu-Gly-OBzl				EtAc-Pe	113-115	-44	Ac	163
Z-pyro-Glu-Gly-OEt				Alc	131-132	-44	Ac	163
α-OBu^t-Z-γ-Glu-Gly-OBu^t	MCA	Tol	85		Oil			660
γ-OEt-Z-Glu-Gly	ONP	DMF	76	Aq	55.5-56.5	-4.2	DMF	630
γ-OEt-Z-Glu-Gly-2,4,6-tri-me-OBzl	DCCI	Acn	73	Alc	148.5-150	-3.5	DMF	630
				Acn	140.5-142.5	-5.4		
γ-Et-nps-Glu-Gly-2,4,6-tri-me-OBzl	DCCI	Chf	87	Be-Cy	64-68	-26	DMF	627
Glu-Abu-Gly				Aq-Alc	176-179.5			382
Glu-Gly					177-178			332
					176			377
γ-Glu-Gly				Aq-Alc	191-192	+10	Aq	384
Glu-Gly-OBzl Hydrobromide					135			754
γ-OMe-Z-Glu-Gly Amide	ONP	TEA	69	EtAc	100.5-101.5	-5.5	DMF	545
γ-OMe-Z-Glu-Gly-OBzl								635
α-OMe-Z-γ-Glu-Gly-OEt	OCH$_2$CN	EtAc	89	Alc-Pe	95-97			331
γ-OMe-Z-α-Glu-Gly-OEt	ONP	Acn	90	EtAc-Pe	93-94	-14	Ac	384
γ-OMe-Z-Glu-Gly-OMe	MCA	Chf	58	Chf-Eth	93	-13	Ac	172
γ-Me-boc-Glu-Gly			90		Oil			9
γ-OMe-boc-Glu-Gly-OBzl	DCCI	MeCl	75	Eth-Pe	67-69	-18	Me	9
γ-OMe-boc-Glu-Gly DCHA Salt				EtAc	137-139	-9.1	Me	9

Compound	Method	Solvent	Yield	Recrystn. solvent	M.p.	[α]	Solvent	Ref.
γ-OMe-Glu-Gly	DCCI	MeCl	49	Aq-Alc	158–160	+35	Ac	422
γ-Me-Glu-Gly-OBu^t	MA	THF	80	EtAc-Pe	69–70	−13	Ac	422
γ-OPAP-Z-Glu-Gly-OEt	DCCI	THF	90	THF-Pe	165–166	−16	THF	24
Pyro-Glu-Gly			79	Me-Eth	164–166	−15	Ac	330
Pyro-Glu-Gly				Me-EtAc	165–167	−58		423
Pyro-Glu-Gly-OTCP				Alc	167–169			423
Pyro-Glu-Gly DCHA Salt				Me-Eth	179–180	−15	DMF	423
					199–200 (dec)			330
Pyro-Glu-Gly Hydrazide	MCA	Chf-MeCl	54	Alc-Aq	197–199	+17	DMF	41
Tos-pyro-Glu-Gly-OEt					132–133			575
Z-Glu-His	DCCI	DMF-Acn	63	Aq	171–174			297
Z-Glu-His-OMe				Me-Pe	120			575
γ-OBu^t-Z-Glu-His				Me-Aq	140–142			575
γ-OBu^t-Z-Glu-His Hydrazide					140–142			298
γ-OBu^t-Z-Glu-His-OMe	DCCI	Acn	80	EtAc-Eth	116–118			575
								298
γ-Bu^t-Z-Glu-His-OMe	ONP	Py	84	Alc-Eth	115–117	−11	Me	582
α-OBzl-Z-γ-Glu-Leu-OEt				THF-Pe	90–93	−9.4	THF	24
γ-OBuzl-Z-D-Glu-Leu-OMe					123			639
Z-Glu-Leu-di-OBzl	DCCI	THF	49	Pe	46			377
Z-Glu-Leu-OBu^t	MCA	Di	71	Eth-Pe	104–105			332
Z-Glu-Leu-OEt	OPh	THF	82	EtAc-Pe	97–98			332
	OPh	THF		EtAc-Pe	93–95			330
Z-Glu-(α-Leu-OEt)-γ-hydrazide				Alc-Eth	134–136	−27	Ac	330
Glu-Leu					197	−11	Ac	377
				Aq	205–206			332
γ-OPAP-Z-Glu-Leu-OEt				Aq	200–202	+8.5	Aq	330
Pyro-Glu-Leu				THF-Pe	155–157	−24	THF	330
				Alc-Eth-Pe	151–152	−36	Aq	24
Pyro-Glu-Leu DCHA Salt				Alc	208–210	−32	Ac	330
								330

Table 2 Dipeptides (continued)

Compound	Method	Solvent	% Yield	Solvent Crystallization	M.P.(°C)	$[\alpha]_D$	Solvent Rotation	Ref.
γ-OBzl-Z-Glu-allo(OH)Lys Lactam	ONP	An	32	EtAc-Me	177–178			538
α-OBzl-Z-γ-Glu-N^ϵ-Lys					204			761
α-OBzl-Z-γ-Glu-N^ϵ-Lys Copper Complex	MCA	THF	70	Alc	200			761
Z-Glu-N^ϵ-Z-Lys DCHA Salt				Alc-Eth	157–158	−3.3	Ac	330
Glu-allo(OH)Lys Lactam				Aq-Alc				538
γ-Glu-N^ϵ-Lys								761
γ-Hydrazino-Z-Glu-N^ϵ-tos-Lys Hydrazide				Alc	154–157	−3.3	DMF	330
Z-Glu-Met DCHA Salt				Alc-Eth	148–150			332
Z-Glu-Met-OMe	OPh	THF		EtAc-Pe	96–98			332
Z-pyro-Glu-Met-OMe				Alc	122–123			332
α-OBzl-Z-γ-Glu-N^δ-Z-Orn-OBzl	DCCl	THF	65	EtAc	130–131	−15	Ac	332
	ONP	Acn	69		131–132	−15	An	385
α-OBzl-Z-γ-Glu-δ-Orn	ONP	THF	68	Aq	184–187	+5.8	Ac	385
α-OBzl-Z-Glu-δ-Orn	ONP	THF	48		197–201	−2	Ac	385
γ-OBzl-Z-Glu-N^δ-Orn-OBzl	ONP	THF	93	Alc	113	−9.6	Ac	385
α-OBzl-Z-γ-Glu-δ-Orn Copper Complex	ONP	THF	58					385
γ-OBzl-Z-Glu-δ-Orn Copper Complex	MCA	THF	75		210			385
Z-Glu-N^δ-Z-Orn				Alc-Aq	178–179	−1.6	Alc	330
Z-Glu-N^δ-Z-Orn DCHA Salt				Alc-Eth-Pe	149–151	−1.4	Ac	330
Z-Glu-Orn-OBu^t	OPh	THF	63	Alc-Eth-Pe	152–153			332
Z-Glu-Orn-OBu^t DCHA Salt				EtAc-Pe-Eth	141–142			332
Z-Glu-N^δ-tos-Orn DCHA Salt				Alc-Eth-Pe	104–106	−1.9	Ac	330
γ-Glu-δ-Orn				Aq-An	115–118	+11	Aq	385
α-Glu-δ-Orn					225 (dec)	+31	1N HCl	385
						−23	1N HCl	385
γ-Glu-Orn					209	+5.2	1N HCl	385

Compound	Reagent	Solvent	Yield	Recryst. solvent	mp (°C)	$[\alpha]$	Solvent	Ref.
Glu-Orn					202–204 (dec)	+14	1N HCl	385
Glu-N$^\delta$-tos-Orn					170–171			332
γ-OBzl-Z-Glu-Phe								355
γ-OBzl-Z-γ-Glu-Phe-OEt	OPAP	EtAc	100	THF-Pe	98–99	+13	THF	24
Z-γ-OBu^t-Glu-Phe-OBu^t					Oil			658
Z-Glu-Phe	OPh	Alc	50	Alc	162–163	+7.0	Ac	330
				Alc-Aq	159–160			332
Z-Glu-Phe-OBu^t DCHA Salt				EtAc-Alc-Pe	160–161			332
Z-Glu-Phe-OEt	DCCI	THF	52	EtAc-Eth-Pe	129–132	+1.4	Ac	330
Z(OMe)-pyro-Glu-Phe-OBu^t				EtAc-Pe	136–137	−28	Me	562
Glu-Phe				EtAc-Pe	129–130			332
				Aq	206	+24	1N HCl	562
γ-OPAP-Z-Glu-Phe-OEt				THF-Pe	191–193			24
Z-Glu-Pro	ONP	THF	71	Chf-Eth	186–189			525
Z-pyro-Glu-Pro	ONP	Py	78	Alc-Aq	70 (dec)	−109	Ac	25
				An-Eth	196–198	−83	Alc	89
Z-pyro-Glu-Pro-ONp				Me-Eth	177–178	−106	Ac	25
Boc-pyro-Glu-Pro	ONP	Chf	70	Alc	141–142	−102	Alc	90
Pyro-Glu-Pro				EtAc-Pe	182–184	−124	Aq	330
Pyro-Glu-Pro DCHA Salt				An	179–180	−100	Ac	330
γ-OBzl-Z-Glu-Ser	MCA	Di-THF	53	EtAc-DiEth	199–200	+1.2	Ac	140
γ-OBzl-Z-Glu-Ser DCHA Salt				Me	62–64			140
Z-γ-Glu-Ser-di-OBzl	DCCI	THF-Acn	75	EtAc-Pe	180	−47	Ac	140
Z-γ-Glu-Ser-OMe	ONP	Chf	82	Aq	118			330
γ-OMe-Z-Glu-DL-Ser Amide					167–169			545
γ-OMe-Z-Glu-Ser-OMe	DCCI	DMF	78		154–157			384
γ-OBzl-Z-Glu-Thr-OMe	ONP	Acn	90		96–97	−9.8	Alc	22
γ-OMe-Z-Glu-DL-Thr Amide					98–101	1.5	DMF	545
Z-Glu-Tyr			92	Aq	182–183	+16	Alc	330

113

Table 2 Dipeptides (continued)

Compound	Method	Solvent	% Yield	Solvent Crystallization	M.P.(°C)	$[\alpha]_D$	Solvent Rotation	Ref.
Z-Glu-Tyr-OBzl	MCA	THF	70	Me	174–175			122
Z-Glu-Tyr-di-OBzl	MCA	Di	76		94			377
Z-Glu-Tyr-OEt	OPh	THF	78	Alc	174–176	+7.1	Ac	330
				Alc-Eth	175–176			332
Z-Glu-Tyr-OEt DCHA Salt					160–161			332
Z-Glu-Tyr-OMe				Me	154–155	+1.8	DMF	330
Glu-Tyr					186–187			377
Glu-Tyr-OBzl Hydrochloride				Me-Eth	70–72			122
γ-OMe-Z-Glu-Tyr-OMe	ONP	Acn	80.5		108–109	−7.1	Alc	384
Z-Glu-Val				EtAc-Pe	124–125	−0.8	DMF	330
Z-Glu-Val-OBu^t	OPh	THF	68	EtAc-Pe	117–118			332
Z-Glu-Val DCHA Salt				Alc-Eth	172–174	−8.3	Ac	330
Z-Glu-Val-OEt	ONP			EtAc	121–122	−16	Ac	330
Z-Glu-Val-OMe				EtAc-Pe	117–118	−13	Ac	330
Z-Glu-Val-OMe-γ-hydrazide	OPh	THF	81	EtAc-Pe	119–120			332
Z-pyro-Glu-Val				Alc-Eth	108–111	−6.2	Ac	330
Z-pyro-Glu-D-Val				EtAc	157–158	−39	Ac	330
Z-pyro-Glu-D-Val-OBu^t	DCCI	THF-DMF-Chf	43	Alc-Eth-Pe	161–163	−10	Ac	330
				Alc	129–130	+11	Ac	330
Z-pyro-Glu-Val-OCH$_2$CN	DCCI	DMF-THF	65	Be	124–125	−37	THF	163
Z-pyro-Glu-D-Val DCHA Salt				Alc	190	−7.8	Ac	330
Z-pyro-Glu-Val DCHA Salt				Alc	190	−26	Ac	330
Glu-Val				Alc	200–201			332
α-OMe-Z-Glu-Val-OBu^t	MCA	Chf	43	EtAc-Pe	105–106			331
α-OMe-Glu-Val				EtAc-Pe	153–155			331
Pyro-Glu-Val					102–105	−30	Ac	330
Pyro-Glu-Val DCHA Salt				Alc	217–219	−19	Ac	330

Compound	Method	Yield	Solvent	M.p.	[α]	Solvent	Ref.
Bz-Gly-dehydro-Ala			Ac	206 (dec)			33
Bz-Gly-dehydro-Ala Amide			Aq-Acn	202			33
Bz-Gly-dehydro-Ala-OMe			Me-Eth	146–148	−22	Alc	33
Z-Gly-Abu-Ala-OBzl	DCCl	53.5		158.5–160.5			125
Z-Gly-Abu-Ala-OBzl Hydrazide				159.5–163			125
Z-Gly-Ala	A	51.7	Alc-Eth	119–121.5			388
	C	64.0		Oil			169
Z-Gly-Ala-OBzl		50	EtAc	130–131	−9.1	Alc	700
			Aq	125–126			156
Z-Gly-Ala-OCH(Ph)CN			Chf-Pe	77–78	−13	An	633
Z-Gly-DL-Ala-OEt			EtAc-Cy	125–126	−15	DMF	156
Z-Gly-Ala-OMe				Oil			155
Z-Gly-Ala-SPh	SPh	75	EtAc-Pe	54–55	−8.1	EtAc	286
Z-Gly-dehydro-Ala	Ac			62–64			169
				Oil			700
N-Z-Gly-dehydro-Ala-OBzl			EtAc-Pe	88–89	−74	Alc	609
Z(NO₂)-Gly-dehydro-Ala			Alc	192–193			469
Z(NO₂)-Gly-dehydro-Ala-OMe			Alc	195–196			33
Z-D-Nᵅ-Ph-Gly-D-Ala	MCA		Be-Pe	94–95			469
Gly-Abu-Ala	MeCl		Alc	197–198 (dec)			469
Gly-Ala			Alc	143–144	−23	DMF	609
			Alc-Aq	141	−26	1N HCl	440a
Gly-DL-Ala			Aq-An	152–155			125
Gly-Ala-OCH(Ph)CN Hydrabromide				238.5–240 (dec)			700
			Aq-Alc	224–226	−46	Aq	33
			Aq-An	224 (dec)			55
N-Tri-me-silyl-Gly-β-Ala-O-trimethylsilyl			Alc-Eth	222–224 (dec)	−48	Aq	633
				Oil			55

Table 2 Dipeptides (continued)

Compound	Method	Solvent	% Yield	Solvent Crystallization	M.P.(°C)	$[\alpha]_D$	Solvent Rotation	Ref.
Di-Np-Gly-Ala					175–176.5	−23	Alc	391
Pht-Gly-α-me-Ala-OMe				EtAc-Pe	179–180			640
Tos-Gly-α-me-Ala	AC	An	71	Aq-Me	177–178.5			365
Tos-Gly-α-me-Ala-OMe	SPh	Ac	63	Aq-Me	113.5–115			365
Tfa-Gly-Ala				EtAc-Eth	131–132	−28	Alc	699
Z-Gly-Arg 2-Naphthylamide Hydrochloride					142–144	+4.5	Ac	484
Z-Gly-N^G-nitro-Arg	DCCI							499
Z-Gly-N^G-nitro-Arg-OMe	MCA	MeCl	80		90–95	−14	DMF	499
Z-D-N^α-Ph-Gly-N^G-nitro-Arg	AC	Py			84			440a
Z-Gly-Asp-di-OBzl								377
Z-Gly-Asp-ONBzl	MCA		67	DMF	165–166	−9.6	DMF	141
Boc-Gly-Asp-ONBzl	DCCI				162–164	+27	Ac	599
For-Gly-β-OBzl-Asp					170			88
Gly-Asp								377
Gly-Asp-ONBzl Hydrobromide				EtAc	222	−18	Aq	141
N-Bz-S-(N-Z-Gly)-Cys-OMe	DCCI	DMF	75		157–158	−52	Me	224
Z-aza-Gly-S-bz-Cys-OEt	DCCI	Chf	59		102–105			154
Z-aza-Gly-S-bzl-Cys-OBzl					107–108	−29	EtAc	156
Z-Gly-S-bz-Cys-OEt					80			154
S-(N-Z-Gly)-N-bz-Cys-OMe				Me	156	−70	DMF	776
Z-Gly-S-bz-Cys-OMe				Be-Pe	101–101.5	−7.2	Me	224
Z-Gly-S-bzl-Cys-OBzl				Alc-Aq	97	−38	Alc	156
Z-Gly-S-bzl-Cys-OEt					76–79	−36	Me	155
Z-Gly-S-bzl-Cys-SePh				Alc-He	93–95	−10	DMF	719
Z-Gly-S-bzl-DL-homo-Cys				Be	138			97
				Chf-Pe	138			
Z-Gly-S-bzl-DL-homo-Cys-OBzl	MCA	Chf		An-Eth	127–128			97
Z-Gly-S-btm-Cys					Oil			231
N-Z-Gly-S-btm-Cys-OMe	A		88					231

Compound	Method	Solvent	Yield (%)	Recryst. Solvent	M.p.	[α]		Ref.
Z-Gly-S-me-Cys-OMe	MCA	EtAc	42	Me	69–70			609
Z-Gly-S-NBzl-Cys-OEt	ONP	Chf	82	Alc	101–102			231
Z(NO$_2$)-Gly-S-Dnp-Cys-OMe	DCCl	DMF	38	EtAc	162–163			609
Z-Gly-N$^\gamma$-xanthyl-Gln				Me-Tol-Aq	198			603
Z-Gly-N$^\gamma$-xanthyl-Gln-OMe	ONP	Chf	76	Di	184			603
Gly-Gln				Alc-Aq	260 (dec)	−1	Aq	603
Z-Gly-γ-OBzl-Glu	A	SPh	47	EtAc-Pe	95–96.6			327
Z-Gly-α-OBzl-Glu	AC	SPh	26	EtAc-Pe	113–114	−4.4	Ac	694
Z-Gly-γ-OBzl-Glu DCHA Salt	AC	Py	66	Alc	133–135	+8.6	Me	694
Z-Gly-Glu-di-OBzl	AC	EtAc	82	EtAc-Pe	58			377
Z-Gly-Glu-di-OEt					57			172
Dnp-Gly-Glu	MCA	EtAc	71	Aq-Alc	194–195	−20	4% NaHCO$_3$	390
Gly-Glu					151.5–152.5			377
Ac-Gly-Gly-OEt				EtAc-Pe	93–95			712
N-Aoc-Gly-Gly					109			248
Aza-Gly-Gly-OEt				Alc	167			154
Aza-Gly-Gly-OEt Hydrobromide				Aq	115–116			154
N-(Azido-ac)-N′-Pht-Gly-Ply-OEt				EtAc	174–175			11
Bz-Gly-Gly Glycolamide Ester					141–142			636
Z-aza-Gly-Gly-OEt					138–141			156
Z-aza-Gly-Gly Hydrazide					124–126			154
Z-Gly-aza-Gly Amide					188–190			154
Z-Gly-aza-Gly α-Bzl-hydrazide					170–171			154
Z-Gly-aza-Gly N-Bzl-hydrazide					170–171			157
Z-Gly-aza-Gly α-Bzl-β-(p-nitro-benzyliden)-hydrazide	MCA		52	Alc-Aq	180–190			154
Z-Gly-aza-Gly N-Bzl-N′-p-nitrobenzyliden-hydrazide					180–190			157
Z-Gly-aza-Gly-OEt				EtAc-Pe	124–125			157
Z-Gly-aza-Gly-ONp					127–128			157

Table 2 Dipeptides (continued)

Compound	Method	Solvent	% Yield	Solvent Crystallization	M.P.(°C)	[α]$_D$	Solvent Rotation	Ref.
Z-Gly-Gly					179-180			29
					178			700
Z-Gly-Gly Anhydride					177-178			29
Z-Gly-Gly-OBzl					111-112			667
Z-Gly-Gly-OBu^t					Oil			564
Z-Gly-Gly-OCH(Ph)CN	DCCI	MeCl	95	EtAc-Cy	105-106			422
	ONP	DMF	80		86-87			633
Z-Gly-Gly-OEt	DCCI	Acn	86		83			154
					82-83			22
	ONP				79-80			178
	A		75		77-79			177
				EtAc-Pe	84-85			711
					79-80			156
	A	THF	77	EtAc-Pe	79-81			249
	CDI		80	Alc-Aq	81-82			155
					81.5-82			23
Z-Gly-Gly-ONBzl	ONP	DMA	85	Alc-Aq	107-108			711
Z-Gly-Gly-ONp				Alc	165-166			637
				Alc	164-165			65
					161-163			29
Z-Gly-Gly-OPAP					219-220.5			23
Z-Gly-Gly-semicarbazide	A		87	Aq	190-193			444
Z-Gly-Gly-SePh					109-110			719
Z-Hydrazino-carbonyl-l-Gly-Gly-OEt				EtAc-Pe	139-141			155
N$^\beta$-Z-DL-α-hydrazino-β-phenyl-propionyl-Gly-Gly-OEt				Alc	103-105			185
[Co(trien)(Gly-Gly-OMe)](ClO$_4$)$_3$								96
[Co(trien)(Gly-Gly-NH$_2$)]Cl(ClO$_4$)$_2$								96

Compound	Cond. agent	Solvent	Yield (%)	Recryst. solvent	m.p. (°C)	Ref.
Dnp-Gly-Gly				Alc-Aq	194–195	391
Gly-aza-Gly Amide Hydrochloride					183–185	154
Gly-aza-Gly-ONp Hydrobromide					95 (dec)	157
Gly-DL-ethionyl-Gly					95	154
Gly-Gly				Aq-An	220 (dec)	97
Gly-Gly-OBzh Hydrochloride				Aq-Alc	138–142	182
Gly-Gly-OBu^t-Hydrochloride					172–173	616
Gly-Gly 2-chloroethylamide				Alc-Eth	179–180	564
Gly-Gly-OCH(Ph)CN Hydrobromide				Ac-EtAc	175–176	422
Gly-Gly-OEt Hydrobromide				Alc	197.5–199	401
2-Iodoethoxycarbonyl-Gly-Gly-OEt	MCA	Chf	72	EtAc-Pe	176	633
DL-Lipoyl-Gly-Gly	MCA		48	Alc	121–122	197
N-[N'-(5,5-Di-me-2-cyclohexen-l-on-3-yl)Gly] Gly Amide	A			Alc	138–139	182
N-[N'-(5,5-Di-me-2-cyclohexen-1-on-3-yl)Gly] Gly-OBzl				Be	185	109
N-[p-Nitro-benzyliden]-aza-Gly-Gly-OEt					126	197
Pht-Gly-Gly				Aq-Alc	174–176	197, 154, 182
Pht-Gly-Gly-OBu^t	TEP	DME	92	Alc	231–232	6
Pht-Gly-Gly-OEt	DCCI	THF	98	Alc-Aq	233–234	6
Tos-aza-Gly-Gly-OEt	Acn	THF	40	Alc-Aq	165.5–166.5	6
Tos-aza-Gly-Gly Hydrazide					165–165.5	712
Tos-Gly-Gly-OBzl					193.5–194.5; 174–177	285, 154
Tos-Gly-Gly-OEt	DCCI			Eth	167–168; 113–115	154, 667
Trt-Gly-Gly-OBzh					88	154
Trt-Gly-Gly-OCH$_2$CN				EtAc-Me	146; Oil	616, 164

Table 2 Dipeptides (continued)

Compound	Method	Solvent	% Yield	Solvent Crystallization	M.P. (°C)	$[\alpha]_D$	Solvent Rotation	Ref.
Trt-Gly-Gly-OEt				Alc	161			774
Z-Gly-N^im-bzl-His Hydrazide				Me	171–171.5			341
Z-Gly-N^im-Z-His-OMe	DCCI	MeCl	85.3	EtAc-Pe	74–75.5	+24	EtAc	261
Z-Gly-His-OMe					Oil			22
Gly-His	AC		55	Aq-Pr	170–175			386
Pht-Gly-His					258–262 (dec)			386
Tfa-Gly-Ile	SPh		93	EtAc-Me-Chf	175–177	+22	THF	699
Tfa-Gly-Ile-OMe				He	72.5–73.5	−20	Alc	699
Aza-Gly-Leu-OEt				Alc	80–100			154
N-(Azido-acl-N'-pht-Gly-Leu-OEt	DCCI	Ac	80	Alc-IPr Eth	119	−22	Chf	11
N-[Bis-(NBzl)-phosphoryl]-Gly-Leu-OBzl	SPh		86	EtAc-Pe	87–88			99
Z-Gly-Leu	C		70		130–133	−17	1N NaOH	700
					134–136	−10	Alc	388
Z-Gly-Leu-OEt					Oil			43
Z-Gly-Leu-OEt Hydrochloride				Alc-Eth	150–160	−35	Alc	43
Z-Gly-Leu-SPh					Oil			700
Z-Gly-DL-nor-Leu					115–116.5			23
Z(NO₂)-allyl-Gly-Leu	MCA	THF	59	Tol	69–73			612
Z(NO₂)-allyl-Gly-Leu-OBzl	DCCI	MeCl	79	MeCl-Pe	146–148			612
Boc-Gly-Leu	DCCI	Chf	73		98–100	−29	Alc	525
Dnp-Gly-Leu Monohydrate					148–149	+34	Aq	391
For-Gly-Leu					225	−35	Aq	389
Gly-Leu					231–232	−34	Aq	99
Gly-Leu-OMe Hydrobromide				Me-Eth	151–153	−36	Aq	667
Succinyl-bis(Gly-Leu)				EtAc-Eth	124	−23	1N NaOH	330
Succinyl-bis(Gly-Leu-OEt)				Alc-Eth	114	−34	Alc	43
Tfa-Gly-Leu	SPh	An		EtAc	175–177	−24	Alc	699

120

Compound	Method	Solvent	Yield (%)	Recryst. solvent	M.p.	$[\alpha]$	Solvent	Ref.
Trt-Gly-Leu	DCCI	THF	80	Eth-Pe	75–85	+7.5	DMF	89
Trt-Gly-Leu-Abu-OMe	MCA	THF	50		75 (dec)			525
Trt-Gly-Leu-OMe	ONP	Ac	58.7					89
Ac-Gly-N$^\epsilon$-ac-Lys	MCA	THF	81	Acn	245–247	−5.6	Alc	32
Z-Gly-N$^\epsilon$-ac-Lys	DCCI	THF	72	EtAc-Pe	126	−6.5	DMF	32
Z-Gly-N$^\epsilon$-Z-Lys				Alc	74–75	−4.5	DMF	754
N$^\epsilon$-(Z-Gly)-N$^\alpha$-Z-Lys-OBzl				Alc-Eth	98–100	+6.2	Alc	53
Bis-Z-Gly-Lys DCHA Salt	MCA	THF-DMF	60-95		124–126			333
Z-Gly-N$^\epsilon$-tos-Lys-OMe					Oil			560
Z(OMe)-Gly-N$^\epsilon$-Z-Lys-OEt				EtAc-Eth	98–99	0	Alc	1
Z(OMe)-Gly-N$^\epsilon$-Z-Lys Hydrazide				DMF-Aq	165–166			1
Boc-Gly-N$^\epsilon$-pz-Lys				Alc-Aq	85–88			599
Gly-N$^\epsilon$-ac-Lys					220–221	−10	1N HCl	32
Gly-Lys Hydrochloride					239–240	+11	Alc	53
Gly-N$^\epsilon$-tos-Lys-OMe Hydrochloride					Oil			560
Trt-Gly-N$^\epsilon$-for-Lys	NHS	Glyme	42	Chf-Dipr	161–162	+12	Chf	7
Trt-Gly-N$^\epsilon$-Lys DCHA Salt	MCA			EtAc-Pe	152–154			220
Z-Gly-Met	MCA	MeCl	69	EtAc-Eth	110–111	+4.2	Alc	700
Z-Gly-D-Met				Di-Eth	110–112	+3	DMF	440a
Gly-Met				Alc-Eth	184–186 (dec)	−10	Aq	700
Z(OMe)-Gly-N$^\delta$-Z-Orn-OEt	DCCI		62		102	−6.0	DMF	337
Z(OMe)-Gly-N$^\delta$-Z-Orn Hydrazide				EtAc-Pe	170–171	−1.3	DMF	337
Ac-Gly-Phe					159–162.5	−0.8	DMF	14
Ac-Gly-Phe-OMe Hydrate	MCA	DMF	79		71.5–82	+11	Me	14
Bz-Gly-Phe	DCCI	THF	69	EtAc-Pe	144.5–148	+39	Alc	14
Bz-Gly-Phe-OMe	DCCI	Acn			123–124	+40	Chf	14
Bz-Gly-Phe-ONp					144–149.5	−21	Chf	14
Bz-Gly-DL-Phe-ONp				Me	174–176			14
Bz-Gly-Phe-ONp Methanol Solvate				Me	61–67	−29	DMF	14

Table 2 Dipeptides (continued)

Compound	Method	Solvent	% Yield	Solvent Crystallization	M.P. (°C)	$[\alpha]_D$	Solvent Rotation	Ref.
Z-Gly-N-me-Phe-ONp	AC	Eth			Oil			176
Z-Gly-N-me-DL-Phe-ONp				Alc-Eth-Pe	99.5–100.5			176
Z-Gly-N-me-Phe Piperizonium Salt				Me-Eth	139–141	−38	Me	176
N-Z-Gly-DL-p-trimethylsilyl-Phe				EtAc-Pe	183			146
N-Z-Gly-DL-p-trimethylsilyl-Phe-OMe	MCA	Di	70	EtAc-Pe	69			146
Z-Gly-p-nitro-Phe	ONP		70	Alc-Aq	182–183	+36	Py	548
Z-Gly-Phe				EtAc-Pe	126–127			43
					120–123	+35	Alc	700
	CD-1, 2,4-T	DMF	78	Chf-Eth	124–125.5			52
	ONP	DMF	74	Aq	123–124			350
	ONP	Chf		EtAc-Pe	125–126.5			519
	MCA	THF						355
Z-Gly-Phe					126.5–127.5	+40	Alc	465
					127			667
	TOSC	THF	34	An-Pe	129.5–130	+38	Alc	712
					128.5–130	+37	Alc	176
	ONP				125–125.5	+12	Acn	119
					68–70	−15	THF	584
				Aq	179–180			23
					127–128	+36	Alc	6
					126			605
Z-Gly-DL-Phe	CDI	THF	70	EtAc-Eth	125–126	+37	An	169
				Alc-Aq	162.5–163.5			465
				Alc-Aq	159–162			176
				An-Aq	161.5–162.5			712

122

Compound	Method	Solvent	Yield (%)	Recryst. solvent	m.p. (°C)	[α]	Solvent	Ref.
Z-Gly-DL-Phe				An-Aq	157–161			119
					161.5–162.5			712
					161			52
Z-Gly-Phe Azlactone	DCCI	Acn	44	EtAc-He	70.5–72			119
Z-Gly-Phe-OBu^t	TEP		99.5	Dipr Eth-Hep	61.5–63.5			6
Z-Gly-Phe 2-Chloroethylamide					147–149			401
N-Z-Gly-Phe-OCH$_2$CN	A		75.5	EtAc-Pe	60–62	−12	DMF	52
Z-Gly-Phe-OEt	AC		77		Oil	−13		757
					Oil			169
Z-Gly-DL-Phe-OEt	CDI	Chf	83	Be-Pe	120–120.5			14
	CDBI	DMF-Acn	69	Be-Pe	133–135			14
N-Z-Gly-Phe-OEt	MCA		80	Alc	91–92			465
	DCCI		86		89.5–91.0			388
Z-Gly-D-Phe Hydrazide	Chf				91–92			43
Z-Gly-Phe-OMe					Oil			681
Z-Gly-Phe-ONp					150–151			22
Z-Gly-DL-Phe-ONp				EtAc-Pe	147	−7.3	Chf	177
				Alc	143–144.5	−6.3	Chf	52
				Alc	133–135			14
					135.5–136.5			177
Z-Gly-Phe Oxazolone					95–96			176
Z-Gly-Phe-SePh	MA	THF	90	Bz-Pe	130–131.5	−59	DMF	52, 176
					105			8
Z-Gly-DL-Phe-SePh	MCA		62		123			719, 52
	MA		88		118–119			121, 719
Z(NO$_2$)-Gly-Phe Hydrazide	MCA		61	Eth	164–166	+5.3	Ac	52, 600

123

Table 2 Dipeptides (continued)

Compound	Method	Solvent	% Yield	Solvent Crystallization	M.P. (°C)	$[\alpha]_D$	Solvent Rotation	Ref.
Z(NO₂)-Gly-Phe-OMe	AC	Eth	78	Alc	109–112			600
Z-D-Nᵅ-Ph-Gly-D-Phe	MCA	MeCl			154–157	−13	DMF	440a
Dnp-Gly-Phe				Aq-Alc	184–185	+8.3	Alc	390
						+18	An	
Et-β-carboxypropionyl-Gly-Phe				EtAc	104	+5.7	Alc	43
Gly-dehydro-Phe Hydrobromide								666
Gly-DL-p-trimethylsilyl-Phe				Aq-Ac	258			146
Gly-Phe					174			605
					240			757
Gly-Phe-OBuᵗ				Aq-Alc	262–265	+40	Aq	218
					34.5–35.5	+17	Alc	6
Gly-Phe-OEt Hydrochloride				Alc-Eth	130–140	+3.2	Alc	43
Gly-Phe-OMe Hydrobromide	DCCI	MeCl	93	Me-EtAc	176–177			406
Gly-Phe 2-Chloroethylamide					185–186			401
Gly-DL-Phe-OEt					oil			6
Gly-DL-Phe-OEt Hydrobromide				Ac-Eth	154–155			6
Succinyl-bis(Gly-Phe)				EtAc	138–140	+28	1N NaOH	43
Succinyl-bis(Gly-Phe-OEt)				Alc-Eth	90	+2.1	Alc	43
Succinyl(Gly-Phe-OEt, Gly-Leu-OEt)				Alc-Eth	130–131	−11	Alc	43
Tfa-Gly-Phe					186.5–187	+41	Alc	6
Tfa-Gly-Phe-OBuᵗ	TEP	DME	83	i-Pr-Aq	119–120	+7.2	Alc	6
Z-Gly-Pro	AC	Eth	15	EtAc	155.5–157	−77	Chf	177
	SPh	Ac	66.0	Sph-Me	155–157			59
	NHS	Aq-DME	55	EtAc-Pe	150–151	−60	Alc	700
	NHP	Aq-DME	75	EtAc	158–159			7
			45		151–154			
Z-Gly-Pro-OMe	AC		88	Eth-Pe	49–50			717
Z-Gly-Pro-ONp				Alc	104–105	−102	EtAc	177
					104–104.5	−102	EtAc	176

Compound	Method	Coupling Solvent	Yield (%)	Recrystn. Solvent	m.p. (°C)	$[\alpha]$	Rotn. Solvent	Ref.
Boc-Gly-Pro	DCCI / Ac	MeCl	92 / 58	EtAc-Pe	142–144 / 158	−68	DMF	9
Dnp-Gly-Pro	DCCI	THF	55		191–192	−71	Alc	113
Pz-Gly-Pro	SPh	Ac	77		135–137	−41	DMF	390
Tfa-Gly-Pro	CDI	THF	53		oil			570
Tfa-Gly-Pro-OBu^t	TEP	DME	69	Mcy	90–91	−83	Alc	699
Tfa-Gly-Pro-OMe				Mcy	89–90	−83	Alc	465
N-Bz-Gly-DL-cyclo-Ser	SPh	Ac	50	i-Pr-Eth	82			6
Z-Gly-OBzl-DL-Ser	DCCI	DMF	69	Alc	196–198			699
Z-Gly-D-Ser				EtAc	137–137.5	−5	DMF	470
Z-Gly-Ser-OBzl				EtAc	121–122	+4.7	Ac	700
Z-Gly-Ser Hydrazide				Me-Eth	149			440a
Z-Gly-Ser-OMe	EDCI	MeCl	69	EtAc-N-He	224	−5.0	DMF	140
Z-Gly-O-tos-DL-Ser-OBzl				Me-Eth	94–95			193
Boc-Gly-2-trt-DL-cyclo-Ser	MCA	EtAc	40	Glyme-Pe	101–103			225
Gly-O-Z-DL-Ser-OBzl				Alc-Eth	201–203			33
N-Gly-DL-cyclo-Ser Hydrobromide				Aq	137			470
Gly-Ser-OMe Hydrochloride				Alc-Aq				33
N-Pht-Gly-OBu^t-Ser	TEP	Glyme	68	Alc-Aq	210			81
N-Pht-Gly-OBu^t-DL-Ser-OBu^t	TEP	Glyme	83	Be-Pe	136.5–137.5			81
N-Pht-Gly-OBu^t-Ser-OBu^t	DCCI	MeCl	75	Chf-Pr	88–89			81
N-Tfa-Gly-2-trt-cyclo-Ser	MCA	MeCl	56	EtAc-Pe	153–156			470
N-Trt-Gly-2-trt-DL-cyclo-Ser	ONp	Ac	70	Alc-Aq	255–256			470
Z-Gly-Trp	NHS	Aq-Acn	83	Alc-Eth	141–142	+33	Alc	700
Z-Gly-Trp	DCCI	MeCl		Alc-Pe	142–143	+32	Alc	7
Z-Gly-Trp-amide						+20	Alc	666
Z-Gly-Trp Benzylammonium Salt					174	+26	An	666
Dnp-Gly-Trp					233–234	−60	Aq-NaHCO₃	390

Table 2 Dipeptides (continued)

Compound	Method	Solvent	% Yield	Solvent Crystallization	M.P. (°C)	[α]$_D$	Solvent Rotation	Ref.
Gly-Trp-amide Toluenesulfonate				Alc-Eth	160-161			666
Gly-Trp-OMe Toluenesulfonate				i-Pr-Eth	176-178			666
N-Trt-Gly-Trp Di-et-ammonium Salt				An	173			666
Trt-Gly-Trp-OMe	DCCI	MeCl	60	An	187			666
Z-Gly-Tyr-OEt	CDI	THF	95		127-128	+18	Alc	465
	PHA	DMF-Acn		EtAc-Pe	123-124	+18	Alc	491
					126-127	+20	Eth	22
				Aq-Alc	126.5-127			466
N-Z-Gly-Tyr-OEt					120			605
Boc-Gly-Tyr Hydrazide	DCCI		84.5	Me	189.5-190	+0.5	DMF	463
Et-N-(1-bz-isopropenyl)-Gly-Tyr	DCCI	Chf	50	EtAc-n-Pen	114-115			228
Gly-Tyr-OEt Hydrochloride				Alc-Eth	239			228
N-Trt-Gly-Tyr-OEt	MCA	EtAc	71	Alc	157-158	+25	THF	548
Z-Gly-Abu-Val-OBzl	DCCI	Acn	66	Alc-Eth	114-116.5	-26	Alc	125
Z-Gly-DL-Val	SPh	Ac	46-93		125-126			700
Z-Gly-Val-OMe	MCA	THF	66	Pe	78			304
Dnp-Gly-Val				Aq-Alc	132-134	-21	Alc	391
For-Gly-Val					244-247	+12	Aq	389
For-Gly-Val-OEt					oil	-14	Alc	389
Gly-Abu-Val				Aq-Alc-An	240.5-241.5	-11	1N HCl	125
Gly-Val					161-162	-6.2	1N HCl	389
Gly-Val-OBu^t Oxalate Salt	Ac	Be	79	Me-Eth		-17	Alc	226
N-Pht-Gly-Val-OBu^t	SPh	Ac		MeCl-He	150-151	+4.7	Chf	226
N-Tfa-Gly-Val				EtAc-Dipr Eth	104			699
N-Tfa-Gly-Val-OMe						-28	Me	699
Histidine								
N^{im}-Bzl-Z-His-Asp-di-ONBzl	EDCI				128-130	-1.4	Me	106

126

Compound	Method	Solvent	Yield (%)	Recrystn. solvent	M.p.	$[\alpha]$	Rotn. solvent	Ref.
N^{im}-Bzl-His-Asp-di-ONBzl Hydrobromide				DMF	115–117	+6.2	DMF	106
Z-His-Asp				Aq	222–222.5 (dec)	−16	Aq-NaHCO$_3$	522
Z-His-Glu				i-Pr-Eth	169–172	−21	Aq-NaHCO$_3$	522
N^{im}-Bzl-Z-His-Gly	DCCI	Py	72	EtAC-Eth	216			386
N^{im}-Bzl-Z-His-Gly-OEt	DCCI		66	DMF-Eth	120–121			386
N^{im}-Bzl-for-His-Gly-OBzl				DMF-Eth	176–180			669
Z-His-Gly					230 (dec)	−20	Aq-NaHCO$_3$	522
His-Gly Hydrochloride					216–217			386
Di-Trt-His-His								386
Di-Trt-His-His-OMe					190–192			386
N^{im}-Bzl-Z-His-Leu	DCCI	MeCl	40	Py-Eth	124–126			386
N^{im}-Bzl-Z-His-Leu-OMe					oil			386
N^{im}-Bzl-Z-His-Leu-ONBzl	DCCI	DMF	89		122–124	+13	Alc	15
N^{im}-Bzl-Z-His-Leu-ONBzl Dihydrobromide				Alc-Aq	188–189	−9.9	Aq-NaHCO$_3$	15
Z-His-Leu	DCCI	MeCl	90					522
Di-Z-His-Leu-OMe				EtAc-Eth	102.5–103.5	−7.6	Me	261
N^{im}-Z-His-Leu-OMe Dihydrobromide	A	EtAc		Di-Eth	95 (dec)	+14	EtAc	261
His-Leu					217–220			386
Z-His-D-Met					117–120	−4	DMF	440a
N^{im}-Bzl-Z-His-D-Phe	DCCI	DMF	77	Me	167–168	+5.4	Me	375
N^{im}-Bzl-Z-His-Phe	DCCI		67	EtAc	127–130	+15	Me	375
N^{im}-Bzl-Z-His-Phe-OMe	DCCI	Acn	79	EtAc	144–145	+5.2	Me	375
N^{im}-Bzl-Z-His-D-Phe-OMe				An	122–123	+11	Me	375
N^{im}-Bzl-Z-His-Phe-ONp					164–166			371
Di-Z-His-Phe					123			522
Z-His-Phe				Alc	231–232 (dec)			522

Table 2 Dipeptides (continued)

Compound	Method	Solvent	% Yield	Solvent Crystallization	M.P. (°C)	$[\alpha]_D$	Solvent Rotation	Ref.
Di-Z-His-Phe Amide					202–203 (dec)			262
Di-Z-His-Phe-OBzl	DCCI	Acn	87.9	EtAc-Eth	126–127	−7.2	Me	261
N^{im}-Z-His-Phe-OBzl Dihydrobromide					127–127.5			261
N^{im}-Z-His-Phe-OBzl Hydrochloride Hydrate					136.5–137 (dec)			261
Z-His-Phe-OBu^t	DCCI		89		225 (dec)			262
Di-Z-His-Phe-OEt					161–162			262
Di-Z-His-Phe Hydrazide			93		200–201			262
Di-Z-His-Phe-OMe	DCCI	MeCl	89.2		123–124			522
	DCCI			EtAc-Eth	135.5–136	+54	Chf	261
	ONp		58					522
	MA		46					
N^{im}-Z-His-Phe-OMe Dihydrobromide					135.5–136 (dec)			261
His-Phe					126.5–127.5 (dec)			264
					214–215 (dec)			386
His-Phe Amide					137–139			262
His-Phe-OMe								407
Di-Trt-His-Phe					150–154 (dec)			386
Di-Trt-His-Phe-OEt	DCCI	MeCl	80		90 (dec)	−53	Me	386
Z-His-Pro-OMe						−35	DMF	190
His-Pro Diketopiperazine				EtAc	168–170	−66	Aq	406
His-Pro-OMe					146 (dec)	−36	Me	190

Compound	Method	Solvent	Yield (%)	Recryst. solvent	M.p. (°C)	[α]	Solvent	Ref.
Di-Trt-His-Pro				An-Cy	115 (dec)	−34	DMF	406
Di-Trt-His-Pro-OMe	DCCI	MeCl	82	An-Cy	212–216	+29	Me	406
N^im-Bzl-Z-His-Ser					180	+10	DMF	47
N^im-Bzl-Z-His-Ser Hydrazide					155			192
N^im-Bzl-Z-His-Ser-OMe	DCCI	Acn	50	EtAc	173–174	+3	DMF	47
N^im-Z-His-Ser	DCCI		72	Aq	173			192
Z-His-Ser Hydrazide					182			192
Z-His-Ser-OMe	A		52	EtAc-Alc-Pe	200–202			559
Di-Z-His-Ser-OMe	DCCI	MeCl	76	Alc	137–139			559
Boc-His-OBu^t-Ser Hydrazide					152–153			593
Boc-His-OBu^t-Ser-OMe	A		79		146–147	−7.3	Me	556
His-Ser					57–65	−2.2	DMF	556
His-Ser-OMe Dihydrochloride					120–130			386
Di-Trt-His-Ser	DCCI	MeCl	85	MeCl-Eth	154–156 (dec)			593
Di-Trt-His-Ser-OMe					227–228			386
Z-His-Thr				An	189.5–190 (dec)	−23	Aq-NaHCO₃	386
D-Z-His-Thr-OBzl				Alc-Eth	130–131	+22	Chf	522
Z-His-Thr Hydrazide					185.5–186 (dec)			522
Di-Z-His-Tyr-OEt	DCCI		91		148–149			522
Z-His-Tyr Hydrazide					210–212 (dec)			262
Z-His-Tyr-OMe	A		45	Alc-EtAc	140.5–142.5 (dec)			262
His-Tyr Amide Acetate					158–160			341
His-Tyr Diketopiperazine				Aq	274–276			262, 341
Z-His-Val				Alc-Eth	196–197.5 (dec)	−20	Aq	278, 522

Table 2 Dipeptides (continued)

Compound	Method	Solvent	% Yield	Solvent Crystallization	M.P. (°C)	$[\alpha]_D$	Solvent Rotation	Ref.
Isoleucine								
Z-Ile-D-Ala	ONp	DMF			161–163	+12	DMF	440a
Z-Ile-N^G-nitro-Arg	ONp	DMF			156–159	+0.5	DMF	440a
Z-Ile-D-Asp	MCA	MeCl			75–90	+17	DMF	440a
Z-Ile-S-bzl-Cys-OEt	MCA	Chf						639
Z-Ile-Cys	SPh	Py		Alc-Aq	158			639
Ile-Cys					165			639
Z-Ile-Gln-ONp	MA	DMF	48	Ac-Alc	217–218.5	−35	DMF	628
Aoc-Ile-Gly-OBzl	DCCI	THF	67	Eth-Pe	68–70.5	−25	Me	517
Z-Ile-Gly					105–106			698
					142–145			
Z-Ile-Gly-OBu^t	DCCI	Acn	62	EtAc-Pe	133–135	−23	Alc	85
Z-Ile-Gly-OEt	DCCI	Acn	87	Me	122–125	−24	Me	698
	ONp	Chf		EtAc	159	−26	Ac	277
Z-Ile-Gly-OMe	MCA	Chf	78	Alc	153.5–154.5			517
Z-Ile-Gly-ONp	ONp	Chf	80	Alc	160–161	−26	Ac	25
Boc-Ile-Gly	MA		75	Eth-He	160–161	−26	Ac	395
Boc-Ile-Gly-OMe	DCCI	Acn	32	Cy	127–130	−11	DMF	443
					212–213			443
Boc-Ile-Gly-ONp	MCA	Chf	63	Eth	132–134			443
					83–84			443
Ile-Gly				Aq-Alc	157–161	+100	Aq	774
Ile-Gly-OBu^t					240 (dec)	+16	Ac	85
Ile-Gly-OMe				Me-Eth	181–182	+16	Ac	395
Ile-Gly-OMe Hydrochloride					181–182			395
Z(NO$_2$)-Ile-Gly				Alc-Cy-He	172–173	+3.0	DMF	631
Z(NO$_2$)-Ile-Gly-2,4,6-tri-me-OBzl	DCCI	Acn	68	EtAc	174–175.5	+1.1	DMF	631

N-Nps-Ile-Gly				Alc-Aq	135–138			774
N-Nps-Ile-Gly DCHA Salt	DCCI		70	Alc	190–192	–57	Me	774
N-Nps-Ile-Gly-OEt	DCCI	THF-MeCl	70	EtAc-Pe	114	–23	Me	774
Z-Ile-N^{im}-bzl-His Hydrazide				Me	191–192			468
Z-Ile-N^{im}-bzl-His-OMe				Be-Pe	115–116	–14	Alc	468
Z-Ile-His Azide								531
Z-Ile-His Hydrazide			74		184–186 (dec)	–52	1N HCl	531
Z-Ile-His-OMe			74	Me-Aq	184–186 (dec)	–52	1N HCl	530
					184–185.5 (dec)	–45	Me-1N HCl	530
					175–176 (dec)	–45	Me-1N HCl	531
Boc-Ile-His Hydrate				Thf-Eth	137–145			466
Boc-Ile-His-OMe	CDI	THF	81	Me-Aq	168.5–170			466
Z(NO$_2$)-N-me-Ile-D-2-hydroxy-3-me-butyryl-N-me-Ile-D-2-hydroxy-3-me-butyric Acid						–90	Be	597
Ile-N$^\epsilon$-boc-Lys				Alc		+6.7	1N NaOH	218
Z-Ile-D-Met	ONp	DMF			123–125	+18	DMF	440a
Z-Ile-D-Phe	DCCI	DMF			159–161	+8	DMF	440a
Z-Ile-Phe	MCA	THF	74		175–176	–25	Me	698
Z-Ile-Phe-OBu^t	DCCI			Pe	127–129	–26	Me	698
Z-Ile-Pro			75					698
For-D-allo-Ile-Pro	DCCI	MeCl		EtAc-Pe	134–135	–14	Me	77
For-D-allo-Ile-Pro-OBzl	DCCI	DMF		EtAc-Pe	124–125	–17	Me	77
Z-Ile-D-Ser					167–168	+1	DMF	440a
Z-Ile-Ser-OBzl	DCCI	DMF	43	EtAc	175	–17	Ac	140
Ile-Trp				Me	144–145	+23	Me	218
Z-Ile-D-Val	DCCI	DMF		EtAc-Pe	153–155	+2	DMF	440a

Leucine

Z-Leu-Ala	SPh	Ac			150	–24	Alc	700
Z-Leu-D-Ala	MCA	MeCl			97–101	–12	Me	440a

132

Table 2 Dipeptides (continued)

Compound	Method	Solvent	% Yield	Solvent Crystallization	M.P. (°C)	$[\alpha]_D$	Solvent Rotation	Ref.
Z-D-Leu-D-Ala	MCA	MeCl			145-148	+31	Me	440a
Z-Leu-D-Ala-OBzl	MCA		67	Chf	120-121	+1.2	Alc	446
Z-Leu-Ala-OBzl	MCA	THF	65	EtAc-Eth-Pe	111	-45	Alc	446
Z-D-Leu-Ala-OMe	MCA		58	EtAc-Pe	131-132	±1.5	Me	527
Leu-Ala				Me-EtAc	255-256			430
				Me-An-Eth		+27		446
					258-259 (dec)			430
Leu-D-Ala						+77	Aq	446
D-Leu-Ala-OMe Hydrochloride								527
Z(NO$_2$)-Leu-Ala					126.5-127.5			430
Z(NO$_2$)-Leu-Ala-OBzl			83	Alc	105.5-107.5			430
Z(NO$_2$)-Leu-Ala-OEt	A	THF	60	Alc-Aq	126-128			430
	MCA		77		131-133			430
Z(NO$_2$)-Leu-Ala Hydrazide				Me	194-196			430
Z-Leu-Asn-2,4,6-tri-me-OBzl				Aq-Alc	174-175	-11	DMF	626
Leu-Asn				Aq-Alc	215.5-221	+15	Aq	626
Leu-β-OBu^t-Asn-OMe Hydrochloride				Eth-Pe	154-156	+5.0	Alc	737
Z-Leu-β-OBu^t-Asp-OMe	DCCI	MeCl		EtAc-Eth-Pe	95-96	-17	Alc	737
Z-D-Leu-S-bzl-Cys	DCCI	MeCl	92		75-77	-6	DMF	440a
Z-Leu-Glu-di-OBzl					80			377
Leu-Glu				Aq	216-217			377
Ac-Leu-Gly					193-194	-50	Alc	607
Ac-Leu-Gly-OEt					99-100	-56	Alc	607
Ac-DL-Leu-Gly-OEt								607
Bz-DL-Leu-Gly				Aq	165			709
Bz-Leu-Gly				EtAc	134-135	-26	Alc	709

Compound	Reagent	Solvent	Yield (%)	Cryst. solvent	m.p.	[α]	Solvent	Ref.
Bz-Leu-Gly-OEt	MCA	THF	93	EtAc-Pe	156.5–157	−34	Alc	709
				Alc	156.5–157	−32	Alc	8
Bz-DL-Leu-Gly-OEt	TEP	Chf	98	EtAc-Pe	153–155			178
Bz-Leu-Gly-OEt				EtAc-Pe	146			709
Z-DL-Abu-DL-nor-Leu-Gly-OEt				EtAc-Pe	153–155			178
Z-Leu-Gly	SPh	Ac	77	EtAc-Pe	135–137	−14	EtAc	23
Z-Leu-Gly 2-Chloroethylamide				EtAc-Pe	116–118	−23	Alc	431
Z-Leu-Gly-OEt				EtAc-Pe	112–113			700
Z-DL-Leu-Gly-OEt	·2,4,6-TBP MCA	DMF-THF	91	EtAc-Pe	137–138			401
Z-Leu-Gly-OMe	MCA	EtAc	67	EtAc-Pe	102			586
Z-Leu-Gly-OMe Hydrochloride				EtAc-Pe	90.5–91	−18	DMF	519
Z-Leu-Gly-ONp	MCA	Acn	56	Alc-Ac	93	−24	Ac	23
Z-Leu-Gly-SPh			77	Alc	93–94	−36	Alc	122
Z-Leu-Gly Tos-hydrazide				Alc	167–168			78
Leu-aza-Gly Amide Acetate				NMe	161			122
Leu-aza-Gly Amide Hydrochloride					165–166			628
Leu-Gly				Aq-An	192–196	+85	Aq	646
					108–110			29
					154–157			700
Leu-Gly Anhydride					236		Aq	445
Leu-Gly 2-Chloroethylamide					115–116			154
Leu-Gly Tos-hydrazide Hydrochloride				Alc	102–104			154
N-[Bis-(NBzl)-phosphoryl]-Leu-Gly-OBzl	DCCI		50	Pr-i-Pr Eth	172–174			520
Z-Leu-His					134–136			99
Leu-His					126–128			29
Nγ-Z-Dbu-Nγ-Z-Dbu-D-Leu-Ile-Nγ-Z-Dbu-OMe Hydrochloride				Me-Eth	200–205 (dec)	−10	Ac	485

Table 2   Dipeptides (continued)

Compound	Method	Solvent	% Yield	Solvent Chrystalization	M.P. (°C)	[α]D	Solvent Rotation	Ref.
Nγ-Z-Dbu-D-Leu-Ile-Nγ-Z-Dbu-OMe Hydrochloride				Me-Eth	155–158	+7.0	Ac	485
Nγ-Z-Nα-Nps-Dbu-Nγ-Z-D-Leu-Ile-Nγ-Z-Dbu-OMe				DMF-Aq	214–217	−19		485
Nγ-Z-Nα-Nps-Dbu-D-Leu-Ile-Nγ-Z-Dbu-OMe				Alc	192–194	−15		485
Nα-Z-Nγ-tos-Dbu-Nγ-tos-Dbu-D-Leu-Ile-Nγ-tos-Dbu-Nγ-pelargonyl-Dbu-OMe	MCA	THF-DMF	80	Aq-Me	162–165	−22	Me	486
Boc-Leu-Ile-OEt				Me-Aq	108–110	−34	Me	549
D-Leu-Ile-Nγ-Z-Dbu-OMe Hydrochloride				Me-Eth	220–222 (dec)	−66	Ac	485
Nps-D-Leu-Ile-Nγ-Z-Dbu-OMe	DCCI	Acn	83	Me	171–173	+15		485
Nγ-Tos-Dbu-Nγ-tos-Dbu-D-Leu-Ile-Nγ-tos-Dbu-Nγ-pelargonyl-Dbu-OMe					149–150	−18		486
Z-Leu-Leu	DCCI			EtAc-Pe	140–150			202
Z-Leu-D-Leu-OBzl					110–112	+2.3	Alc	446
Z-D-Leu-Leu DCHA Salt	DCCI				163.5–164.5			202
Leu-D-Leu				Aq		+68	1N HCl	446
Leu-Leu						−13	1N NaOH	446
D-Leu-Leu Dihydrate								202
Leu-Leu Hydrate					95–99			202
Tos-Leu-Leu Hydrazide			89	Aq-Alc	192–193			299
Tos-Leu-Leu-OMe	Ac	EtAc-Aq	89	EtAc-Pe	123–124			299
Leu-threo-Nε-Z-Lys-OBzl				Aq-Alc-An	139–141	−17	Me	197a
Aoc-Leu-Met Amide	ONp	DMF		EtAc-Pe	104–106	−37	Me	517
Z-Leu-D-Met	ONp	DMF			92–93	−39		440a
Z-D-Leu-D-Met	MCA	MeCl			98–100	+1	DMF	440a
Z-Leu-Met Amide	MCA	Chf	62.5		210–211	+7	Me	25

134

Compound	Method	Solvent	Yield (%)	Recrystn. solvent	M.p.	[α]	Solvent	Ref.
Boc-Leu-Met Amide					154–155	−35	DMF	395
Leu-Met Amide					129–131	−6.5	Aq	443
Leu-Met Amide Hydrochloride					126–127	+10	Aq	395
N-Trt-Leu-Met				i-Pr	85–87	+7.3	Aq	25
N-Trt-Leu-Met-OMe	DCCI	Acn	80	Be-Pe	138	−26	DMF	48
Boc-D-Leu-N^δ-Z-Orn-OEt	DCCI	Chf-THF	77	Eth-Pe	101	−19	DMF	48
D-Leu-δ-Z-Orn-OEt Hydrochloride				EtAc-Pe	88	+11	Ac	301
Z-Leu-Phe					102–104			301
Z-D-Leu-Phe	MCA	MeCl		EtAc-Pe	55–60	−12	Me	697
Z-D-Leu-D-Phe	MCA	MeCl			oil	+20	Me	440a
Z-Leu-Phe 2-Chloroethylamide				EtAc-Pe	146–148			440a
					123–125			401
Z-Leu-Phe-OEt	MCA	THF	80	EtAc-Pe	94–95			129
Z-Leu-Phe Hydrazide	MCA	THF			186–188			697
N-Z-Leu-Phe-OMe	MCA	THF	74	Me	81	−26	Me	129
Z-Leu-Phe-SPh	MCA	MeCl	54	EtAc-Pe	150			697
N-[Bis-(*p*-bromo-bzl)-phosphoryl]-Leu-Phe-OMe				EtAc-Pe	118			697
N-[Bis-(*p*-bromo-bzl)-phosphoryl]-Leu-Phe-OMe Hydrazide					196			99
Leu-Phe				Me	190–192			99
Leu-Phe-OEt Hydrochloride				Me-Eth	217–219			218
Leu-D-Phe-OMe				Me-Eth	105–106			129
Z(OMe)-Leu-Phe-vinyl Ester	MCA	THF	87	Be-Pe	50–55	−40	Alc	130
Z-Leu-D-Ser	MCA	MeCl		EtAc-Pe	116	−15	DMF	52
Z-Leu-Ser-OMe	MCA	TEA	57	Me-Eth	170 (dec)	−17	Me	440a
Leu-Ser-OMe Hydrochloride				Cy-Pe	146–152	−35	Me	120
For-Leu-OBu^t-Thr-OBu^t	MCA	Be		Eth-Pe	154–156	−45		120
Z(OMe)-Leu-O-[2,2,2-trifluoro-1-Z-amino-et]-Thr DCHA Salt	TEP			EtAc-Pe	164			195
								701

Table 2 Dipeptides (continued)

Compound	Method	Solvent	% Yield	Solvent Crystallization	M.P. (°C)	[α] D	Solvent Rotation	Ref.
Z(OMe)-Leu-Thr-OMe	DCCI	MeCl	79	Eth-EtAc	oil			701
Z-Leu-Trp-OBzl	MCA	THF	84	EtAc	110			707
Z-D-Leu-Trp 2-Hydroxyethylamide					169–170			527
Leu-Trp-OMe	ONp	THF	82	EtAc-Pe	134–136	+4	Me	197a
Z-Leu-OBu^t-Tyr-OMe	NHS	THF	87		87–89	−10	DMF	328
					87–89	−11	DMF	
Boc-Leu-Tyr-OMe					113–114			78
Z-Leu-Val Amide	ONp	DMF	90	Alc	234–236			66
Z-Leu-DL-Val-OBzl	DCCI	MeCl	60	EtAc-Pe	oil			446
Z-Leu-Val Hydrazide	PHA	DMF			163			674
Z-Leu-Val-OMe	DCCI	DMF			oil			179
Z-Leu-Val-ONp				Eth-Pe	126			307
Boc-Leu-Val-OMe				He-EtAc	144–147			356
Leu-DL-Val						+17	1N HCl	446
Leu-Val				Me-Eth		+18	1N HCl	218
Leu-Val Hydrate						+55	Aq	446
Leu-D-Val Hydrate								446
Leu-Val-OMe Acetate								179
Leu-Val-OMe Hydrochloride								179
Lysine								
N$^\varepsilon$-Z-N$^\alpha$-Nps-Lys-Ala-OMe	DCCI	Dipr Eth-EtAc	88		74–77	−36	Di	774
N$^\varepsilon$-Boc-Z-Lys-Ala-OBu^t	DCCI	EtAc	80	An-Pe	88–90	−13	An	403
	A		51		91–93	−10	An	560a
N$^\varepsilon$-Boc-Z-Lys-Ala-OEt	ONp		90	Alc-Eth	85–88			
					98–99	−24	Alc	583
N$^\varepsilon$-Boc-Z-Lys-Ala Hydrazide					132–133	−27	Ac	583

136

Compound	Method	Solvent	Yield (%)	Recryst.	M.p. (°C)	$[\alpha]$	Solv.	Ref.
N^ϵ-Tos-Z-Lys-Ala-OBu^t	A	DMF	80	Alc-Aq	137	−9.6	An	542
N^ϵ-Tos-Z-Lys-Ala-OMe	ONp	Acn	94	EtAc-Pe	133–134			308
N^ϵ-Tos-Z-Lys-D-Ala-OMe	DCCI	EtAc	63	EtAc-Pe	133–135	−22	Me	761a
N^ϵ-Tos-Lys-Ala-OMe Hydrobromide	DCCI	Py-Chf	80		143–145	+7.0	Me	767
N^ϵ-Boc-Z-Lys-N^G-tos-Arg Amide	MA		64					767
N^ϵ-Tos-Z-Lys-N^G-nitro Arg				Alc-Aq	95–105	−5.5	Me	761a
N^ϵ-Tos-Z-Lys-N^G-nitro-Arg-OMe	DCCI	THF-DMF	54	EtAc-Pe	108–112	−8.2	Py	492
N^ϵ-Tos-Lys-N^G-nitro-Arg-OMe Hydrobromide					142–144	−12	Di	560
N^ϵ-Boc-Z-Lys-Asp-di-OBu^t						+1.6	Aq	560
N^ϵ-Boc-Lys-Asp-di-OBu^t	DCCI	THF-DMF	81		95–99	−14	Me	560
N^ϵ-For-Z-Lys-Asp				Me-EtAc	154–156	+0.7	Me	573
N^ϵ-For-Z-Lys-Asp-di-OMe	MCA		87	EtAc	141–143	−11	Me	573
N^ϵ-For-Lys-Asp				Aq-Eth	173–176	+24	Aq	747
N^ϵ-For-Lys-Asp-di-OMe					oil			747
N^ϵ-For-Lys-Asp-di-OMe Hydrochloride	MCA	THF-DMF		Me-Eth	179–180	+12	Me	747
N^ϵ-For-Lys-β-OMe-Asp Diketopiperazine				Me	158–160			747
N^α,N^ϵ-Di-Z-Lys-S-bzl-Cys	MCA	THF			115–119	−12	DMF	747
Di-Z-DL-Lys-S-bzl-D-Cys	DCCI	MeCl	87		174–176	+9	DMF	746
N^α,N^ϵ-Di-Z-Lys-S-bzl-Cys Hydrazide Monohydrate				Me	144–147			440a
N^α,N^ϵ-Di-Z-Lys-S-bzl-Cys-OMe	DCCI	Acn	65	Me	115–116	−16	DMF	746
Lys-S-bzl-Cys Dihydrobromide					225–226	−37	Me	746
N^ϵ-Ac-Z-Lys-Gly-OBzl	MCA	Chf	80	Chf-Eth	91.5–93	−23	Me	746
N^ϵ-Ac-Lys-Gly				Aq-Alc	92–93			32
Di-Z-Lys-Gly-OEt				EtAc-Pe	121–123			32
N^ϵ-Boc-Z-Lys-Gly Amide				EtAc-Pe	67–68			712
N^ϵ-Boc-Z-Lys-Gly-OBu^t	A	DMF	83		118	−3	Me	249
N^ϵ-Boc-Lys-Gly Amide	OTCP		79		oil	−13	Me	259
Lys-Gly						+12	Me	686
N^ϵ-Tos-Z-D-Lys-Gly Amide	ONp	EtAc	92	Eth-Pe		−14	Me	769

Table 2 Dipeptides (continued)

Compound	Method	Solvent	% Yield	Solvent Crystallization	M.P. (°C)	$[\alpha]_D$	Solvent Rotation	Ref.
N^{ϵ}-Tos-Z-D-Lys-Gly-OEt	MA				153–154	+4.9	Chf	769
N^{ϵ}-Tos-Z-Lys-Gly-OEt	DMchf	Chf	73	Alc-Aq	154–156	−4.7	Chf	62
N^{ϵ}-Tos-Z-Lys-Gly-OMe Hydrochloride	MCA	EtAc	71–77	EtAc-Pe	155–156	−5.0	Chf	765
	DCCI	EtAc	70	Me-Eth	165			122
N^{ϵ}-Tos-thia-Lys-Gly-OEt	DCCI	DMF	80		103–105	−22	DMF	215
N^{α},N^{ϵ}-Di-tos-Lys-Gly			40	Alc-Aq	100–102	−4	Me	419
N^{ϵ}-Tos-Lys-Gly-OEt Hydrobromide				Alc-Eth	180–181	+17	Aq	765
N^{ϵ}-Tos-Lys-Gly-OMe Hydrobromide					175–176	−9.0	Ac	122
N^{ϵ}-Tfa-Z-Lys-Gly				EtAc-Pe	96–98	+25	Ac	422
N^{ϵ}-Tfa-Lys-Gly				Aq-Alc	246–248 (dec)			422
N^{ϵ}-Tfa-Lys-Gly-OBu^{t}	ONp	Py	90	Alc-Eth	71–76	+16	Ac	422
N^{ϵ}-Boc-Z-Lys-Ile Hydrazide	DCCI	Acn		Me	161–162	−32	Ac	583
N^{ϵ}-Boc-Z-Lys-Ile-OMe				EtAc-Pe	40–42	−15	Me	583
N^{ϵ}-Boc-Z-Lys-N^{ϵ}-boc-Lys-OMe	DCCI	Acn		Eth	78–84	−5.3	An	576
N^{ϵ}-Boc-Lys-N^{ϵ}-boc-Lys-OMe					oil			576
N^{ϵ}-Boc-Pz-Lys-N^{ϵ}-boc-Lys-OMe				Eth	124–127	−2.0	Me	576
N^{ϵ}-Boc-N^{α}-trt-Lys-N^{ϵ}-boc-Lys					75–100	+1.0	Me	576
N^{ϵ}-Boc-N^{α}-trt-Lys-N^{ϵ}-boc-Lys-OMe				Eth-Pe	134–137	+3.7	Me	576
N^{ϵ}-For-Z-Lys-N^{ϵ}-for-Lys				Me	204–206			239
N^{ϵ}-For-Z-Lys-N^{ϵ}-for-Lys Amide	MCA	Di	44	Alc-Eth	117–118			239
N^{ϵ}-For-Z-Lys-N^{ϵ}-for-Lys-OMe	ONp	DMF	77		112–114			239
N^{ϵ}-Tos-Z-Lys-N^{ϵ}-tos-Lys-OBzl					145–146	−7.5	DMF	373
N^{ϵ}-Tos-Z-Lys-N^{ϵ}-tos-Lys Hydrazide					113–115	−7.2	Ac	373
Di-Z-Lys-D-Met	WRK	Acn	85	EtAc-He	105–106			440a
N^{ϵ}-Z-N^{α}-boc-Lys-Phe-OMe					118–120	+2	DMF	356a
Di-Z-DL-Lys-Phe	DCCI	DMF			118–120	+6	Me	440a
Di-Z-DL-Lys-D-Phe	DCCI	DMF			118–121	+1	DMF	440a

Compound	Method	Solvent	Yield (%)	Recrystn. solvent	M.p. (°C)	[α]	Solvent	Ref.
Bis-Z-Lys-Phe				Me	187–188	−4.9	Ac	355
N^ε-Boc-Z-Lys-Phe Hydrazide	MCA			EtAc-Pe	130–131			400
N^ε-Tos-Z-Lys-Phe-OBzl				Me-Eth	152–153			122
N^ε-Tos-Z-Lys-Phe-OBzl Hydrobromide					oil			122
Bis-Z-Lys-Pro	Ac			Eth	128–129			333
Di-Z-Lys-Pro-OBzl	MCA	Py	90		oil			717
Bis-Z-Lys-Pro DCHA Salt				Alc-Eth	144	−4.8	Ac	333
Bis-Z-Lys-Pro-OMe			83	EtAc-Pe	oil	+3.6	DMF	333
Lys-Pro Hydrochloride								717
Di-Z-Lys-Ser-OBzl					123–125			140
N^ε-Tos-Z-Lys-OBu^t-Thr-OBu^t					115–120	−4	DMF	408
Di-Z-allo(OH)-Lys-OBzl-Tyr-OBzl					150–152	+3.0		538
Di-Z-allo(OH)-Lys-Tyr-OBzl					186–187	−2.3	DMF	538
Di-Z-DL-Lys-D-Val	DCCI	DMF		Pe	101–103	−17	Ac	440a
N^ε-Tos-Z-Lys-Val				Alc-Eth	oil	−15	Alc	560
N^ε-Tos-Z-Lys-Val Hydrazide								560
N^ε-Tos-Z-Lys-Val-OMe								560
N^ε-Tos-Z-Lys-Val-OMe Hydrochloride	MCA	THF-DMF	60	An-Eth				560
Methionine								
Z-Met-D-Ala	MCA	MeCl	84		169–170	−3	DMF	440a
Z-D-Met-D-Ala	MCA	MeCl			161–163	+5	DMF	440a
Boc-Met-Ala-OMe	ONp	DMF		He	86–88			356a
Z-Met-N^G-nitro-Arg	MCA	MeCl			140–143	−3	DMF	440a
Z-Met-D-Asp	MCA	Aq-Di	41		125–130	−21	Me	440a
Z-Met-Gln				Me	159–161	−13	Alc	241
Z-Met-Gln Hydrazide				Me	220–223 (dec)			241
Z-Met-Gln-OMe				Me-Pe	193–194	−6.6	Me	241
Met-Gln				Alc	232–233	+17	NH_4OH	241
Z-Met-Glu	MCA	THF		EtAc-Pe	139–141			358
Ac-DL-Met-Gly-OEt	MCA	THF		EtAc-Eth	114			358

Table 2 Dipeptides (continued)

Compound	Method	Solvent	% Yield	Solvent Crystallization	M.P. (°C)	$[\alpha]_D$	Solvent Rotation	Ref.
Bz-DL-Met-Gly	DCCI	MeCl		EtAc-Pe	177–179			358
Bz-DL-Met-Gly-OEt				Alc	118–120	−20	DMF	358
Z-Met-Gly-OEt				Chf	98			22
N-Tos-DL-Met-Gly				Aq-Alc	66–67			419
Z-D-Met-D-Leu	MCA	MeCl		EtAc-Pe	80–83	+12	DMF	440a
Boc-Met-N$^\varepsilon$-Lys-OMe	A		71	EtAc-Pe	93–94	−17	Me	557
Boc-Met-N$^\varepsilon$-boc-Lys Hydrazide					123–124	−21	DMF	557
Z-D-Met-D-Met	MCA	MeCl			118–120	+9	DMF	440a
Z-Met-D-Met	MCA	MeCl			106–108	+4	DMF	440a
Z-Met-Met-OMe								615
Met-Met				Alc	227	+27	Aq	99
N-Trt-Met-Met-OMe				Me	112–113			99
Z-D-Met-Phe	MCA	MeCl			97–100	−5	DMF	440a
Z-D-Met-D-Phe	MCA	MeCl			125–127	+2	Me	440a
Z-Met-D-Phe	MCA	MeCl			123–126	−21	Me	440a
Z-Met-D-Ser	MCA	MeCl			162–163			440a
Z-Met-Tyr	MCA	THF		Aq	141.5–143.5			358
Z-D-Met-DL-Tyr	MCA	MeCl			oil	+12	Me	440a
Met-Tyr				Aq-Alc	259–265 (dec)			218
Z-Met-D-Val	MCA	MeCl			125–127	−14	DMF	440a
Ornithine								
N$^\delta$-Pht-Z-Orn-Ala	MCA			EtAc-Cy	183–183.5	+4.4	DMF	630
N$^\delta$-Pht-Z-Orn-Ala-2,4,6-tri-me-OBzl	MCA	DMF	82	Ac-Alc	194–195.5	−6.0	DMF	630
N$^\delta$-Pht-Orn-Ala	MA		21	Aq-Alc	242–243	+6.3	1N HCl	630
N$^\delta$-Z-N$^\alpha$-Z(OMe)-Orn-Gly-OBzl	DCCI		50	EtAc-Eth	141–143			337

Compound	Method	Solvent	Yield	Recryst.	M.p.	[α]	Solvent	Ref.
N^δ-Pht-Z-Orn-Gly Amide	ONp		65		143-144	-3.0	DMF	63
N^δ-Tos-Z-Orn-Gly-OEt	ONp	Acn	87	i-Pr	190-193.5	+7	DMF-Ac	256
N^δ-Z-boc-D-Orn-Pro-OEt	DCCI	THF	84		135-136			301
	DCCI	Chf	89		oil			
N^δ-Z-D-Orn-Pro-OEt Hydrochloride	ONp		53		oil			301
Phenylalanine								
Z-aminoisobutyryl-Phe-Ala-OMe					151.5-152	-43	Chf	429
Z-aminoisobutyryl-Phe-D-Ala-OMe				Tol	45.5-47.5	-57	Chf	429
Z-aminoisobutyryl-DL-Phe-DL-Ala-OMe	A		35	EtAc-Pe	187-189	-50	Chf	173
Z-Phe-Ala					165			173
Z-Phe-D-Ala	MCA	MeCl			116-117	-1	Me	169
Z-DL-Phe-DL-Ala-OEt	C		50	Alc-Aq	100-101.5			440a
Z-Phe-Ala Hydrazide					207-208	-7.2	DMF	388
Z-Phe-Ala-OMe	Ac	Py	81	Me-Aq	130-131	-24	Me	553
N-For-DL-p-tri-me-silyl-Phe-DL-Ala-OEt	DCCI	Acn	47	EtAc-Pe	152			169
Phe-Ala-OMe Hydrochloride					237			146
DL-p-Tri-me-silyl-Phe-DL-Ala				Ac	120-124			169
Aoc-Phe-N^G-nitro-Arg-OBzl				EtAc-Pe	115-120	-15	Alc	146
Bz-Phe-N^G-nitro-Arg					97-104	+3	DMF	518
Z-p-chloro-D-Phe-N^G-nitro-Arg	ONp	DMF	88		125-128	-3	Me	440a
Z-p-fluoro-Phe-N^G-Arg-OMe					90-95	+2	DMF	440a
Z-p-fluoro-D-Phe-N^G-Arg-OMe	ONp	DMF	83		94-97			438
Z-D-Phe-N^G-Arg-OMe	MCA	Di	84		90-92			438
Z-Phe-N^G-Arg-OMe	MCA	MeCl	87	EtAc-Pe	176-180	-3.0	Py	438
Z-D-Phe-N^G-nitro-D-Arg	ONp	Chf Py		Alc	105-110	+3	Me	438
Z-Phe-N^G-nitro-D-Arg					173-176			744
Z-Phe-N^G-nitro-Arg								440a
								456

Table 2 Dipeptides (continued)

Compound	Method	Solvent	% Yield	Solvent Crystallization	M.P. (°C)	$[\alpha]_D$	Solvent Rotation	Ref.
Z-Phe-N^G-nitro-Arg-OMe					160–161	−15	Me	22
				Me	150–152			456
N-(N$^\alpha$-Z-Phe-N^G-nitro-Arg)-5-OMe-tryptamine	MCA	THF	86	EtAc-Eth	125	+7.3	Me	740
Z-Phe-N^G-nitro-Arg-ONBzl	MCA	THF	72	EtAc-Eth	174			70
	ONp	DMF	84	EtAc	172–173	−44	Me	652
Boc-Phe-N^G-nitro-Arg				Pe	169	−11	Me	137
Mz-Phe-Arg-OMe Hydrochloride	MCA	THF			115–120	−8	DMF	440a
Mz-Phe-Arg-OMe Hydrochloride Sulfate				Alc	145–146			297
Phe-^{14}C-Arg								297
Phe-Arg								218
N-(Phe-Arg)-5-OMe-tryptamine Diacetate								218
Phe-N^G-nitro-Arg-OMe					175	+3.9	Aq	740
Phe-N^G-nitro-Arg-OMe Dihydrobromide								297
Phe-N^G-nitro-Arg-ONBzl Hydrobromide								297
Pht-Phe-N^G-nitro-Arg	MCA	MeCl			188–190	−111	DMF	70
Tos-Phe-N^G-nitro-Arg	MCA	MeCl			120–125	+5	DMF	440a
Trt-Phe-N^G-nitro-Arg	MCA	MeCl			135–140	+1	DMF	440a
Z-D-Phe-Asp					60–65	+5	DMF	440a
Z-Phe-D-Asp					60–68	−7	DMF	440a
Z-D-Phe-D-Asp					64–72	+13	DMF	440a
Z-Phe-β-OMe-Asp					132–133.5	−17	Acn	440a
Z-Phe-β-OMe-L+D L-Asp Azlactone					97.5–100	−53	Acn	119
Z-Phe-Cit	ONp	THF	55	EtAc-Alc	155–157			119
				Alc	170–173			456
Z-Phe-Cit-OMe					170–171			456
N-Bz-S-(N-Z-Phe)-Cys-OMe	MCA	Chf	64	Me	132.5–133	−91	Me	123
Z-D-Phe-S-allyl-Cys	MCA	MeCl		Me	75–80	+2	DMF	224
								440a
Z-Phe-S-bz-Cys-OMe	DCCI	Chf			139–140	38	Me	224

Compound	Method	Solvent	Yield (%)	Recryst. solvent	M.p.	[α]	Solvent	Ref.
Z-Phe-S-et-Cys	MCA	MeCl			73–78	−20	DMF	440a
Z-Phe-S-me-Cys	MCA	MeCl			111–116	−19	DMF	440a
N-Pht-Phe-S-bzl-Cys-OEt				Alc-Aq	111.5–112.5	−141	Alc	42
Z-Phe-N$^\gamma$-xanthyl-Gln			80	Me-Aq	188–189.5 (dec)			603
Z-Phe-N$^\gamma$-xanthyl-Gln-OMe	ONp	Chf			215–216			603
Z-D-Phe-Glu	MCA	MeCl			147–155	+2	DMF	440a
Z-Phe-D-Glu	MCA	MeCl			163–168	−11	DMF	440a
Z-D-Phe-D-Glu	MCA	MeCl			168–171	+14	DMF	440a
Phe-Glu					209–210	+51	Aq	603
Aza-Phe-Gly-OEt					79–80			154
Bz-Phe-Gly-OMe					120–121			680
Z-aminoisobutyryl-DL-Phe-Gly-OEt	DCCI	Acn	84	EtAc	161.5–162.5			429
Z-aminoisobutyryl-Phe-Gly-OEt				Eth	93.5–95 / 161.5–162.5	−47	Chf	429 / 173
Z-aminoisobutyryl-DL-Phe-DL-phenyl-Gly-OMe				Eth	208–210	−39	Chf	173
Z-aminoisobutyryl-Phe-DL-phenyl-Gly-OMe				EtAc	98.5–99.5	−102	Chf	173
Z-aminoisobutyryl-Phe-D-phenyl-Gly-OMe				EtAc	128–130	−20	EtAc	429
Z-Phe-aza-Gly-ONp	ONp				133–134			157
Z-Phe-Gly	SPh	Ac	60		149–150	−10	Ac	584
	MCA	MeCl	85		149–151			700
	TOSC	THF	52	Alc-Eth				440a
Z-D-Phe-Gly	DCCI		80	Alc	130–131	+21	DMF	667
Z-Phe-Gly-OBzl					130			99
N-[N'-(5,5-Di-me-2-cyclohexen-1-on-3-yl)-Phe-Gly-OBzl	A			Me-Eth	164			197
Z-DL-Phe-Gly 2-Chloroethylamide					150–151 / 109.5–110			401 / 23
Z-Phe-Gly-OEt	OPAP		77	EtAc-Cy	90.5–94	−14	Alc	623

Table 2 Dipeptides (continued)

Compound	Method	Solvent	% Yield	Solvent Crystallization	M.P.(°C)	$[\alpha]_D$	Solvent Rotation	Ref.
Z-Phe-Gly-OEt	ONp	DMF			110-112	-24	DMF	168
	CBHA	DMF		EtAc-Pe	108-110			615
				EtAc-Pe	109.5-110			178
	C	THF	70	EtAc-Pe	109-110	-17	Alc	712
				EtAc-Pe	108-110	-14		388
	2,4,6-TBP	Chf		EtAc-Pe	110			584
								586
Z-Phe-Gly-OEt	ONp	Chf	78	EtAc-Pe	106-109	-17	Alc	354
	PHA	Acn	60	EtAc-Pe	107-109	+20	Me	491
Z-D-Phe-Gly-OEt	DCCI	Chf	83		109-110			18
Z-D-Phe-Gly-OMe					120-121			681
Z-Phe-Gly-ONp				An	175-179	-97	DMF	649
Z-Phe-Gly-SPh				EtAc-Pe	133-135	-14	Alc	700
Z-Phe-phenyl-Gly-OMe				Chf	166-167.5	+31	Di	429
Z-Phe-DL-phenyl-Gly-OMe	ONp	DMF		Di	162-165	+18	Di	429
Z-Phe-D-phenyl-Gly-OMe	ONp	DMF			210-212	-67	Di	429
Boc-Phe-Gly Hydrazide				EtAc	213-214	-75	Di	555
N-For-DL-p-tri-me-silyl-Phe-Gly-OEt			50	EtAc-Pe	129-130	+6.5	Me	146
For-Phe-Gly					125	+14	0.5N NaOH	389
For-Phe-Gly-OEt				Ac	204-205			389
p-Tri-me-silyl-DL-Phe-Gly				Alc	130-131	+11	Alc	146
N-[p-Nitro-benzylidene]-aza-Phe-Gly-OEt				Alc	232			154
N-[Bis(p-nitro-bzl)-phosphoryl]-Phe-Gly-OBzl	DCCI	Chf	83	EtAc-Pe	135	-8	Chf	99
N-Nps-Phe-Gly				Alc	188-190	+32	DMF	774
N-Nps-Phe-Gly-OEt	DCCI		70	EtAc-Pe	121	+27	DMF	774

144

Compound	Method	Solvent	Yield (%)	Recryst. solvent	M.p.	[α]	Solvent	Ref.
Nps-Phe-Gly-ONp	MCA	Chf	70	EtAc-Cy	121–122	−12	DMF	631
Phe-Gly	MCA		44	Ac-Aq-An	140–141	+95	Aq	667
Phe-Gly-OBu^t Oxalate Salt					249–250 (dec)	+98	Aq	774
DL-Phe-Gly 2-Chloroethylamide				Alc	258 (dec)	+103	Ac	700
Phe-Gly-OEt Hydrobromide				An	257–259 (dec)	+71	1N HCl	389
D-Phe-Gly-OEt Hydrochloride				Me-Eth	164 (dec)	+95	Aq	99
Phe-Gly-OMe					186–188	+8.0	DMF	229
D-Phe-Gly-OMe				Acn	134–137			401
N-Pht-Phe-Gly-OBu^t	DCCI	MeCl	84	An-He	167–168.5	−101	Chf	354
N-Pht-Phe-Gly-OEt	MCA	MeCl	66	Alc	160–161			18
N-Trt-Phe-Gly-OEt		MeCl		Alc	137–138			680
N-Trt-sulfenyl-Phe-Gly-OEt	MCA	MeCl		Alc	113–114	−54	DMF	681
Z-Phe-His				Me-Aq	183–185 / 201 (dec)			229, 42, 99, 774
Z-Phe-D-His	MCA	MeCl			171–172	−24	DMF	386
Z-D-Phe-His	MCA	MeCl			165–168	+38	Me	120
Z-D-Phe-D-His	MCA	MeCl			210–211	+4	DMF	440a
Z-Phe-His-OMe	MCA, DCCI	DMF	50		119			440a, 120
Phe-His	ONp	DMF	92	MeCl-Cte	84–86 / 121–124 / 170–175	−19	DMF	386, 123
Z-D-Phe-Ile	MCA	MeCl			110–112	+22	DMF	440a
Z-Phe-D-Ile	MCA	MeCl			107–109	−23	DMF	440a
Z-D-Phe-D-Ile	MCA	MeCl			150–152	−4	DMF	440a

Table 2 Dipeptides (continued)

Compound	Method	Solvent	% Yield	Solvent Crystallization	M.P. (°C)	[α]_D	Solvent Rotation	Ref.
Z-Phe-Ile-OMe	DCCI	THF		EtAc-Pe	106-107	-10	Alc	89
	ONp	Chf	76		106			525
β-S-Bzl-propionyl-Phe-Ile Hydrazide				DMF-Me	208-210	-19	DMF	253
β-S-Bzl-propionyl-Phe-Ile-OMe				Eth-Pe	102	-13	DMF	253
Phe-Ile-OMe					74-76	+6.2	Alc	89
Z-Phe-Leu				Aq-Alc	141-142	-20	Me	487
				EtAc	139.5-140.5			712
Z-D-Phe-Leu	MCA	MeCl		Aq-Alc	126-127	-4.5	Me	487
Z-Phe-D-Leu					113-115	+2	Me	440a
Z-Phe-Leu 2-Chloroethylamide					148-150			401
Z-Phe-Leu-OEt	DCCI	Di	63	EtAc-Pe	114-115			87
Z-Phe-Leu Hydrazide				Me	194-195	-22	Me	87
Z-D-Phe-Leu Hydrazide				Me	183-184.5	-49	Me	87
Z-Phe-Leu-OMe	DCCI	Me-Di	68	EtAc-Pe	109-109.5			712
	DCCI	EtAc	76	EtAc-Pe	110-111	-25	Me	487
Z-D-Phe-Leu-OMe	DCCI	EtAc	45.5	Me-Pe	125-126	-19	Me	487
	MCA	Cte	58	Alc	124-126			
N-[Bis-(p-nitro-bzl)-phosphoryl]-Phe-Leu-OBzl					108			
Phe-Leu				Alc	258-260	+4.8	N/3 HCl	99
					258-260	+6.5	0.1N HCl	99
D-Phe-Leu				Aq-i-Pr	249-251	-98	1N HCl	487
					160	-0.5	DMF	218
Phe-Leu-OBzl Hydrochloride	DCCI		75		159-160			487
	MCA		75		160			774

146

Compound	Method	Solvent	Yield (%)	Recrystn. solvent	M.p. (°C)	[α]	Rotn. solvent	Ref.
Phe-Leu 2-Chloroethylamide	WRK			Aq-Ac	201–203			401
D-Phe-Leu Diketopiperazine				An-Pe	247–249			57
Phe-Leu-OEt Hydrobromide				Me-EtAc	158–160			87
Phe-Leu Hydrazide Dihydrobromide				Me-EtAc	247–248			87
D-Phe-Leu Hydrazide Dihydrobromide				An-Pe	245–247			87
D-Phe-Leu Hydrobromide				An-Pe	197–198			487
Phe-Leu Hydrobromide					106–108 (dec)		1N HCl	487
D-Phe-Leu-OMe				Me-Pe	101–103			487
D-Phe-Leu-OMe Hydrobromide				An-Eth-Pe	171–173	−89	Me	487
Z-Phe-Nα-Z-Lys	MCA	Chf		Alc	166–168			53
Z-Phe-Nα-Z-Lys-OBzl			60		153–155			53
Z-Phe-Lys	MCA	Chf	70	Alc	198–200			53
Nε-Z-Phe-Lys-OMe Hydrochloride	DCCI		74.5	Me-Acn	189–190			53
Z-Phe-Nε-trt-Lys					131–133	−10	Me	722
Boc-Phe-Nε-Z-Lys-OBzl					273–275			53
Phe-Lys				Alc	146–147.5	−6.2	Me	722
Phe-Nε-Lys-OBzl					216–218			53
Nε-Phe-Lys Hydrochloride	MCA	MeCl			118.5–119.5	+8	Me	440a
Z-Phe-D-Met	DCCI	DMF			140–143	−8	DMF	440a
Z-Phe-D-Met Sulfoxide	DCCI	DMF			105–115	+10	DMF	440a
Z-D-Phe-D-Met Sulfoxide	DCCI	DMF			123–125	+10	DMF	440a
Z-D-Phe-Met Sulfoxide	A			Tol	81–83	−87	Chf	429
Z-aminoisobutyryl-Phe-D-Phe-OMe	A				137–138	−13	Chf	429
Z-aminoisobutyryl-Phe-Phe-OMe	MCA	THF			167–169			173
Z-aminoisobutyryl-D L-Phe-DL-Phe-OMe			55	Alc-Eth-Pe	126–128			451
Z(OMe)-Phe-D-Phe-OEt			79		209–211			23
Z-Phe-DL-Phe	DCCI				93–94			262
Z-Phe-Phe-OBuᵗ	DCCI			EtAc	219–221			284
Z-DL-α-Phe-DL-α-Phe DCHA Salt					138–139			262
Z-Phe-Phe-OEt								

Table 2 Dipeptides (continued)

Compound	Method	Solvent	% Yield	Solvent Crystallization	M.P. (°C)	[α]$_D$	Solvent Rotation	Ref.
Z-Phe-Phe-OMe	OCP	DMF			148–149	−17	DMF	255
β-S-Bzl-propionyl-Phe-Phe Hydrazide	DCCI		72		229	−26	0.3N HCl-Ac	255
β-S-propionyl-Phe-Phe-OMe				DMF-Me	134–135	−21	DMF	255
For-Phe-Phe-OBu^t				Be-Pe				659
OMe-Z-Phe-D-Phe Hydrazide				DMF-Eth-Pe	194–195	−3.4	DMF	451
Phe-Phe-OBu^t Acetate					101–103			262
Phe-Phe-OEt Hydrobromide					176–178			262
Tos-Phe-Phe				EtAc-Pe	197	+22	DMF	520
Tos-Phe-Phe-O-i-Pr	Ac	THF	74	EtAc-Pe	125.5–126.5	+15	DMF	520
Tfa-DL-Phe-DL-Phe				Be	142–145			284
Tfa-DL-α-Phe-DL-α-Phe-OMe	O	Acn	96.7		160–162.5			284
Z-Phe-Pro	ONp	DMF	65.6	EtAc-Pe	105–106.5	−64	Py	519
	ONp	Py	81	EtAc-He	109–111			354
Z-D-Phe-Pro	MCA	MeCl			55–61	−35	DMF	440a
Z-D-Phe-DL-Pro	MCA	MeCl			55–62	−10	DMF	440a
Z-D-Phe-Pro-OEt	MCA	Chf	86		oil			451
Z-Phe-Pro-OMe	Ac	Py	91.5		oil			717
D-Phe-Pro-OEt Hydrochloride					oil			451
Z-D-Phe-Sar-OEt	DCCI	Chf	86		oil			16
D-Phe-Sar-OEt Hydrochloride								16
Aoc-Phe-Ser Hydrazide				Alc	175–177	−4.0	DMF	518
Aoc-Phe-Ser-OMe				EtAc-Pe	60–90	−3.2	DMF	518
Z-Phe-Ser	ONp	Py	65	EtAc-Eth	155–156			65
Z-Phe-D-Ser	MCA	MeCl			134–136	−28	DMF	440a
Z-Phe-Ser Hydrazide				DMF	187–188			439
				Me	193			70

Compound	Method	Solvent	Yield (%)	Recryst. solvent	M.p. (°C)	[α]	(solv.)	Ref.
Z-D-Phe-D-Ser Hydrazide	DCCI	Acn	91	Pe	187–188	−6.4	DMF	439
Z-Phe-Ser-OMe	MCA	MeCl	95	EtAc-Pe	188–190	+8	Ac	681
					125			70
Z-D-Phe-D-Ser-OMe	DCCI	MeCl		EtAc-Pe	122–123	−5.7	DMF	439
Phe-Ser-OMe Hydrochloride					126–127			681
Z-Phe-Thr-OMe	MCA	MeCl		EtAc-Pe	184–185			683
Z-D-Phe-Trp	MCA	MeCl			120–122	+6	Ac	98
Z-Phe-D-Trp	MCA	MeCl			172–174	−1	Me	440a
Z-Phe-Trp	DCCI	MeCl			127–128	−3	DMF	440a
Z-Phe-Trp-OBzl	DCCI	MeCl		EtAc-Eth	137–142	−10	Me	440a
Z-Phe-Trp-OEt			70		135	−4	Me	707
Phe-Trp					123–125			262
Z(NO$_2$)-Phe-Tyr-OMe	DCCI	Acn	82	Me-Alc	161–163			707
Z-Phe-OBu^t-Tyr-OBu^t	TEP	Glyme	47	Alc	70–70.5			600
Z-Phe-OBu^t-Tyr-OMe				Eth-Pe	103–105	−14	Me	81
Z-Phe-OEt-carbonyl-Tyr-OMe	MCA	THF	69	EtAc-Pe, An-Aq	170.5–171.5	−16	Me-DMF	403
Z-D-Phe-Tyr	MCA	MeCl			109–112	+8	DMF	160
Z-Phe-Tyr					181.5–183			440a
Z-Phe-Tyr-OEt	ONp	DMF	86.5	Eth-Be	156–158			160
	NHS	DMF	85	Alc-Aq	156–158			350
	DCCI				159–160			7
Phe-OBu^t-Tyr Diketopiperazine				DMSO	269–271	−9.1	Alc	262
Phe-Tyr Diketopiperazine					283–285			403
Phe-Tyr-OEt Hydrobromide					162–164	−167	Fm	403
Phe-Tyr-OMe Hydrobromide					168–169			262
					201–203			350
Z-Phe-D-Val	DCCI	DMF		Me-Eth	146–148	−15	DMF	600, 440a
Z-D-Phe-Val	DCCI	DMF		Me-Eth	147–149	+22	DMF	440a
Z-Phe-Val-OBu^t	SmA	Acn	83		104–106	−19	Me	727
Z-Phe-Val Boc-hydrazide	NHS	EtAc				−23		543

Table 2 Dipeptides (continued)

Compound	Method	Solvent	% Yield	Solvent Crystallization	M.P.(°C)	$[\alpha]_D$	Solvent Rotation	Ref.
Z-Phe-Val Hydrazide				Me	214-216			543
Boc-Phe-Val Hydrazide					167			715
Boc-Phe-Val-OMe					120-122	-11	DMF	168
Coc-Phe-Val Boc-hydrazide								543
Phe-Val								543
Phe-Val-OBu^t				Pe	66-67	-29	Me	727
Phe-Val Hydrazide Hydrochloride					221	-18	Aq	715
Phe-Val-OMe								168
Phe-Val-OMe Hydrochloride								179
N-Pht-Phe-Val Boc-hydrazide	DCCI	Acn	87	Alc-Dipr Eth	223	-114	Me	719
N-Pht-Phe-Val Hydrazide Trifluoroacetate				EtAc-Alc	146	-84	Me	719
Proline								
Z-Pro-Ala					161-162	-57	Me	565
					161-162	-59	Alc	690
Z-Pro-D-Ala	ONp	DMF			oil	-33	Me	440a
Z-Pro-Ala Boc-hydrazide					93-95	-93	Me	565
Z-Pro-Ala Hydrazide					144-145	-37	DMF	553
Z-Pro-Ala-OMe					79-80	-74	Alc	553
Z-Pro-Ala-ONBzl	MCA	THF	92	EtAc-Pe	134-135	-83	Me	468
Pro-Ala Boc-hydrazide					96-98	-86	Me	565
Pro-Ala-ONBzl Hydrobromide				Alc-Pe	150-151	-47	Me	468
Z-Pro-N^G-nitro-Arg	MCA	Di	70	An-Aq	197-198			643
Z-Pro-N^G-nitro-Arg-OMe	MCA	MeCl		Me-Eth	130-132			643
Z-DL-Pro-D-Asp	MCA	MeCl			65-70	-0.4	Me	440a
Z-Pro-D-Asp	ONp	Py-Aq	82		60-65	-46	Me	440a
Z-Pro-Gly	NHS	Alc-Aq	72	EtAc-Pe	122-123			456
					119-121			584
					124-125			7

150

Compound	NHP	Aq-DME	Solvent	M.p.	[α]	Solvent	Ref.
Z-Pro-Gly Amide	DCCI	28	Aq-DME	106–108	–52	Me	652
	ONp	68.5	Me-THF	oil	–30	DMF	605
Z-Pro-Gly-di-OBzl	DCCI		THF · Eth	120	–49		193
Z-Pro-Gly Boc-hydrazide	MCA	77	DMF · EtAc-Pe	89–90			615
Z-Pro-Gly-ONBzl	MCA	46	Chf · Alc-Ac	119	–56	Ac	70
Z-Pro-Gly-ONp	ONp	92		97			652
Z-Pro-Nγ-pht-Dbu-Gly Amide	MCA	79	Chf · Alc	143.5–145	–25	DMF	456
Pro-Gly			Eth-Pe	196–197			771
				230–232			178
			Alc-Aq	69	–23	Aq	699
Pro-Gly Boc-hydrazide			EtAc-MeCl-Pe	194–201			35
Pro-Nγ-tos-Dbu-Gly Amide	SPh	32	Ac · Aq-Me	113–115	–104	Alc	771
Pro-Nγ-tos-Dbu-Gly Amide Picrate	ONp	76	MeCl · Chf-He	191–192	–22	Aq	771
Tfa-Pro-Gly	MCA		Aq-THF · Chf-Cte	133–135	–66	Chf	699
Pro-His	MCA		THF · i-Pr-Aq	138.5–139.5			406
Z-Pro-D-Leu	MCA		EtAc	118.5–119.5	–62	Me	546
Z-Pro-Leu	MCA	94	THF · Hep-i-Pr	190–191	–37	Me	83
	TEP		DiP · Hep	89–90	–76	Me	6
Z-Pro-Leu Amide	ONp	77	MeCl · Aq	91.5–92			276
Z-Pro-Leu-OBu^t		97	THF-Aq	149–150			6
Z-Pro-Leu Hydrazide	MCA	96	THF · He-Eth	128–129			444
Z-Pro-Leu Me-amide		94	EtAc-He	131–132	–73	Alc	72
Z-Pro-Leu-OMe	ONp	84.5	Chf · NMe	74–75			444
	ONp		EtAc · Alc-Aq	76.5–78	–42	DMF	83
Z-Pro-Leu Semicarbazide				212–213			444
Boc-Pro-Leu-OBu^t	TEP	91	DME · Alc-Aq	93–94 / 107–108	+53	DMF	6
Pz-Pro-Leu-OMe	MA	65.1	THF · EtAc-Pe	146–147	–78	Me	721

Table 2 Dipeptides (continued)

Compound	Method	Solvent	% Yield	Solvent Crystallization	M.P.(°C)	$[\alpha]_D$	Solvent Rotation	Ref.
Pro-Leu				Aq-DME	249.5–250.5	−79	Aq	6
Pro-Leu Semicarbazide Hydrobromide								
Z-Pro-N^ϵ-Z(NO_2)-Lys	ONp	DMF	77		139–141			444
Z-Pro-N^ϵ-tos-Lys-OBu^t	MCA	Chf	96		101–104	−41	DMF	600
Z-Pro-N^ϵ-tos-Lys N-(β-tos-amino)et Amide	ONp	DMF	82		oil			542
					oil			767
Z-Pro-N^ϵ-tos-thia-Lys Hydrazide				Me	163–164	−50	DMF	215
Z-Pro-N^ϵ-tos-thia-Lys-OMe	DCCI	EtAc	85	EtAc-Pe	104–106	−38	DMF	215
Pro-N^ϵ-Z(NO_2)-Lys				Aq	213–214			600
Pro-N^ϵ-Z(NO_2)-Lys-ONp Benzenesulfonate				Alc-Eth	126–127			600
Pro-N^ϵ-tos-Lys N-(β-Tos-amino)et Amide								767
Z-Pro-D-Met	DCCI	DMF			95–97	−25	DMF	440a
Z-Pro-Met	DCCI	DMF			135–137	−30	DMF	440a
Z-D-Pro-D-Met	MCA	MeCl			133–135	+22	DMF	440a
Z-Pro-D-Phe	DCCI	DMF			53–57	−15	DMF	440a
Z-Pro-Phe-OBzl	MA				128–129 (dec)	−12	Py	530
Z-D-Pro-D-Phe-OBu^t	MA				69	−46	Me	684
Z-Pro-Phe-OBu^t					70–71	+34	Chf	550
Z-Pro-Phe-OEt	DCCI	Chf	78	EtAc-Eth-Pe	65–68	−34	Chf	15
	MA	THF	71		65–68	−33	Alc	
Z-Pro-Phe-OMe	DCCI	TEA	70	EtAc-Cy	oil	−28	DMF	22
Z-Pro-Phe-ONBzl	DCCI	Di-THF	90	Alc-Eth	91–92	−53	Chf	406
Z-Pro-Phe-N^γ-tos-Dbu-OMe	CDI	THF	98	i-Pr	162–164	−47	DMF	683
Boc-Pro-Phe-OMe	DCCI		70	i-Pr-EtAc	74–76			466
					91–92			
N-Nps-Pro-Phe-OMe	MA		80		91–92	−7.6	DMF	774

Compound			Yield (%)	Recryst. solvent	m.p. (°C)	[α]	Solvent	Ref.
Pro-Phe				Aq	236–237.5	−41	6N HCl	218
				Aq-Ac	234–236 (dec)	−37	1N HCl	406
Pro-^{14}C-Phe Amide								218
Pro-Phe-OBzl Hydrobromide					120–121	−27	6N HCl	530
D-Pro-D-Phe-OBu^t					61	+25	Me	684
Pro-Phe-OBu^t					65–66	−26	Me	552
					65–66	−23	Me	550
Pro-Phe-OMe	DCCI	MeCl	66	Me-Eth	177–178.5	−41	Aq	466
Pro-Phe-OMe Hydrobromide				EtAc	171–172	−33	Me	405
Pro-Phe-OMe Hydrochloride				An-Eth	159			774
Pro-Phe-ONBzl				i-Pr-Ac-He	74–75			406
Pro-Phe-N$^\gamma$-tos-Dbu-OMe					oil			683
Aoc-Pro-Pro				EtAc-Pe	155–158	−113	Alc	518
Bz-Pro-Pro	DCCI	Acn	53		186–188			680
Z-D-Pro-D-Pro	ONp	THF	80	Alc	191–193	+82		681
Z-Pro-Pro	ONp	Py	70	Me	187–190			354
Z-Pro-Pro-OMe	Ac	Py	82	EtAc-Pe	76–78			717
Boc-Pro-Pro				EtAc	187–187.5			474
Boc-Pro-Pro-OMe	MCA	THF	70		117–120	−32	DMF	474
	DCCI	DMF						
Z-Pro-D-Ser					185–186	−76	Ac	440a
Z-Pro-Ser Hydrazide				Eth-Pe				395
Boc-Pro-Ser-OMe	DCCI	MeCl	79		188–190	+17	Me	525
Z-DL-Pro-D-Trp	MCA	MeCl	70	Alc	183			440a
Z-Pro-Trp	DCCI	MeCl						707
Pro-Trp				Dipr-Eth	108.5–109.5			707
Z-Pro-OBu^t-Tyr-OBu^t	ONp	MeCl	86		122–123	−6.2	Me	81
Z-Pro-Tyr	ONp	MeCl	71	Me-Aq	59–68			268
Z-Pro-Tyr-OBu^t								81
Z-Pro-Tyr Hemihydrate				EtAc-Pe	204–205	−64	Me	741
Z-Pro-Tyr Hydrazide				Me	164–165	−41	Ac	741
								753

Table 2 Dipeptides (continued)

Compound	Method	Solvent	% Yield	Solvent Crystallization	M.P. (°C)	$[\alpha]_D$	Solvent Rotation	Ref.
Z-Pro-Tyr-OMe	MA		76		61-64	-31	Me	753
	DCCI	DMF	93	EtAc-Eth	77-79	-24	Alc	741
	DCCI	MeCl	91	EtAc-Eth	72-74	-20	Alc	268
	MCA	THF	98.7	EtAc-Eth	74-77			606
Boc-Pro-Tyr Hydrazide				Alc-Eth	174-176	-14	DMF	606
Boc-Pro-Tyr-OMe	MCA	THF	90		63-64	-61	Me	741
Pro-Tyr				Alc	213-215	-36	Me	741
Pro-Tyr-OMe Hydrobromide				Me-Eth	158-161	-8.2	Aq	606
Z-DL-Pro-D-Val	MCA	MeCl			oil	-24	Me	440a
Z-Pro-Val				Me-Aq	134-136	+10	Me	560
Z-Pro-Val Amide				Me-Aq	201-203	-57	Me	240
Z-Pro-Val Hydrazide				Alc-Aq	170-171	-80	Ac	560
Boc-Pro-Val Amide	MCA	THF	44.1		84	-40	DMF	571
Pro-Val Amide Acetate				Alc-Eth	137-138			571
					138-140			244
Pro-Val Amide Hydrochloride				Me-Eth	266-268	-57	Aq	240
Pro-Val Amide Trifluoroacetate				Me	163-165			571
Sarcosine								
Z-Sar-β-Ala					121-122			23
Z-Sar-Gly					158-159.5			23
Z-Sar-Gly-OMe	DCCI			EtAc-Eth	123-124			752
Z-Sar-Gly-ONp				EtAc-Eth	86-87			752
Bz-Sar-Phe				Alc	98-100			752
				Aq-Me	193-196	+24	Me	14
Bz-Sar-Phe-OMe				EtAc-Pe	110-112	+11	EtAc	14
Bz-Sar-Phe-ONp				Alc	135-143	-13	Chf	14
N-Z-Sar-Phe				Aq-Alc	112-116.5	+24	Me	14

Compound	Method	Solvent	Yield (%)	Cryst. solvent	m.p. (°C)	[α]	Rot. solvent	Ref.
N-Z-Sar-Phe Ethyl Acetate Solvate				Alc	95	+22	Me	14
Z-Sar-Phe Hydrazide	DCCI	MeCl		Eth-Pe	157–158	+7.1	DMF	752
N-Z-Sar-Phe-OMe			95	Eth-Pe	73–76.5	+24	EtAc	14
Z-Sar-Phe-OMe				Alc	71–72	+3.1	Me	752
N-Z-Sar-Phe-ONp					136–138 / 118–121	−8.3	Chf	14
N-Z-Sar-N-me-Val-OBu^t	DCCI		96		oil	−83	Me	410

Serine

Compound	Method	Solvent	Yield (%)	Cryst. solvent	m.p. (°C)	[α]	Rot. solvent	Ref.
Z-D-Ser-D-Ala	MCA	MeCl		EtAc-Eth	157–158	+13	Me	440a
N-Z-Ser-Ala-OBzl					76.5	−22	Ac	140
Z-DL-Ser-DL-Ala-OEt	DCCI	Acn						22
Ser-Ala				Aq-An	223–225 (dec)	−31	1N HCl	296
Ser-Ala-OBzl	DCCI	DMF	43	EtAc	76–78	−14	Ac	140
N-Z-Ser-N^G-nitro-Arg-OBzl				EtAc-Eth	106–108	−12	DMF	135
N-Pht-OBu^t-Ser-N^G-nitro-Arg Z-hydrazide	MCA	THF-DMF	77	Aq-Alc	105–108	−13	DMF	727
Ser-Arg Acetate				Me	145–147	−22	Me	135
OAc-Z-Ser-γ-OMe-Glu-ONp	MCA	DMF	56		170–171	+7.6	Aq	620
OAc-Ser-γ-OMe-Glu-ONp Toluenesulfonate					308–312 (dec)	−37	DMF	620
Ser-Glu-di-OBzl				Me-EtAc	191–192.5	−19	DMF	140
N-Tos-Ser-Glu	MCA			Aq	176 / 197–198	+8 / +23	Alc / Di	419
OBzl-N-boc-Ser-Gly-ONp	MCA		74	EtAc-Cy	85.5–86	−6.0	DMF	619
OBzl-N-for-Ser-Gly-OBzl	DCCI		81		91–92	+2.2	Ac	142
OBzl-N-for-Ser-Gly-OEt	DCCI	Di	75	EtAc-Eth	91–92	+2.2 / +0.2	Ac / Alc	213
OBzl-Ser-Gly-OBzl Hydrochloride	DCCI	THF			63–64	+4.1	Alc	213
OBzl-Ser-Gly-OBu^t-Toluenesulfonate				EtAc-Eth-Pe	111.5–112	+8.3 / +10	Alc / Aq	213 / 88

Table 2 Dipeptides (continued)

Compound	Method	Solvent	% Yield	Solvent Crystallization	M.P.(°C)	[α]_D	Solvent Rotation	Ref.
OBzl-Ser-Gly-OEt Hydrochloride	DCCI				oil			213
OBzl-tfa-Ser-Gly-OBu^t	DCCI				oil			88
N-Z-Ser-Gly-OBzl		MeCl	71	EtAc-Pe	105–106			667
Z-Ser-Gly-OEt	DCCI	MeCl		Alc	98–101			584
Z-Ser-Gly-ONBzl	DCCI	DMF-Acn	70	Alc	121–123	−8.5	Ac	269
					121–123	+1.5	THF	
Z-Ser-Gly-ONp	DCCI	Acn	75	DMF-Me	170–171			118
N-Boc-Ser-Gly-OBzl	DCCI	MeCl		EtAc-Pe	77–79	−13	Me	668
Nps-Ser-Gly				EtAc-Cy	130–131	−51	DMF	632
Nps-Ser-Gly-OEt	DCCI		80	EtAc	139–140	−47	DMF	632
Nps-Ser-Gly-ONp				EtAc	148–150	−64	DMF	632
Ser-Gly						+30	1N HCl	667
Ser-Gly-OBzl					176	+8.2	Ac	140
Ser-Gly-OBzl Benzenesulfonate				i-Pr-Eth	170 (dec)	+7.4	Ac	667
Ser-Gly-OEt Hydrochloride				Alc-EtAc	104.5–106.5	+22	Aq	632
Ser-Gly-ONBzl				Acn	55–58	+28	DMF	481
				DMF-Acn	140–145			269
					94–96			
Ser-Gly-ONp Hydrobromide					173–173.5			118
O-Tos-N-boc-Ser-Gly-OBzl				Alc	101–103	+15	Chf	668
O-Tos-N-Z-Ser-Gly-OBzl				Alc	87–89	+15	Chf	668
N-Tos-DL-Ser-Gly				Aq	157–158			419
N-Z-Ser-N^{im}-bzl-His-OBzl	DCCI	THF	54	EtAc	136–138	−4	THF	319
N-Z-Ser-N^{im}-bzl-His Hydrazide				Me	199			192
OBu^t-Z-Ser-N^{im}-bzl-His-OMe				DMF-Me	198–200	−3	DMF	319
OBu^t-Z-Ser-N^{im}-bzl-His Hydrazide	NHS-DCCI	THF	86		oil			534
					126–128			534

Compound	Method	Solvent	Yield	Recrystn. solvent	M.p.	[α]	Rot. solvent	Ref.
N-Z-Ser-N^{im}-bzl-His-OMe	DCCI	Acn-Py	76	EtAc-Me	167			192
Z-Ser-Leu Amide	A	EtAc-DMF	74	Alc-Aq	181–183			304
Z-Ser-nor-Leu-OMe	DCCI	Chf		EtAc-Pe	71			525
Z-Ser-N$^\epsilon$-boc-Lys	A				125–126	+3.6	Me	85
Z-Ser-N$^\epsilon$-boc-Lys-OMe					103–105	–1	DMF	85
N-Z-Ser-N$^\epsilon$-boc-Lys-OMe	WRK	Acn	49	Eth	106.5–107.5	–11	Me	100
Boc-Ser-N$^\epsilon$-boc-Lys-OMe	A	EtAc	72	Eth-Pe	45–50			525
Ser-N$^\epsilon$-Z-Lys-OMe					80			89
Ser-N$^\epsilon$-boc-Lys-OMe					oil			85
N-Trt-Ser-N$^\epsilon$-Z-Lys-OMe	DCCI	Acn-DMF	91	EtAc-Pe	127–128	–38	Alc	100 / 89
Z-Ser-Met-OMe	DCCI		91.1	EtAc-Pe	101–102	–29	Me	371
N-Boc-Ser-Met-OMe	DCCI			EtAc	66–67.5	–16	Me	463
Ser-Met-OMe					84–85 / 86–88			463 / 371
Z-D-Ser-Phe	DCCI	DMF			133–135	–19	Me	440a
Z-D-Ser-D-Phe	A	EtAc			138–139	–15	DMF	440a
Z-Ser-D-Phe	DCCI	DMF			137–139	–9	DMF	440a
Z-Ser-Phe-OBzl	DCCI	DMF	80	EtAc	121–122			120
N-Z(OMe)-Ser-Phe-OMe	A / DCCI	THF	68 / 81	EtAc-Pe	118–119	–8.4	Me	701
Ser-Phe				Alc / THF	315 (dec) / 170–171	+26	Ac	120 / 701
Ser-Phe-OBzl Toluenesulfonate								120
O-[2,2,2-Trifluoro-1-Z-amino-et]-N-Z(OMe)-Ser-Phe				EtAc-Pe	140			701
O-[2,2,2-Trifluoro-1-Z-amino-et]-N-Z(OMe)-Ser-Phe-OMe				EtAc-Pe	162			701
O-[2,2,2-Trifluoro-1-Z-amino-et]-Ser-Phe-OMe Hydrochloride					90 / 169 (dec)			701
N-Z-Ser-Pro	A	EtAc	67	EtAc	107–109	–70	Me	748

Table 2 Dipeptides (continued)

Compound	Method	Solvent	% Yield	Solvent Crystallization	M.P.(°C)	[α]$_D$	Solvent Rotation	Ref.
Z-Ser-Pro-OBzl	DCCI		87		105–107	–77		722
N-Z-Ser-Pro Hydrazide				Me	137–141	–93	Ac-Aq	747
N-Z-Ser-Pro-OMe				Me	117–121	–68	Me	747
N-Z-Ser-Pro-ONp			60			–95	Me	605
Ser-Pro					189	–108	Aq	722
Z-D-Ser-D-Ser	DCCI	DMF		EtAc	190–192	–23	DMF	440a
N-Z-Ser-D-Ser	DCCI	THF-Acn	65		160–161			335
N-Z-Ser-Ser Hydrazide					212–213			335
Z-Ser-Ser Hydrazide				Alc-Aq	215–218	–10	DMF	135
Z-Ser-Ser-OMe	2,4-DNPO	Chf			143–145	–5.5	DMF	22
O,O'-(N,N-Bis-2-chloro-et-amido)-phosphoryl-D-Ser-D-Ser Hydrochloride				Alc-Eth	96	–4.2	Me	655
O,O'-(N,N-Bis-2-chloro-et-amido)-phosphoryl-Ser-Ser Hydrochloride						+4.1	Me	655
O,O'-(N,N-Bis-2-chloro-et-amido-phosphoryl)-Ser-Ser Hydrochloride				Alc-Eth	88 (dec)			655
O-[2,2,2-Trifluoro-1-Z-amino-et]-N-boc-Ser-Ser DCHA Salt	DCCI-NHS	THF	67	EtAc-Pe	143			701
O-[2,2,2-Trifluoro-1-Z-amino-et]-N-boc-Ser-Ser-OMe	DCCI	MeCl	70	EtAc-Eth	129–130			701
O-[2,2,2-trifluoro-1-Z-amino-et]-Ser DCHA Salt								701
O-[2,2,2-Trifluoro-1-Z-amino-et]-N-boc-Ser-O-[2,2,2-trifluoro-1-Z-amino-et]-Ser Hydrazide				Me-Aq	173–175			701

Compound	Method	Solvent	Yield (%)	Recrystn. solvent	M.p. (°C)	[α]	Solvent	Ref.
O-[2,2,2-Trifluoro-1-Z-amino-et]-N-boc-Ser-O-[2,2,2-trifluoro-1-Z-amino-et]-Ser-OMe				EtAc-Pe	151			701
Z-Ser-Thr Hydrazide				Me	220–223		DMF	399
Z-Ser-Thr-OMe	ONp	Chf	60	Alc-Eth	126–127	+6.7	DMF	399
	DCCI	EtAc	87	EtAc-Pe	125–126	+6.5	Ac	
N-Z-Ser-Trp Hydrazide	A		93	DMF-Alc-Aq	234–234.5	−14	Me	549
Z-Ser-Trp-OMe				Alc-Aq	101.5–103.5	+7.1		549
N-Ac-Ser-O-ac-Tyr				Aq	193–197	−16	Aq	241
N-Ac-Ser-Tyr				Aq	192–194	+18	Aq	241
OBzl-N-boc-Ser-Tyr Hydrazide	DCCI		81.7	Alc	179–181	−12	DMF	463
Z-Ser-Tyr-azide								241
N-Boc-Ser-Tyr-OMe	A			Eth	115–118	−5.0	Me	463
N-Boc-Ser-Tyr Hydrazide					193–195 (dec)	−19	Aq-Alc	463
Ser-Tyr	A	Chf	69	Eth-EtAc	256–260 (dec)	+43	Aq	241
Z-Ser-nor-Val-OMe	DCCI				70			525
OBu^t-N-Z-Ser-Val-OBu^t	DCCI	THF	79	Alc-Aq	73.5–76.5	−2.2	Alc	602
OBu^t-Ser-Val-OBu^t Hydrochloride	MCA				170–173	−15	Alc	602
Threonine								
Z-Thr-Ala				EtAc-He	129–130.5	−18	Me	106
Z-Thr-Ala-OMe	EDCI			EtAc	132.5–134	−34	Me	106
Boc-Thr-Ala-OBzl	DCCI	MeCl	55		130–130.5			78
N-Z(OMe)-Thr-Ala-OMe			81		98–101			356a
O-[2,2,2-Trifluoro-1-Z-amino-et]-N-Z(OMe)-Thr-Ala	DCCI-NHS	Aq	42		126–128			701
				EtAc-Pe	185–186			701
O-[2,2,2-Trifluoro-1-Z-amino-et]-N-Z(OMe)-Thr-Ala-OMe					159–161			701

Table 2 Dipeptides (continued)

Compound	Method	Solvent	% Yield	Solvent Crystallization	M.P.(°C)	$[\alpha]_D$	Solvent Rotation	Ref.
Actinocinyl-bis-[Thr-D-allo-Ile-OMe]					107–110			77
Z-OBu^t-Thr-Phe-OMe	DCCI	MeCl	75	Chf-Pe	oil			736
Z-DL-Thr-D-Phe	DCCI	DMF			135–138	−13	Me	440a
Z-Thr-Phe					151–152	+19	DMF	47
N-Z-Thr-Phe-OMe	DCCI		78.5		105–107	+4.0	DMF	47
	A		86.5	Pe-EtAc	105–106	+1.6	Alc	559
Z-Thr-Phe-OMe	A		86.5		105–106			559
OBu^t-Thr-Phe-OMe Hydrochloride				Me-Eth	162–163	+26	DMF	736
N-Nps-Thr-Phe	DCCI	Chf	60		110	−17		774
Pht-Thr-Phe								728
Pht-Thr-Phe-OBzl	DCCI		91.6		130–130.5			728
Pht-Thr-Phe Boc-hydrazide	DCCI		93.5		188–189			728
Pht-Thr-Phe Hydrazide Trifluoroacetate								21
Thr-Phe					147–150	−32	Me	701
Thr-Phe-OMe				Alc-Eth	150–151	−17	Me	559
O-[2,2,2-Trifluoro-1-Z-amino-et]-N-Z(OMe)-Thr-Phe				EtAc-Pe	167–168	+16	Aq	559
O-[2,2,2-Trifluoro-1-Z-amino-et]-N-Z(OMe)-Thr-Phe-OMe	DCCI	Chf	45		130–131	+9.3	Aq	701
Thr-Pro-OMe Hydrochloride				Me-EtAc	190–191	−95	Aq	701
Z-Thr-Ser Hydrazide				Aq	210–214			774
				Me-Aq	264–265			559
N-Z-Thr-Ser-OMe	DCCI		60	EtAc	132–133	−45	N HCl	476
								47
Z-Thr-Ser-OMe	EDCI		52	Pe-EtAc	158.5–159	−7	Me	476
OBu^t-N-Z-Thr-OBu^t-Ser	A		53		127–129			559
OBu^t-N-Z-Thr-OBu^t-Ser-OMe	2,4-DNPO	Acn	100		oil			22
	DCCI	MeCl			oil	+11	DMF	735
								735

160

N-Z(OMe)-Thr-Ser-OMe	DCCI	MeCl			126–127	−4.5	Me	701
N-Pht-Thr-OBzl-Ser Z-hydrazide	DCCI				132–133.5			728
Thr-OBzl-Ser Z-hydrazide					114–115			728
Thr-Ser-OMe								47
O-[2,2,2-Trifluoro-1-Z-amino-et]-N-Z(OMe)-Thr-O-[2,2,2-trifluoro-1-Z-amino-et]-Ser			54	EtAc-Pe				701
O-[2,2,2-Trifluoro-1-Z-amino-et]-N-Z(OMe)-Thr-O-[2,2,2-trifluoro-1-Z-amino-et]-Ser-OMe			92	EtAc-Pe	168–169			701
N^γ-Z-Dbu-Thr-N^γ-Z-Dbu-OMe Hydrochloride Hydrate				Me-Eth	201–204 (dec)	+9.9		485
N^γ-Z-N^α-Nps-Dbu-Thr-N^γ-Dbu-Z-Thr-OMe				Aq-Di	217–219	+6.2		485
N^α-Z-N^γ-Tos-Dbu-Thr-N^γ-tos-Dbu-Thr Hydrazide				Me-Aq	160 (dec)	−14		486
N^α-Boc-N^γ-pelargonyl-Dbu-N^γ-Z-Dbu-Thr-N^γ-Z-Dbu-Thr Hydrazide					220 (dec)			485
N^α-Boc-N^γ-pelargonyl-Dbu-N^γ-Z-Dbu-Thr-N^γ-Z-Dbu-Thr-OMe Sesquihydrate				Me-Aq	185–195 (dec)			485
Nps-Thr-N^γ-Z-Dbu-Thr-OMe				Me	183–184	−52		485
Thr-N^γ-Z-Dbu-Thr-OMe Hydrochloride				Me-Eth	146–149	+2.6		485
Tryptophan								
Z-D-Trp-D-Ala	MCA	MeCl			149–150	+18	DMF	440a
Z-Trp-D-Ala	MCA	MeCl			75–80	−26	DMF	440a
Z-Trp-Ala-OBzl	DCCI	MeCl	80	EtAc	153	−27	Me	707
Trp-Ala				EtAc	153	+28	Aq	707
Z-Trp-N^G-nitro-Arg	MCA	MeCl			68–75	−17	DMF	440a
Z-D-Trp-S-Bzl-Cys	MCA	MeCl			65–70	+13	DMF	440a

Table 2 Dipeptides (continued)

Compound	Method	Solvent	% Yield	Solvent Crystallization	M.P.(°C)	$[\alpha]_D$	Solvent Rotation	Ref.
Z-D-Trp-Gly	OCH$_2$CN	THF	70		158-161	+19	Me	742
Z-Trp-Gly-OBzl	MCA	THF	42	EtAc-Pe	124-125	-20	Me	375
	DCCI	EtAc	66	EtAc-Pe-Eth	117-119			666
	MCA	THF	25					297
	WRK	Acn	89	EtAc-Pe	117-119			666
Z-Trp-Gly-OBu^t	DCCI	EtAc	94		oil			369
	DCCI	THF	92					370
Z-Trp-Gly-OEt	OPAP				124.5-125	-7.2		23
Z-Trp-Gly-OMe	MCA	THF	74	Eth-Pe	156-158			162
Z-D-Trp-Gly-OMe					158-159	+11	Ac	742
Mz-Trp-Gly-OBzl	CMCI	EtAc	63	Acn	152-153	-54	1N HCl	297
Me-D-Trp-Gly Hydrochloride Monohydrate								742
Trp-Gly-OBzl								375
Trp-Gly-OBu^t								369
								370
Trp-Gly Diketopiperazine				EtAc-Pe	292-303			235
Trp-Gly-OMe Hydrochloride								235
D-Trp-Gly Monohydrate					164-165	-93	Aq	162
Trp-Gly-ONBzl Hydrochloride					150-153			742
Z-Trp-Leu					144-146			297
Z-Trp-Leu-OBzl	DCCI	Acn	96	EtAc-Pe	114			720
Z-Trp-Leu-OBu^t	DCCI		54		oil	-33		707
Z-Trp-Leu Boc-hydrazide					130			719
Z-Trp-Leu-OEt	OTCP	DMF	85	EtAc-Cy	109-110	-39	Me	720
Z-Trp-Leu Hydrazide				Me	204-205			424
								424
Z-Trp-Leu-OMe	DCCI		71		113-114			720

Compound	Method	Solvent	Yield (%)	Recryst.	M.p. (°C)	$[\alpha]$	Solvent	Ref.
Z-Trp-Leu-OMe	DCCI	MeCl	91	EtAc-Pe	112–113.5	−30	Me	28
Z-Trp-Leu-OMe	DCCI		63		114–116	−28	Me	260
Z-Trp-N-me-nor-Leu Hydrazide	DCCI	EtAc			oil			424
Z-Trp-N-me-nor-Leu-OMe	AC	EtAc			oil			424
Trp-Leu					oil			707
Trp-Leu-OBu^t				Me	105–107	−18	Me	719
Trp-Leu-OBu^t Acetate								719
Trp-Leu Boc-hydrazide								720
Trp-Leu-OMe								260
Aoc-Trp-Met Hydrazide	DCCI	Chf-THF	63.1	Alc-Aq	158–163	−22	DMF	520
Boc-Trp-Met Hydrazide	DCCI	Chf	89	EtAc	177–178			111
Boc-Trp-Met-OMe	OTCP	DMF		Dipr-Eth	98–99			111
Trp-Met-OMe Hydrochloride								111
Z-D-Trp-Phe	MCA	MeCl			90–100	+23	DMF	440a
Z-D-Trp-D-Phe	MCA	MeCl			142–145	+36	DMF	440a
Z-Trp-D-homo-Ser Hydrazide					193–195			424
Z-Trp-homo-Ser Hydrazide					193–195			424
Z-Trp-D-homo-Ser Lactone				EtAc-Pe	155–160			424
Z-Trp-homo-Ser Lactone				EtAc-Pe	155–160			424
Z-Trp-D-Ser	MCA	MeCl			oil	−45	DMF	440a
Z-Trp-D-Val	MCA	MeCl			105–110	−36	DMF	440a
Tyrosine								
N-Tos-Tyr-S-bzl-Cys-OEt	DCCI	THF	87	EtAc-Pe	139–140	−33	Alc	42
OBzl-N-Z-Tyr-Gly-OMe	OTCP	DMF	76	Me	128–130			423
Z-Tyr-Gly Amide	DCCI	MeCl		Me	126–127			160
N,O-Di-Z-Tyr-Gly-OEt	ONp	Chf		Me-Aq	114–116			22
Z-Tyr-Gly-OMe	DCCI	MeCl	78	Chf	165	−2.5	Chf	28
OBu^t-N-Z-Tyr-Gly OMe	DCCI	EtAc	96	EtAc-Eth	141–143; oil	−22	DMF	28

Table 2 Dipeptides (continued)

Compound	Method	Solvent	% Yield	Solvent Crystallization	M.P.(°C)	$[\alpha]_D$	Solvent Rotation	Ref.
O-Ethoxycarbonyl-N-Z-Tyr-Gly-amide	MCA	THF	91	Alc-Aq	157–159	−24	DMF	160
Tyr-Gly-OMe Acetate					oil			423
Tyr-Gly-OMe Acetate Hydrochloride				Eth-Alc	92–95 (dec			423
OAc-N-for-Tyr-Ile-OMe	DCCI	EtAc	66	THF-Eth	152–153			569
	MCA	THF	31		150–153			
OBzl-Tyr-Ile-OEt	MCA	THF	77	EtAc-Pe	128	+10	Ac	15
O,N-Di-Z-N-me-Tyr-Ile-OBu^t	ONP				oil	+9	DMF	258
						−17	Me	
O,N-Di-Z-N-me-Tyr-Ile Boc-hydrazide	ONP	THF	67	Be-Pe	97	−40	Ac	258
O,N-Di-Z-me-Tyr-Ile-OMe	MCA	Chf	98			−18	Me	258
	DCCI	AcN	76			+10	DMF	
						−21	Me	
						+10	DMF	
Di-Z-Tyr-Ile-OMe	OTCP	Alc	67		158	+2.7	Ac	253
β-S-Bzl-propionyl-Tyr-Ile Hydrazide					253–254	−12	DMF	253
β-S-Bzl-propionyl-Tyr-Ile-OMe	DCCI		98			−8	DMF	253
N-For-Tyr-Ile-OMe	DCCI	THF	74	EtAc-Pe		−14	Me	569
N-Me-Tyr-Ile-OBu^t						−18	DMF	258
N-Me-Tyr-Ile-OMe Hydrobromide					190	+6	Me	258
Tyr-Ile-OEt Hydrochloride					oil			15
Tyr-Ile-OMe					oil			569
OBzl-Z-Tyr-Leu Hydrazide					191–193			733
OBzl-Z-Tyr-Leu-OMe	P		80		132.5–133	−14	Me	733
OBzl-N-Z-Tyr-Leu-OMe	ONP	DMF	75	Me	127	−16	Me	166
N-Z-Tyr-Leu 1-Hydroxypiperidine Ester				EtAc-Dipr Eth	150–151	+1.6	Chf	199
N-Z-Tyr-Leu Hydrazide				Me	225–226	−17	DMF	199
N,O-Di-Z-Tyr-Leu-OMe	WRK	AcN	55	EtAc-Dipr Eth	163.5–164.5	−17	Me	199

Compound	Method	Solvent	Yield (%)	Recryst. solvent	M.p.	[α]	Solvent	Ref.
Z-Tyr-D-Met	ONP	DMF	85	EtAc	168–169	−12	DMF	166
Di-Z-Tyr-Phe-OMe	DCCI	DMF	69		68–70	−8	DMF	440a
Z-Tyr-Phe-OMe	OTCP		75		187–188	−15	DMF	259
3-Benzylthiopropenyl-Tyr-Phe Hydrazide	MA			DMF-AQ	132–133	−24	Me	753
β-S-Bzl-propionyl-Tyr-Phe Hydrazide					249–251	−21	DMF	768
β-S-Bzl-propionyl-Tyr-Phe-OMe	OTCP	DMF	68		147–149	−17	DMF	255
3-Benzylthiopropenyl-Tyr-Phe-OMe	A	Aq-DMF	97	Aq-Alc	147–149	−17	DMF	255
N-Propenyl-Tyr-Phe Hydrazide					151–152	−17	DMF	768
N-Propenyl-Tyr-Phe-OMe					268–269	−22	DMF	259
Tyr-Phe-OMe Hydrochloride					156	−14	DMF	259
Z-Tyr-Pro-amide				EtAc-Me	204–206			753
N-Z-Tyr-Ser Hydrazide	DCCI	Acn	62	Me	187–190	−4.9	DMF	645
					226–227	−20	1N HCl	100
Z-Tyr-Ser Hydrazide	DCCI	Di-Acn	79		226–228	−5.3	DMF	565
N-Z-Tyr-Ser-OMe	DCCI	Acn	81		151–152	−3.3	Me	100
N,O-Di-Z-Tyr-Ser-OMe	A		57	EtAc-Pe	176–177	−4.2	DMF	100
Z-Tyr-Ser-OMe					156–158			559
Tyr-Ser				Aq-Alc	260 (dec)	+26	1N HCl	218
Tyr-Ser-OMe					130–135			559
								270
OBuᵗ-Z-Tyr-OSu	DCCI-NHS	Pe-MeCl	96		118	−16	Di	403
Z-Tyr-Tyr-OMe	DCCI				170–173	−11	DMF	50
OBuᵗ-Tyr-OBuᵗ-Tyr Diketopiperazine				Py-Pe or DMSO	265–269	−73	DMSO	328
Z(OMe)-Tyr-Tyr	DCCI	THF	96	Me-Aq	170–173			50
Tyr-Tyr Hydrochloride				Me-Be	210–211			50
Tyr-Tyr-OMe Hydrochloride	MCA	THF	71		210–211	+11	DMF	50
N,O-Di-Cbo-Tyr-Val				EtAc-Pe	181–183	+2	Alc	685
N-[N,O-Di-Cbo-Tyr-Val]-β-D-glucosamine				Alc	211–213	+37	DMF	685
Valine								
Z-Val-Ala	MCA	MeCl		EtAc-Pe	172–173	+18	Me	332
Z-Val-D-Ala	MCA				160–164			440a

Table 2 Dipeptides (continued)

Compound	Method	Solvent	% Yield	Solvent Crystallization	M.P.(°C)	[α]D	Solvent Rotation	Ref.
Z-Val-Ala DCHA	MCA			EtAc-Alc-Pe	167-168			332
Z-Val-Ala Hydrazide	MCA	THF	71	Me-Aq	219-222			588
Z-Val-Ala-OMe	MCA	THF	75	EtAc	164-165			332
				EtAc-Pe	162.5-163			588
N(Chloro-ac)Val-Ala-OEt Isomeric Mixture	DCCI			EtAc	175-176			318
	MA				144-145			
Val-Ala				Aq-Alc	257-258			332
Val-D-Ala-OBzl					117-119	+56	Alc	863
Val-Ala-OMe						-16	Me	863
Z-Val-N^G-nitro-Arg	MCA	MeCl		Alc-Aq	175-177	-9.3	Alc	504
Z-Val-D-Asp	DCCI	MeCl			65-75	-17	Me	440a
Z-D-Val-S-bzl-Cys	ONp	DMF	91		95-100	-30	DMF	440a
Z-Val-S-bzl-Cys Amide				Aq-Ac	215			307
				Ac-Aq	217			307
Z-Val-S-btm-Cys-OMe	MCA	THF	83	Aq-Me	112			304
For-Val-S-btm-Cys-OMe	DCCI	THF		Me-Aq	128-129			304
Nps-Val-S-bzl-Cys-ONp				Alc	168-168.5	-97	DMF	631
Val-S-btm-Cys-OMe			26		161-162			304
N-Z-Val-γ-OBu^t-Glu-OEt				EtAc-Pe	70-71	-26	Alc	305
				EtAc-He	135-135.5			
Z-Val-Glu								755
Z-Val-Glu-di-OEt	ONp	Chf	93	Cte	120-120.5			755
Z-Val-Glu-di-OMe	ONp	Chf			127-128			755
Z-Val-α-OMe-Glu-ONp	ONp	DMF						147
Z(NO$_2$)-Val-Glu	Ac	Eth	84	Alc	162-163			430
Z(NO$_2$)-Val-Glu-di-OEt					138-141			430
Val-Glu					219-222			755
				Aq-An	220-222			430
Val-Glu-di-OBzl Toluenesulfonate					111-114	+6.0	Chf	669

Compound	Method	Solvent	Yield	Recryst.	m.p. (°C)	[α]	Solvent	Ref.
Val-Glu-di-OEt	MCA		45	Alc-Eth	119–120	+2.2		755
Val-α-OMe-Glu					201–202		EtAc	635
Val-γ-OMe-Glu-ONp Hydrobromide								147
Z-Val-Gly	MCA		82	Be	120–125			239
Z-Val-Gly-OEt	MCA	MeCl	63	Alc	169–170	−6	Me	36
	DCCI			Me	166–167	−10		615
	DCCI				167	−31	Alc	277
					166			178
Z-Val-Gly Hydrazide				Me	175–176	−4	Me	36
Z-Val-Gly-melphalan-OEt					159–160			36
Z-Val-Gly-OMe	ONp	Di	80	Me-Aq	160–161	−25	Me	373
	MCA		73	Alc	204–205	−40	Ac	239
N-Z-Val-Gly-ONp								646
Z-Val-melphalanyl-Gly-OEt								36
Boc-Val-Gly-OEt	DCCI	THF	50	Acn-Eth	98–99			535
N-(Chloro-acl)-Val-Gly OET	DCCI	Chf		Alc	149–150			318
N-(5-Chlorosalicylidene)-Val-Gly-OEt	DCCI	MeCl	40	MeCl-Eth	124.5–127	+31	Di	592
For-Val-Gly	DCCI		70	Aq	206–208 (dec)	−49	Alc	527
For-Val-Gly-OEt	DCCI	Chf		EtAc	219–221	−48	Alc-Aq	389
N-For-Val-Gly-OEt				Alc	154	−50	Alc-Aq	389
Nps-Val-Gly-2,4,6-tri-me-OBzl					157–158.5	−61	Alc	592
Val-Gly					183–184	−49	DMF	625
					152–153	+17	Aq	389
Val-Gly-OEt Hydrochloride				Aq-A	255–260			239
Val-Gly-2,4,6-tri-me-OBzl Hydrochloride				Di	70			592
Val-Gly-OMe				Me-Eth	185.5–187	−24	DMF	625
Val-Gly-OMe Hydrochloride					oil			373
Z-D-Val-D-His Hydrazide					199	+13	DMF	267
					191.5–192	+10	Ac	684
Z-Val-His Hydrazide					192–193	−10	Ac	563
					192–193	−10	Ac	552
								563

Table 2 Dipeptides (continued)

Compound	Method	Solvent	% Yield	Solvent Crystallization	M.P.(°C)	[α]D	Solvent Rotation	Ref.
Z-D-Val-D-His-OMe					164-165	+22	Alc	684
Z-Val-His-OMe					163-164	-18	Alc	563
Z-Val-D-His-OMe					160-162	+17	Alc	563
Val-His						+44	Aq	218
Z-Val-Leu-OBzl	MCA		93	Aq-Alc	105-108	-41	Ac	396
Z-Val-Leu-OEt				Aq-Me	103-105	-42	Alc	36
Z-Val-Leu Hydrazide					135-173			36
Z-Val-Leu-melphalane-OEt								36
Z-Val-Leu-OMe	MCA		75		93-96	-39	Ac	396
Boc-Val-Leu-OBzl	MCA		98		74-78	-25	Ac	396
Boc-Val-Leu-OBu^t	MCA		70		89-93	-58	Ac	396
Boc-Val-Leu-OMe	MCA		70		125-126	-62	Ac	396
				EtAc-Pe	125-126			396
N-Tos-DL-Val-Leu				Me-Eth	107-109			344
					154-155			
N-Tos-DL-Val-Leu-OEt	DCCI		95	EtAc-Pe	111-113	-32	Aq	344
Val-Leu-OBzl Hydrochloride					188-190	-6.0	6N HCl	396
Val-Leu Hydrochloride					217-218	-12	Aq	396
Val-Leu-OMe Hydrochloride					174-176			396
Z-Val-N$^\alpha$-Z-N$^\epsilon$-Lys-OBzl	DCCI	THF	50	Alc	239-240			53
Z-Val-N$^\epsilon$-boc-Lys Hydrazide	DCCI	Acn	77	Pe	180-182			645
Z-Val-N$^\epsilon$-boc-Lys-OMe					111-113			645
Z-Val-Lys Hydrazide				EtAc-Pe	210-213			130
Z-Val-N$^\epsilon$-tos-Lys					139-144			560
Z-Val-N$^\epsilon$-tos-Lys-OBzl	MCA	Di	73.5	Me	212	-19	Ac	130
Z-Val-N$^\epsilon$-tos-Lys-OEt	MCA	Di	84	DMF-Aq	208-209	-4.5	DMF	130
Z-Val-N$^\epsilon$-tos-Lys Hydrazide								494
								560

Compound	Method	Solvent	Yield %	Recryst. solvent	m.p.	[α]	Rot. solvent	Ref.
Z-Val-Nε-tos-Lys-OMe	ONp	EtAc	83	Eth	131-132	-14	Ac	494
Boc-Val-Nε-Z(OMe)-Lys Hydrazide	MCA	THF	77	An-Eth-Pe	128-129			560
Pz-Val-Nε-boc-Lys				Me	192-193			580
Val-Nε-Lys	MCA	Di	70		167-169			298
				EtAc	167-169			578
Val-Nε-Tos-Lys-OMe Hydrochloride				Alc-Aq	208-210	+0.9	Aq	53
				Alc-Eth	198-200	+11	Ac	560
Z-D-Val-D-Met	MCA	MeCl	76	Me-Eth-Pe	179-181	-1	DMF	440a
Z-Val-D-Met	MCA	MeCl			152-153	+22	DMF	440a
Z(OMe)-Val-Nδ-Z-Orn-OEt	MCA	THF			140-144	-7.8	Ac	302
Z(OMe)-Val-Nδ-Z-Orn Hydrazide	MCA	Aq-DMF			211-212 (dec)	-4.2	DMF	302
Z-Val-Orn-OBzl	MCA	THF	58	EtAc-Pe-Me	138-139			129
Z-Val-Nδ-Tos-Orn-OEt	MCA	THF	71	EtAc-Pe	116-118			129
Boc-Val-Nδ-Z-Orn-OEt	MCA	THF		EtAc-Eth-Pe	123-125	-8.2	Ac	301
Boc-Val-Nδ-Z-D-Orn Hydrazide					174	-9.6	Alc	301
Boc-Val-Nδ-Z-Orn Hydrazide	MCA	Aq-DMF		Alc-Eth-Pe	175	-14	DMF	451
Z-D-Val-Phe	MCA	MeCl			132-134	-15	DMF	440a
Z-Val-D-Phe	MCA	MeCl			118-120	+12	DMF	440a
Z-D-Val-D-Phe	MCA	MeCl			176-178	-13	DMF	440a
Z-Val-Phe	DCCI	EtAc		Me	172-174	-13	Me	147
Z-Val-Phe-OMe	MCA				132-134	+14	Di	147
N-Z-Val-Phe-OMe	DCCI	MeCl	70	Me	136			122
N-(5-Chlorosalicylidene)-Val-Phe-OMe	DCCI	MeCl	78	Me	139-140	-5	DMF	774
N-(2-Hydroxy-1-naphthal)-Val-Phe-OMe	DCCI	MeCl	65	Me	150-151	+32	MeCl	592
Nps-Val-Phe-OMe	DCCI	Chf	83	EtAc-Pe	123-124	-25	Di	592
	MA		70		121-122	-6.8	DMF	774
Val-Phe-OMe Hydrochloride	MCA		60	Me-Eth	196			122
			35	Me-Eth	196.5-199 (dec)	+19	Aq	592

Table 2 Dipeptides (continued)

Compound	Method	Solvent	% Yield	Solvent Crystallization	M.P.(°C)	[α]D	Solvent Rotation	Ref.
Val-Ser				Me-Eth	193-195	+21	Aq	774
				Aq-Alc		+33	DMF	218
Z-D-Val-D-Ser	MCA	MeCl			174-176	-17	Me	440a
Z-Val-Trp				EtAc	217-218	-6		476
Z-Val-Trp-OBzl	DCCI	MeCl		EtAc-Pe	129	+71	Chf	707
Z-Val-Trp-OMe	EDCI	MeCl	70	Me-Aq	145-147	+12	Me	476
Z-D-Val-DL-Tyr	MCA	MeCl			90-95	+13	DMF	440a
Z-D-Val-D-Tyr					238-239	-42	Me	563
Z-Val-Tyr Boc-hydrazide	ONp	DMF			128-131	-11	DMF	190
						-23	Py	
						-20	Ac	
Z-D-Val-D-Tyr-OMe				Alc-Aq	153	-12	Py	684
Z-Val-Tyr Hydrate					164-166	-13		569
					95			569
Z-Val-Tyr Hydrazide				Me	237-238	+13	DMF	563
					247-248	-10		494
Z-D-Val-D-Tyr Hydrazide					240	+13	DMF	684
Z-Val-Tyr Hydrazide					192-193	-10	Ac	552
Z-Val-Tyr-OMe	DCCI		81	EtAc	150	-18	Me	494
					146-148	+13	Py	563
						+57	Chf	
Z-D-Val-D-Tyr-OMe	MCA	THF	80	Me-Aq	148-149	+16	Me	99
	NHS	CHF-DMF						519
Boc-Val-Tyr-OEt				EtAc-Pe		-13	Me	563
Val-Tyr Boc-hydrazide	DCCI	THF	72	EtAc	147-148	-13	Me	466
					135			190
Val-Tyr-OEt				MeCl-Pe	113.5-114.5	-8.4	DMF	466

Compound	Method	Solv.	Yield (%)	Recryst.	m.p. (°C)	$[\alpha]_D$	Solv.	Ref.
Z-Val-Val	MCA			Pe	114–115.5	+7.7	An	330
Z-D-Val-D-Val	DCCI	MeCl	50	Me-Aq	132–134	–6.8	An	564
Z-Val-Val-OBzl	DCCI	Chf	64	Alc	134–135	+5	DMF	440a
Z-Val-Val-Ophenacyl	MCA	THF	71		174–175	–9.8	EtAc	564
Z-Val-Val-OBzh	MCA	THF	80	Thf-Eth	111–112	–22	Chf	616
N^4-(Z-Val-Val)-Sulfanilamide	MCA	THF	73		162–163	–35	THF	616
Z-D-Val-D-Val-OBu^t				EtAc-Eth-Pe	136–137			590
Z-Val-Val-OEt					257–259	–14	THF	564
N-[N-(5,5-Di-me-cyclohex-2-en-1-on-3-yl)-DL-Val]-DL-Val-OMe					oil			330
N-Pht-D-Val-D-Val Bzl-Amide	DCCI	Py		EtAc	90–92	–43	DMF	196
N-Tfa-Val-OMe Racemic Mixture	DCCI-NHS			Alc				564
Val-Val				Alc	205–206	+14	1N HCl	693
D-Val-D-Val					176–177	–14	1N HCl	564
Val-Val Anilide								564
D-Val-D-Val Bzl-amide Hydrobromide				Alc-Eth	239–240	+1.3	Alc	590
D-Val-D-Val Bzl-amide Hydrochloride					272–273	+21	Aq	564
D-Val-D-Val-OBu^t					oil			564
Val-Val-OEt-hydrochloride								564
Val-D-Val-OMe Hydrochloride				Me-Eth	214	+59	Me	330
Val-Val-OPhenacyl Hydrobromide					196–197	–18	Me	527
Val-Val-OPhenacyl Hydrochloride					198	–22	Me	616
Val-Val-OBzh Hydrochloride	DCCI	Chf		THF-Eth	180–181	–14	DMF	616
N^4-(Val-Val)-sulfanilamide				Me	284–287			590

Part 2

Tripeptides to Decapeptides

Introduction

The tripeptides and each successive increment of one amino acid unit through the decapeptides have been entered in Part 2. The glossary listing of amino acids reflects those appearing in the tables and, with exception of the amino-butyric acids, each is considered one unit when determining the choice of table. One other exception involves derivatives of glycolic acid, hydroxy-proline and hydroxy-isovaleric acid, which appear in Part 3 among the depsipeptides.

The method column of each table indicates the peptide bond-forming reagent (see glossary) and whether, e.g., see Table 3, an N-terminal amino acid was condensed with a preformed dipeptide (1+2) or by condensing an N-protected dipeptide unit with a C-terminal amino acid (2+1). Similarly, condensing an N-terminal tetrapeptide unit with a C-terminal hexapeptide component of a decapeptide will appear along with the peptide bond-forming reagent as 4+6 in the method column.

Condensing two peptide units was frequently accomplished using the azide technique. The azide reaction is one of the most reliable for avoiding racemization when joining preformed peptide units to other peptides or amino acids. Consequently, a brief review of variations in the azide method appearing in Parts 2 and 3 should prove useful and now follows. Various procedures utilizing the peptide hydrazide include sodium nitrite in water-hydrochloric acid-tetrahydrofuran,[91] water hydrochloric acid-dimethylformamide at $-15°$[103] or in water hydrochloric acid-acetic acid at $-10°$.[765] Experimental difficulties with the sodium nitrite approach have been circumvented using butyl nitrite with approximately $2M$ hydrogen chloride in tetrahydrofuran at $-25°$,[249] t-butyl nitrite with hydrochloric acid in dimethylformamide-water at $-40°$,[668] isoamyl nitrite with hydrogen chloride in dioxane-dimethylformamide at $-10°$[520] or by nitrosyl chloride in tetrahydrofuran-dioxane at $-25°$.[249] Less common approaches include N-bromosuccinimide in tetrahydrofuran and iodine in di-methylacetamide-water.[711] The latter method of azide formation seems particularly promising as only 1-2% racemate could be detected in the reaction between Z-Gly-Phe hydrazide and Gly-OEt.

3

Tripeptides

Many of the tripeptides appearing in Table 3 were originally prepared prior to 1960. The procedures summarized in Table 3 are those appearing in the literature from 1960-1968. The peptide bond forming reagents listed in Table 3 have all seen service in dipeptide syntheses (Table 2, Part 1). Comparison of methods for synthesis of the same tripeptide provide especially useful entries in Table 3. Some interesting examples include reports from different laboratories of preparing the same tripeptide by different methods, for example, the synthesis of Z-Pro-Val-Gly-OEt by use of DCCI[576] and MCA[277] (both by 1+2).

Tripeptides are particularly amenable to removing impurities by extraction procedures which, in Table 3, generally involved washing an ethyl acetate solution successively with 10% citric acid, 5% ammonium hydroxide and water,[747] 1N ammonium hydroxide, water, 1N hydrochloric acid and water[652] or 1N hydrochloric acid, water, 5% sodium bicarbonate and water.[261] A similar procedure entails washing a chloroform solution successively with 1N sodium hydroxide, 5% citric acid and water.[398] Following removal of solvent, crystallization and recrystallization from ethyl acetate-hexane was commonly used to obtain pure specimens. In a number of cases, the crude tripeptide was simply triturated with petroleum ether or diethyl ether and the solid thereby obtained was used for analytical purposes. The solvent listed in Table 3, however, corresponds to a precipitation or a crystallization and recrystallization sequence. Except where crystallization solvents are given, sharp melting point values, for example, 230° must be viewed with some reservation.

Again, in Table 3 and elsewhere in Parts 1-3, optical rotation values were not included in those instances where the sign of rotation was missing in the original literature. Also, peptides such as diethyl N,N'-bis-Z-Cystinyl-bis(S-trt-Cys-Gly) appear in Table 3.

Recently, syntheses of Phe-Gly-Leu and Leu-Thr-Ala have been completed using the controlled aceylation of amino acid N-carboxyanhydrides.[342] Other recent literature pertaining to tripeptide syntheses may be found by consulting references included in the introduction to each of the other tables.

Table 3 Tripeptides

Compound	Method	Solvent	% Yield	Solvent Crystallization	M.P.(°C)	[α]D	Solvent Rotation	Ref.
Alanine								
Z-Ala-Ala-Ala Azide								535
Z-Ala-Ala-Ala-OEt	1+2 DCCI							535
Z-Ala-Ala-Ala Hydrazide					192	−17	DMF	507
Z-α-me-Ala-Ala-α-me-Ala				Aq-Me	205–206			535
2-(1'-Z-α-me-Ala-α-me-Ala-α-me-Ala-amino-1'-me)-et-4,4-dimethyloxazolone				Be-Pe	200–201			284
Z-α-me-Ala-α-me-Ala-α-me-Ala-OBu^t				EtAc-Pe	166.5–167.5			284
Z-α-me-Ala-α-me-Ala-α-me-Ala-OMe				Aq-Me	145–146			365
Tos-α-me-Ala-α-me-Ala-α-me-Ala				Aq-Me	205–207			365
Tos-α-me-Ala-α-me-Ala-α-me-Ala-OMe				Be-Pe	156–158			365
Tfa-α-me-Ala-α-me-Ala-α-me-Ala-OMe				EtAc	197–199			365
Z-DL-Ala-DL-Ala-Gly-OEt	2+1 OPAP		72	EtAc	197–198			284
Z-DL-Ala-Ala-Phe-OEt	2+1 OPAP		80		112–114			23
Z-Ala-Ala-O-chlorocarbonyl-Ser-OMe				Be	175 143.5–144 (dec)	−3.7	Di	23
Z-Ala-Ala-Ser-OMe	2+1 A	EtAc Eth-Chf	65	An	197–198			296
N-Z-Ala-Ala-Tyr-OMe					197–198	−50	Me	296
Ala-Gln-β-OBu^t-Asp-OMe	1+2 ONP	MeCl		Alc-Aq	182–183	−12	Ac-Aq	98
Ala-Gln-β-OBu^t-Asp-OMe Acetate				EtAc	107–109	−9.6	Me	726
				EtAc	112–114	−7.4	Me	726

179

Table 3 Tripeptides (continued)

Compound	Method	Solvent	% Yield	Solvent Crystallization	M.P. (°C)	$[\alpha]_D$	Solvent Rotation	Ref.
Ala-Gln-β-OBu^t-Asp-OMe Hydrobromide				Acn	158 (dec)	−4.4	Me	726
Ala-Gln-β-OBu^t-Asp-OMe Hydrochloride				Aq-Alc	163–164	−22	Me	726
Z-Ala-Gln-β-OBu^t-Asp	1+2							726
Z-Ala-Gln-β-OBu^t-Asp-OMe	DCCI	Acn-DMF	73	Me	174–176	−30	Me	726
Ala-Gln-S-bzl-Cys Dihydrate	1+2			Aq	241–243 (dec)	−46	1N HCl	746
Z-Ala-Gln-S-bzl-Cys-OMe	DCCI	DMF	61	Me	198–200	−29	DMF	746
Z-Ala-Gln-S-bzl-Cys Monohydrate	1+2 MCA	THF	58	Me	194–198	−17	DMF	746
Tos-α-me-Ala-Gly-α-me-Ala-OMe				EtAc-An	193–194.5			365
β-Ala-Gly-Asn-SPh Hydrobromide				Alc-Eth	164–167	−71	Aq	383
Z-β-Ala-Gly-Asn-SPh				EtAc-DMF	183–184	−51	DMF	383
Z-β-Ala-Gly-γ-OMe-Glu-SPh				EtAc	109	−52	DMF	384
Z-DL-Ala-Gly-Gly	2+1							233
Z-Ala-Gly-Gly	HA	Di	76	Alc-Aq	110	−6.1	Alc	700
Z-Ala-Gly-SPh	2+1SPh	Ac	84	Aq	161–163	+5.1	DMF	700
Z-Ala-Gly-Gly-OCH(Ph)CN	2+1 WRK		86	EtAc-Pe	141–142	+4.5	DMF	633
	1+2 DCCI	Acn	86	EtAc-Cy	98–99	+4.6	DMF	
β-Chloro-Z-Ala-Gly-Gly-OEt	DCCI	Acn	74	EtAc-Cy	98.5–99.5			708
Z-Ala-D-Leu-Ala-OMe	1+2 MCA		71	EtAc-Pe	159–160 / 152–153	−5.4	Me	527
Ala-Leu-Ile Hydrazide				DMF	243–244	−55	Ac	549
Ala-D-Leu-Ala-OMe Acetate					Oil			527
Z-Ala-Leu-Ile-OEt	1+2 MCA	DMF	71	EtAc-Pe	132–134	−53	Alc	549
Z-Ala-Leu-OBu^t-Tyr Hydrazide					206–208	−31	DMF	328
Z-Ala-Leu-OBu^t-Tyr-OMe	1+2 OSu	THF	88	EtAc-Pe	164–166	−15	DMF	328
N-Trt-Ala-Leu-OBu^t-Tyr Hydrazide					220	−43	DMF	328

Compound	Method	Solvent	Yield (%)	Recryst. solvent	M.p. (°C)	[α]	Solvent	Ref.
Trt-Ala-Leu-OBu^t-Tyr-OMe				EtAc-Pe	155–157	−31	DMF	328
Boc-Ala-N$^\epsilon$-Z-Lys-Phe-OMe	2+1 A	DMF	83	EtAc-He	111–114	+30		356a
Boc-Ala-Phe-Ala-OMe	2+1 A		50	EtAc-Eth	167	−41	Me	525
Ala-Phe-N^G-nitro-Arg-OMe Hydrobromide						−8.5	1N NaOH	553
Z-Ala-Phe-N^G-nitro-Arg-OMe	2+1 A		91	Alc-Aq	126–128	−25	DMF	553
Z-Ala-Phe-Ile				Alc	183–186	−44	Alc	89
Z-Ala-Phe-Ile Hydrazide	1+2 DCCI	THF		EtAc-Pe	230–232		DMF	89
Z-Ala-Phe-Ile-OMe					154–156		Alc	89
Boc-Ala-Phe-Ile Hydrazide					250			525
Boc-Ala-Phe-Leu	1+2 ONP				106–108	−30	DMF	168
Boc-Ala-Phe-Leu-OMe					85–87			168
Boc-Ala-Phe-Val	1+2 ONP				173–174	−10	DMF	168
Boc-Ala-Phe-Val-OMe	1+2 DCCI	Chf-Acn	77	Alc-Aq				168
Boc-Ala-Ser-N$^\epsilon$-Boc-Lys-OMe	MCA	THF	81	Alc	60	−25	Alc	525
Z-Ala-OBu^t-Ser-Val-OBu^t					101–103			602
Boc-β-Ala-Trp-Met Hydrazide					218–219 (dec)			111
Boc-β-Ala-Trp-Met-OMe	1+2 OTCP	DMF	75	EtAc	138–139	+11		111
Ala-Tyr-Gly-OMe				EtAc	152–153	−39		423
Ala-Tyr-Gly-OMe Acetate Hydrate				Ac-EtAc	138–139		DMF	423
Z-Ala-OBu^t-Tyr-Gly-OMe	1+2 OTCP	DMF	86		102–103	−17	Chf	28
Z-Ala-Tyr-Gly-OMe	1+2 DCCI	DMF-Acn	75	EtAc-Pe	149–151	−18	DMF	423
Z-Ala-Tyr-Phe-OMe	1+2 OTCP	DMF	64		148–149	−18	DMF	28
Ala-Val-Leu-OMe Hydrochloride				Alc-Eth	171 191–192	−16	DMF DMF	259 549
Arginine								
Arg-Arg-Ala					172–174	−17	Aq	102
N^G-Nitro-Arg-Arg-N^G-nitro-Arg-Ala-OBzl					114			732

181

Table 3 Tripeptides (continued)

Compound	Method	Solvent	% Yield	Solvent Crystallization	M.P.(°C)	$[\alpha]_D$	Solvent Rotation	Ref.
N^G-Nitro-Z-Arg-N^G-nitro-Arg-Ala	1+2 MCA DCCI	THF	67	Me-Di-Pe	172–176	−7	DMF	102
N^G-Nitro-Z-Arg-N^G-nitro-Arg-Ala-OMe			70		98–104	−18	Me	102
N^G-Nitro-Boc-Arg-N^G-nitro-Arg-Ala-OBzl	1+2 MCA		93		95–105			732
N^α-Z-Arg-Arg-Arg 2-Naphthylamine Trihydrochloride	1+2 MCA				125			484
N^G-Nitro-Arg-N^G-nitro-Arg-Pro-OBu^t	1+2 DCCI	Acn	56	Bu	120			503
N^G-Nitro-Arg-N^G-nitro-Arg-Pro-OMe	1+2 DCCI				120			574
N^G-Nitro-Z-Arg-N^G-nitro-Arg-Pro-OMe	1+2 DCCI	Acn	43		136–160			574
N^G-Nitro-N^α-trt-Arg-N^G-nitro-Arg-Pro-OBu^t								298
								503
N^G-Tos-Arg-N^G-tos-Arg-Pro						−8.8	Me	455
N^G-Tos-Arg-N^G-tos-Arg-Pro-OBu^t								372
N^G-Tos-Z-Arg-N^G-tos-Arg-Pro					118–120	−16	Me	455
N^G-Tos-Z-Arg-N^G-tos-Arg-Pro Amide					125–130	−25	Me	492
N^G-Tos-Z-Arg-N^G-Tos-Arg-Pro-OBu^t					Me			372
N^G-Tos-N^α-Z-Arg-N^G-Tos-Arg-Pro-OBu^t						−33	Me	372
Arg-Glu-β-Pz-Ala Amide						+3.4	Aq-Ac	232
N^G-Nitro-Z-Arg-Glu-β-Pz-Ala Amide	1+2 MCA 1+2 DCCI		80 53		179–181	−15	Ac-Aq	232
Arg-Lys-Gly-Diacetate								686
Arg-Lys-Gly Diacetate Di(O-p-Toluoyl)-D-Tartrate				Me-Eth	166–168	−5	Me	686
N^G-Nitro-Z-Arg-N^ε-boc-Lys-Gly-OBu^t	1+2 DCCI	MeCl	81	Acn	87–88	−16	Me	686
N^G-Nitro-Z-Arg-Lys-Gly				Me	206–208	−11	Ac-Aq	686
N^G-Nitro-Z-D-Arg-D-Phe-D-Pro					124–126 (dec)	+30		681

Compound	Method	Solvent	Yield (%)	Solvent	m.p. (°C)	$[\alpha]$	Solvent	Ref
N^G-Nitro-Z-Arg-Phe-Pro	1+2 WRK	DMF	61	Acn	163–165			354
N^G-Nitro-Bz-Arg-Phe-Pro	2+1 DCCI	DMF	76	EtAc-Pe	118–121			680
N^G-Nitro-Bz-Arg-Phe-Pro-OMe					118–121	+28		680
N^G-Nitro-Z-D-Arg-D-Phe-D-Pro-OMe	2+1 ONP	Di	74	Me	165–167	16; −42; −52	Me; DMF; Ac	681
N^G-Nitro-Z-Arg-Phe-Pro-ONp						−67; −45; −59	Me; DMF; Ac	354
N^G-Nitro-Z-Arg-Pro-Gly								193
N^G-Nitro-Z-Arg-Pro-Gly-ONp					95			193
Arg-Pro-Val Amide Diacetate Dihydrate								244
N^G-Nitro-Z-Arg-Pro-Val Amide								244
Z-D-Arg-D-Trp-Gly-OMe	1+2 MCA	THF	64		128–130	+25	Me	742
N^G-Nitro-Arg-Trp-Gly-OMe Dihydrobromide	1+2 MCA	Di	48		122–125	−18	Me	162
N^G-Nitro-D-Arg-D-Trp-Gly-OMe Dihydrobromide Trihydrate								742
N^G-Nitro-Z-D-Arg-Trp-Gly-OMe	1+2 DCCI	Me-Eth	73	Alc	92	−22	Me	743
N^G-Nitro-Z-Arg-Trp-Gly-OMe	1+2 DCCI	Acn	71	EtAc	123–125			162
N^G-Tos-Arg-Trp-Gly-OBu^t					156–157			370
N^G-Tos-Arg-Trp-Gly-OMe								544
N^G-Tos-Z-Arg-Trp-Gly-OBu^t	1+2 DCCI	Acn	84		106–112			370
N^G-Tos-Z-Arg-Trp-Gly-OMe	1+2 DCCI	Acn	80					544
N^G-Tos-Z-Arg-Tyr-Gly-OBu^t								369
Arg-Val-Tyr Boc-hydrazide					175 (dec)	−19; −25	Me; DMF	190
Z-Arg-Val-Tyr Boc-hydrazide	1+2 DCCI	Py	71	EtAc-Me	160 (dec)	−26; −12; −16	Me; DMF; Ac	190
Z-Arg-Val-Tyr Boc-hydrazide					163 (dec)			190
N^G-Nitro-Z-Arg-Val-Tyr		Alc			183–186	−30; −10	Me; DMF	569

Table 3 Tripeptides (continued)

Compound	Method	Solvent	% Yield	Solvent Crystallization	M.P.(°C)	[α]D	Solvent Rotation	Ref.
N^G-Nitro-Z-Arg-Val-Tyr	1+2 DCCI	THF		Alc-Aq	182–183	+7.1	Py	569
N^G-Nitro-Z-Arg-Val-Tyr-OMe	1+2 DCCI	THF	56		211–214	+5.0	DMF	569
N^G-Nitro-Z-Arg-Val-Tyr-OMe	1+2 DCCI	THF	36	Alc-Aq	180–185			569
Asparagine								
Z-Asn-Ala-Pro	1+2 OTCP	DMF	60		178	82	Me	259
Z-Asn-Ala-Pro-OBu^t				Aq	188–189	–54	1M Ac	259
Asn-Asn-S-Bzl-Cys-OMe	1+2 MA	Chf	52–56	Ac-Aq	219–221	–28	DMF	765
Z-Asn-Asn-S-Bzl-Cys-OMe					oil			765
Asn-S-Bzl-Cys-Tyr-OEt Hydrobromide	1+2 ONP	DMF	66	DMF-Aq	148–152	–37	DMF	452
Z-Asn-S-Bzl-Cys-Tyr-OEt					oil			452
Asn-Gln-Tyr-OEt Hydrobromide	1+2 ONP	DMF	72	DMF-Eth	224–225 (dec)	–11	DMF	451
Z-Asn-Gln-Tyr-OEt								451
Asn-Ser-Gly				Aq-Me	230–234	–12 / –9.0	Aq / 1N HCl	269
Z-Asn-Ser-Gly				Aq	185–186	–8.4	Ac	269
Z-Asn-Ser-Gly-OEt				Me	224–226			491
Z-Asn-Ser-Gly-ONBzl	1+2 DCCI	Acn	45	DMF-Me	210–212	–12 / –1.5	Ac / DMF	269
Aspartic Acid								
Boc-Asp-Ala-Phe-OMe	1+2 ONP	DMF	52	Eth-EtAc	174	–29	Aq	525
Asp-Cys-Gly					180	–18	Ac	382
β-OBzl-Z-Asp-S-bzl-Cys-Gly	1+2 DCCI		72	Alc	149–151			382
Asp-Gly-Gly Amide				EtAc-Pe-Eth	126–128			545
β-OBzl-Z-Asp-Gly Amide	1+2 DCCI	DMF	65	Eth-Pe	168			545
β-OBu^t-Asp-Phe-Val-OBu^t				EtAc	98–100	–11	Me	727
β-OBu^t-Z-Asp-Phe-Val-OBu^t	1+2 MCA	THF	85		121–122	–37	Me	727

Compound	Method	Solvent	Yield (%)	Recryst. solvent	m.p. (°C)	$[\alpha]$	Solvent	Ref.
Z-Asp-Ser-Ala-di-OBzl	1+2 DCCI	THF-Acn			131	−17	Ac	140
Z-Asp-Ser-Glu-tri-OBzl	1+2 DCCI	EtAc-Pe	80		80-82	−20; −36	Py; Py-Aq	140; 118
Asp-OAc-Ser-Gly-ONp Hydrobromide				Acn	143-144.5	−15	Py	269
Asp-Ser-Gly					230-234	−15	Ac	142
Asp-Ser-Gly				Aq-Alc	174-176	−7.3	Aq	213
β-OBzl-Asp-OBzl-Ser-Gly-OEt Hydrobromide					174-176 (dec)	−7.3	Aq	213
β-OBzl-Z-Asp-OBzl-Ser-Gly-OBzl	1+2 DCCI	THF	77	EtAc-Pe	129-131	−4.7	Di	142
α-OBzl-Z-Asp-OBzl-Ser-Gly-OEt	DCCI	Di	78	EtAc-An-Pe	134-136	−5.6	Alc	213
β-OBzl-Z-Asp-Ser-Gly-ONp	1+2 DCCI	Acn		DMF-Acn	121-124; 148; 162			213
β-OBzl-N-for-Asp-OBzl-Ser-Gly-OEt	DCCI	Di	89	EtAc	91-93	−5.8	Ac	213
Z-Asp-OBzl-Ser-Gly-di-OBzl	DCCI	Di	41	EtAc	129-131	−4.7	Di	213
Z-Asp-Ser-Gly					185-186			269
Z-Asp-Ser-Gly-di-OBzl*	1+2 DCCI	Acn	74	EtAc	120	−8.9; −8.0	Py; Ac	140
Z-Asp-Ser-Gly-ONBzl	DCCI	DMF	45	Me	209-211			269
β-OBu^t-Boc-Asp-Ser-Gly				EtAc-He	132-134	−13; −16	Ac	573
β-OBu^t-Boc-Asp-Ser-Gly-ONBzl	1+2 DCCI	Acn	53	EtAc	131-133	−15	Me	573
β-OMe-Asp-Ser-Gly-ONp-Toluenesulfonate				DMF-Acn	150-151			118
β-OMe-Z-Asp-OAc-Ser-Gly-OBzl				EtAc-He	135-136			118
β-OMe-Z-Asp-Ser-Gly-ONBzl	1+2 DCCI	Acn	73	EtAc	136-137	−5.9; −11	Chf	269

*Material having unsharp m.p. (105-115) and higher optical rotation ($[\alpha]_D^{26}$ ranging between −12.9 and −19.4) was obtained in cases where a slight excess (10%) of triethylamine was used in the condensation step, or when the reaction product was washed extensively with aqueous bicarbonate solution.

Table 3 Tripeptides (continued)

Compound	Method	Solvent	% Yield	Solvent Crystallization	M.P. (°C)	[α]D	Solvent Rotation	Ref.
β-OMe-Z-Asp-Ser-Gly-ONp	1+2 DCCI	Acn	78	EtAc	187–188			118
β-OMe-Pz(OMe)-Asp-Ser-Gly-ONBzl				Acn	149–151			269
Asp-Tyr-Ser-OMe					189–191			559
Z-Asp-Tyr-Ser-OMe	1+2 ONP	EtAc-DMF	72.5	Eth-Pe	217–221			559
Cysteine								
S-Bzl-Z-Cys-Ala-Gln	1+2 MCA	THF	82	Me	154–156	−13	DMF	746
S-Bzl-Z-Cys-Ala-Gln Hydrazide				DMF-Eth	204–210	−17	DMF	746
S-Bzl-Z-Cys-Ala-Gln-OMe				Me	194–196	−23	DMF	746
S-Bzl-Z-Cys-Ala-Gly	1+2 MCA			Aq-Ac	154–157	−17	DMF	290
S-Bzl-Z-Cys-Ala-Gly-OEt	1+2 ONP	DMF	72	Aq-Ac	156–157	−16	DMF	305
S-Bzl-Z-Cys-Ala-Gly-OMe					156–157	−17	DMF	305
S-Bzl-Z-Cys-Ala-Gly-2,4,6-tri-me-OBzl	1+2 ONP	DMF	96		180	−13	DMF	314
S-Bzl-Z-Cys-Ala-Gly-2,4,6-tri-me-OBzl				EtAc-Cy	161.5–163	+18	DMF	625
S-Bzl-Z-Cys-Ala-Gly-2,4,6-tri-me-OBzl Hydrochloride				Me-EtAc	173.5–175			625
S-Bzl-Nps-Cys-Ala-Gly				Aq-Ipr	190–193	+7.4	5N-HCl	290
S-Bzl-Nps-Cys-Ala-Gly-OEt	1+2 DCCI	Chf	82	Aq-An	171–172			290
S-Bzl-Nps-Cys-Ala-Gly-2,4,6-tri-me-OBzl	1+2 MCA			Aq-An	167–169	+17		290
		DMF		DMF-Alc	186–189	+17	DMF	625
S-NBzl-Z-Cys-Ala-Gly-OEt	MCA	THF	85	Ac-Aq	212			304
S-Bzl-Z-Cys-Ala-Ser-OMe	2+1 A		72	Alc	198–201			249
S-Bzl-Z-Cys-Asn-Tyr-OEt				DMF-Aq	154–155	−22	DMF	452
S-Bzl-Cys-Asn-Tyr-OEt Hydrobromide					oil			452
*Di-Z-Cystinyl-bis(Gly-OEt)	WRK	Acn			165–166			187

*The base showed thermochromic changes. Green-blue at 100° and golden brown at −78°; warming to 25° restored the greenish color.

186

Compound	Method	Solvent	Yield (%)	Cryst. solvent	M.p. (°C)	$[\alpha]$	Solvent	Ref.
N,N′-Di-for-Cystinyl-bis(Gly-OEt)				EtAc	184–185	−80	DMF	187
N,N′-Di-Tos-Cystinyl-bis(Gly-OEt)				EtAc-Pe	173–175	−22	5N HCl	187
N,N′-Di-Z-Cystinyl-bis-Val-di-OBu^t					173–174			510
Cystinyl-bis-Val					184–185			510
S,N-Di-Z-Cys-S-NBzl-Cys-Ala-OMe	1+2 DCCI	Chf	61.4	Ac-Aq	152–153	−9.7	DMF	304
Bzh-Z-Cys-S-bzh-Cys-Gly	1+2 DCCI	MeCl	30	Alc	165–166	−42	DMF	223
S-Bzh-Z-Cys-S-bz-Cys-Gly-OEt				Alc	137–139	−19	DMF	223
S-Bzh-Z-Cys-Cys-Gly-OEt				Me	192–194	−26	DMF	223
N-S-Bz-Z-Cys-S-trt-Cys-Gly-OEt	DCCI	Chf	65.5	EtAc	136–138	−10	DMF	225
N-Z-S-Bzh-Cys-S-trt-Cys-Gly-OEt					152–153	−133	DMF	223
N-Z-S-(N′-Z-Cys)-Cys-Gly-OBzh				Me	131–132	−26	DMF	223
Z-Cys-S-bzh-Cys-Gly-OEt				Me	197–198.5	−9.5	DMF	227
Z-Cys-S-trt-Cys-Gly-OEt				MeCl-He	132–134	−95	DMF	223
Diethyl N,N′-Di-Z-Cystinyl-bis(S-bzh-Cys-Gly				EtAc-He	137–138	−63	DMF	223
Diethyl N,N,N-Di-Z Cystinyl-bis(S-trt-Cys-Gly)					184–185			225
S-(N-Z-S-Diphenyl-me-Cys)-N-bz-Cys-Gly-OEt	1+2 ONP	DMF	39.7	An-Pe	184–184.5	−91	DMF	224
S-Trt-Z-Cys-S-bzh-Cys-Gly-OBzh	DCCI	Chf	59	EtAc	184–185	−17	DMF	228
S-Trt-Z-Cys-S-bzh-Cys-Gly-OEt	DCCI	Chf	54	EtAc	183.5–185	−17	DMF	228
S-Trt-Z-Cys-S-bzh-Cys-Gly-ONp	1+2 DCCI	DMF	37.5	EtAc	187–190	−17	DMF	228
Z-S-Bzl-Cys-γ-OEt-Gly-γ-OEt-α-ONp-Glu	1+2 ONP	Chf	62	EtAc	169.5–170.5	−11	DMF	631
S-Bzl-Z-Cys-Glu-di-OBzl	1+2 DCCI	Acn	71	Alc	75	−35	DMF	674
S-Ac-Z-Cys-Gly-Gly-OEt					128			708
S-Bzl-Z-Cys-Gly-Gly	2+1 A		60	EtAc-Pe	121–123	−42	DMF	637
S-Bzl-Z-Cys-Gly-OEt					114–115	−10	Alc	263
S-Bzl-Z-Cys-Gly-Gly Hydrazide	1+2 MCA	DMF		EtAc-Eth	173			263
S-Bzl-Z-Cys-Gly-Gly-ONp				EtAc-Cy	117–119.5	−20	DMF	637

Table 3 Tripeptides (continued)

Compound	Method	Solvent	% Yield	Solvent Crystallization	M.P.(°C)	[α]D	Solvent Rotation	Ref.
Z-Se-Bzl-Cys-Gly-Gly-OEt	MCA	Chf			98–100			145
Se-Bzl-Z-DL-Cys-Gly-Gly					149			145
Se-Bzl-Z-Cys-Gly-Gly-OEt					85			145
Se-Bzl-DL-Cys-Gly-Gly-OEt					196–197			145
N,N'-Di-Bzhoc-Cystinyl-di-Gly-OEt				EtAc-n-He	166–168	−15	Chf	222
N,N'-Di-Z-Cystinyl-di-Gly-OEt								225
N,N'-Di-Z-diseleno-Cystinyl-di-Gly				Alc	223 (dec)			144
N,N'-Di-Z-diseleno-Cystinyl-bis Gly-OEt								144
N,N'-Bis-Z-Cystinyl-bis-Gly-OMe								777
Diseleno-Cystinyl-bis-Gly								144
N,N'-Di-Tos-Cystinyl-bis-Gly				i-Pr-Aq	136	+144	Alc	419
N,N'-Di-Tos-Cystinyl-bis-Gly-OEt				Alc	183–184	+18	Di	419
S-Bzl-Cys-Gly-Ser-OEt				Alc-Eth-Pe	147.5–148.5			41
S-Trt-Cys-Gly-Val-OBu^t	EDCI	MeCl		Me-Eth-He	162–163	+0.6	Alc	226
S-Trt-Cys-Gly-Val-OBu^t	1+2	MeCl	82		151–153			226
N,S-Di-Trt-Cys-Gly-Val-OBu^t	EDCI			Chf-Pe	105–110	+68	Alc	226
N,S-Di-Trt-Cys-Phe-Gly-OBu^t								229
S-Trt-Cys-Phe-Gly-OBu^t Oxalate Salt	1+2	MeCl	17	Eth		+7.4	DMF	229
S-Trt-Cys-N-Pht-Phe-Gly-OBu^t	EDCI					−5.5	DMF	229
S-Trt-Nps-Cys-Phe-Gly-OBu^t	EDCI	MeCl	92			−10	Me	229
S-Bzl-Z-Cys-Phe-Phe Azide				Me	208			68
S-Bzl-Z-Cys-Phe-Phe Hydrazide				Me	163	−38	DMF	68
S-Bzl-Z-Cys-Phe-Phe-OMe						−25	Py	68
S-Bzl-Z-Cys-Phe-Tyr Azide	2+1 DCCI	Acn	75			−36	DMF	68
S-Bzl-Z-Cys-Phe-Tyr Hydrazide					234	−35	DMF	68

Compound	Method	Solvent	Yield %	Recryst. solvent	M.p.	$[\alpha]$	Solvent	Ref.
S-Bzl-Z-Cys-Phe-Tyr-OMe	DCCI		63	EtAc-Eth-Pe	152	-24 / -25	Me / DMF	68
S-Bzl-Z-Cys-Pro-Abu-Gly Amide	1+2 OTCP	DMF	79	EtAc	143-144	-83	Ac	275
S-Bzl-Z-Cys-Pro-Gly Amide	1+2 ONP	DMF		Me	100-103	-46	Me	276
S-Bzl-Z-Cys-Pro-Leu Me-amide	1+2 ONP	DMF	57	EtAc-Me	75-76	-68	Alc	72
S-Bzl-N-for-Cys-Ser-Leu Amide	1+2 DCCI	DMF	76	Alc-Aq	219			304
S-Bzl-Z-Cys-Thr-Ser-OMe	1+2 ONP	DMF		Me-Aq	185-187	-16	DMF	317
S-Bzl-Cys-Tyr-Gly				Aq-Alc	187-190			292
S-Bzl-N-tos-Cys-Tyr-cyclohexy-Gly Hydrazide				Aq-Ac	249-253			128
S-Bzl-N-tos-Cys-Tyr-D-cyclohexyl-Gly Hydrazide				Alc-Aq	234-236		Me	128
S-Bzl-N-tos-Cys-Tyr-cyclohexyl-Gly-OMe	2+1 A	EtAc	84	Me	228-229	-37		128
S-Bzl-N-tos-Cys-Tyr-D-cyclohexyl-Gly-OMe	2+1 A	EtAc	81	Me	252-255	-34		128
S-Bzl-N-tos-Cys-Tyr-cyclopentyl-Gly Hydrazide				DMF-Aq	201-203		Me	128
S-Bzl-N-tos-Cys-Tyr-cyclopentyl-Gly-OMe	2+5 A	Chf-EtAc	81	Aq-Me	185-190	-47		128
S-Bzl-Z-Cys-N-me-Tyr-Ile			100		oil	-75	Ac	258
S-Bzl-Z-Cys-N-me-Ile-OBu^t	1+2 DCCI	THF	95		oil			258
S-Bzl-Z-Cys-N-me-Tyr-Ile-OMe	1+2 DCCI	Chf	94		180-182	-80	Ac	258
S-Bzl-Z-Cys-Tyr-Ile	2+1 DCCI	Acn		Eth-Pe	155-156	-61	Ac	51
S-Bzl-Z-Cys-Tyr-Ile-OMe			67.5	Eth-Pe	154-156	-29	An	51
S-Bzl-N-tos-Cys-OMe-Tyr-Ile-OMe	2+1 DCCI			Alc	154-156			295
S-Bzl-N-tos-Cys-D-Cys-OMe-Tyr-Ile-OMe	2+1 A				169			295
S-Bzl-N-tos-Cys-Tyr-Ile ONp	2+1 A		78		163	-35	Me	276
Se-Bzl-Z-Cys-Tyr-Ile	2+1 DCCI	Acn			193	-4	DMF	145
S-Bzl-N-Tos-Cys-Tyr-Leu-OMe	MCA / 2+1 A / 2+1 A	Aq	79 / 83.5	Aq-Me	191-192 / 191-192			437 / 249 / 249
S-Bzl-Z-Cys-OMe-Tyr-Phe Hydrazide	2+1 A		78.5	Aq-Me	219-220			604

189

Table 3 Tripeptides (continued)

Compound	Method	Solvent	% Yield	Solvent Crystallization	M.P.(°C)	[α]D	Solvent Rotation	Ref.
S-Bzl-Z-Cys-OMe-Tyr-Phe-OMe	2+1 DCCI	DMF-Acn		76	167-168 203			604
S-Bzl-Cys-Tyr-Phe-OMe								192
S-Bzl-Cys-Tyr-Phe-OMe Hydrobromide								192
S-Bzl-N-Tos-Cys-Tyr-Phe-OMe	2+1 A	Aq-Ac		Aq-Me	180-181	-43	Me	765
S-Bzl-N-Tos-Cys-Tyr-Phe Hydrazide					241-245	+7.0	DMF	765
S-Btm-Z-Cys-Tyr-Phe Hydrazide					232.5-235	-44	DMF	103
S-Btm-Z-Cys-Tyr-Phe-OMe	2+1 A	DMF-Aq	43	Me-Aq	172-173	-43	DMF	103
S-Bzl-N-Tos-Cys-Tyr-OMe-Thr Hydrazide				DMF-Aq	204-207			91
S-Bzl-N-Tos-Cys-Tyr-OMe-Thr-OMe	2+1 A	Aq-THF	83	EtAc-Pe	178-181			91
S-Bzl-Z-Cys-Tyr-Tyr Azide				Me	238			68
S-Bzl-Z-Cys-Tyr-Tyr Hydrazide	2+1 DCCI	Py	82	EtAc	177	-18	Me	68
S-Bzl-Z-Cys-Tyr-Tyr-OMe						-29	DMF	68
S-Bzl-N-Tos-Cys-Tyr-nor-Val-OMe	2+1 DCCI	THF	55	EtAc	186.5-187.5			68
Glutamine								
Z-Gln-Asn-S-bzl-Cys Hydrazide	1+2 MCA	Chf-DMF	75-81	Aq-DMF	259-260			765
Z-Gln-Asn-S-bzl-Cys-OMe				Aq-Ac	238-240	-38	Ac	765
Z-Gln-Asn-Se-bzl-Cys	MCA	THF-Di			200-201			145
Z-Gln-Asn-Se-bzl-Cys-OMe					229-230			145
Gln-Asn-S-bzl-Cys-OMe				Aq	192-194	-46	Ac	765
Gln-Asp-S-bzl-Cys-OMe Hydrobromide				Me-Eth	184-185			643
Z-Gln-S-bzl-Cys-His Monohydrate	1+2 MCA	DMF-THF	73	Me	191-194	-22	DMF	746
Z-Gln-Trp-Leu-OBu^t	1+2 MCA	THF	84	Alc-Aq	204-205	-42	Alc	719
Z-Gln-Trp-Leu Boc-hydrazide	1+2 ONP	Py	70	DMF-Aq	247 (dec)	-28	DMF	719
Gln-Trp-Leu-OBu^t					134-136	-21	Me	719
Gln-Trp-Leu Boc-hydrazide					105-118	-31	Me	719

Compound	Method	Solvent	Yield (%)	Recryst.	M.p.	[α]	Solvent	Ref.
Tfa-Gln-Trp-Leu Boc-hydrazide	1+2 DCCI		64		265	−26	DMF	720
Tfa-Gln-Trp-Leu Hydrazide					249–252	−23	DMF	720
α-OBzl-Z-Glu-Ala-Gly-OBzl	MCA		50		140–142			382
α-OBzl-Z-Glu-Ala-Gly-ONp					129–131			382
Glu-Ala-Gly								321
γ-Glu-dehydro-Ala-Gly								609
γ-OBu^t-Z-Glu-Ala-Phe-OMe	1+2 A	DMF	73		142–145	−26	Me	395
γ-OBu^t-Glu-Ala-Phe-OMe						−12	Me	395
γ-OBzl-Z-Glu-N^G-Tos-Arg-Gly	1+2 ONP		77	An-Eth	82–85	−7.5	An	539
γ-OBzl-Z-Glu-N^G-Tos-Arg-Gly-ONp				EtAc	105–108	−7.5		539
α-OBu^t-Z-Glu-N^G-nitro-Arg-Gly				Aq-Alc	125–127	−10	DMF	403
γ-OBu^t-Z-Glu-N^G-nitro-Arg-Gly					126–128	−16	Alc	536
γ-OBu^t-Z-Glu-N^G-nitro-Arg-Gly-OMe	1+2 ONP	DMF	68		116–119	−20	Alc	536
γ-OBu^t-Z-Glu-N^G-tos-Arg-Gly	1+2 ONP		97		88–94	−5.4	DMF	542
γ-OMe-Z-Glu-N^G-nitro-Arg-Gly	1+2 ONP	THF	47	DMF-EtAc	178–179	−9.3	DMF	351
γ-OBzl-Z-Glu-Asn-Tyr Boc-hydrazide	1+2 ONP		62.3		210–215	−16	DMF	762
γ-OBu^t-Z-Glu-Asn-Tyr Boc-hydrazide	1+2 ONP		38		210–212	−22	Ac	762
α-γ-Glu-Bis-α-Orn					185–202 (dec)			385
Z-α-γ-Glu-Bis-N$^\delta$-Z-Orn-OBzl	ONP	THF	70	EtAc-Pe	182–183	−9.5	Ac	385
Z-Glu-Bis-Val-OMe	DCCI	DMF	91	Alc	126–127	−18	Alc	330
Z-α-me-S-bzl-Cys-β-Ala-OEt	1+2 DCCI	Me	47		140–142	+35		435
γ-OBzl-Z-Glu-S-bzl-Cys-Gly	1+2 ONP	Py-Acn	62		100–107	−22	Ac	382
γ-OBzl-Z-Glu-S-bzl-Cys-Gly-OBzl	1+2 ONP	Acn	82		165–166	−25	Ac	382
	DCCI		90		149–150	−35	Ac	382
γ-OBzl-Z-Glu-S-Z-Cys-Gly-OBzl	1+2 DCCI				158–159	−35	Me	610
α-OBzl-Z-Glu-Se-bzl-Cys-Gly-OBzl	1+2 DCCI	MeCl		Alc	161–163	−26	DMF	668
Z-α-OBzl-γ-Glu-Se-bzl-Cys-Gly-OBzl	DCCI	MeCl		Alc	161–163	−26	DMF	668
Z-α-OEt-γ-Glu-Se-bzl-Cys-Gly-OEt	MCA	THF	31	Alc	103–106			143
Z-γ-Glu-Se-bzl-Cys-Gly	AC	Py	71	Alc	103	−29	DMF	144
Dnp-Glu-S-Dnp-Cys-Gly					139			609
Glu-Cys-Gly					190–192	−21	Aq	382

Table 3 Tripeptides (continued)

Compound	Method	Solvent	% Yield	Solvent Crystallization	M.P.(°C)	[α]$_D$	Solvent Rotation	Ref.
Glu-S-Dnp-Cys-Gly	1+2 MCA	THF	50	Aq	211			609
γ-OMe-Z-Glu-Se-bzl-D-L-Cys-Gly-OEt					oil			144
α-OMe-N-Dnp-Glu-S-Dnp-Cys-Gly-OMe				Alc	131			609
Z-γ-di-Glu-Glu-tetra-OBzl	2+1 DCCI	THF	61	Alc-Aq	140	-4.4	Ac	694
Z(OMe)-γ-di-Glu-Glu-tetra-OBzl				EtAc-Pe	147-149	-5.4 / -16	Ac / DMF	694
Z-di-(γ-OMe-Glu)-Glu-di-OEt	2+1 MCA	DMF	87	Alc	114	-16	Di	175
γ-OEt-Z-Glu-γ-OMe-Glu-γ-OEt-Glu-ONBzl	1+2 DCCI		65		126-127	-11	DMF	635
Glu-Glu-tetra-OBzl	MCA	Di	35	Me	139-142			80
γ-OMe-Z-D-Glu-γ-OMe-Glu-Glu-di-OEt	1+2 MA	THF		EtAc-Pe	97-101	-9.9	Di	175
N-Nps-Glu-γ-bz-Glu-Glu-OBzl				EtAc	174-177	-20	DMF	775
Z-Glu-Gly-Tri-OEt					149			377
Z-di-(γ-OMe-Glu)-Gly-OMe	2+1 ONP	DMF-Chf	72	EtAc	151-152	-6.9	DMF	172
γ-OEt-Z-Glu-γ-OEt-Glu-Gly	1+2 ONP	DMF	82	Alc-Eth	181.5-182	-5.8	DMF	627
γ-OEt-Z-Glu-γ-OEt-Glu-Gly-2,4,6-tri-me-OBzl	1+2 ONP	DMF	73	Alc	181.5-182	-5.4	DMF	627
Glu-Glu-Gly Hydrobromide					119-120			377
γ-OMe-Z-Glu-γ-OEt-Glu-Val-ONBzl					152-154	-9.5	DMF	635
γ-OMe-Z-Glu-α-OMe-Glu-Val-ONBzl					124	-10	DMF	635
Z-Glu-Glu-Asp-tri-OBzl					145			377
Glu-Gly-Asp								377
Z-Glu-Gly-Glu-tri-OBzl	MCA	Chf	67	Pe	74-76			377
Glu-Gly-Glu				An-Aq	168			377
γ-OBzl-N-for-Glu-Gly-Gly-Gly-OCH$_2$CN	1+2 DCCI	MeCl	34	EtAc-Eth	56-58	-2.5	DMF	422
γ-OBzl-N-tfa-Glu-Gly-Gly				EtAc-Pe	130-132	-4.8	Ac	422
γ-OBzl-N-tfa-Glu-Gly-Gly-OBu^t	1+2 DCCI	MeCl	61		104	-2.1	Ac	422

Compound	Method	Solvent	Yield (%)	Recryst. solvent	M.p.	$[\alpha]$	Solvent	Ref.
γ-OEt-Z-Glu-Gly-Gly	1+2 MCA	Acn		EtAc-Eth	118.9–119	+2.1	Chf	637
γ-OEt-Z-Glu-Gly-Gly-OCH$_2$-CN				EtAc-Cy	105–106	−2.7	DMF	637
γ-OEt-Z-Glu-Gly-Gly-ONp				Alc	130.5–133	−4.0	DMF	637
Glu-Gly-Gly					159–161	−1.5	DMF	422
γ-OMe-Glu-Gly-Gly				Aq-Alc	169–171	+40	Ac	422
γ-OMe-Glu-Gly-Gly-OBu^t				Chf-Pe	96	+6.0	Ac	422
N-Tfa-Glu-Gly-Gly				EtAc-Pe	137	−5.4	Aq	422
Z-γ-Glu-Gly-Leu-OMe	OPh	THF	69	EtAc-Pe	124–126			332
Z-γ-Glu-Gly-Leu-OMe DCHA Salt				Alc-Eth	138–139			332
γ-OMe-Boc-Glu-Gly-Pro	2+1 DCCI	MeCl	70	EtAc	100–102	−46	Me	9
γ-OMe-Boc-Glu-Gly-Pro DCHA Salt					165–168	−6	Ac	9
γ-OBzl-Z-Glu-His-Phe-OMe	DCCI		79		172–173	−3.7	DMF	407
γ-OBu^t-Z-Glu-His-Phe				Acn	161–162	−11	DMF	261
γ-OBu^t-Z-Glu-N^{im}-Z-His-Phe-OMe	1+2 DCCI	MeCl	95					261
Glu-His-Phe-OMe					185–189 (dec)	−12	Me	407
γ-OMe-N-for-Glu-His-His-Phe	1+2 DCCI	Acn	87.2	MeCl	165–165.5 (dec)	−12	DMF	261
γ-OMe-N-for-Glu-N^{im}-Z-His-Phe-OBzl								261
γ-OBzl-Z-Glu-Phe-Gly-OMe	2+1 OPAP	THF	77	THF-Pe	143–145	+7.6	THF	355
Z-Glu-Phe-Gly-di-OEt	1+2 DCCI	MeCl	67	EtAc-Pe	129–131	−28	Alc	24
γ-OBu^t-Z-Glu-Phe-Thr-OMe	DCCI	Acn	69		60			98
Bz-pyro-Glu-Pro-N$^\varepsilon$-Z-Lys-OMe	DCCI	Acn-MeCl	69					525
Bz-pyro-Glu-Pro-Ser-OMe								525
Z-Glu-Ser-Ala-di-OBzl	1+2 DCCI		78	EtAc-Eth	166–168	−16	Ac	140
γ-OMe-Z-Glu-OAc-Ser-γ-OMe-Glu-ONp				Me	309–312 (dec)	−33	DMF	620
γ-OMe-Z-Glu-OAc-Ser-γ-OMe-Glu-ONp p-toluenesulfonate								620
γ-OBzl-Z-Glu-OBzl-Ser-Gly-OEt	DCCI	Di		An-EtAc	146–147	−1.8	Di	213
Z-Glu-OBzl-Ser-Gly-di-OBzl	1+2 DCCI	Acn-THF	66	EtAc	109–112	−7.7	Ac	213
Z-Glu-Gly-di-OBzl				EtAc	121			140

Table 3 Tripeptides (continued)

Compound	Method	Solvent	% Yield	Solvent Crystallization	M.P.(°C)	[α]D	Solvent Rotation	Ref.
α-OEt-Z-Glu-Ser-Gly-OEt	DCCI	Chf	57	Alc-Aq	145-147	-2.5	EtAc	491
Glu-Ser-Gly	OTCP	DMF	99		191-192 (dec)	+8.6	Aq	213
Bz-pyro-Glu-Ser-N$^\epsilon$-boc-Lys-OMe					106-108			525
Z-Glu-Trp-Leu-OMe				EtAc	198-201	-23	DMF	260
Glu-Trp-Leu-OMe								260
Z-γ-Glu-Val-Ala	OPh	THF	74	Aq-Alc	173-174			332
Z-γ-Glu-Val-Ala DCHA Salt					171-172			332
Z-Glu-Val-Val-OEt				Alc-Eth	186-187	-39	Ac	330
Z-Glu-Val-Val-OEt-γ-hydrazide				Alc-Aq	215	-36	Ac	330
Glycine								
N-Z-Gly-3-chloro-Ala-Ala-OMe				EtAc-Pe	140.5-141			790
Ac-aza-Gly-aza-Ala-Gly-OEt					100-135			154
Z-Gly-DL-Ala-Gly	1+2 SPh		57	Aq	150.5-151			700
Z-Gly-Ala-Gly Azide					183-184			540
Z-Gly-Ala-Gly-OEt	2+1 A				144-145			540
Z-Gly-DL-Ala-Gly-OEt	1+2 MCA	THF	68.5	Alc-Aq	139			233
Z-Gly-β-chloro-Ala-Gly-OEt	1+2 DCCI		80		132	-9.4	DMF	708
Z-Gly-Ala-Phe	MA	Py		EtAc	163-164	-19		169
Z-Gly-Ala-Phe-OEt				EtAc-Pe	122-123	-24		169
Boc-Gly-Ala-Phe Hydrazide	MCA		77		177-183	-27	Ac	394
Boc-Gly-Ala-Phe-OMe	1+2 MCA	Chf	80		107-108	-24	Me	394
N-Trt-Gly-Ala-Phe-OEt				An	150-151.5			158
Boc-Gly-As-Gly-OBu^t								599
Boc-Gly-βONBzl-Asp-Gly-OBu^t					108-110	-14	Ac	599
Z-Gly-Arg-Arg 2-Naphthylamide	ONP	DMF	69	Alc	119-120			484
Ac-Gly-S-bzl-Cys-Gly-OEt					162.5-			760
Ac-Gly-S-bzl-Cys-Gly-N-Me-amide								760

Compound	Method	Solvent	Yield (%)	Recryst. solvent	M.p. (°C)	[α]	Rot. solvent	Page
Ac-Gly-Cys-Gly-N-Me-amide				Alc	193-194	-28	DMF	760
Z-Gly-S-ac-Cys-Gly-OEt				Eth-An-Pe	92-95	-29	DMF	481
Z-Gly-S-bz-Cys-Gly-OEt	1+2 MCA	Chf	49		94	-30	DMF	708
Z-Gly-S-bzl-Cys-Gly-OBzl	2+1 MCA	Chf	85	An-Pe	105-108			481
Z-Gly-S-bzl-DL-homo-Cys-Gly-OBzl				EtAc-Pe	110-114			97
Gly-S-et-Cys-Gly	1+2 DCCI	Chf		EtAc-Pe	110-114			97
Z(NO₂)-Gly-S-Z-Cys-Gly-OBzl				Aq-Ac	220 (dec)			97
Z(NO₂)-Gly-S-Dnp-Cys-Gly				EtAc	135-136			609
Z-Gly-S-bzl-Cys-OMe-Tyr Hydrazide	2+1 A			Ac-Aq	113			609
Z-Gly-S-bzl-Cys-OMe-Tyr-OMe	MCA	Chf	58	DMF-Aq	215-217	-25	DMF	772
Z-Gly-S-bzl-Cys-Tyr Amide	MCA	Chf	60	Aq-Me	137-138	-22	DMF	772
Z-Gly-S-bzl-Cys-Tyr-OEt	1+2 MCA	Chf	63	EtAc-Pe	183-185			292
Z-Gly-S-bzl-Cys-Tyr Hydrazide				i-Pr-Pe	87-88	-9.8	Di	295
Gly-S-bzl-Cys-Tyr-Amide				EtAc-Pe	153-155			299
Gly-S-bzl-Cys-Tyr-OEt				Aq-Me	207-209			295
Z-Gly-Glu-Tri-OMe				Me-Eth	126-130	-12	Alc	292
Z-Gly-γ-OMe-Glu-Glu-di-OEt	1+2 MCA	EtAc-DMF	85	EtAc-Pe	107-111			299
Z-Gly-γ-OMe-Glu-Gly-OEt	2+1 DCCI	TEA	68.5	EtAc-Eth-Pe	78-80			377
Z-Gly-γ-OMe-Glu-Gly-OMe	1+2 MCA	EtAc	49	EtAc-Eth	84-85			172
Gly-Gly-β-Ala-SePh Hydrobromide					82-85			384
Gly-Gly-DL-Ala-SePh Hydrobromide					110-111			172
Ac-Gly-Gly-Arg 2-Naphthylamide Hydrochloride				Alc-Eth				719
Z-Gly-Gly-Arg 2-Naphthylamide Hydrochloride								719
β-Carboxyproprionyl-Gly-Gly-Arg 2-Naphthylamide Hydrochloride								484
Z-Gly-Gly-Asp-SPh	2+1 MCA	THF	65.5	EtAc-DMF	204-205	-56	DMF	383
Z-di-Gly-S-bzl-Cys-OBzl	MCA	Chf	49		113.5-114.5	-34	Aq-Py	279
Di-Gly-S-bzl-Cys-OBzl Hydrobromide				Alc-Eth	147-148	-38	Aq-Py	279
Di-Gly-Cys								279

Table 3 Tripeptides (continued)

Compound	Method	Solvent	% Yield	Solvent Crystallization	M.P.(°C)	$[\alpha]_D$	Solvent Rotation	Ref.
Z-Gly-Gly-Gln-γ-OMe-α-ONp	2+1 MCA	THF	90	EtAc-Pe	108-109	−30	DMF	384
Z-Gly-Gly-Gln-γ-OMe-α-SPh				EtAc-Pe	104	−49	DMF	384
Gly-Gly-Gln-γ-OMe-α-SPh Hydrobromide				Alc-Eth	175-176	−78	Aq	384
Gly-Gly-Glu-γ-OMe-α-ONp Hydrobromide					148-149	−48	Aq	384
Gly-Gly-Glu-γ-OMe-α-SePh Hydrobromide								719
Aza-Gly-aza-Gly-Gly-OEt					192			154
N-Bzhoc-Gly-Gly-Gly					189-189.5 (dec)			219
N-Bzhoc-Gly-Gly-Gly-OEt	DCCI	DMF			175-176			219
Z-aza-Gly-aza-Gly-Gly-OEt					190-193			154
Z-Gly-Gly-aza-Gly Amide	1+2 SPh	Ac	76		184-186 (dec)			154
Z-tri-Gly								700
Z-Gly-Gly-Gly Anhydride				EtAc	194-195			29
Z-Gly-Gly-Gly-OBu^t	MCA		64	Alc-Aq	127-128			220
Z-Gly-Gly-Gly-OEt	2+1 ONP	Py	75	Alc	167-169			65
Z-Gly-Gly-Gly-ONp				Alc	167.5-168			712
Z-Gly-Gly-Gly-SPh					218-220			65
[Co(trien)(GlyOEt)(Gly-Gly-OEt)] Cl$_3$					132			700
Gly-Gly-Gly								96
Gly-Gly-Gly-OBu^t					oil			29
Gly-Gly-Gly-OEt Hydrobromide					191-194			220
Gly-Gly-Gly-OEt Hydrochloride								65
Gly-Gly-Gly-SePh Hydrobromide								164
Pht-tri-Gly-OEt								719
Z-Gly-Gly-His								11
Z-Gly-Gly-His-OMe				Alc-Eth	189-190			386
Gly-Gly-His								386

196

Compound	Method	Solv.	Yield (%)	Recryst.	M.p. (°C)	[α]	Solv.	Ref.
Z-Gly-aza-Gly-Leu-OEt					64–67	+1.6	Alc	154
Z-Gly-Gly-Leu	1+2 SPh	Ac	87.5	Aq	146–148			700
	1+2 ONP	Aq	88		144–145			30
For-Gly-Gly-Leu	2+1 CMEC	Aq	82		130	−28	Aq	334
Gly-Gly-Leu					197–198 (dec)	−28	Aq	700
Pht-Gly-Gly-Leu-OEt	2+1 A		70	Aq-Alc	155–156	+7	Chf	30
	2+1 DCCI		55		155–156			11
Z-di-Gly-N^ϵ-Z-Lys-OBzl				EtAc-Eth	99–100	−11	DMF	1
Z-di-Gly-N^ϵ-Z-Lys Hydrazide				Alc-Eth	174–175	−4.2	DMF	1
Di-Gly-N^ϵ-Z-Lys-OBzl Hydrochloride					155–160			1
Gly-Gly-Lys								1
Di-Gly-Lys Monohydrochloride								1
Trt-di-Gly-N^ϵ-Z-Lys-OBzl				EtAc-Pe	115–117	−10	DMF	1
For-Gly-Gly-Phe	2+1 CMCI	Aq	70	Alc	174–175			334
For-Gly-Gly-Pro	2+1 CMCI	Aq			oil			334
For-Gly-Gly-Ser	2+1 CMCI	Aq	84					334
For-Gly-Gly-Tyr	2+1 CMCI	Aq	77					334
Z-Gly-His-Gly	A	Chf	55	Aq	170–173			341
Z-Gly-His-Gly-OEt				Alc	172	−8	DMF	22
Z-Gly-N^{im}-His-Gly				EtAc-Chf	202–204			341
Z-Gly-N^{im}-His-Gly-ONBzl	2+1 A			Aq	173–174			341
Gly-His-Gly				EtAc	224			341
Z-Gly-N^{im}-Z-His-Leu-OMe	1+2 DCCI	MeCl	90	MeCl	152–152.5	−9.2	Me	261
Z-Gly-His-Phe					200 (dec)	+15	Me	261
Z-Gly-N^{im}-Z-His-Phe-OMe	1+2 DCCI	MeCl	89	MeCl	154–155	−8.6	Me	264
Gly-N^{im}-Z-His-Phe-OMe Dihydrobromide					154–154.5			261
Z-Gly-His-Ser								261, 264, 593

Table 3 Tripeptides (continued)

Compound	Method	Solvent	% Yield	Solvent Crystallization	M.P. (°C)	[α]$_D$	Solvent Rotation	Ref.
Z-Gly-His-Ser Hydrazide					208.5–209.5			593
Z-Gly-His-Ser-OMe	1+2 A	Aq	9.8	Me	166–167			593
Gly-His-Ser				Aq-Alc	202–203 (dec)			593
Gly-His-Ser-OMe					149–150	+4.3	DMF	549
Boc-Gly-Ile-Gly Hydrazide				Eth-Pe	163–165			333
Z-Gly-Leu-Gly	2+1 SPh	Ac	68		oil	−43	Aq	700
Z-Gly-DL-nor-Leu-Gly-OEt	2+1 OPAP		97		108.5–110.5			23
Z-Gly-Leu-Gly-OMe				EtAc-Pe	128–132			286
Z-Gly-Leu-Leu				EtAc-Pe	131–132			202
Z-Gly-Leu-D-Leu					145–147			202
Z-Gly-Leu-D-Leu-OMe					118			202
Z-Gly-Leu-Leu-OMe				Eth-Pe	133–134			286
Trt-Gly-Leu-nor-Leu-OMe	2+1 DCCI	Acn	69	Eth-Pe	75 (dec)			525
Boc-Gly-Leu-Met Amide	2+1 A	Aq	62	EtAc-Eth	107–110			525
	1+2 MCA		65		159–160	−30	Ac	395
Gly-Leu-Met Amide					156–158	−50	Aq	89
Gly-Leu-Met Amide Hydrochloride				EtAc	202–204	−48	Ac	395
N-Trt-Gly-Leu-Met Amide	2+1 DCCI	MeCl	66		214–216	−19	Alc	89

198

Compound	Method	Solvent	Yield	Recryst. solvent	M.p.	[α]	Rot. solvent	Ref.
Z-Gly-Leu-Val Amide	1+2 ONP	DMF	86	Aq	187–190	−30	Ac	66
Z-Gly-Leu-Val-OMe	2+1 DCCI-NHS	MeCl	86		oil			701
Gly-Leu-Val-OMe				EtAc-Pe	115–117	−50	Me	701
Trt-Gly-Leu-nor-Val-OMe	2+1 DCCI	Acn	71	Eth-Pe	80 (dec)			525
Z-Gly-N^ε-ac-Lys-Gly-OBzl	1+2 MCA	Chf	46	Acn	170–171			32
Z-Gly-N^ε-Z-Lys-Gly-OEt	2+1 MCA	THF	46.5	EtAc	155–158			754
Z-Gly-N^ε-tos-Lys-Gly Amide	1+2 ONP	DMF	87	Alc-EtAc	159–161	−14	Ac	336
Z-Gly-N^ε-tos-Lys-Gly-OEt				Di-Me	162–163 (dec)	−3.8	DMF	336
Z(OMe)-Gly-N^ε-Z-Lys-Gly				Di-Me-Eth	153–154	−6.9	DMF	1
Z(OMe)-Gly-N^ε-Z-Lys-Gly-OBzl	2+1 A	Ac-Aq	95					1
Z(OMe)-Gly-N^ε-Z-Lys-Gly-ONp								1
Boc-Gly-Lys-Gly-OBu^t	2+1 DCCI		76	Aq-Alc	125–130	−11	Alc	599
Boc-Gly-N^ε-Pz-Lys-Gly-OBu^t					245–246			599
Gly-N^ε-ac-Lys-Gly					177–182			32
Gly-N^ε-Z-Lys-Gly-OBzl Hydrochloride								1
Gly-N^ε-Z-Lys-Gly-ONp Trifluoroacetate								1
Gly-N^ε-tos-Lys-Gly Amide	1+2 MCA DCCI	THF	80	Eth	110 (dec)			336
N-Trt-Gly-N^ε-Z-Lys-N^ε-Z-Lys			67	Me-Eth-Pe				71
N-Trt-N-Gly-N^ε-Z-Lys-N^ε-Z-Lys-OMe								71
Z-Gly-Phe-Ala	2+1 MCA	THF	68		164–165.5	−10	Me	169
Z-Gly-Phe-Ala-OMe			80.4		106–108	−14	An	169

199

Table 3 Tripeptides (continued)

Compound	Method	Solvent	% Yield	Solvent Crystallization	M.P.(°C)	$[\alpha]_D$	Solvent Rotation	Ref.
Z-Gly-Phe-Arg-OMe	1+2 ONP	DMF	66	EtAc-He	110–112			65
Bz-aza-Gly-aza-Phe-Gly-OEt	2+1 DCCI	MeCl	81	EtAc-Pe	136–137			154
N-Z-Gly-p-nitro-Phe-Gly-OEt	2+1 OCH$_2$CN	Ac-THF	51		129–130			548
					129–130	+4	Ac	
N-Z-Gly-p-nitro-Phe-Gly-ONp	NHS	DME	92	Me-Aq	147–149	−11	Di	548
Z-Gly-Phe-Gly					157–158			7
Z-Gly-DL-Phe-Gly-OEt	MCA	DMF-THF	85	An-Aq	132–133			712
Z-Gly-Phe-Gly-OEt	2+1 OPAP		80	Alc	120–121			8
Z-Gly-Phe-Gly-OEt	2+1 A				121–122			23
	2+1 A	THF-NBS	62		116–117			711
		DMF-Aq	68		116–117			
	PHA	DMF-Acn	78		117–119	−13	Alc	491
	2+1 Sph	THF	80		114–115			121
	*2+1 TOSC	THF	47		132–133	0.0	Alc	667
	*2+1 TOSC	Acn	50		132–133			
	*2+1 Ac	THF	45	Alc	126–128	−0.7	Alc	
	2+1 MA		32		110	−12	Alc	99

*May correspond to Z-Gly-DL-Phe-Gly-OEt.

Compound	Method	Solvent	Yield (%)	Recryst. solvent	M.p. (°C)	$[\alpha]$	Rot. solvent	Ref.
Z-Gly-Phe-Gly-OMe	2+1 MCA	Chf						519
Boc-Gly-Phe-Gly-OEt	2+1 DCCI	Chf						355
Gly-p-nitro-Phe-Gly-ONp Hydrobromide	1+2 NHS	DME	79	Alc-Aq	100.5–101.5	−9.7	Me	7
Z-Gly-D-Phe-Leu				Me-An-Eth	178–180			548
Z-Gly-Phe-Leu-OEt	1+2 DCCI	EtAc	73	EtAc-Pe	91–94			56
Z-Gly-D-Phe-Leu Hydrazide				Aq-Me	166–167	−2.7 / 0 / −33	Ac / DMF / Me	87 / 87 / 87
Z-Gly-Phe-Leu Hydrazide	1+2 DCCI	EtAc	85	Me-Aq	173	−5.2	Ac	87
Z-Gly-D-Phe-Leu-OMe				EtAc-Pe	106–107	0	Me	87
Z-Gly-Phe-Leu-OMe	DCCI	EtAc		Eth-Pe	84–86			56
Boc-Gly-D-Phe-Leu-OMe	1+2 DCCI	Di	63		150–151.5	−17	Ac	87
Gly-D-Phe-Leu				Alc-Eth	210–215 (dec)			56
Gly-Phe-Leu-OEt Hydrobromide								87
Gly-D-Phe-Leu Hydrazide Dihydrobromide				Me-EtAc	233–234			87
Gly-Phe-Leu Hydrazide Hydrobromide				Eth-Me	108–109			87
Gly-Phe-Leu-OMe					178	−10	DMF	87
Gly-D-Phe-Leu-OMe Hydrobromide					144.5			87
Z-Gly-Phe-Phe	2+1 A	Aq-Ac	73	EtAc-Pe	144–146			757
Z-Gly-Phe-Phe-OEt	1+2 DCCI		78		226–228 (dec)			757
Gly-Phe-Phe								262
Gly-Phe-Phe-OEt Acetate				Me-Eth	97–98.5	−1.6	Me	757, 262

201

Table 3 Tripeptides (continued)

Compound	Method	Solvent	% Yield	Solvent Crystallization	M.P.(°C)	[α]D	Solvent Rotation	Ref.
Z-Gly-D-Phe-D-Ser-Hydrazide				DMF-Alc	189-191	+3.5 / -7.2	Ac	681
Z-Gly-D-Phe-D-Ser-OMe	2+1 A		75		146-148	0 / -12	Ac	681
Z-Gly-Pro-Ala					141-142			59
Z-Gly-Pro-Ala-OMe	WRK	Acn	64	EtAc-He	159-160	-128	Me	59
	DCCI	MeCl	81		158-159			716
Z-Gly-Pro-Ala-ONp				MeCl-He	153-155			59
Hoc-Gly-Pro-Ala					178			113
Hoc-Gly-Pro-Ala-ONBzl					173			113
Gly-Pro-Ala	2+1 MCA	Chf	78	Alc-Aq		-132	Ac	59
Gly-Pro-Ala-OMe Hydrobromide				Me-Eth	172-174			59
Gly-Pro-Ala-ONp Hydrobromide				Me-Eth	177-178			59
Z-Gly-Pro-Gly				EtAc	141	-79	Acn	496
					137-139	-80	Aq	59
					129-131			113
Z-Gly-Pro-Gly-OEt	2+1 DCCI	MeCl	80		oil			716
					oil			177
								615
Z-Gly-Pro-Gly-ONp	2+1 MA	Chf	50	Acn-Eth	151-153	-67	Alc	496
	DCCI	MeCl	96	i-Pr	146.5-148	-82	Alc	496
Z-Gly-Pro-Gly-ONp Hydrobromide				Acn-Eth	175-176 (dec)	-65	DMF	496
Gly-Pro-Gly						-101	Aq	59
Gly-Pro-Gly Dihydrate								113
Gly-Pro-Gly-OEt Hydrochloride				Alc	216-217 (dec)	-106	Aq	615
Gly-Pro-Gly-ONp Hydrobromide				Me-i-Pr	196-197 (dec)			59

Compound	Method	Solvent	Yield (%)	Recryst. solvent	M.p. (°C)	[α]	Solvent	Ref.
Pz-Gly-Pro-Gly	2+1 MCA	Chf	74		179–181	−48	DMF	570
Pz-Gly-Pro-Gly-OEt					166–167	−60	DMF	570
Pz-Gly-Pro-Gly Hydrazide					130–132	−50	DMF	570
Pz-Gly-Pro-Gly-ONp	1+2 A	Alc	63		192–193			570
Z-Gly-Pro-Leu Semicarbazide			35		179–180			444
Boc-Gly-Sar-N$^\epsilon$-bz-Lys	2+1 DCCI		96	An-Pe	230–232	−4.5	Di	75
Z-Gly-O-chlorocarbonyl-Ser-Ala-OMe				Alc	126.5–127			296
Z-Gly-Ser-Ala Hydrazide				Aq	198–201			711
Z-Gly-Ser-Ala-OMe	2+1 A		50	Alc-Aq	135.5–137	−38	Me	296
Gly-Ser-Ala Hydrazide Dihydrobromide					163–165			711
Z-Gly-Ser-Gly-OEt	1+2 DCCI	DMF	48	EtAc	153–155	+1.4	DMF	481
Z-Gly-Ser-Gly-ONp	1+2 DCCI	Acn	67	DMF-Acn	195			118
Z-Gly-O-Tos-Ser-Gly-OEt				An-Aq	102–103	+4.2	DMF	481
Z-Gly-Ser-His-OMe	1+2 ONP	DMF	84	Me	168–169	−18	DMF	244
Z-Gly-DL-Tyr-Gly-OEt	2+1 DCCI	THF	77	EtAc-Pe	112–113			278
Z-Gly-Tyr-Gly-OEt				EtAc-Pe	115–116			22
Gly-Tyr-Gly-OEt Hydrobromide	2+1 A / 2+1 DCCI	THF	70	Alc	190–192	−7.0	Alc	548
Boc-Gly-Val-Gly	1+2 MCA	Chf	72	Alc	155–157			267
Boc-Gly-Val-Gly-OMe				Alc	150 (dec)			267
N-Trt-Gly-Val-Phe	MCA	Chf	80.5		185			158
N-Trt-Gly-Val-Phe-OEt				Be				158
Histidine								
His-Gly-His	2+1 DCCI	MeCl	83	Me-Eth	145–160			386
Di-Trt-His-Gly-His	1+2 DCCI	MeCl	92					386
Di-Trt-His-Gly-His-OMe								386
Di-Trt-His-Gly-Phe-OMe				An-Cy	110–115	−8	Me	406

203

Table 3 Tripeptides (continued)

Compound	Method	Solvent	% Yield	Solvent Crystallization	M.P. (°C)	$[\alpha]_D$	Solvent Rotation	Ref.
Di-Z-His-N^{im}-Z-His-Phe-OBzl	1+2 DCCI	MeCl	81		138-140			264
	1+2 DCCI	MeCl	81		138-140	-17	Me	261
Di-Z-His-Phe-Arg Hydrate								297
N-(N^{α}-Z-His-Phe-Arg)-5-OMe-tryptamine	1+2 A	Me-EtAc-DMF	63	Me	154-156	-6.0	Me	740
Di-Z-His-Phe-Arg-OMe Carbonate				Me	131-135			297
Di-Z-His-Phe-Arg-OMe Hydrobromide	DCCI	Acn	70					297
Di-Z-His-Phe-N^{G}-nitro-Arg-OMe				Me	125-128			297
His-Phe-Arg-OMe Acetate				Eth-Me				297
N-(His-Phe-Arg)-5-OMe-tryptamine								740
Z-N^{im},bzl-His-Phe-N^{δ}-Z-Orn	2+1 DCCI	EtAc-THF	60	Di-Acn	149-150	-17	DMF	375
Z-N^{im},bzl-His-Phe-N^{δ}-Z-Orn-OMe				Di	157-158	-17	Di	375
Z-His-Phe-N^{δ}-Z-Orn				An-Aq	163-166	-15	Me	375
Z-His-Phe-N^{δ}-Z-Orn-OMe	2+1 A				191-193	-25	Me	375
N^{im}-Bzl-Z-His-Pro-Phe-OEt					oil			15
N^{im}-Bzl-Z-His-Pro-Phe Hydrazide								15
His-Pro-Phe					130-145 (dec)			406
His-Pro-Phe-ONBzl	1+2 DCCI	MeCl	89	Cy	135-155	-36	Me	406
Di-Trt-His-Pro-Phe				Cy	112-115	-1	Me	406
Di-Trt-His-Pro-Phe-OMe	1+2 DCCI	MeCl	68		131-140	-6	Chf	406
Di-Trt-His-Pro-Phe-ONBzl Cyclohexane Solvate				EtAc-Cy	202-204 (dec)	-20	Me	406
Z-His-Phe-Phe	1+2 A		68		154-156			262
Z-His-Phe-Phe-OBu^t	1+2 ONP		92		159-160 (dec)			262
Di-Z-His-Phe-Phe-OEt								262

Compound	Method	Solvent	Yield (%)	Recryst. solvent	m.p. (°C)	[α]	Rotation solvent	Ref.
Z-His-Phe-Phe-OEt					187–188	−23	Aq-Ac	262
Z-His-Phe-Trp-OEt	1+2 A		51		189–190	−24	Me	262
Z-His-Phe-Tyr-OEt					168–169	−27	Me	262
Di-Z-His-Phe-Tyr-OEt	1+2 ONP		92		156–158			262
N^{im}-Bzl-N^{α}-Z-His-Pro-Phe-OMe	1+2 AC	Py	98					717
N^{im}-Bzl-His-Pro-Phe-OMe Dihydrobromide	1+2 DCCI	DMF	90.5		211–214			405
His-Pro-Phe-OMe								216
Z-His-Tyr-Tyr-OEt	2+1 A		68		110–114	−24	Me	262

Isoleucine

Compound	Method	Solvent	Yield (%)	Recryst. solvent	m.p. (°C)	[α]	Rotation solvent	Ref.
N-Ac-Ile-S-bzl-Cys-Leu Amide	2+1 DCCI			Alc-EtAc	278			639
Z-Ile-S-bzl-Cys-Leu	2+1 MCA	THF		Alc	165			639
Ile-Cys-Leu					145			639
Z-Ile-S-bzl-Cys-Ser Hydrazide				DMF-Aq	224–225	−22	DMF	317
Z-Ile-S-bzl-Cys-Ser-OMe				Me-Aq	196–198	−31	DMF	317
Z-Ile-Gln-Asn Hydrazide	1+2 MCA	Chf	74	HMPA-Eth	219–221			289
Z-Ile-Gln-Asn-OMe				Aq-Ac	250–253	+35	DMF	289
Ile-Gln-Asn-OMe				Me	163–166			289
Z-Ile-Gln-Asp-ONBzl	1+2 ONP	DMF	63		247–250	−10	DMF	141
Ile-Gln-Asp-ONB					214–217	−34	0.5N KHCO$_3$	141
Z-Ile-Gly-Asp-ONB	1+2 ONP	DMF	88		218–222	−9.5	DMA	141
Ile-Gly-Asp					185–190	+50	Aq	141
Z-Ile-Gly-Val-OBu^t								698
Z(NO$_2$)-Ile-Gly-Val-ONBzl	2+1 MCA	DMF-Acn	73	Me-Eth	180–180.5	−3.0	DMF	631
N^{β}-Z-Ile-N^{α}-boc-hydrazino-ac-Leu-Met Amide				EtAc	180–182	−32	DMF	443
N^{β}-Boc-Ile-N^{α}-boc-hydrazino-ac-Leu-Met Amide	1+2 MA	Py	62		195–198			443
B$^{\beta}$-Ile-hydrazino-ac-Leu-Met Amide Acetate				Chf-Eth	201–202			443
Z-Ile-D-Phe-N^{im}-bzl-His-OEt	2+1 A			Alc	136			639
Z-Ile-D-Phe-N^{im}-bzl-His-OEt Hydrazide				Alc	194			639

Table 3 Tripeptides (continued)

Compound	Method	Solvent	% Yield	Solvent Crystallization	M.P.(°C)	$[\alpha]_D$	Solvent Rotation	Ref.
Z-Ile-Phe-Val-OBu^t								698
D-Allo-Ile-Pro-Sar-OBzl Hydrochloride	2+1 DCCI	MeCl	70			-106	Aq	77
For-D-allo-Ile-Pro-Sar-OBzl						-37	Me	77
Z-Ile-Pro-Val-OBu^t								698
Z-Ile-Val-α-OBu^t-Glu-OEt	1+2 ONP	DMF	92	MeCl-Eth	186-189			305
Z-Ile-Val-Glu-α-et-γ-OBu^t	1+2 ONP	DMF	92	MeCl-Eth	186-189	-18	Chf	305
Z-Ile-Val-Gly-2,4,6-tri-OMe-bzl	1+2 ONP	DMF	91	Ac	227.5-228.5	-33	Ac	625
Leucine								
Z-Leu-Ala-Thr-OMe	1+2 DCCI	THF	70-80	EtAc-Pe	154-155			704
Boc-Leu-Ala-Thr-OMe	1+2 DCCI	THF	60	EtAc-Pe	182-183			704
Leu-Ala-Thr-OMe Trichloroacetate								704
Leu-Ala-Val				Alc-Aq	240-242			430
Leu-Ala-Val Hydrate				Alc	243-247			430
Z(NO$_2$)-Leu-Ala-Val				Aq-Alc	160-161			430
Z(NO$_2$)-Leu-Ala-Val-OBzl	2+1 A		79	Aq-Alc	162-165			430
Z(NO$_2$)-Leu-Ala-Val Hydrazide					249.5-251.5			430
Z(NO$_2$)-Leu-Ala-Val-OMe	2+1 A		86	Me	199-200			430
Boc-Leu-N^G-di-Z-Arg-Leu-OMe	2+1 MCA	THF	57	Eth-Pe	155-156			183
Leu-Arg-Leu-Tfa				Alc-Acn	196			183
Z-Leu-Asp-Phe Amide	1+2 OTCP	Me	50	Aq-Me	224-226	-49	DMF	323
Z-Leu-β-OBu^t-Asp-Ser-OMe	EDCI		74		131-132.5	-34	Me	199
Leu-β-OBu^t-Asp-Ser-OMe					oil			199
Z-Leu-S-bzl-Cys-Gly-OEt	1+2 ONP	DMF	69	EtAc-Pe	127-130			350
N-Tos-D-Leu-S-bzl-Cys-Tyr-OEt	1+2 AC	EtAc	92	Aq-i-Pr / EtAc-Pe	114-118 / 58-62	+4.7	Di	299

Compound	Method	Solvent	Yield (%)	Recryst. solvent	mp (°C)	[α]		Ref.
N-Tos-Leu-S-bzl-Cys-Tyr-OEt	AC	Chf	85	Aq-Alc	131–137			293
Z-D-Leu-Gly-Gly					145–147			202
Z-Leu-Gly-Gly Anhydride	1+2 MCA				145–146			29
Z-D-Leu-Gly-Gly-OEt	1+2 MCA			EtAc-Eth	102–103			202
Z-Leu-Gly-Gly-OEt	2+1 ONP		60	EtAc	104–105			202
Chloroacetyl-Leu-Gly-Gly					147–148			30
Z-Leu-Gly-Leu					oil			29
Z-Leu-Gly-Pro-OEt	2+1 MCA	THF	74		oil			431
Z-Leu-Gly-Pro-OMe	2+1 AC	Py	86		58–59			717
Leu-Gly-Pro-OEt Hydrochloride					oil			431
Z-Leu-Gly-Ser-OBzl	2+1 DCCI	THF-Acn	80	EtAc-Eth	128	−2.3	Ac	140
Z-Leu-Leu-Gly				EtAc-Pe	148–150			202
Z-Leu-Leu-Gly				Me-Eth	180–181			202
Z-Leu-Leu-Gly DCHA Salt				Aq-Alc	123–124			202
Z-D-Leu-Leu-Gly-OMe				Eth	111–112			286
Z-Leu-Leu-Gly-OMe	1+2 ONP	Chf	70	Be-Eth	110	−51	Me	78
Boc-Leu-Leu-Gly-OMe					139–140			286
Leu-Leu-Gly-OMe Hydrochloride				Me-Eth	170–171			266
For-Leu-N$^\epsilon$-boc-Lys-N$^\epsilon$-boc-Lys					oil			266
For-Leu-N$^\epsilon$-boc-Lys-N$^\epsilon$-boc-Lys-OMe					oil			18
Z-Leu-D-Phe-Gly-OEt	2+1 MCA	Chf	80	EtAc-Eth	122–124	+13	Me	18
Leu-D-Phe-Gly-OEt Hydrochloride	1+2 DCCI				oil			337
For-Leu-Phe-N$^\epsilon$-boc-Lys					182–184	+68	DMF	266
For-Leu-Phe-N$^\epsilon$-boc-Lys-OMe					oil			266
Z-Leu-D-Phe-Pro-OEt	MCA	Chf	96		oil			451
Z-Leu-Phe-Pro-OMe	2+1 A		40	Eth-Pe	109–110			129
Leu-D-Phe-Pro-OEt Hydrochloride					oil			451
Leu-Phe-Pro-OMe Hydrochloride				Me-Eth	221–223			129
Z-Leu-D-Phe-Sar-OEt					oil			16
Leu-D-Phe-Sar-OEt Hydrochloride					oil			16
Z-Leu-Phe-Val	1+2 MCA	Chf-THF	66	EtAc-Pe	180–181			693

Table 3 Tripeptides (continued)

Compound	Method	Solvent	% Yield	Solvent Crystallization	M.P. (°C)	[α]$_D$	Solvent Rotation	Ref.
Z-Leu-Phe-Val-OBu^t	2+1 NHS	THF	90		oil			693
Z-Leu-Phe-Val-OMe	PHA	Acn		EtAc-Pe	152–154			697
Leu-Phe-Val-OMe Hydrochloride				Me-Eth	246–248			179
Z(OMe)-Leu-Phe-Val-OBu^t								179
Z-Leu-Tyr-Leu Hydrazide								52
Z-Leu-Tyr-Leu-OMe	1+2 ONP	DMF	88	Me	237	−39	DMF	679
Z-Leu-Val-S-bzl-Cys Amide	1+2 ONP		93	EtAc	177–178	−51	Me	166
Z-Leu-Val-Glu	1+2 ONP			Aq-Ac	230–231			307
Z-Leu-Val-Glu-γ-OBu^t-α-OMe	1+2 ONP	THF	81	Alc-EtAc-He	210–212	−28	DMF	755
				Alc	189–192			329
Z-Leu-Val-Glu-di-OEt	1+2 ONP	Chf	90	Alc	176–177			755
Z-Leu-Val-Glu-γ-OMe	1+2 ONP	THF	76	Alc	172–173	−16	DMF	319
Z-Leu-Val-Glu-di-OMe	1+2 ONP	Chf	97	Me-Eth	190.5–191			755
Leu-Val-Glu				An	216–218			755
Leu-Val-Glu-di-OEt Hydrochloride	ONP	DMF						755
Lysine								
Z-boc-Lys-D-Ala-D-Ala-ONBzl					129–130	+9.8	DMF	662
Z-Lys-D-Ala-D-Ala-ONBzl Toluene sulfonate					163	+23	DMF	662
N$^\alpha$-Z-N$^\epsilon$-boc-Lys-N^G-tos-Arg-N^G-tos-Arg-δ-aminovaleryl-OMe					82–85	−11	Me	454

208

Compound	Method	Solvent	Yield %	Recryst.	m.p. (°C)	[α]	Solv.	Ref.
N^ε-Boc-N^α-Z-Lys-N^G-nitro-Arg-N^G-nitro-Arg Amide	1+2 NHS	THF	71.8	n-Bu	111–114	−15	Me	461
N^ε-Boc-N^α-Z-Lys-N^G-nitro-Arg-N^G-nitro-Arg-OBzl	1+2 MCA	THF	65.6	n-Bu	110–120	−15	Me	461
N^ε-Boc-Z-Lys-N^G-tos-Arg-N^G-tos-Arg Amide	1+2 ONP		87	Acn	112–118	−20	Me	492
N^ε-Boc-Lys-Arg-Arg Amide Triacetate						−12	Ac-Aq	461
N^ε-Boc-Lys-Arg-Arg Di-acetate						+2.7	Ac-Aq	461
N^ε-Boc-Lys-N^G-tos-Arg-N^G-tos-Arg-δ-aminovaleryl-OMe						+5.3		454
Di-Z-Lys-N^G-Arg-Pro	1+2 MCA A	THF	76	Alc-Eth		−37	Ac	558
Di-Z-Lys-N^G-nitro-Arg-Pro-OMe			78			−40	Ac	558
Di-Boc-Lys-γ-OBu^t-Glu-Thr Hydrazide	1+2 MCA	THF	89	EtAc-Eth	113–114	−15	DMF	535
Di-Boc-Lys-γ-OBu^t-Glu-Thr Azide					99–101	−4.7	DMF	535
N^ε-Z-boc-Lys-di-Gly						−2.8	DMF	1
N^ε-Z-boc-Lys-di-Gly-OBzl	1+2 DCCI	MeCl	72	EtAc-Eth	80–83	−4.6	DMF	1
N^ε-Z-boc-Lys-di-Gly Boc Hydrazide				Alc-Eth	110–112	−0.7	Alc	1
N^ε-Z-N^α-for-Lys-Gly-Gly	1+2 MA	MeCl	84	Chf		+8.4	Ac	422
N^ε-Z-Lys-Gly-Gly-OBu^t								422
N^ε-Z-Lys-di-Gly Hydrazide Dihydrochloride					oil			1
Lys-Gly-Gly	1+2 DCCI	MeCl	71	EtAc-Pe	108–109	−6.4	Ac	422
N^ε-Tfa-Z-Lys-Gly-Gly				EtAc-Pe	107–108	−6.1	Ac	422
N^ε-Tfa-Z-Lys-Gly-Gly-OBu^t								422

Table 3 Tripeptides (continued)

Compound	Method	Solvent	% Yield	Solvent Crystallization	M.P. (°C)	$[\alpha]_D$	Solvent Rotation	Ref.
N^{ϵ}-Tfa-Lys-Gly-Gly				Aq-Alc	226–228 (dec)	+28	Ac	422
N^{ϵ}-Tfa-Lys-Gly-Gly-OBu^t Hydrochloride	1+2 ONP		83	Me-Eth	163–164	+26	Ac	422
N^{ϵ}-Boc-Z-Lys-N^{ϵ}-boc-Lys-N^G-tos-Arg Amide								492
N^{ϵ}-Boc-Lys-N^{ϵ}-boc-Lys-N^G-tos-Arg Amide	2+1 A		80		130–132	−15	Me	492
N^{ϵ}-Tos-Z-Lys-N^{ϵ}-tos-Lys-N^G-tos-Arg-OBzl					90–95	−13	Me	373
N^{ϵ}-Boc-N^{α}-for-Lys-N^{ϵ}-boc-Lys-Phe					82–86	−4	DMF	373
N^{ϵ}-Boc-N^{α}-for-Lys-N^{ϵ}-boc-Lys-Phe-OMe	2+1 MCA	Chf	94	Me-Eth	147–149			266
					115–117			266
N^{ϵ}-For-Lys-Phe-γ-OBu^t-Glu-OMe					145.5–146.5	−26	DMF	535
Di-Z-Lys-Phe-Gly-OMe	ONP	DMF	87	Acn				355
N^{ϵ}-Boc-N^{α}-Z-Lys-Pro-Val Amide	MCA		76.6		161–163			571
N^{ϵ}-Boc-Lys-Pro-Val Amide Toluenesulfonate								571
N^{ϵ}-For-N^{α}-Z-Lys-Pro-Val Amide	MCA	Di	43	Alc-Eth	217–218			239
N^{ϵ}-For-Lys-Pro-Val Amide Hydrochloride								239
N^{ϵ}-Pht-N^{α}-boc-Lys-Pro-Val Amide	MCA	THF	56	EtAc-Eth	172.5–173			571
N^{ϵ}-Pht-Lys-Pro-Val Amide Hydrochloride								571
N^{ϵ}-Tos-Lys-Pro-Val Amide Hydrochloride	1+2 MCA					−52		240
N^{ϵ}-Z-α-carbethoxy-Lys-Ser-Gly-OBzl	1+2 MCA	Chf-DMF	78	Eth-Alc	185–186	−17	Ac	667
N^{ϵ}-Boc-N^{α}-Z-Lys-Trp-Gly-OBu^t	ONP			EtAc	97–99	−19	Me	94
N^{ϵ}-For-N^{α}-Z-Lys-Trp-Gly-OMe					172–174		Me	743
N^{ϵ}-For-Lys-Trp-Gly-OMe Acetate								743

Compound	Method	Solvent	Yield (%)	Recryst. solvent	M.p.	[α]	Solvent	Ref.
Nᵉ-Tos-Nᵅ-Z-Lys-Trp-Gly-OBuᵗ	1+2 ONP	EtAc	69	Me	98–100	–19	DMF	94
N-[di-Z-Lys-Val]-β-D-Glu	MCA	DMF–THF	53	Alc-Eth	188–190	–54	Ac	685
Di-Boc-Lys-Val-Leu Hydrazide				EtAc-Pe		–56	Ac	549
Di-Boc-Lys-Val-Leu-OMe								549
Methionine								
Met-Asn-OBuᵗ-Thr-OBuᵗ				Be	137	–33; –7	DMF; Alc	48; 720
[1-Methyl-2-benzoyl-vinyl]-Met-Asn-OBuᵗ-Thr-OBuᵗ	1+2 MCA	DMF–THF	80	Alc	161.5–163	+78	Alc	720
N-Pht-Met-Asn-OBuᵗ-Thr-OBuᵗ	1+2 ONP	DMF	81		165	–9	DMF	48
Boc-Met-D-Asp-D-Phe Amide	1+2 OTCP	DMF	72	Me-EtAc	188–189 (dec)	+44	DMF	111
Boc-D-Met-D-Asp-D-Phe Amide	1+2 OTCP	DMF	74		204–205 (dec)	+39	DMF	111
Boc-Met-Asp-Phe Amide	1+2 OTCP	DMF	81	Eth-Alc	209–210 (dec)			111
Boc-D-Met-Asp-Phe Amide	OTCP	DMF	75	Aq-Alc	189–190 (dec)	–43	DMF	111
Boc-Met-Asp-Phe-OMe	1+2 OTCP	DMF		DMF				111
Met-Asp-Phe Amide					223–225 (dec)		DMF	111
Met-D-Asp-D-Phe Amide Hydrochloride Hemihydrate	1+2 OTCP	DMF	100	EtAc-Me	197–198 (dec)	+82	DMF	111
D-Met-D-Asp-D-Phe Amide Hydrochloride Hemihydrate	1+2 OTCP	DMF	100		182 (dec)	+12	DMF	111

Table 3 Tripeptides (continued)

Compound	Method	Solvent	% Yield	Solvent Crystallization	M.P.(°C)	$[\alpha]_D$	Solvent Rotation	Ref.
Met-Asp-Phe Amide Hydrochloride Hydrate				Me-EtAc	185 (dec)	−12	DMF	111
D-Met-Asp-Phe Amide Hydrochloride Monohydrate					192–194			111
Met-β-bzl-Asp-Phe Amide				i-Pr-Me	174–175			111
Met-β-OBu^t-Asp-Phe Amide				EtAc-Pe	152–153			111
Met-β-OBu^t-Asp-Phe Amide Hydrochloride				EtAc	204–205			111
N-Nps-Met-β-OBzl-Asp-Phe Amide				Alc-Eth	193–194.5			111
N-Nps-Met-β-OBu^t-Asp-Phe	1+2 DCCI		71	Alc	168–169			111
Z-Met-Asp-OBu^t-Thr-OBu^t	1+2 OTCP WRK	DMF	52.4		147–147.5	−22	Me	101
Z-Met(sulfone)-Asp-OBu^t-Thr-OBu^t					196–197	−29	Me	101
Met-Asp-OBu^t-Thr-OBu^t					146–148	−21	Me	101
Tfa-Met-Asp-OBu^t-Thr-OBu^t	1+2 A	Chf	36		124	−21	Me	720
Z-Met-Gly-Gly-OEt	1+2 ONP			An-Aq	131–132	+3	DMF	22
					132.5–133.5			712
Ornithine								
Di-Z-Orn-N^G-nitro-Arg-Pro	1+2 ONP	THF	70	Alc-Eth		−38	Me	558
Di-Z-Orn-N^G-nitro-Arg-Pro-OMe	DCCI		45	Chf-Eth		−43	Ac	558
N$^\delta$-Boc-N$^\alpha$-Z-Orn-Gln-His-OMe	1+2 ONP	Py	82	Alc-EtAc	151–154	−17	Alc	400
N$^\delta$-Boc-N$^\alpha$-Z-Orn-γ-OBu^t-Glu-His-OMe	1+2 ONP	Py	57	Alc-Pe	99–101	−13	Alc	582
N$^\delta$-Boc-N$^\alpha$-for-DL-Orn-N$^\delta$-boc-DL-Orn-N$^\delta$-boc-DL-Orn Hydrazide					179–181			432
N$^\delta$-Boc-N$^\alpha$-for-DL-Orn-N$^\delta$-boc-DL-Orn-N$^\delta$-boc-DL-Orn-OMe								432

212

Compound	Method	Solvent	Yield (%)	Recryst. solvent	M.p. (°C)	[α]	Solvent	Ref.
N$^\delta$-Boc-N$^\alpha$-for-DL-Orn-DL-Ser-N$^\delta$-boc-DL-Orn Hydrazide					158–160 (dec)			432
N$^\delta$-Boc-N$^\alpha$-for-DL-Orn-DL-Ser-N$^\delta$-boc-DL-Orn-OMe	1+2 DCCI	DMF	61					432
N$^\delta$-Boc-DL-Orn-DL-Ser-N$^\delta$-boc-DL-Orn-OMe Hydrochloride								432
N$^\delta$-For-N$^\alpha$-Z-Orn-Trp-Gly-OMe	1+2 DCCI			Me	144–146	+4.2	Me	743
N$^\delta$-For-Orn-Trp-Gly-OMe Acetate Hydrate					113–116	–6.3	Me	743
N$^\delta$-Pht-Z-Orn-Trp-Gly-OBu^t	1+2 DCCI	EtAc	67	EtAc-Pe	115–120	–7	DMF	63
N$^\delta$-Tos-N$^\alpha$-Z-Orn-Trp-Gly-OMe						–3.4	Ac	375
Phenylalanine								
Phe-Ala-Asn Amide					135–137			436
Z-Phe-Ala-Gly-OEt	1+2 ONP	DMF	63	Me	84–87	–26	Alc	168
Z-Phe-N^G-tos-Arg-N$^\epsilon$-tos-Lys-OMe	1+2 MCA	Chf	62		178–179	–10	DMF	409
Phe-N^G-tos-Arg-N$^\epsilon$-tos-Lys-OMe					195			409
Z-Phe-S-bz-Cys-Gly-OMe	1+2 MCA	Chf	70		110	–62	DMF	777
Z-Phe-S-bz-Cys-Gly-ONp	1+2 DCCI	Chf	84		173–174	–44	DMF	777
Z-Phe-S-Z-Cys-Gly-OEt	1+2 DCCI		55	Alc	170	–40	Alc	610
Z-Phe-S-Z-Cys-Gly-ONBzl					118	–37	DMF	777
Z-Phe-Cys-Gly-OEt					117–122	–17	DMF	610
Z-Phe-S-Eac-Cys-Gly-OEt	1+2 OTCP		78	EtAc-Pe / Aq-i-Pr / DMF-Eth / Me-Eth	104–107	–47	DMF	188
Phe-S-bzl-Cys-Tyr-OEt	1+2 MCA	Chf			213–215			188
Z-Phe-Gln-Asn-OMe	1+2 MCA	Chf	83		172–174	–13	DMF	299
Phe-Gln-Asn-OMe					148–150			289
Aza-Phe-aza-Gly-Gly-OEt					148–149			289, 154
Z-Phe-aza-Gly-Gly-OEt	2+1 SPh	Ac	54	Alc-Aq	146–147	–2.7	Alc	157, 154
Z-D-Phe-Gly-Gly-OEt	1+2 DCCI	Chf	67	EtAc-Eth	95–96	+17	DMF	337

Table 3 Tripeptides (continued)

Compound	Method	Solvent	% Yield	Solvent Crystallization	M.P. (°C)	[α]_D	Solvent Rotation	Ref.
N-[p-Nitro-benzylidene]-aza-Phe-aza-Gly-Gly-OEt					212			154
Nps-Phe-Gly-Gly-2,4,6-tri-me-OBzl	2+1 MCA	DMF	74	EtAc-Cy	118.5-119	+20	DMF	631
D-Phe-Gly-Gly OEt Hydrochloride					oil			337
Z-Phe-Gly-Pro	1+2 ONP	Py-Aq	90	Alc	212			65
Z-Phe-Gly-Pro-ONp				Alc-Ac	85-90			65
Z-Phe-His-Gly				DMF	202 (dec)			120
Z-Phe-His-Gly-OMe	2+1 DCCI	DMF	50	EtAc-Pe	167-170	-20	Me	120
Z-D-Phe-His-Leu-ONBzl	1+2 DCCI	Acn	81	EtAc-Pe	124-127	+5.9	DMF	190
Z-Phe-His-Leu-ONBzl	1+2 DCCI	Acn	82	EtAc-Pe	156	-30 / -18	Me / DMF	190
D-Phe-His-Leu-ONBzl Dihydrobromide	1+2 ONP	THF	72		166 (dec)	-31 / -20	Me / DMF	190
Phe-His-Leu-ONBzl Dihydrobromide				i-Pr-EtAc	245	-4.0 / -4.0	Me / DMF	190
Aoc-Phe-Ile-Gly-OBzl	ONP	DMF	98	Me-Aq	142-144	-13 / -33	DMF / Me	517
Z-Phe-Ile-Gly-OBu^t	1+2 DCCI		83	Me	153-155	-34	Alc	85
Z-Phe-Ile-Gly-OEt	1+2 ONP	Py	78	Alc	180-181	-30	Me	25
	1+2 ONP	DMF		Ac	179.5-180.5	-21	Ac	517
Phe-Ile-Gly-OBu^t					169	-17	Me	85
Z-Phe-Leu-Gly	1+2 MCA		69	Alc-Aq	162	-30	Me	120
Z-Phe-Leu-Gly-OMe				EtAc-Pe	196-199			120
Phe-Leu-Gly-OMe Hydrochloride				Me-Eth				286
N-For-Phe-Leu-N^ε-boc-Lys	2+1 MCA	Chf	85		oil			266
N-For-Phe-Leu-N^ε-boc-Lys-OMe								266

214

Compound	Method	Solvent	Yield (%)	Recryst.	M.p. (°C)	[α]	Rot. solv.	Ref.
Z(OMe)-D-Phe-D-Leu-L-Leu-N$^\delta$-Z-Orn-OEt	MCA	Chf-THF	74	Alc-Eth-Pe	159	+8.4	Ac	301
Z(OMe)-D-Phe-D-Phe-Leu-N$^\delta$-Z-Orn Hydrazide	1+2 MCA	EtAc	66	Me	201-202	+9.7	DMF	301
Z-Phe-Leu-Ser Hydrazide	PHA	DMF			175	-8.2	Ac	120
Z-Phe-Leu-Ser-OMe	1+2 DCCI	Acn-DMF			139-140	-26	Me	120
Z-Phe-Leu-Val-OMe					139-140			179
Phe-Leu-Val-OMe				Me-Eth	203-204	-34	Alc	179
Z-Phe-boc-Lys-Gly					173-174			324
Z-Phe-N$^\alpha$-Z-Lys-Tyr-OBzl	2+1 DCCI	Chf	50	Alc	120			53
N$^\epsilon$-Phe-Lys-Tyr Hydrochloride				An	161-162			53
Z-Phe-N$^\alpha$-Lys(α-OMe)-N$^\epsilon$-Z-Val	2+1 DCCI			Me	170-173			53
Z-Phe-N$^\alpha$-Lys-N$^\epsilon$-Z-Val				Me	150-153			53
Phe-N$^\alpha$-Lys-N$^\epsilon$-Val Hydrochloride					145-146			53
Z-ABu-Phe-Phe-Gly-OMe	1+2 A	DMF	53	EtAc-He	172	+23	Chf	429
Z-Phe-DL-Phe-Gly-OEt	2+1 OPAP	MeCl	71		187-190			23
Z-Phe-Phe-Gly-OEt	1+2 ONP	DMF			185-190	-29	DMF	168
Z-D-Phe-Phe	MCA, ONP	MeCl, DMF			187-191	-6	DMF	440a
Tfa-DL-α-Phe-DL-α-Phe-DL-α-Phe-OMe	1+2 O	Acn	50	Aq-Me	120-130	+15	Me	284
Z-D-Phe-D-Phe-D-Ser	ONP	DMF			199-203			440a
Z-Phe-Phe-Tyr	MCA, ONP	MeCl, DMF		Alc-Aq	199-201	+16	Me	350
Z-D-Phe-D-Phe-D-Tyr	1+2 ONP	DMF	80	DMF-Aq	180-185			440a
Z-Phe-Phe-Tyr-OEt					249-251	-28	DMF	350
Z-Phe-Phe-Tyr Hydrazide					230			539
Phe-Phe-Tyr					192-195			350
Z-D-Phe-D-Phe-D-Val	MCA, ONP	MeCl, DMF	75		105-106	+21	DMF	440a
Z-Phe-Pro-Gly-OEt					93-95	-52	DMF	302
Z-Phe-Pro-Gly-OEt					215-217	-55	Alc	168
D-Phe-Pro-Gly-OEt					123-125			302
Z-D-Phe-D-Ser-D-Pro Hydrazide	MCA	THF		DMF-Alc		+34	DMF	681
Z-D-Phe-D-Ser-D-Pro-OMe	1+2 ONP	DMF	82	EtAc-Eth		+48		681

Table 3 Tripeptides (continued)

Compound	Method	Solvent	% Yield	Solvent Crystallization	M.P. (°C)	[α]D	Solvent Rotation	Ref.
Boc-Phe-Ser-Pro	1+2 ONP				122-124 (dec)	-58	Me	722
Z-Phe-Thr-Ser OMe	1+2 ONP	DMF	55	Me-Aq	182-184	-6.8	DMF	458
Proline								
Z-Pro-Ala-N^G-nitro-Arg-OMe	2+1 A		78			-68	Ac	553
Pro-Ala-N^G-nitro-Arg-OMe Hydrobromide Hydrate					191-192	-16	DMF	553
Z-Pro-Ala-Gly Amide			62		195-196	-90	Aq	275
Z-Pro-Ala-Gly-OMe					133-134.5	-39	DMF	690
Z-Pro-N^G-nitro-Arg-Gly Amide	1+2 ONP	DMF	71	i-Pr	102-104	-81	Alc	690
Z-Pro-N^G-nitro-Arg-Gly Amide Hydrate	2+1 MCA	DMF-THF	60	Py-EtAc				103
Z-Pro-N^G-nitro-Arg-Gly Amide Hydrate								643
Diflavianate					181-183			643
Z-Pro-N^G-Tos-Arg-Gly Amide								257
Z-Pro-N^G-Tos-D-Arg-Gly Amide						-30	Ac-Aq	769
Z-Pro-N^G-Tos-Arg-Gly-OEt	1+2 MCA	THF	88					257
Z-Pro-N^G-Tos-D-Arg-Gly-OEt	1+2 MCA	Chf	92			-28	Ac	769
Pro-Arg-Gly Amide Dihydrobromide								643
Pro-N^G-Tos-D-Arg-Gly Amide						-17	Aq	769
Z-Pro-Cit-Gly Amide	1+2 ONP	DMF		Me	217-221			61
Boc-Pro-Cit-Gly-OEt	1+2 ONP	Py	66		198-199			61
Z-Pro-S-bzl-Cys-Gly Amide				Alc-Aq	161-163	-78	DMF	215
Z-Pro-S-bzl-Cys-Gly-OMe	1+2 MCA	Chf	53	EtAc-Pe	121-122	-71	DMF	215
Z-Pro-S-bzl-Cys-Tyr-OEt	1+2 MCA	Chf	65	EtAc-Pe	148-150	-39	Di	299
Z-Pro-S-bzl-Cys-Tyr Hydrazide				Aq-Alc	189-192			299

216

Compound	Method	Solvent	Yield (%)	Cryst. solvent	m.p. (°C)	[α]	Solvent	Ref.
Z-Pro-Gly-Gly Amide	2+1 ONP	DMF	61	Alc	146	−51	Ac	275
						−63	Aq	605
Z-Pro-Gly-Phe	ONP	Chf			159–160.5	−12	Alc	22
Z-Pro-Gly-Phe-OMe					92	−21	DMF	605
Pro-Gly-Phe					220			605
Z-Pro-Gly-Tyr	2+1 DCCI	DMF	96.5		102	−12	Alc	605
Z-Pro-Gly-Tyr-OEt	1+2 MCA		91		60	−20	Alc	605
Pro-Gly-Tyr					60	−11	Alc	277
Z-Pro-Ile-Gly Amide				EtAc	178	−69	Me	277
Z-Pro-Ile-Gly-OEt	1+2 MCA	Chf	86		151	−80	Ac	277
Pro-Ile-Gly Amide					118	−63		291
Z-α-aminosuberyl-Pro-Leu-Gly Amide OMe				EtAc-He	85–89	−36	DMF	567
N-Z-S-bzl-penicillaminyl-Pro-Leu-Gly Amide					207–210			154
Z-Pro-Leu-aza-Gly Amide				Aq-Me	165–165.5	−70	Alc	628
Z-Pro-Leu-Gly Amide					161–163	−74	Alc	83
Z-Pro-D-Leu-Gly Amide	2+1 MCA	THF		Aq	167–168	−10	Alc	546
Z-Pro-Leu-Gly-OEt	2+1 MCA	THF		Aq	150–151.5	−80	Alc	520
	1+2 ONP	Chf		Alc-Aq	150–152			83
Z-Pro-Leu-Gly-ONp	2+1 MCA	THF		Alc	142.5–143.5	−47	DMF	628
	1+2 MCA	DMF	94	EtAc-Eth				
Z-Pro-Leu-Gly N^{α}-Tos-hydrazinoacetamide	1+2 ONP	DMF	52		193–195	−75	DMF	445
Pro-Leu-aza-Gly Amide Hydrobromide						−37	Aq	154
Pro-Leu-Gly Amide					119–120	−53	DMF	628
Pro-Leu-Gly N^{α}-Tos-hydrazinoacetamide	MCA				155–158	−21		445
Z-Pro-Leu-Sar Amide								84
Pro-Leu-Sar Amide								84
Z-Pro-Leu-Val-OMe	1+2 DCCI		92	EtAc-He	126–127	−92	Me	88
Boc-Pro-Leu-Val-OMe	1+2 OSu					−83		356

Table 3 Tripeptides (continued)

Compound	Method	Solvent	% Yield	Solvent Crystallization	M.P. (°C)	$[\alpha]_D$	Solvent Rotation	Ref.
Z-Pro-N^ϵ-boc-Lys-Ala-OBu^t	ONP		78	EtAc	132–134	−41	DMF	403
	1+2 ONP		78		132–134	−41	DMF	536
Z-Pro-N^ϵ-tos-Lys-Ala Amide					169–171	−48	Me	767
Z-Pro-N^ϵ-tos-Lys-D-Ala Amide	1+2 MCA	Chf	85	Me-Aq	194–195	−43	Me	767
Z-Pro-N^ϵ-tos-Lys-D-Ala-OMe	1+2 ONP	DMF	71	EtAc	140–143	−36	Me	767
Z-Pro-N^ϵ-tos-Lys-Ala-OMe	1+2 DCCI	Acn	76	Alc-Aq	129			308
	1+2 DCCI	EtAc	72	EtAc-Pe	125–127	−53	Me	761a
	ONP		84		125–127	−52	Me	767
N-Nps-Pro-N^ϵ-Z-Lys-Ala-OMe	1+2 DCCI	Chf	50	Me	175–176	−44	DMF	774
Pro-N^ϵ-Z-Lys-Ala-OMe Hydrochloride					133–135	−60	Aq	774
Z-Pro-N^ϵ-for-Lys-Asp-di-OMe	1+2 MCA	THF	64	EtAc	133–135	−55	Me	747
Pro-N^ϵ-boc-Lys-β-OBu^t-Asp-OBu^t								573
								573
Pro-N^ϵ-for-Lys-Asp	DCCI	Acn		Aq-Alc	143 (dec)	−42	Aq	747
Pro-N^ϵ-for-Lys-Asp-di-OMe Hydrochloride	1+2 DCCI	Acn		Aq-Me	oil	−35	Me	747
Z-Pro-N^ϵ-tos-Lys-Gly Amide					184–185	−40	DMF	765
Z-D-Pro-N^ϵ-tos-Lys-Gly Amide					184–185	−33	DMF	414
Pro-N^ϵ-tos-Lys-Ala Amide						+13	Me	336
Pro-N^ϵ-tos-Lys-D-Ala Amide								767
Pro-N^ϵ-tos-Lys-Ala-OMe Hydrochloride								767
								761a
Z-Pro-N^ϵ-boc-Lys-β-OBu^t-Asp-OBu^t	DCCI	Acn		Bu^t	104–105	−43	Alc	573
	1+2 DCCI	Acn		EtAc-Eth	104–105	−43	Alc	573
Z-Pro-N^ϵ-for-Lys-Asp	1+2 MCA	Aq-DMF-THF	50	Me-EtAc	170–173	−43	Me	747
Z-Pro-N^ϵ-tos-Lys-Gly-OEt	1+2 ONP	Aq-Di	93	Me-EtAc	178–180	−48	Me	573
				EtAc-Pe	153–154	−57	Ac	765

Compound	Method	Solvent	Yield (%)	Recrystn. solvent	m.p. (°C)	$[\alpha]$	Solvent	Ref.
Z-Pro-N$^\epsilon$-tos-D-Lys-Gly-OEt	1+2 ONP	DMF	83	EtAc	152–153	−56	Ac	62
Z-D-Pro-N$^\epsilon$-tos-Lys-Gly-OEt	1+2 ONP	DMF	87	Aq-Alc	129–131	−18	Ac	414
Z-Pro-N$^\epsilon$-tos-Lys-Gly-OEt Hydrate	1+2 DMCHF	Chf	77–82	Alc-Aq	133–135	+18	Ac	769
				EtAc-Aq-Pe	120–125	−49		336, 765
Z-Pro-N$^\epsilon$-tos-thia-Lys-Gly Amide	1+2 DCCI	EtAc	53	EtAc-Pe	144–146	−49	DMF	215
Z-Pro-N$^\epsilon$-tos-thia-Lys-Gly-OEt	2+1 A		70	Alc	122–124	−50	DMF	215
D-Pro-N$^\epsilon$-tos-Lys-Gly Amide					123–124	−49	DMF	336
Pro-N$^\epsilon$-tos-Lys-Gly Amide					oil			765
Pro-N$^\epsilon$-tos-D-Lys-Gly Amide					195–198			769
Pro-N$^\epsilon$-tos-thia-Lys-Gly Amide					150			215
Z-Pro-N$^\epsilon$-tos-Lys-OBu^t-Thr-OBu^t	1+2 ONP		90	EtAc-DMF	129–131	+37	DMF	408
Z-Pro-N$^\epsilon$-pht-Orn-Gly Amide			86		80–86	−29	DMF-Ac	63
Z-Pro-tos-Orn-Gly Amide					106–108			256
Z-Pro-N$^\delta$-tos-Orn-Gly-OEt	1+2 DCCI	Acn	93		95–98			256
Z-Pro-Phe-Ala-OMe	2+1 A		82	EtAc-Eth	115–117			553
Aoc-Pro-Phe-N^G-nitro-Arg-OBzl				Me-Eth	137–139	−72	Me	553, 518
Z-Pro-p-fluoro-Phe-N^G-nitro-Arg-OMe				Me-Aq	137–139	−46	Aq	438
Z-Pro-p-fluoro-D-Phe-N^G-nitro-Arg-OMe				EtAc-Eth	137–139	−39	Alc	438
Z-Pro-Phe-N^G-nitro-Arg Hydrobromide	1+2 ONP	DMF	85		138–140			439
Z-Pro-D-Phe-N^G-nitro-Arg-OMe	2+1 A		75	Alc-Eth	115	−43	DMF	438, 555
Z-Pro-Phe-N^G-nitro-Arg-OMe	1+2 ONP	DMF	87		72–89	−42	DMF	439, 456, 439
	1+2 ONP	DMF	60					
Z-Pro-Phe-N^G-nitro-Arg-ONBzl	1+2 MCA	Chf	90	EtAc-Pe	112 (dec)	−10	Me	558, 70
Z-Pro-Phe-N^G-nitro-Arg-ONBzl	1+2 ONP	DMF	70					652, 137

219

Table 3 Tripeptides (continued)

Compound	Method	Solvent	% Yield	Solvent Crystallization	M.P.(°C)	$[\alpha]_D$	Solvent Rotation	Ref.
Pro-Phe-N^G-nitro-Arg Hydrobromide								439
Pro-Phe-N^G-nitro-Arg-OMe Hydrobromide								555
Pro-Phe-N^G-nitro-Arg-ONBzl-Hydrobromide							Ac	558
Z-Pro-Phe-Cit-OMe	1+2 ONP		46	EtAc-Alc	196-197			70
					187-190	−43	DMF	456
Z-Pro-Phe-His-OMe	1+2 ONP		70		160-162	−38	DMF	123
Z-Pro-Phe-N$^\delta$-boc-Orn-OMe	2+1 A		76		120-122	−52	Me	123
Pro-Phe-N$^\delta$-boc-Orn-OMe					120-122	−25	Me	565
Bzl-Pro-Pro-N^G-nitro-Arg-ONBzl	2+1 DCCI	Acn						565
Z-Pro-Pro-N^G-nitro-Arg-OMe	2+1 MCA	Acn	76	Me-Eth				680
Z-D-Pro-D-Pro-N^G-nitro-D-Arg-ONBzl						+54		354
Pro-Pro-N^G-nitro-Arg-ONBzl								681
D-Pro-D-Pro-N^G-nitro-D-Arg-ONBzl								680
Aoc-Pro-Pro-Gly	2+1 DCCI	Chf	80.5	EtAc-Pe	109-112	−132	Alc	518
Z-D-Pro-D-Pro-Gly					99-102	+83		681
Z-Pro-Pro-Gly-OBzl	2+1 DCCI		81		120-122	−115	Me	722
Z-D-Pro-D-Pro-Gly-OEt	2+1 DCCI	Acn-DMF	78		oil			681
Pro-Pro-Gly					112-114	−97	Me	722
Z-Pro-Sar-N-Me-Val-OBu^t				Eth-Pe	50			410
Boc-Pro-Ser-nor-Leu-OMe	2+1 A		56					525
Z-Pro-Ser-N$^\epsilon$-boc-Lys-OMe	2+1 A		88		120-123	−52	Me	395
Boc-Pro-Ser-N$^\epsilon$-boc-Lys-Abu-OMe	2+1 A		67		135 (dec)	−67	Ac	524
							DMF	
Boc-Pro-Ser-N$^\epsilon$-boc-Lys-OMe	2+1 A		68		55-60	−37		525
Pro-Ser-N$^\epsilon$-boc-Lys-OMe					oil			395
								395
Boc-Pro-Ser-nor-Val-OMe	2+1 A		66		75			525

Peptide	Method	Solvent	Yield (%)	Recryst. solvent	M.p. (°C)	[α]	Solvent	Ref.
Z-Pro-Trp-Leu-OMe	1+2 DCCI	MeCl	98	Me	227–228	−40	DMF	28
	1+2 MCA		98					28
Pro-Trp-Leu-OMe					109–111	−51	Alc	268
Z-Pro-OAc-Tyr-N$^{\epsilon}$-tos-Lys-OMe	2+1 DCCI	DMF	69		105–108			573
Z-Pro-Tyr-N$^{\epsilon}$-boc-Lys-OMe	2+1 DCCI	Acn	60	Me	134–136			268
Z-Pro-Tyr-N$^{\epsilon}$-tos-Lys								268
Z-Pro-Tyr-N$^{\epsilon}$-tos-Lys-OMe				DMF-Me	224–226	−16	DMF	269
Boc-Pro-Tyr-N$^{\epsilon}$-tos-Lys-OMe						−36		269
Boc-Pro-Tyr-N$^{\epsilon}$-tos-Lys-OMe								269
Pro-Tyr-N$^{\epsilon}$-tos-Lys				EtAc	85–87	−15	Alc	269
Pro-Tyr-N$^{\epsilon}$-tos-Lys-OMe				Me	198–200	−19	Aq	269
Pro-Tyr-N$^{\epsilon}$-tos-Lys-OMe Hydrochloride					161–162	−59	Me	753
Z-Pro-Tyr-Phe-OMe	2+1 A		47		161–162	−60	Me	753
	1+2 ONP	DMF	74					753
Pro-Tyr-Phe-OMe Hydrochloride	1+2 MCA	Di	54	EtAc-Be	228–229	−32	Me	239
Z-Pro-Val-Gly				EtAc-Eth	191–193			239
				EtAc	193–195			277
Z-Pro-Val-Gly Amide					188	−61	Me	277
Z-Pro-Val-Gly-OEt	1+2 MCA	Chf	61	Alc	155	−78	Me	373
Z-Pro-Val-Gly-OMe	1+2 ONP	EtAc	67		130–132	−90	Me	239
	1+2 MCA	Di	62		125–127			371
	2+1 DCCI	MeCl	90	MeCl-P2	111–112			239
Pro-Val-Gly				Aq-Alc	228–234			277
Pro-Val-Gly Amide					132	−46	Ac	239
Pro-Val-Gly-OBzl Hydrochloride				Alc-Eth	183–186			576
Pro-Val-Gly-OEt				Alc-Eth	127–128	−74	Alc	576
Pro-Val-Gly-OMe				Me-Eth	127–128			373
					143–144	−76	Me	
Sarcosine								
Z-Sar-β-Ala-Gly-OEt	2+1 OPAP		65		102–104			23
N-Tos-Sar-S-bzl-Cys-Tyr Hydrazide								295

Table 3 Tripeptides (continued)

Compound	Method	Solvent	% Yield	Solvent Crystallization	M.P. (°C)	$[\alpha]_D$	Solvent Rotation	Ref.
Z-Sar-Gly-Gly-OEt	2+1 OPAP		60		142–143			23
Z-Sar-Phe-N^G-nitro-Arg								752
Sar-Phe-N^G-nitro-Arg Hydrobromide								752
Serine								
OBzl-boc-Ser-(Ala)$_2$-OBzl	1+2 2,4-DNPO		100	Glyme	168–169			356a
Z-Ser-Ala-Ala-OBu^t		Chf	74	Alc-Pe	166–167	−44	Alc	398
Z-Ser-Ala-Ala-OEt	1+2 2,4-DNPO	Chf	70	EtAc-Pe	177–179	−6.0	DMF	399
Ser-Ala-Ala-OEt				Alc-Eth	150–152	−20	DMF	399
OBzl-boc-Ser-N^G-nitro-Arg-Leu Z-hydrazide	1+2 ONP	DMF	70	EtAc	115–118	−37	Me	458
OBzl-boc-Ser-N^G-nitro-Arg-Leu-OMe						−25	DMF	458
OBzl-boc-Ser-Asp-Gly Z-hydrazide	1+2 ONP	DMF	80	EtAc	83–84	−12	DMF	458
OBzl-Ser-Gln-Gly-ONBzl Trifluoroacetate					85–89	−11	Me	734
OBzl-boc-Ser-Gln-Gly					156–158			734
OBzl-boc-Ser-Gln-Gly-ONBzl					146.5–147.5	−11	Me	734
OBu^t-Z-Ser-Glu-Gly	1+2 MCA	DMF		Aq	158–159	−9.0	Alc	736
OBu^t-Z-Ser-Glu-Gly-OMe				Alc	185–186	−9.2	Alc	736
						−15	Ac-Aq	
N-Ac-DL-Ser-Gly-Gly				Me	179–181			34
N-Ac-Ser-Gly-Gly-OBzl					156–157	−9.3	Me	34
N-Ac-DL-Ser-Gly-Gly-OBzl				Acn	137–139			34
OAc-N-Z-DL-Ser-Gly-Gly-OBzl				Alc	112–113			34
OAc-N-Z-Ser-Gly-Gly-OBzl				Alc	105–107	+2.9	Ac	34
OAc-Z-DL-Ser-Gly-Gly-OEt	ONP	Chf						22
OAc-DL-Ser-Gly-Gly				Aq-Alc	165–169			34
OAc-Ser-Gly-Gly-OBzl								34

Compound	Method	Solvent	Yield (%)	Recryst.	M.p. (°C)	$[\alpha]$	Solvent	Ref.
OAc-DL-Ser-Gly-Gly-OBzl	1+2 DCCI	Acn		NMe	144–146			34
Z-DL-Ser-Gly-Gly-OBzl	1+2 DCCI	Acn	64	Aq	134–135			34
Z-Ser-Gly-Gly-OBzl			60		151–152	−4.2	Ac	34
Z-DL-Ser-Gly-Gly-OEt	1+2 DCCI	DMF	60	EtAc	130–131			22
DL-Ser-Gly-Gly				Aq-Alc	196–200 (dec)			545
								34
Ser-Gly-Gly-OBzl Hydrobromide				Alc	181.5–183	19	Aq	708
DL-Ser-Gly-Gly-OBzl Hydrobromide				Alc	174–175			34
Z-Ser-N^{im}-bzl-His-Asp-ONBzl	1+2 EDCI				195–196.5	−21	DMF	106
Ser-N^{im}-bzl-His-Asp-ONBzl Dihydrobromide					93–103 (dec)	−4	DMF	106
OBzl-Z-Ser-N^{im}-Z-His-Leu-OMe	1+2 DCCI	MeCl	86	EtAc-Eth	105–106	+7.8	EtAc	261
Z-Ser-N^{im}-bz-His-Leu Hydrazide	1+2 DCCI	THF	68	DMF-Me	180–184	−12	DMF	319
Z-Ser-N^{im}-bzl-His-Leu-OMe				THF-Eth	111–113	−8	THF	319
Z-Ser-Leu-Tyr-OMe	A	EtAc	40	THF-Eth	112–114	−14	DFM	78
Z-Ser-Met-Gln	1+2 A	Aq	54	Aq-Me	176.5–177	−14	DMF	241
Ser-Met-Gln				Aq-Alc	228 (dec)	−24	NH$_4$OH	241
Z-Ser-Met-Glu Hydrazide					211–212	−17		241
N-Boc-DL-Ser-N^{δ}-boc-DL-Orn-N^{δ}-boc-DL-Orn Hydrazide					182–183	−13		432
N-Boc-DL-Ser-N^{δ}-boc-DL-Ser-N^{δ}-boc-DL-Orn-OMe								432
N-Boc-DL-Ser-N^{δ}-boc-DL-Orn-DL-Ser Hydrazide					124–125			432
N-Boc-DL-Ser-N^{δ}-boc-DL-Orn-DL-Ser-OMe								432
OAc-Z-Ser-Phe-Gly-OEt	1+2 ONP	Py	67	Alc	172–174			354
OBzl-Ser-Phe-Gly-OMe	1+2 DCCI	Me-DMF	79	Me	142–146			680
Z-Ser-Phe-Gly Hydrazide					192–196			354
Z-D-Ser-D-Phe-Gly-OMe					143–145	+8.3		681
Ser-Phe-Gly-OMe					118–120			680

Table 3 Tripeptides (continued)

Compound	Method	Solvent	% Yield	Solvent Crystallization	M.P. (°C)	$[\alpha]_D$	Solvent Rotation	Ref.
D-Ser-D-Phe-Gly-OMe	2+1 ONP	Di	71		130–133	−2	Di	681
Z-Ser-Pro-Phe	1+2 A	EtAc	57	EtAc	60–70	−61	Me	605
Z-Ser-Pro-Phe-OMe	2+1 MCA	THF	53	Me	97–99	−65	Me	123
Z-Ser-Pro-Pro-OBzl				Aq-Alc	129–131	−134	Aq	748
Ser-Pro-Pro					177–181 (dec)	−186	Aq	748
Z-Ser-Ser-N^G-nitro-Arg-OBzl	2+1 A	EtAc	54	Alc	107–109	−7	DMF	135
Ser-Ser-Arg Acetate				Aq-Alc	132–136	−9	Aq	135
Ser-Ser-N^G-nitro-Arg				Aq	183–184	−6.2	Aq	135
N-Boc-DL-Ser-DL-Ser-N$^\delta$-tos-DL-Orn-OMe								432
DL-Ser-DL-Ser-N$^\delta$-tos-DL-Orn-OMe Hydrochloride								432
Z-Ser-Ser-OBzl	1+2 A	EtAc	47	Me-Aq	207–208			335
N-Boc-DL-Ser-DL-Ser-DL-Ser-OMe								432
O-Phosphoryl-Ser-O-phosphoryl-Ser-O-phosphoryl-Ser					137–139			335
DL-Ser-DL-Ser-DL-Ser-OMe Hydrochloride								432
Z-Ser-Trp-Ile-OBu^t	2+1 A	EtAc	84	EtAc-He	152–153	−33	Me	549
Ser-Trp-Ile-OBu^t						−21	Me	549
Boc-Ser-Tyr-Ser Hydrazide				Aq	184–187	−3.4	DMF	270
						−24	Ac-Aq	270
						−9	Py	270
Boc-Ser-Tyr-Ser-OMe	1+2 A	THF	63	An	124–127	−24	Me	270
Ser-Tyr-Ser-OMe								270
Threonine								
Z(OMe)-Thr-S-bzl-Cys-Gly-OEt				EtAc-Pe	134–136	−16	DMF	452
Z(OMe)-Thr-S-bzl-Cys-Gly Hydrazide				DMF-Eth	214–215	−20	DMF	452

Compound	Method	Solvent	Yield %	Recryst. solvent	M.p. (°C)	$[\alpha]$	Solvent	No.
N^l-Z-N$^\alpha$-Nps-Dbu-Thr-N^l-Z-Dbu-N^l-Z-Dbu-D-Leu-Ile-N^l-Z-Dbu-OMe				DMF-Aq	205–213	–22		485
Nps-Thr-N$^\gamma$-Z-Dbu-N$^\gamma$-Z-Dbu-D-Leu-Ile-N$^\gamma$-Z-α,γ-Dbu-OMe				DMF-Aq	208–212 (dec)	–31		485
Z-Thr-Pro-N$^\epsilon$-Z(NO$_2$)-Lys-ONBzl	1+2 DCCI	MeCl	93		oil			600
Thr-Pro-N$^\epsilon$-Z(NO$_2$)-Lys-ONBzl Hydrobromide				i-Pr	120–155	–26	Chf	600
N$^\alpha$-Z-N$^\gamma$-tos-Dbu-Thr-N$^\gamma$-tos-Dbu-Thr-N$^\gamma$-tos-Dbu-N$^\gamma$-tos-Dbu-D-Leu Hydrazide	1+2 DCCI		86		132–136	–40	Me	486
Z-Thr-Val-γ-OBzl-Glu-OBzl					248–250 (dec)	–33	Aq	669
Thr-Val-Glu					169–172	–27	Me	669
Thr-Val-Glu-di-OBzl								669
Tryptophane								
Z-Trp-S-bzl-Cys-Tyr-OEt	1+2 MCA	Chf	85	EtAc-Pe	101–104	–5.5	Di	300
Z-Trp-Gly-Trp Amide	1+2 MCA	THF	80	Acn-Eth	212–214			666
Z-Trp-Gly-Trp-OMe	1+2 MCA	Di	69	DMF-Eth	180–182			666
Trp-Gly-Trp-amide Toluenesulfonate								666
Z-Trp-D-Leu-Trp 2-Hydroxyethylamide								527
Trp-D-Leu-Trp 2-Hydroxyethylamide								527
Tyrosine								
OBzl-Z-Tyr-S-NBzl-Cys-Asn-ONBzl	1+2 ONP		62	Ac-Aq	209–211	–27	DMF	309
OBzl-Z-Tyr-S-bzl-Cys-Asp-ONBzl					209–211	+32		315
OBzl-Nps-Tyr-S-bzl-Cys-Asp-2,4,6-tri-me-OBzl				DMF-Alc	207–208.5	+25	DMF	625
O-Tos-Nps-Tyr-S-bzl-Cys-Asp-2,4,6-tri-me-OBzl	1+2 MCA	DMF	65	Alc	157.5–158.5		DMF	625
O-Tos-Tyr-S-bzl-Cys-Asp-2,4,6-tri-me-OBzl Hydrochloride				Aq-DMF	226–227	–16	DMF	625

Table 3 Tripeptides (continued)

Compound	Method	Solvent	% Yield	Solvent Crystallization	M.P. (°C)	$[\alpha]_D$	Solvent Rotation	Ref.
OBzl-Z-Tyr-S-bzl-Cys-Tyr-OEt	1+2 MCA	Chf	84	EtAc-Pe	115–118	−3.7	Di	300
OBzl-Z-Tyr-Gln-Leu-OMe	1+2 ONP	DMF	85	Alc-Aq	219–221			311
Z-Tyr-Gly-Gly					214–215			341
Z-Tyr-Gly-Gly Hydrazide					167–169			341
OBzl-Z-Tyr-Leu-β-OBu^t-Asp	2+1 A	Acn						733
OBzl-Z-Tyr-Leu-β-OBu^t-Asp-OEt	1+2 DCCI NHS	DMF			130–136			733
OBu^t-Z-Tyr-Leu-β-OBu^t-Asp-OMe								737
OBu^t-Tyr-Leu-β-OBu^t-Asp-OMe				Dipr-Eth	115–116.5	−20	Alc	737
Tyr-Leu-β-OBu^t-Asp					oil			733
Z-Tyr-Leu-Gly	1+2 DCCI			EtAc-Pe	170			122
Z-Tyr-Leu-Gly-OMe				EtAc-Pe				122
Z-Tyr-Pro-Phe	1+2 ONP	Chf						406
Z-Tyr-Pro-Phe-OMe					oil	−25	Me	406
Tyr-Pro-Phe						−9	Aq	406
N-Z-Tyr-Ser-Gly-OMe	2+1 A ONP	Chf	71	Aq-Me	204–206	−7	DMF	100
OBzl-N-Z-Tyr-Ser-N$^\epsilon$-boc-Lys-OMe	1+2 OTCP	EtAc	59	EtAc-Eth	118–120	−8.4	Me	100
N, O-Di-Z-Tyr-Ser-N$^\epsilon$-boc-Lys-OMe	2+1 A	THF-Aq-DMF		THF-Pe	116–118	−8.3	Me	100
N-Z-Tyr-Ser-N$^\epsilon$-boc-Lys-OMe						−6.2	DMF	100
Tyr-Ser-N$^\epsilon$-boc-Lys-OMe	1+2 DCCI	DMA-Acn	74	Ac	103–105	−5.1	Me	100
O-Ethoxycarbonyl-N-for-Tyr-Ser-Met				Me	164–166	−8.1	Me-Aq	160
N-For-Tyr-Ser-Met Hydrazide					208–210	−8.1	Ac-Aq	160
Valine								
Bzhoc-Val-Ala-Gly				EtAc-Chf-He				227
Bzhoc-Val-Ala-Gly-OBzh			76		188–189	−28	Chf	227
Bzhoc-Val-Ala-Gly-OMe	1+2 DCCI	MeCl						227

Compound	Method	Solvent	Yield (%)	Recryst.	mp (°C)	[α]	Solvent	Ref.
N-Nps-Val-Ala-Gly-OBzh	1+2 EDCI	MeCl	75	THF-Eth	191–192	−81	Chf	227
Val-Ala-Gly-OBzh				EtAc-He	112–114	−73	Chf	227
Val-Ala-Gly-OBzh Hydrochloride				THF-Eth	103–108	−21		227
Z-Val-Asn-Leu-OBu^t	1+2 ONP	DMF	80		205–206	−37		641
Val-Asn-Leu-OBu^t					152–154	−12		641
Bzhoc-Val-S-trt-Cys-Gly-OBzl	1+2 EDCI		73	EtAc-He	191.5–192.5		Chf	225
Z-Val-S-bzl-Cys-Gly	1+2 ONP	DMF		Ac	195–197	−25	DMF	166
Z-Val-S-bzl-Cys-Gly-OEt	1+2 ONP	DMF	85		173	−26	DMF	310
Z-Val-S-bzl-Cys-Gly-OMe	1+2 ONP	DMF	71.5	Alc	178–180	−26	DMF	350
Z-Val-S-bzl-Cys-Gly-ONp			88	Alc	179–180	−24	DMF	166
Nps-Val-S-bzl-Cys-Gly-OBzl-(OMe)	DCCI	Chf	99	DMF	217–219	−53	DMF	619
Val-S-bzl-Cys-Gly				Alc	161.5–162	−63	Ac	166
					188–190	+6.5	DMF	166
Val-S-bzl-Cys-Gly-OMe Hydrobromide				Ac	166–167	−0.8	Ac	411
Val-S-trt-Cys-Gly-OEt Hydrochloride	1+2 DCCI	MeCl	55	2-Pr-Pe	130–131	−46	DMF	228
Z-Val-S-bz-Cys-Ser-OMe	1+2 MCA	Chf	80	Me	201–202	−19	DMF	776
Z-Val-S-bzl-Cys-Ser Hydrazide					228–230	−29	DMF	315
Z-Val-S-bzl-Cys-Ser-OMe	1+2 ONP	Chf	50		199	−41	DMF	315
Boc-Val-S-bzl-Cys-Ser-OMe	1+2 MCA	Chf	50	EtAc	150–152	−105	DMF	776
N-Nps-Val-S-bz-Cys-Ser-OMe	1+2 MA	Chf	71	EtAc-Pe	206	−20	DMF	776
N-Nps-Val-Cys-Ser-OMe				Me	148–150	−3	DMF	479
N-Trt-Val-S-trt-Cys-Ser-OMe				Me-EtAc	183–184	−14	Me	776
Val-S-bz-Cys-Ser-OMe Hydrochloride	1+2 MA	THF	32		204	−10	DMF	776
Val-S-Nps-Cys-Ser-OMe Hydrochloride				Me-Eth	187	−60	DMF	479
Val-S-Nps-Cys-Ser-OMe Toluenesulfonate				Me-Eth	144–147	−25	DMF	479
Val-S-trt-Cys-Ser-OMe Hydrochloride	1+2 ONP		85		100 (dec)	+26	Me	776
Z-Val-γ-OBu^t-Glu-Ala-OMe				Pr	145–146	−15	DMF	411
Z-Val-γ-OMe-Glu-γ-OEt-Glu-ONBzl					171–172	−10	DMF	635
Z-Val-Gly-Gly-OEt				Alc	155–157	+1	Alc	36
Z-Val-Gly-Gly Hydrazide					178–180			36

Table 3 Tripeptides (continued)

Compound	Method	Solvent	% Yield	Solvent Crystallization	M.P. (°C)	$[\alpha]_D$	Solvent Rotation	Ref.
Z-Val-Gly-Gly-melphalan-OBzl								36
Val-Gly-Gly-melphalan-OEt								36
Z-Val-His-Pro				EtAc-Eth	176	-44	Me	190
Z-Val-His-Pro Boc-hydrazide	2+1	EtAc	70		150	-21	DMF	190
Z-Val-His-Pro Hydrazide				Alc-Eth	172-175 (dec)	-78	Me	190
						-38	DMF	
Z-Val-His-Pro-me	2+1 A	EtAc	70	EtAc-Pe	96-98	-55	Me	190
	1+2 MCA	THF	49			-73	1N HCl	
	1+2 DCCI	Acn	48			-32	Py	
	1+2 ONP	Acn	48					
Z-Val-Leu-Gly-OMe				MeCl-Dipr-Eth	174-175	-66	Me	286
Val-Leu-Gly-OMe Hydrochloride					188-189	-53	Me	286
Z-Val-N^{ϵ}-boc-Lys-Val-OBu^t	1+2 A	DMF	49	Ac-Pe	146-147	-37	Me	644
Z-Val-N^{ϵ}-tos-Lys-Val-OMe	2+1 A	EtAc	70-75	DMF-THF	174-175.5	-28	Alc	580
	1+2 MCA	THF-DMF	75					
Val-N^{ϵ}-boc-Lys-Val-OBu^t				Alc-Aq	145-155	-24	Alc	644
Val-N^{ϵ}-tos-Lys-Val-OMe Hydrochloride	2+1 A	EtAc	75	Alc-Eth-Pe	220-223	-16	Aq	560
Z-Val-N^{δ}-tos-Orn-Phe-OEt				Aq-Di	201-203			129
Boc-Val-N^{δ}-Z-D-Orn-Pro					oil			301
Boc-Val-N^{δ}-Z-D-Orn-Pro-OEt	1+2 MCA	Chf-THF / DMF-EtAc	79		oil			301
Val-N^{δ}-Z-D-Orn-Pro-OEt Hydrochloride	2+1 A	EtAc	81		oil			301
Val-N^{δ}-Z-D-Orn-Pro Hydrochloride					oil			301

Compound	Method	Solvent	Yield (%)	Recryst. solvent	m.p.	[α]		Ref.
Z-Val-Trp-Pro-OBzl	2+1 A	EtAc	75	EtAc	191–192			494
Val-Trp-Pro	1+2 MCA		80	Me-Aq	177–178	−20	Ac	494
Z-Val-Tyr-Ile-OEt				Me-Eth	191			15
Z-Val-Tyr-Ile Hydrazide				DMF-EtAc	279–280			15
Z-Val-Tyr-Ile-OMe	1+2 DCCI	EtAc	69	Me	214–217			569
	2+1 DCCI	DMF	65		215–217			569
	2+1 MCA	THF	38		213–216			569
Z-Val-D-Tyr-Ile-OMe								569
Val-Tyr-Ile-OMe				Acn-Aq	146–148			569
Z-Val-Tyr-Pro Amide	1+2 MCA	THF	87	EtAc-Pe	173–175	−17	Me	645
Z-Val-Tyr-Pro-OBu^t	2+1 A	EtAc	13	Me-EtAc	170–171	−29	Me	578
	2+1 DCCI	Acn	51.5	Acn	50–60			578
Val-Tyr-Pro-OBzl	2+1 DCCI			Aq-EtAc	215–217			494
Val-Tyr-Pro-OBu^t				An-Aq	217–218			298
Z-Val-Tyr-Tyr-OEt	2+1 DCCI			Alc-Aq	168–170			691
Z-Val-Tyr-Tyr Hydrate					175–177			502
Z-Val-Tyr-Tyr-OMe	2+1 DCCI	DMF		Me				502
For-D-Val-D-Val-Gly								691
Z-Val-Val-Val-OEt								164
Z-D-Val-Val-D-Val-OMe								330
Val-Val-Val-OEt Hydrochloride	2+1 MCA	THF	89	Alc	172–174	−13	DMF	527
	1+2 MCA		83	EtAc-Pe	205–206			330

4

Tetrapeptides

A majority of the tetrapeptide syntheses summarized in Table 4 were accomplished by an active ester (ONP, DCCI, EDCI, WRK, NHS or OTCP), mixed anhydride (primarily MCA), azide (A) or thio ester (SPh) method. While DCCI was among the most frequently used reagents, its limitations begin to appear in tetrapeptide syntheses. A number of examples were encountered where use of DCCI led to mixtures, for example, in the 2+2 synthesis of Z-Gly-Try-Gly-Gly.[666] Difficulties encountered using DCCI were usually rectified by application of the MCA procedure. The syntheses of Z-Gly-Pro-Trp-Leu-OMe hydrate[28] by MCA (2+2), DCCI (2+2), and OTCP (1+3) and the 2+2 preparation[422] of N$^{\epsilon}$-Tfa-Z-Lys-Gly-γ-OMe-Glu-Gly-OBu^t, by DCCI, MA and ONP methods provide particularly useful examples. The experimental techniques summarized in both references 422 and 28 include special assessment of purity (for example by tlc and amino acid analysis) and are especially noteworthy. Other method comparisons include OTCP (1+3) with A (2+2)[111] and OTCP (1+3) with EDCI (1+3).[199]

Partial purification of Z-Leu-Pro-Thr-N^G-nitro-Arg-ONBzl (1+3, by ONP in DMF)[653] by washing an ethyl acetate solution successively with 1N ammonium hydroxide, water, 1N hydrochloric acid and water provides a typical illustration. Another useful washing sequence utilizes 1N sodium bicarbonate in place of ammonium hydroxide.[652] In many cases this elementary expedient followed by recrystallization led to a pure tetrapeptide. More involved purification problems were solved by column chromatography using silica gel[179,48,225] or carboxymethylcellulose[744] as adsorbent. Column chromatographic purification of Z-Pro-Leu-Phe-Val-OMe (1+3 synthesis with DCCI)[179] provides an example.

Countercurrent distribution techniques were utilized for more difficult separation problems.[190,415,455,372,235,94,410,269] Purification of Z-Arg-Arg-Pro-Val-OMe by a 190 transfer countercurrent distribution with n-butanol-acetic acid-water (4:1:5) followed by ion exchange (amberlite IRA-410) chromatography and recrystallization from methanol outlines a useful approach.[71] Isolation of N^ϵ-Boc-Z-Lys-N^ϵ-Boc-Lys-N^G-Tos-Arg-N^G-Tos-Arg-δ-aminovaleric-OMe and confirmation of purity using three paper chromatographic and four thin layer chromatographic solvent systems typifies a very careful assessment of purity.[454]

Pertinent literature concerning tetrapeptides appearing after July 1968 concern a His-Ser-Glu-Gly tetrapeptide sequence of glucagon,[198] synthesis of tetrapeptides using the new acyoxyphosphonium salt method[159] and synthesis of D-Ser-tetrapeptides.[326]

Table 4 Tetrapeptides

Compound	Method	Solvent	% Yield	Solvent Crystallization	M.P.(°C)	[α]$_D$	Solvent Rotation	Ref.
Alanines								
Ala-Ala-Ala-Ala				Aq-Alc	268-273 (dec.)			759
Z-Ala-Ala-Ala-Ala	2+2 MCA	DMF	59	Aq-Alc	241-243 (dec.)			759
Z-α-me-Ala-α-me-Ala-α-me-Ala-α-me-Ala				Aq-Me	243-244			284
2-(1'-Z-α-me-Ala-α-me-Ala-α-me-Ala-α-me-Ala-amino-1'-me)et-4,4-dimethyloxazolone				EtAc-Pe	233-234			284
Z-α-me-Ala-α-me-Ala-α-me-Ala-α-me-Ala-OBu^t	3+1 O	Acn	98.5	EtAc-Pe	176-178			284
Tos-α-me-Ala-α-me-Ala-α-me-Ala-α-me-Ala				Me	260-262			365
Tos-α-me-Ala-α-me-Ala-α-me-Ala-α-me-Ala-OMe					218-219			365
Tfa-α-me-Ala-α-me-Ala-α-me-Ala-α-me-Ala-OMe				EtAc-He	238-240			284
N-(3-phenyl-N-[3-(1-thia-5-oxa-4-me-hexyl)-N-(N-carboxy-3-[(2-[3-(phenyldithio)pro-pionamido]et)dithio]-N-bzl-Ala]-Ala]-Ala)Gly-OBu^t				EtAc-He	120-121	−15	Chf	222
Boc-(Ala)$_2$-N$^\epsilon$-Z-Lys-Phe-OMe			91	EtAc-He	162-165			356a
			43	EtAc-He	198-203			356a
Z-Ala-S-bzl-Cys-Asp-Tyr-OEt	1+3 ONP		68	DMF-Aq	184-187	−14	DMF	452
Z-Ala-S-bzl-Cys-Asp-Tyr Hydrazide				DMF-Eth	255-257 (dec)	−29	DMF	452
Z-Ala-Gln-S-bzl-Cys-His Monohydrate	1+3 O	DMF	55	Me	195-200	−26	DMF	746
Z-DL-Ala-aza-Gly-aza-Gly-Gly-OEt				Aq-Alc	180-182			157
					177-178			154
					180-182			154
Z-Ala-Gly-Gly-Gly-OCH(Ph)CN	2+2 WRK	Acn	73	Alc-Cy	149.5-150	−1	DMF	633
	2+2 ONP	DMF	81	Alc-Cy	77.5-79.5	−0.5	DMF	633

Compound	Method	Solvent	Yield (%)	Recryst. solvent	M.p. (°C)	[α]	Solvent	Ref.
Z-Ala-Gly-Gly-Leu	1+3 SPh	Ac	68	Aq	158.5–159.5		Alc	700
Z-Ala-Gly-Gly-Leu	3+1 SPh	Ac	61	Aq	122–123	−18	Alc	113
Z-Ala-Gly-Pro-Ala-ONBzl			65		123–124	−18	Alc	113
Z-DL-Ala-aza-Gly-aza-Sar-Gly-OEt			89		168			154
Nps-Ala-Gly-Ser-Gly	2+2 ONP	DMF	85	DMF-EtAc	148	−34	DMF	632
Nps-Ala-Gly-Ser-Gly-OEt	2+2 MCA	DMF		Alc-Eth	140–147	−33	DMF	632
Nps-Ala-Gly-Ser-Gly-ONp					179–180	−36	DMF	632
Z-Ala-Leu-Tyr-Leu	1+3 ONP	Ac-DMF	78	Acn-Eth	152.5–153.5	−38	DMF	166
Z-Ala-Leu-Tyr-Leu Hydrazide	1+3 ONP	DMF			136–137	−36	DMF	166
Z-Ala-Leu-Tyr-Leu-OMe			93	EtAc-He	223–224	−41	DMF	166
Boc-Ala-Phe-Ala-Gly-OEt					280–281	−47	Me	168
Ala-Phe-Ile-Gly					231–232	0	Ac	25
Z-Ala-Phe-Ile-Gly	1+3 DCCI				205–207	−39	Ac	25
Z-Ala-Phe-Ile-Gly-OBu^t	1+3 ONP	Py	92	Alc	250	−49	Alc	85
Z-Ala-Phe-Ile-Gly-OEt				Alc-Pe	211–212	−30	Ac	25
Boc-Ala-Phe-Ile-Gly Hydrazide	2+2 A		7		214–216	−25	Ac	395
Boc-Ala-Phe-Ile-Gly-OMe	1+3 ONP	DMF			226–227	−34	Alc	395
Boc-Ala-Phe-Phe-Gly-OEt	1+3 ONP	DMF			217–219	−43	Alc	168
Boc-Ala-Phe-Pro-Gly	1+3 ONP	DMF	64		201–204	−99	Ac	168
Boc-Ala-Phe-Pro-Gly-OEt	1+3 ONP	DMF			180–181	−72	Alc	168
Z-β-Ala-Pro-Phe-N^G-nitro-Arg-ONBzl	1+3 MCA		77	EtAc-Pe	100–105	−10	Ac	651
Ala-D-Val-Val-D-Val-OMe Hydrochloride					60–65			527
Z-Ala-D-Val-Val-D-Val-OMe								527
Arginine								
Arg-D-Ala-Arg-D-Ala				Aq	215	+15	Aq	401
Arg-Ala-Arg-Ala								203
N^G-Nitro-Z-Arg-Ala-N^G-nitro-Arg-Ala-OBzl	2+2 DCCI	DMF	79		212–213			203

233

Table 4 Tetrapeptides (continued)

Compound	Method	Solvent	% Yield	Solvent Crystallization	M.P. (°C)	$[\alpha]_D$	Solvent Rotation	Ref.
N^G-Nitro-Z-Arg-D-Ala-N^G-nitro-Arg-D-Ala-OBzl					197	+4.4	Me	401
Arg-Ala-Gln-Asp-β-OBu^t-α-OMe Acetate						21	Alc	726
Arg-Ala-Gln-β-OBu^t-Asp Hydrochloride						-18	Aq	726
Tri-Z-Ala-Gln-Asp-β-OBu^t-α-OMe	1+3 ONP	DMF	99		225	-9.7	Ac	726
Z-Arg-Ala-Gln-Asp-β-OBu^t-α-OMe Hydrobromide	1+3 NHS-DCCI	DMF	80	Me-EtAc	171–173	-27	Me	726
Z-Arg-Ala-Gln-Asp-β-OBu^t-α-OMe Hydrochloride	1+3 DCCI	DMF	65		167–169 (dec)	-28	Me	726
Z-Arg-Ala-Gln-β-OBu^t-Asp				Me-Aq	237 (dec)	-19	Ac-Aq	726
Arg-Arg-Pro-Val Amide Acetate Hydrate								244
Arg-Arg-Pro-Val-OBu^t Trihydrochloride								644
Arg-Arg-Pro-Val-OMe Trihydrobromide								71
Z-Arg-Arg-Pro-Val-OMe	DCCI	DMF	51	Me-MeCl	170–175		Me	71
Z-Arg-Arg-Pro-Val-OMe Dihydrobromide				Me	195–200			71
N^G-Nitro-Arg-N^G-nitro-Arg-Pro-Val Amide	1+3 MCA	THF	58					644
N^G-Nitro-Z-Arg-Arg-Pro-Val Amide Acetate Hydrate	3+1 MCA	DMF-THF	45					244
N^G-Nitro-Z-Arg-N^G-nitro-Arg-Pro-Val Amide								644
N^G-Nitro-Z-Arg-Gly-Gly-Gly-OEt	2+2 ONP	Py	72	Alc-Aq	174–178	-20	DMF	65
N^G-Nitro-Z-Arg-Leu-Val-Glu-di-OEt	1+3 MCA	THF	67	An	182–184	-101 -73	Me DMF	165
N^G-Nitro-Z-Arg-Pro-Gly-Pro	2+2 ONP	Di	46		150 (dec)	-94 -66	Ac-Aq Me	193
N^G-Nitro-Z-Arg-Pro-Gly-Pro-ONp				EtAc-Eth	160	-76 -100	DMF Ac-Aq	193

Compound	Method	Solvent	Yield	Recrystn.	m.p.	[α]$_D$	Solvent	Ref.
N^G-Nitro-Z-Arg-Pro-Pro-Ala Boc-hydrazide	2+2 DCCI		46		148–150	−112	Me	565
N^G-Nitro-Z-Arg-Pro-Pro-Ala Hydrazide Hydrochloride					140–142	−105	Me	565
N^G-Nitro-Z-Arg-Pro-Pro-Gly-boc-hydrazide Hydrochloride	2+2 DCCI	Acn-DMF	83		115			70
N^G-Nitro-Z-Arg-Pro-Pro-Gly Hydrazide Hydrochloride					123			70
N^G-Nitro-Z-Arg-Val-Tyr-Ile-OMe	3+1 DCCI	EtAc-DMF	27	Alc	178–181			569
	DCCI	DMF			180–182			
	DCCI	DMF			140–180			

Asparagine

Compound	Method	Solvent	Yield	Recrystn.	m.p.	[α]$_D$	Solvent	Ref.
Z-Asn-N^G-nitro-Arg-Val-Tyr-OEt	2+2 DCI	DMF	55	Ac	224–225			466
Z-Asn-N^G-nitro-Arg-Val-Tyr Hydrate					188–189.5			466
Z-Asn-S-bzl-Cys-Pro-Abu-Gly Amide	1+4 OTCP	DMF	92		222	−77	Ac	275
Z-D-Asn-S-bzl-Cys-Pro-Gly Amide	1+3 ONP	DMF	93	Alc-EtAc	240	−50	DMF	276
Z-Asn-S-bzl-Penicillaminyl-Pro-Leu-Gly Amide	1+4 ONP				101–105	−44	DMF	567
Z-Asn-Tyr-S-NBzl-Cys-Asn-ONBzl	2+2 DCCI	DMF	47	Ac-Aq	213–216	−453	DMF	309
	2+2 MCA	DMF		Ac-Aq	213–216			
Asp-Ala-Phe-Ile-OMe					230 (dec)	−17	Ac	85
					170 (dec)	−17	Ac-Aq	524
						−41	DMF	
β-OBzl-Z-Asp-Ala-Phe-Ile-OMe	1+3 MCA	THF	82	Alc-Aq	133–135	−20	Ac	85
Z-Asp-Ala-Phe-Ile-OMe	1+3 ONP	DMF	43		240–245	−23	Ac-Aq	524
						−40	DMF	
β-OBu^t-Z-Asp-Ala-β-OBu^t-Ser-Val-OBu^t					163–166	−22	Alc	602
β-OBzl-Z-Asp-Arg-Val-Tyr Boc-hydrazide	1+3 DCCI	DMF	71		142–144 (dec)	−24	Me	190
						−11	DMF	

235

Table 4 Tetrapeptides (continued)

Compound	Method	Solvent	% Yield	Solvent Crystallization	M.P.(°C)	[α]D	Solvent Rotation	Ref.
β-OBzl-Z-Asp-Arg-Val-Tyr Hydrazide					168–172	−29	Me	190
					168–	−29	Me	190
					172 (dec)			
Asp-OAc-Ser-Gly-Gly						−12	DMF	34
O-α-Asp-N-ac-Ser-Gly-Gly Tetrahydrate				Aq-Alc	156 (dec)	+11	Aq	34
					157–	+3.7	Aq	34
					160 (dec)			
β-OBzl-Z-Asp-DL-Ser-Gly-Gly Amide	1+3 DCCI	DMF	60	Me	178–180			545
Z-Asp-OAc-Ser-Gly-Gly				Alc	132–134	−24	Acn	34
Z-O-α-Asp-N-ac-Ser-Gly-Gly Tetrahydrate	1+3 DCCI	Py	55	Acn	169–170			34
			69					
Z-Asp-O-tos-Tyr-S-bzl-Cys-Asn-2,4,6-tri-me-OBzl	1+3 ONP	DMF		DMF-Alc	228–229	−35	DMF	625
Z-Asp-Tyr-OBzl-Cys-Asp-ONBzl	2+2 MCA		75		281–220	−34	DMF	315
β-OBu^t-Z-Asp-Tyr-Ser-N$^\epsilon$-boc-Lys Hydrazide				Me	186–188			100
β-OBu^t-Z-Asp-Tyr-Ser-N$^\epsilon$-boc-Lys-OMe	1+3 2,4,5-OTCP	DMF	68		94–96	−26	Me	100
	1+3 ONP							
Cysteines								
S-Bzl-Z-Cys-Ala-Gln-S-bzl-Cys	1+3 MCA	THF	52		208–210	−27	DMF	746
S-Bzl-Z-Cys-Ala-Gln-S-bzl-Cys Hydrazide				DMF-Eth	236–239	−25	DMF	746
S-Bzl-Z-Cys-Ala-Gln-S-bzl-Cys-OMe				DMF-Eth	221–222	−30	DMF	746
S-Bzl-Cys-Ala-Gln-S-bzl-Cys				Aq	188–190	−33	DMF	746
S-Bzl-Z-Cys-Ala-Gly-Val-OMe	2+2 MCA	THF	66.5		200		Aq-Ac	304
S-Bzl-Cys-Ala-Gly-Val-N$^{\alpha'}$-Z-cystathione α'-hydrazide				Aq-Me	175–176	−9.2	Ac	290

236

Compound	Method	Solvent	Yield (%)	Recryst.	M.p. (°C)	$[\alpha]$	Solvent	λ
Nα'-Z-α'-hemicystathionyl-S-bzl-Cys-Ala-Gly-Val-α-hemicystathione				Aq-DMF	294–296	−14	HMPA	290
α'-Hemicystathionyl-S-bzl-Cys-Ala-Gly-Val-α-hemicystathione				Ac-Eth	240–242	†1.7	Ac	290
Nps-S-bzl-Cys-Ala-Gly-Val-Nα'-Z-cystathione α'-OMe				Aq-DMF	140–145			290
Nps-S-bzl-Cys-Ala-Gly-Val-ONp	3+1 MCA	Chf	66	Aq-An	150–155	−29	DMF	290
S-Bzl-Z-Cys-S-bzl-Cys-Ala-Gly-OEt	1+3 ONP	DMF	82	Aq-Ac	188–190	−29	DMF	305
S-Bzl-Z-Cys-S-bzl-Cys-Ala-Gly-OMe	1+3 ONP	DMF	96	DMF-Alc	194–195	−18	DMF	314
S-Bzl-N-Nps-S-bzl-Cys-S-bzl-Cys-Ala-Gly-2,4,6-tri-me-OBzl					168.5–170.5			625
S,N-di-Z-Cys-S-NBzl-Cys-Ala-Gly-OEt	1+3 DCCI	Di	76	Ac-Aq	197–198		Ac-Aq	304
S,N-di-Z-Cys-S-NBzl-Cys-Ala-Gly Hydrate								304
S-Btm-N-for-Cys-S-NBzl-Cys-Ala-Gly-OEt	1+3 DCCI	Di	58	Ac-Aq	212–215	−80	Ac-Aq	304
N,N'-bis(N-Z-bzh-Cys)-Cystine-di-Gly-di-OEt					182–184		DMF	225
N,N'-Bis(Z-S-bz-Cys)-Cystine-di-Gly-di-OEt	1+3 ONP	DMF	74	Di	209–223	−107	DMF	225
S-Bzl-Z-Cys-S-bzl-Cys-Thr-Ser-OMe				Ac-Aq	174–178	−26	DMF	317
N-Z-S-(N'-Z-Cys-Gly-OEt)-Cys-Glu-α-OEt-γ-OBu^t	3+1 EDCI	MeCl	75	EtAc-He	105–107	−108	DMF	227
S-(N'-Z-Cys-Gly-OEt)-Z-Cys-Glu-α-OEt-γ-OBu^t				EtAc-He	151–153	−121	DMF	225
N-Z-S-(N'-Z-Cys-Gly OEt)-Cys-Gly N,N-di-et-amine Salt								227
S-(N'-Z-Cys-Gly-OEt)-Z-Cys-Gly N,N-di-et-amine Salt				An-Eth	151–153	−129	DMF	227
S-(N'-Z-Cys-Gly-OEt)-Z-Cys-Gly-OEt N,N-di-et-amine Salt				An-Eth	151–153	−129	DMF	227
N-Z-S-(N'-Z-Cys-Gly OEt)-Cys-Ser-OMe	3+1 EDCI	MeCl-DMF	79		115–117		DMF	227
S-bzl-Z-Cys-Gly-Gly-S-bzl-Cys-OBzl	3+1 A			EtAc-He	162–164	−117	DMF	225
S-bzl-Z-Cys-Gly-Gly-S-bzl-Cys Hydrazide					178–179	−40	Py	263
Cys-Gly-Gly-Cys					162			263

Table 4 Tetrapeptides (continued)

Compound	Method	Solvent	% Yield	Solvent Crystallization	M.P.(°C)	$[\alpha]_D$	Solvent Rotation	Ref.
S-Bzl-Z-Cys-di-Gly-Gly-OEt	1+3 MA	Py	63	Chf-Eth	124.5-126	-23	Di	279
S-Trt-Z-Cys-Gly-Gly-Gly								220
S-Trt-Z-Cys-Gly-Gly-Gly-OBu^t	1+3 DCCI		84		176-178	+23	An	220
S-Bzh-N-pht-Cys-Gly-Phe-Gly					110-114	-85	An	229
S-Bzh-N-pht-Cys-Gly-Phe-Gly-OBu^t	2+2 DCCI	MeCl	94	An-He	165-167	-62	DMF	229
S-Bzl-Z-Cys-Pro-Ala-Gly Amide	1+3 ONP	DMF	60		147-149	-47	DMF	690
	1+3 OTCP				144	-46 / -86	DMF / Ac-Aq	275
S-Bzl-Z-Cys-Pro-N^G-tos-Arg-Gly Amide	1+3 OTCP	DMF	88			-35	DMF	255
S-Bzl-Cys-Pro-N^G-tos-Arg-Gly Amide								255
S-Btm-Z-Cys-Pro-N^G-nitro-Arg-Gly Amide	1+3 ONP	DMF	34	Dipr Eth-DMF	92-94	-43	DMF	103
S-Bzl-Z-Cys-Pro-Cit-Gly Amide	1+3 ONP	DMF-Py	68	Me	185-187			61
S-Bzl-Z-Cys-Pro-Gly-Gly Amide	1+3 OTCP	DMF	67	Me-Aq	149	-36	DMF	275
S-Bzl-Z-Cys-Pro-Ile-Gly Amide	1+3 ONP	DMF	92		167			189
S-Bzl-Cys-Pro-Ile-Gly Amide								189
S-Bzl-Z-bz-Cys-Pro-Leu-Gly Amide					104-105	-61	DMF	610
S-Bzl-Z-Cys-Pro-Leu-Gly Amide	1+3 DCCI		85		158-160	-62	DMF	51
	ONP		83		141.5-142.5 168-169.5	-58	DMF	628
S-Bzl-Z-Cys-Pro-D-Leu-Gly Amide	1+3 ONP	DMF		Me-Aq	171-172	-13	DMF	519
S-Bzl-Cys-Pro-Leu-Gly Amide Hydrobromide	1+3 ONP	DMF			125-130	-67	Alc	546
N-Z-S-4,4'-di-Omediphenylme-Cys-Pro-Leu-Gly Amide								51
S-4,4'-di-OMe-diphenylme-N-Z-Cys-Pro-Leu-Gly Amide	1+3 ONP	DMF		Me	156-158	-37	DMF	200

238

Table (rotated 90°; top header row and left-hand column captions are cut off at the page edge):

Compound	Coupling	Solvent	Yield (%)	Solvent ([α])	m.p. (°C)	[α]	Recryst. solvent	No.
…Leu-Gly Amide			54					~200
S-Eac-Z-Cys-Pro-Leu-Gly Amide	1+3 OTCP	DMF	95		204	−80	Ac-Aq	188
						−66	DMF	188
S-Eac-Cys-Pro-Leu-Gly Amide					170	−66	DMF	668
Se-bzl-Z-Cys-Pro-Leu-Gly	1+3 A	DMF-Aq	78	Alc-Aq	163-164	−54	DMF	687
Se-bzl-Z-Cys-Pro-Leu-Gly Amide	1+3 ONP	DMF		Aq-Me	162-163	−52	DMF	668
Se-bzl-N-Z-Cys-Pro-Leu-Gly Amide	1+3 A	DMF		Alc-Aq	163-164	−54	DMF	62
S-Bzl-Z-Cys-Pro-N$^\varepsilon$-tos-Lys-Gly Amide	1+3 ONP	THF	84.5		130-132	−29	Chf	62
					130-132	−29	Chf	414
S-Bzl-N-Z-Cys-Pro-N$^\varepsilon$-tos-Lys-Gly-OEt	1+3 MCA	THF	69		127-130	−25	Chf	62
S-Bzl-Z-Cys-Pro-N$^\delta$-pht-Orn-Gly Amide			79	Alc-Aq	108-110	−39	DMF-Ac	63
S-Bzl-Z-Cys-Pro-N$^\delta$-tos-Orn-Gly Amide	1+3 OTCP	DMF	78		177-180	−38	DMF	254
S-Bzl-Cys-Pro-N$^\delta$-tos-Orn-Gly Amide						−38	Ac	254
S-Bzl-N-Z-Cys-Pro-Leu-Sar Amide	1+3 ONP	Chf	76		195-200	−61	DMF	84
S-Bzl-Z-Cys-Tyr-Tyr					224-235	−19	DMF	50
S-Bzl-Z-Cys-Tyr-Tyr-OEt	2+2 DCCI					−23	DMF	50
Z-Gln-Ala-Ala-Tyr-OMe	1+3 ONP	DMF	55		203-205	−24	Ac-Aq	98
Z-Gln-Asp-Ala-Pro-OTcp	1+3 MCA	THF		Alc	191	−71	Me	259
Z-Gln-(β-OBu^t)-Asp-Phe-Val-OBu^t					208-209	−36	DMF	727
Gln-β-OBu^t-Asp-Phe-Val-OBu^t Hydrochloride						−13	Me	727
Tfa-Gln-β-OBu^t-Asp-Phe-Val-Z-hydrazide	2+2 DCCI	DMF	84		235-236	−37	DMF	715
Tfa-Gln-β-OBu^t-Asp-Phe-Val Hydrazide					236	−33	DMF	715
Z-Gln-Gln-Asn-Asn-2,4,6-tri-me-OBzl	2+2 ONP	DMF			248-249.5 (dec)	+0.8	DCA	626
Gln-Gln-Asn-Asn				Aq-Alc	205.5-207.5 (dec)	−25	Aq	626
Z-Gln-Gly-Leu-Val Amide	1+3 ONP	DMF	95		239-241 (dec)	−27	Ac	66

Glutamine (section heading preceding the Z-Gln- compounds)

Table 4 Tetrapeptides (continued)

Compound	Method	Solvent	% Yield	Solvent Crystallization	M.P. (°C)	[α]$_D$	Solvent Rotation	Ref.
Z-Gln-Gly-Thr-Phe Methanol Solvate	2+2 DCCI				170	−4	DMF	47
Z-Gln-His-Phe-Arg Gelatine	1+3 A	DMF		Aq	159–160			297
Z-Gln-His-Phe-Arg-OMe Acetate				Me-EtAc	162–165	−53	Ac-Aq	297
Z-Gln-Pro-Ser-N$^\epsilon$-Z-Lys	2+2 DCCI	MeCl	60	THF-Aq	168–172	−29	DMF	573
Z-Gln-Pro-Ser-N$^\epsilon$-Z-Lys Hydrazide				Alc	163–165	−50	Alc	89
Z-Gln-Pro-Ser-N$^\epsilon$-Z-Lys-OMe				An-Eth-Pe	65			89
Gln-Pro-Ser-Lys					200 (dec)			89
Pyro-Gln-Pro-Ser-Lys					180 (dec)			89
γ-OBu^t-Z-Glu-Ala-OBu^t-Tyr-Gly-OMe	1+3 2,4,5-OTCP	DMF	80	Chf-Pe	141–142	−33	Chf	28
γ-OBu^t-Z-Glu-Ala-Tyr-Gly-OMe	1+3 2,4,5-OTCP			Py-Eth	158–160	−16	DMF	28
γ-OBu^t-Glu-Ala-Tyr-Gly-OMe Acetate		Ac-DMF	93	EtAc	163–164	−14	DMF	423
Bis-[γ-Glu]-di-Se-Cys-di-Gly (Se-Se-Glutathion)					118–120			144
Bis-[N-Tfa-γ-Glu(α-OEt)]-di-Se-Cys-di-Gly-di-OEt					198–200 (dec)			144
γ-OBzl-bz-Glu-γ-OBzl-Glu-γ-OBzl-Glu-γ-OBzl-Glu-OBzl	1+3 MCA		59	Me-Aq	148–150	−17	DMF	80
γ-OEt-Z-Glu-γ-OMe-Glu-γ-OEt-Glu-Val-ONBzl					149.5–152	−13	DMF	635
γ-OMe-Z-Glu-γ-OMe-Glu-OAc-Ser-γ-OMe-Glu-ONp	1+3 MCA		92	Me	181.5–183.5	−27	DMF	620
γ-OMe-Glu-γ-OMe-Glu-OAc-Ser-γ-OMe-Glu-ONp p-Toluenesulfonate								620
γ-OBzl-N-for-di-Gly-N$^\epsilon$-Z-Lys-OMe	3+1 OCH$_2$CN	THF	31	DMF-Eth	171–172	−8.8	DMF	422

Compound	Method	Solvent	Yield	Recryst.	m.p.	[α]	Solvent	Ref.
Glu-Gly-Lys-Gly					170–172 (dec)			422
γ-Z(OMe)-Glu-Gly-Nᵉ-tfa-Lys-Gly	2+2 DCCI	Py	65	Et-Ac-Pe	109–111	−18	Ac	422
γ-Z(OMe)-Glu-Gly-Nᵉ-tfa-Lys-Gly-OBuᵗ				Et-Ac-Pe	96–98	−23	Ac	422
γ-OMe-Glu-Gly-Nᵉ-tfa-Lys-Gly	MCA	THF-DMF	64.5	Alc-Eth	158–160	−7	Ac	422
Z-Glu-Gly-Thr-Phe-OMe				DMF-Aq	219–220			559
Glu-Gly-Thr-Phe-OMe				Alc-Aq-Eth	162–165			559
Z-Glu-Ile-Val-γ-OBuᵗ-Glu Hydrazide	2+2 A		73		243–244	−14	DMF	314
Z-Glu-Ile-Val-γ-OBuᵗ-Glu-OMe					171–174	−13	DMF	314
Boc-Glu-Nᵉ-Z-Lys-D-Ala-D-Ala-di-ONBzl						164		662
γ-OBuᵗ-Z-Glu-Nᵟ-boc-Orn-γ-OBuᵗ-Glu-His-OMe	1+3 ONP	Py	74	Me	117–118	−16	Alc	582
γ-OBuᵗ-Z-Glu-Nᵟ-boc-Orn-Glu-His-OMe	1+3 ONP	Py	78	Me-Eth	140–142	−21	Me	400
Z-Glu-Pro-Ser-Nᵉ-Z-Lys					100–103	−18	Alc	89
Z-Glu-Pro-Ser-Nᵉ-Z-Lys-OMe	2+2 DCCI	MeCl	66		110 (dec)	−54	Ac-Aq	524
						−61	Me	
						−36	DMF	
Z-Pyro-Glu-Pro-Ser-Nᵉ-boc-Lys-OMe	1+3 DCCI ONP	Chf	81		115–127	−67	Me	169
Glu-Pro-Ser-Lys-OMe					60 (dec)	−63	Ac-Aq	85
						−58	Me	524
Pyro-Glu-Pro-Ser-Nᵉ-boc-Lys-OMe								85
Pyro-Glu-Pro-Ser-Lys Hydrazide	EDCI	DMF	56		125 (dec)	−64	Me	85
γ-OBzl-Z-Glu-Ser-Ala-Gly-OEt					167–170			594

Glycine

Compound	Method	Solvent	Yield	Recryst.	m.p.	[α]	Solvent	Ref.
Z-Gly-Ala-Gly-Tyr-OBzl	3+1 A	EtAc	47	EtAc	161–163	−13	Me	540
Z-Gly-Ala-D-Leu-Ala-OMe	1+3 MCA		71	EtAc-Pe	116–119			527
					160			
Gly-Ala-D-Leu-Ala-OMe Acetate					174–175	−31	MeOAlc	527
Z-Gly-Ala-Phe-Gly	2+2 DCCI	Di-Acn	17.2	Me	85–89		Di	700
Z-Gly-(β-OBzl)-Asp-OBzl-Ser-Gly-OEt	EDCI	DMF	60	EtAc-Eth	135–137	−13		213
Z-Gly-β-OBzl-Asp-Ser-Gly-OEt			35					594

Table 4 Tetrapeptides (continued)

Compound	Method	Solvent	% Yield	Solvent Crystallization	M.P.(°C)	$[\alpha]_D$	Solvent Rotation	Ref.
N-For-Gly-Asp-Ser-Gly-OBu^t					125–127	–36		88
N-For-Gly-β-OBzl-Asp-OBzl-Ser-Gly					213–214 (dec)	–10		88
N-For-Gly-β-OBzl-Asp-OBzl-Ser-Gly-OBu^t	2+2 DCCI				122–123	–18		88
Z-Gly-di-(γ-OMe-Glu)-Gly-OMe	1+3 MCA	DMF		EtAc	136–139			172
Z-Gly-γ-OBzl-Glu-Ser-Gly-OEt	2+2 MCA	THF	45	EtAc-Pe	119–121.5			327
Gly-Glu-Ser-Gly-OEt				Me-Eth				327
Z-Gly-β-Ala-Gly								55
Z-Gly-Gly-S-bzl-Cys-Tyr-OEt	1+3 MCA	Chf	65	EtAc-Pe	142–144	–24	Di	299
Z-Gly-Gly-γ-OBzl-Glu-Gly-OEt	2+2 MA	Py	42	Aq-An	136–138	–4	Chf	422
Z-Gly-Gly-Gly-N^G-nitro-Arg-OMe	3+1 ONP	DMF	59	Me-Aq	148–150			65
Aza-Gly-Gly-aza-Gly-Gly-OEt Hydrobromide					85–120			154
Z-aza-Gly-aza-Gly-aza-Gly-Gly-OEt					182–184			154
Z-aza-Gly-Gly-aza-Gly-Gly					100–155			154
Z-aza-Gly-Gly-aza-Gly-Gly-OEt					193–194			154
Z-aza-Gly-Gly-aza-Gly-Gly Hydrazide					172–173			154
Z-Gly-aza-Gly-aza-Gly-OEt					189–191			154
				Alc-Aq	189–190			157
Z-Gly-Gly-Gly-Gly					188–190			154
N-[p-Nitro-benzylidene]-aza-Gly-Gly-aza-Gly-OEt					228–229			29
Tos-aza-Gly-Gly-aza-Gly-Gly-OEt					187–194			154
Z-Gly-Gly-Gly-Leu				Me	173–175			154
Gly-Gly-Gly-Leu				Aq-Alc				30
Z-Gly-Gly-Leu-Gly	2+2 ONP		78	Aq-An	133–134			30
Z-Gly-Gly-Leu-Gly-ONp Hydrate				Alc	149–150			30

Compound	Method	Solvent	Yield (%)	Recryst. solvent	M.p. (°C)	[α]	Solvent	Ref.
Gly-Gly-Leu-Gly				Aq-Alc				30
Z-Gly-aza-Gly-aza-Phe-Gly-OEt					161–163	−8.0	Me	154
Z-Gly-Gly-Phe-Phe-OEt					166–168	−7.7	DMF	262
Gly-Gly-Phe-Phe-OEt Acetate					153–155	−32	Chf	262
Z(NO$_2$)-Gly-Ile-Val-Glu-OBu^t	1+3 ONP	DMF	72	MeCl-Eth	176–179	−42	Me	305
Z(NO$_2$)-Gly-Ile-Val-Glu-α-et-γ-OBu^t	1+3 ONP	DMF		DMF-Eth	183–186	−23	KHCO$_3$	305
Z-Gly-Ile-Val-Gly				Alc	189.5–190	−26	Aq	625
Z-Gly-Leu-Gly-Gly						−34	Ac-Aq	30
Gly-Leu-Gly-Gly					70 (dec)	−27	DMF	30
Gly-Leu-Met-Gly Amide							DMF	524
N-Trt-Gly-Leu-Met-Gly Amide	3+1 DCCI	DMF	35.5	MeCl-Eth	120 (dec)	−5.5	Me	524
Z-Gly-Phe-Phe-Tyr	3+1 A	THF	59	Me-Aq	212.5–215.5	−14		350
Z-Gly-Phe-Phe-Tyr-OBzl	2+2 DCCI	THF	85	Pe	186–188			757
Z-Gly-Phe-Phe-Tyr-OEt					185–187			350
Gly-Phe-Phe-Tyr				Aq-Alc	208–212			757
Z(NO$_2$)-Gly-Phe-Phe-Tyr Hydrazide	2+2 A	THF	55	Alc-Aq	205–210			350
Z(NO$_2$)-Gly-Phe-Phe-Tyr-OMe				Alc-Aq	215–218			600
Z-Gly-D-Phe-D-Ser-D-Pro Hydrazide	3+1 A	DMF	73	DMF-Alc	222–224			600
Z-Gly-D-Phe-D-Ser-D-Pro-OMe					141.5–143	+27		681
Boc-Gly-Pro-Ala-Thr-OMe					228–230			681
Z-Gly-Pro-S-bzl-Cys-Tyr-OEt	2+2 MCA	Chf	75	Pr	107–110	−49	Di	78
Z-Gly-Pro-Leu-aza-Gly Amide					141–145			300
Z-Gly-Pro-Leu-Val	1+3 DCCI				230–232	−90		154
Z-Gly-Pro-Leu-Val-OMe					135–136			88
Gly-Pro-Leu-Val					oil			88
Z-Gly-Pro-Trp-Leu-OMe Hydrate	2+2 MCA, 2+2 DCCI, 1+3	MeCl	100, 55	Aq-An	219 (dec), 115–118	−67	Me	88, 28

Table 4 Tetrapeptides (continued)

Compound	Method	Solvent	% Yield	Solvent Crystallization	M.P.(°C)	$[\alpha]_D$	Solvent Rotation	Ref.
Boc-Gly-Pro-Trp-Leu-OMe	2,4,5-OTCP 1+3	DMF						
	2,4,5-OTCP	DMF	81	i-Pr	188–189	−76	Me	28
	2+2 DCCI MCA	MeCl	94 / 77	i-Pr	188–189	−74	Me	28
Gly-Pro-Trp-Leu-OMe Trifluoroacetate				Me-Eth	129–132 (dec)	−57	Me	28
Boc-Gly-Pro-Trp-Met-OMe	DCCI	MeCl	95	EtAc-Pe	116–118	−59	DMF	9
For-Gly-O-bzl-Ser-N^{im}-Z-His-Leu-OMe	2+2 DCCI	MeCl	66.8		131–132	+1.6	EtAc	261
Z-Gly-Ser-Phe-N^G-nitro-Arg-ONBzl	2+2 A	DMF-EtAc	55	i-Pr	130 (dec)	−18	Me	193
Gly-Ser-Phe-N^G-nitro-Arg-ONBzl				Di-Eth	130 (dec)	−12	DMF	193
						−30	Me	
Z-Gly-Trp-Gly-Trp Amide	1+3 MCA	THF	34	Alc-Aq	196–198	−24	Ac-Aq	666
Gly-Trp-Gly-Trp Amide p-Toluenesulfonate	1+3 WRK	DMF						666
Boc-Gly-Tyr-Ser-Met Hydrazide Hydrate				Aq	202–204 (dec)	−17	Ac-Aq	463
Boc-Gly-Tyr-Ser-Met-OMe	3+1 A		61.5	Acn	183–185	−16	Me	463
Boc-Gly-Val-Gly-Gly				Alc-Aq	201–203			267
Boc-Gly-Val-Gly-Gly-OMe				An	160–162			267
Gly-Val-Gly-Gly					240–242 (dec)			267
N-trt-Gly-Val-Phe-Ala-OEt	3+1 DCCI	MeCl	89	Be	193			158
Histidine								
N^{im}-Bzl-Z-His-Leu-S-bzl-Cys-Gly	1+3 DCCI	MeCl	81	Alc-Aq	195–196			764
N^{im}-Bzl-Z-His-Leu-S-bzl-Cys-Gly-OEt				Alc	145–147			764

Compound	Method	Solvent	Yield (%)	Solvent	M.p. (°C)	$[\alpha]$	Solvent	Ref.
Z-His-Leu-S-bzl-Cys-Gly	1+3 A		79	Alc	196–198	−31	Ac	758
Z-His-Leu-S-bzl-Cys-Gly-OEt	1+3 A	DMF	88		165–168	−57	Me	758
Z-His-Leu-Val-Gln-γ-OBu^t-α-OMe	1+3 DCCI	Acn	65		204–205	−38	DMF	329
N^{im}-Bzl-Z-His-Leu-Val-Glu-di-OEt	EDCI	DMF	54		177–179			755
Di-Z-His-Leu-Val-Glu-di-OEt	EDCI	DMF	42	Alc	157–158			594
His-Leu-Val-Glu-OEt Dihydrochloride					175–176			594
Di-Z-His-Phe-Ala-Asn Amide	ONP	DMF	92.5	Alc-Eth	209–211			755
His-Phe-Ala-Asn Amide					184–186	−12	DMF	436
His-Phe-Arg-Gly Acetate Hydrate								436, 235
Boc-His-OBzl-Ser-Asp-Gly-Z-hydrazide	1+3 A	DMF	70	Aq-Alc	174–176	−12	DMF	458
Boc-His-Ser-Asp-Gly Hydrazide						−18	DMF	458
N^{im}-Bzl-Z-His-Ser-Gln-Gly	2+2 DCCI		21		190–192	−2	DMF	47
N^{im}-Bzl-Z-His-Ser-Gln-Gly-OEt	1+3 A				170	−3	DMF	47
Boc-His-OBzl-Ser-Gln-Gly-ONBzl					144–146	−32	Aq	734
Boc-His-Ser-Gln-Gly					166–168	−18	Me	734
N^{im}-Bzl-His-Thr-Val-Glu-di-OBzl Di-p-toluenesulfonate								669

Isoleucine

Compound	Method	Solvent	Yield (%)	Solvent	M.p. (°C)	$[\alpha]$	Solvent	Ref.
Z-Ile-Gly-Leu-Met Amide	2+2 ONP	DMF-Ac	70	Eth-DMF	235–236	−18	DMF	443
N^{β}-Boc-α-hydrazino-β-phenyl-propionyl-Ile-Gly-Leu-Met Amide	1+3 MCA			Aq	208–212	−23	DMF	185
					214–216	−20	DMF	443
						−32	DMF	
Boc-Ile-Gly-Leu-Met Amide	MCA	THF	65	DMF-Aq	207–209	−33	Ac	395
					218	−32	Ac	524
				Me-Eth	136	−22	DMF	524
Ile-Gly-Leu-Met Amide				Me-Eth	145–147	−6	Ac	443
						−38	DMF	
						−36	Me	
						−33	DMF	

245

Table 4   Tetrapeptides (continued)

Compound	Method	Solvent	% Yield	Solvent Crystallization	M.P. (°C)	$[\alpha]_D$	Solvent Rotation	Ref.
Ile-Gly-Leu-Met Amide Hydrochloride						-27		563
Z-Ile-N^{im}-bzl-His-Pro-Ala-ONBzl	2+2 A	Di-EtAc			oil	-25	Me	395
Ile-N^{im}-bzl-His-Pro-Ala-ONBzl Hydrobromide								468
Z-Ile-N^{im}-bzl-His-Pro-Phe-OMe	1+3 DCCI	MeCl	93	Me-EtAc	106-110	-37	Me	468
Z-Ile-His-Pro-Phe-OBzl	2+2 A		70		81-85	-61	Me	405
Z-Ile-His-Prp-Phe-ONBzl	1+3 MCA	Aq-THF	98	EtAc-Pe	92-100	-63	Me	531
Boc-Ile-His-Pro-Phe-OMe Hydrate	2+2 CDI	DMF	64					19
Ile-N^{im}-bzl-His-Pro-Phe-OMe								466
Ile-His-Pro-Phe-OBzl Dihydrobromide					156-160 (dec)	-46	6N HCl	405
Ile-His-Pro-Phe-OMe Dihydrobromide Hydrate				Me-Pe	159-168			531
Ile-His-Pro-Phe-ONBzl Dihydrobromide								466
Ile-His-Pro-Phe-ONp Dihydrobromide								19
Z-Ile-His-Pro-Tyr-OMe	A	DMF	67.9	Me	201.5-204.5	-32	DMF	588
Ile-His-Pro-Tyr-OMe Dihydrobromide	1+3 DCCI	MeCl	61	Alc-Eth	168-172	+30	DMF	606
For-D-allo-Ile-Pro-Sar-N-me-Val-OMe						-99	Me	606
D-Allo-Ile-Pro-Sar-N-me-Val-OMe Hydrochloride						-143	Me	76
Leucine								
Leu-Ala-Gly-Val	3+1 A			Alc-Di	194.5-196	+18	Alc	415
Leu-Ala-Val-Glu Hydrochloride	3+1 A			Alc-EtAc	178-186			430
Z(NO$_2$)Leu-Ala-Val-Glu-di-OBzl		EtAc	50	Alc	220-223			430
Z(NO$_2$)Leu-Ala-Val-Glu-di-OEt		EtAc	45	Aq-Alc	225	-28		430
Z-Leu-γ-OBu^t-Glu-Asp-Tyr Boc-hydrazide								762
Z-Leu-Gly-Ala-N^G-nitro-Arg-ONBzl	2+2 ONP	DMF	71	Di-Eth	128-129	0.0	Ac	646
Z-Leu-Gly-Asn-Asn-Tyr Boc-hydrazide	1+3 ONP		84		220-226		Ac	762

Compound	Method	Solvent	Yield	Recryst.	M.p.	[α]	Solv.	Ref.
Z-Leu-aza-Gly-aza-Gly-Gly-OEt				Alc	136–138			154
Z-Leu-Gly-Gly				Aq-Alc	157–159			29
Z-Leu-Gly-Gly-ONp					154–156			29
Leu-Gly-Gly-Gly								29
Boc-Gly-Leu-Met Amide	1+3 MCA		72		196–203	−35	Ac	394
Leu-Gly-Leu-Met Amide Hydrochloride					200–216	−29	Aq	394
Z-Leu-Gly-Leu-Val Amide	1+3 ONP		60		228–230	−32	Ac	367
N-Tos-Leu-S-bzl-Cys-Tyr-OEt	2+2 A	Aq-DMF		EtAc-Pe	205–208	−20	Di	299
Leu-Met-Asn-OBu^t-Thr-OBu^t								48
Leu-Met-Asn-OBu^t-Thr-OBu^t Picrate	1+3 ONP	DMF	74	Alc	133–135	+8	DMF	48
N-Pht-Leu-Met-Asn-OBu^t-Thr-OBu^t	1+3 MCA	THF	75	Hep-Be	oil	+6	DMF	48
Z-Leu-D-Phe-Gly-Gly-OEt								337
Leu-D-Phe-Gly-Gly-OEt Hydrochloride	1+3 MCA	THF	97		oil			337
Z-Leu-D-Phe-Pro-Gly-OEt								302
Leu-D-Phe-Pro-Gly OEt Hydrochloride	1+3 ONP	DMF	44	EtAc	111–113	−46	Ac	302
Z-Leu-Pro-Phe-N^G-nitro-Arg-ONBzl								653
Boc-Leu-OBzl-Ser-N^G-nitro-Arg-Leu Z-hydrazide				Alc	202–203	−21	DMF	458
Boc-Leu-OBzl-Ser-N^G-nitro-Arg-Leu-OMe	1+3 ONP	DMF	86	Alc	169–170	−32	Me	458
Z-Leu-Tyr-Gln-Leu Hydrazide				Alc	246–249	−29	DMF	315
Z-Leu-Tyr-Gln-Leu-OMe				EtAc-Pe	226–229			311
Z-D-Leu-Trp-D-Leu-Trp 2-Hydroxyethylamide	2+2 DCCl	MeCl	66	MeCl-Pe	195–202			527
Z-Leu-Val-S-bzl-Cys-Gly-OEt	1+3 ONP	DMF	91		208	−44	MeCl	674
				EtAc-Chf-Pe	170			310
					202			674
Z-Leu-Val-S-bzl-Cys-Gly Hydrazide	1+3 ONP		83	DMF-Alc	198–199	−34	DMF	411
Z-Leu-Val-S-bzl-Cys-Gly-OMe					209–210	−28	DMF	351
Z-Leu-Val-S-bzl-Cys-Gly-ONp					204–206	−2.1	DMF	411
Leu-Val-S-bzl-Cys-Gly-OMe Hydrobromide						−22	Ac	411
Z-Leu-Val-γ-OBu^t-Glu-Ala-OMe	1+3 ONP		95		225–226	−20	DMF	411
	1+3 OSu							534

Table 4 Tetrapeptides (continued)

Compound	Method	Solvent	% Yield	Solvent Crystallization	M.P. (°C)	$[\alpha]_D$	Solvent Rotation	Ref.
Lysine								
Nᵉ-Boc-Z-Lys-NG-tos-Arg-NG-tos-Arg-Pro	1+3 ONP	DMF			106–109	−22	Me	455
Nᵉ-Boc-Z-Lys-NG-tos-Arg-NG-tos-Arg-Pro Amide	1+3 ONP	Acn			120–126	−26	Me	492
Nᵉ-Boc-Nα-Z-Lys-NG-tos-Arg-NG-tos-Arg-Pro-OBut	ONP		94.5		108–112	−33	Me	372
NG-Boc-Lys-NG-tos-Arg-NG-tos-Arg-Pro					105–110	−14	Me	455
Nᵉ-Tos-Nα-Z-Lys-NG-tos-Arg-NG-tos Arg-Pro-OBut	1+3 ONP		92	An-Eth	120–125	−32	Me	372
Nᵉ-Tos-Z-Lys-NG-tos-Arg-NG-tos-Arg-Pro-OMe	1+3 ONP		84		110–115			371
Di-Boc-Lys-Asn-Ala-Phe								392
Di-Boc-Lys-Asn-Ala-Phe Hydrazide				DMF-Aq	213–214	−38.6	DMF	443
Di-Boc-Lys-Asn-Ala-Phe-OMe					163–166	−8.5	Ac	392
Di-Boc-Lys-γ-OBut-Glu-Phe-Thr-OMe	1+3 ONP	DMF	60	EtAc	151–152	−23	Ac-Aq	98
Lys-Gly-Glu-Gly					192–194 (dec)	+17	Ac	422
Nᵉ-Tfa-Z-Lys-Gly-γ-OMe-Glu-Gly-OBut	2+2 DCCl	Py	65	EtAc-Pe	86–88	−10	Ac	422
	2+2 MA	Py	60		83–85	−9		
	2+2 ONP	Py	71	EtAc-Pe	85–87	−8		
Nᵉ-Tfa-Lys-Gly-γ-OMe-Glu-Gly				Alc-Eth	163–165	+16	Ac	422
Nᵉ-Boc-Z-Lys-Nᵉ-boc-Lys-NG-tos-Arg-NG-tos-Arg Amide	1+3 ONP	Acn	76		115–125	−10	Me	492
Nᵉ-Boc-Z-Lys-Nᵉ-boc-Lys-NG-tos-Arg-NG-tos-Arg-δ-aminovaleric-OMe	ONP				83–88	−143	Me	454
Nᵉ-Boc-Lys-Nᵉ-boc-Lys-NG-tos-Arg-NG-tos-Arg-δ-aminovaleric-OMe				Me-Eth	95–100	−9.6	Me	454
Di-Aoc-Lys-Phe-Ile-Gly				Me-Aq	127–133 (dec)	−17.2	DMF	517
Di-Aoc-Lys-Phe-Ile-Gly-OBzl	1+3 ONP	DMF	88	Alc-Aq	151–152	−17	DMF	517
Di-Aoc-Lys-Phe-Ile-Gly-OEt	1+3 ONP	DMF	73		162–163	−18	DMF	517

Compound	Method	Solvent	Yield (%)	Recryst. solvent	M.p. (°C)	$[\alpha]$	Solvent	Ref.
Di-Boc-Lys-Phe-Gly-OEt	1+3 ONP	DMF	85.2		162-164	-32	Alc	168
Di-Z-Lys-Pro-Pro-Gly	1+3 ONP		96		190	-102	Me	722
N^{ϵ}-Boc-Z-Lys-Pro-Pro-Gly	1+3 ONP				170	-109		722
N^{ϵ}-Boc-Z-Lys-Pro-Val-Gly					117-118	-131	Me	368
					72-95	-72	Me	577
N^{ϵ}-Boc-Z-Lys-Pro-Val-Gly-OEt	1+3 DCCI	Acn	87	An	142-144	-77	Alc	576
N^{ϵ}-Boc-Z-Lys-Pro-Val-Gly-OMe	1+3 ONP	EtAc	76	EtAc	137-138	-86	Me	368
N^{ϵ}-Boc-Lys-Pro-Val-Gly-OEt								576
N^{ϵ}-Boc-N^{α}-Pz-Lys-Pro-Val-Gly	1+3 DCCI	Acn	60	An	127-130	-64	Me	576
N^{ϵ}-Boc-N^{α}-Pz-Lys-Pro-Val-Gly-OEt				An-Acn	149-150	-70	Me	576
N^{ϵ}-Boc-N^{α}-trt-Lys-Pro-Val-Gly				Eth-Pe	102-120	-7.7	2N NH$_4$OH	576
N^{ϵ}-Boc-N^{α}-trt-Lys-Pro-Val-Gly-OEt				Eth-Pe	100	-17	Me	576
N^{ϵ}-For-Z-Lys-Pro-Val-Gly-OMe	1+3 MCA	Di	61	Me	166-167			239
N^{ϵ}-For-Lys-Pro-Val-Gly Hydrate				Me-Eth				239
Lys-Pro-Val-Gly								576
N^{ϵ}-Tos-Z-Lys-Pro-Val-Gly	1+3 ONP	EtAc	76	EtAc	109-110			371
N^{ϵ}-Tos-Z-Lys-Pro-Val-Gly-OMe				EtAc	139-140			371
N^{ϵ}-Tos-Z-Lys-Pro-Val-Gly-ONp				Alc-Ac	152-153			371
N^{ϵ}-Tos-Boc-Lys-Pro-Val-Gly	1+3 ONP	EtAc	84		104-106	-68	Me	373
N^{ϵ}-Tos-boc-Lys-Pro-Val-Gly-OMe	1+3 DCCI	DMF-MeCl	93	Alc	109-110	-73	Me	373
N^{ϵ}-Boc-Z-Lys-OBu^t-Tyr-Leu-β-OBu^t-Asp-OMe					164.5-165	-25	Alc	737
N^{ϵ}-Boc-Z-Lys-Tyr-Leu-γ-OBu^t-Asp	1+3 MCA	Alc			142-144 (dec)	-25	Me	733
N^{ϵ}-Boc-Lys-OBu^t-Tyr-Leu-β-OBu^t-Asp-OMe			96	Dipr-Eth	67	-31		737
N^{ϵ}-Boc-Lys-Tyr-Leu-γ-OBu^t-Asp			91.5	EtAc-Pe	195-196	-10	Alc	730
N^{ϵ}-Boc-Z-Lys-Val-Tyr-Pro-OBu^t	1+3 DCCI	Acn			110	+11	Ac-Aq	578

Phenylalanine

Compound	Method	Solvent	Yield (%)	Recryst. solvent	M.p. (°C)	$[\alpha]$	Solvent	Ref.
Z-Phe-Ala-Pro-Phe-N^{G}-nitro-Arg-ONBzl	2+2 A		56		188-189	-43	DMF	553

Table 4 Tetrapeptides (continued)

Compound	Method	Solvent	% Yield	Solvent Crystallization	M.P.(°C)	[α]$_D$	Solvent Rotation	Ref.
Phe-Ala-Pro-Phe-N^G-nitro-Arg-ONBzl Hydrobromide						−29	DMF	553
Z-D-Phe-N^G-nitro-D-Arg-Trp-Gly				Me	227 (dec)	−1.9	DMF	744
Z-D-Phe-N^G-nitro-D-Arg-D-Trp-Gly					205–209	+21	DMF	744
Z-Phe-N^G-nitro-Arg-Trp-Gly Dihydrate					190–193			235
Z-Phe-N^G-nitro-Arg-Trp-Gly-OMe	2+2 DCCI	Acn-MeCl	78	Me	136–140			297
N$^\alpha$-Z-D-Phe-N^G-nitro-D-Arg-D-Trp-Gly-OMe	2+2 MCA	THF-DMF	54		146–150	+14	Me	744
Z-D-Phe-N^G-nitro-Arg-Trp-Gly-OMe	2+2 MCA	DMF-THF	63	Me-EtAc	202 (dec)	−7	DMF	744
Z-Phe-N^G-nitro-Arg-Trp-Gly-OMe Dihydrate	2+2 MCA	THF	67		145–148			600
	1+3 MCA	THF	63		148–150			162
Z-D-Phe-N^G-nitro-Arg-D-Trp-Gly-OMe Hydrate	1+3 MCA	Di	84.1		145–148	+20	Me	742
Z-Phe-N^G-nitro-D-Arg-Trp-Gly-OMe Monohydrate					110	−14	DMF	743
Z-D-Phe-N^G-nitro-Arg-D-Trp-Gly-OMe Monohydrate					134	+5.2	DMF	743
Z-Phe-N^G-tos-Arg-Trp-Gly-OBu^t	1+3 WRK	Acn	84	EtAc	160–162			370
	1+3 WRK							369
D-Phe-D-Arg-D-Trp-Gly						−3.7	1N HCl	744
Phe-Arg-Trp-Gly Acetate Hydrate				Me-Eth				235
D-Phe-N^G-nitro-D-Arg-Trp-Gly Hydrobromide						−5.9	Me	744
Phe-N^G-nitro-Arg-Trp-Gly Hydrate								235
Phe-N^G-nitro-Arg-Trp-Gly Dihydrobromide Hydrate								235
Phe-N^G-nitro-Arg-Trp-Gly-me								575
Phe-N^G-nitro-Arg-Trp-Gly-OMe								298
D-Phe-N^G-nitro-D-Arg-D-Trp-Gly-OMe Hydrobromide						−5.6	Me	742

Compound	Coupling	Solvent	Yield (%)	Recryst. solvent	M.p. (°C)	[α]	Solvent	Ref.
Phe-N^G-nitro-Arg-Trp-Gly-OMe Dihydrochloride				DMF-Aq	223–224	−87	DMF	297
Phe-N^G-tos-Arg-Trp-Gly-OBu^t				Ac-Me	246	−18	DMF	369
N,N'-Z-Phe-Cystine-bis(Gly-OEt)				Aq-An	233–235	−21	1N HCl	370
N,N'-bis-Z-Phe-Cystine-di-Gly Di-OMe								188
Z-Phe-Gln-γ-OBzl-Glu-Gln-OBzl								777
Phe-Gln-Glu-Gln								775
Z-Phe-Gly-Ala-Val	2+2 SPh	Ac	85	EtAc	193–195	−18	Alc	700
Z-Phe-N^ε-boc-Lys-Trp-Gly OBu^t	1+3 WRK	Acn	70	Me	183–184	−26	Me	94
Z-Phe-N^ε-tos-Lys-Trp-Gly-OBu^t	1+3 WRK	Acn	79	EtAc	140–141	−26	Me	94
Z-Phe-N^δ-pht-Orn-Trp-Gly-OBu^t	1+3 ONP		79		167–169	−15	DMF	63
Z-Phe-Phe-Tyr-Thr				Aq-Alc	209–210	−33	Me	351
Z-Phe-Phe-Tyr-Thr-OMe	1+3 DCCI	DMF-THF	72	Alc	205–206	−21	DMF	351
Z-Phe-Pro-Tyr-Phe-OMe	1+3 ONP		85					753
Phe-Pro-Tyr-Phe-OMe								753
Z-Phe-Ser-Pro-Phe-OMe	1+3 ONP		87	Alc-Eth	156–159	−40	DMF	123
Z-D-Phe-Ser-D-Pro-D-Phe-OMe	1+3 A	EtAc	72		115–117	−51		681
D-Phe-D-Ser-D-Pro-D-Phe-OMe					oil	+38		681
Z-Phe-Val-Asn-Gln Boc-hydrazide								543
Z-Phe-Val-Asn-Gln Hydrazide								543
Z-Phe-Val-Asn-Gln-OMe								543
Proline								
Z-Pro-Gly-Phe-Gly	1+3 NHS	Aq-Alc	76	Alc-Aq	154–155	−27	Di	7
Z-Pro-Gly-Phe-Ser			80	Di-Pe				683
Z-Pro-Gly-Phe-Ser-OMe	2+2 DCCI	DMF-THF	41	EtAc-Eth	107–109			683
Pz-Pro-Leu-Gly-Pro-OMe	1+2 P	THF	68	EtAc-Pe	121–123			721
Z-Pro-Leu-Phe-Val-OMe	1+3 DCCI	DMF	80	EtAc-Pe	176–178			179
Pro-Leu-Phe-Val-OMe Hydrochloride				Me-Eth	125–145			179
Z-Pro-Phe-N^{im}-Z-His-Leu-OMe	2+2 DCCI			An-Eth	144.5–145 (dec)	−56	Me	261

Table 4 Tetrapeptides (continued)

Compound	Method	Solvent	% Yield	Solvent Crystallization	M.P. (°C)	$[\alpha]_D$	Solvent Rotation	Ref.
Z-Pro-Phe-Leu-Val-OMe	1+3 DCCI	Acn		EtAc-Pe	122-125			179
Pro-Phe-Leu-Val-OMe Hydrochloride					128-135			179
Z-Pro-Pro-N^ϵ-boc-Lys-Asp-di-OBu^t	1+3 DCCI	Acn	72	Eth	78-85	-72	Alc	573
Z-Pro-Pro-N^ϵ-for-Lys-Asp	ONP	Aq-Di	90			-96	Me	747
Z-Pro-Pro-N^ϵ-for-Lys-Asp DCHA Salt					230 (dec)			747
Pro-Pro-N^ϵ-boc-Lys-Asp-di-OBu^t				Me-Eth	147-149	-73	Me	573
Pro-Pro-N^ϵ-for-Lys-Asp						-109	Aq	747
Pro-Pro-Pro-Tyr					163-166 (dec)			573
Pro-Pro-Pro-Tyr Hydrazide	DCCI	Acn	29	DMF-Me	217-219	-77	DMF	573
Pro-Pro-Pro-Tyr-OMe	2+2 A	EtAc	32		226-228	-85	DMF	573
Boc-Pro-Ser-Asp-N^ϵ-boc-Lys-OMe					125 (dec)	-53 / -28	Ac-Aq / DMF	524
Pro-Tyr-Arg-Met Acetate Trihydrate	2+2 A	EtAc			181-183	-23	Aq	741
Z-Pro-Tyr-N^ϵ-tos-Lys-Met(sulfoxide)OMe				Me				268
Boc-Pro-Tyr-N^ϵ-tos-Lys-Met	3+1 DCCI	Acn						269
Boc-Pro-Tyr-N^ϵ-tos-Lys-Met-OMe					223-226	-42	5N KHCO$_3$	269
Pro-Tyr-N^ϵ-tos-Lys-Met					223-226			269
Pro-Tyr-N^ϵ-tos-Lys-Met(sulfoxide)					237-238			268
Z-Pro-Val-Asn-Leu-OBu^t	1+3 ONP	DMF	70	Alc	218-219	-41		641
Pro-Val-Asn-Leu-OBu^t					198	-40		641
Z-Pro-Val-Gly-N^ϵ-tos-Lys DCHA Salt				Eth-Alc	175-177 / 212-			560
Z-Pro-Val-Gly-N^ϵ-tos-Lys Hydrazide	1+3 MCA	THF	76.5	DMF-Aq	213.5	-21	DMF	560
Z-Pro-Val-Gly-N^ϵ-tos-Lys-OMe	2+2 A	EtAc	75	EtAc-Pe / DMF-THF	135-137.5 / oil	-32	Alc	560

Serine

Compound	Method	Solvent	Yield %	Recryst.	m.p.	[α]	Solvent	M
OBzl-boc-Ser-N^G-nitro-Arg-N^G-nitro-Arg-Ala-OBzl	1+3 MCA		91		173–176	−26	Py	732
OBzl-Ser-N^G-nitro-Arg-N^G-nitro-Arg-Ala-OBzl			86		175–178	−7.6	Ac	732
Z(OMe)Ser-Asn-S-bzl-Cys-Tyr-OEt	A	DMF-EtAc	56	Alc-Eth-Pe	174–177	−25	DMF	452
Ser-Asn-S-bzl-Cys-Try OEt Trifluoroacetate								452
O[2,2,2-trifluoro-1-Z-et]Ser-Gly-Leu-Val-OMe					72–74			701
N[Z(OMe)]-O-[2,2,2-trifluoro-1-Z-amine-et]Ser-Gly-Leu-Val-OMe								701
OAc-Z-Ser-Pro-Phe-Arg-OMe	1+3 ONP	DMF	70	EtAc-Pe	140			440
OBzl-Z-Ser-Pro-Phe-N^G-nitro-Arg-OMe	1+3 ONP	DMF	66	Me-Eth	166–168	−55		456
OBzl-N-Nps-Ser-Pro-Phe-N^G-nitro-Arg-ONBzl				EtAc-Me-Eth	100–102			137
Z-Ser-Pro-Phe-N^G-nitro-Arg-OMe	A	EtAc	64	Me	128–130	−42	DMF	439
	1+3 ONP	Py	56	EtAc	170–172	−70		456
	1+3 A	EtAc-DMF	64	Me	128–130	−35	Ac	439
Z-Ser-Pro-Phe-N^G-nitro-Arg-ONBzl	3+1 DCCI	DMF	92		101	−58		605
N-Boc-Ser-Pro-Phe-N^G-nitro-Arg-ONBzl	1+3 A	DMF	76	EtAc-Pe	91–100			652
Ser-Pro-Phe-N^G-nitro-Arg-ONBzl					95–103			605
OAc-Z-Ser-Pro-Phe-Cit-OMe	1+3 ONP	DMF	52	Acn-Aq	170–172	+5	DMF	456
Z-Ser-Ser-Gly-Gly-OEt	2,4-DNPO	Chf						22
Z-Ser-Trp-Ser-Met Hydrazide		Di			245–246(dec)			371
OAc-Ser-Tyr-Ser-Met Hydrazide		Aq			256			571
OAc-Ser-Tyr-Ser-Met-OMe					200–211			571
OBzl-boc-Ser-OBzl-Ser-Met-OMe	2+2 A	EtAc	61.3	EtAc-Pe	127–129	−11	Me	463
Z-Ser-Tyr-Ser-Met Hydrazide	2+2 A				187–189(dec)			407
Z-Ser-Tyr-Ser-Met-OMe					191–193			407
Boc-Ser-Tyr-Ser-Met Hydrazide	A	EtAc	52	Aq	115–125	−35	Me-Aq	463
Boc-Tyr-Ser-Met-OMe	2+2 A	EtAc	44	EtAc	129–134	−36	Aq-Me	270
						−29	Me	270
Ser-Tyr-Met-OMe Trifluoroacetate				Me	211	−29	Me	463
								571

Table 4 Tetrapeptides (continued)

Compound	Method	Solvent	% Yield	Solvent Crystallization	M.P.(°C)	[α]D	Solvent Rotation	Ref.
Threonine								
Z-Thr-Ala-Ala-Ala-OEt	1+3				201–202	−12	DMF	507
Boc-Thr(Ala)$_3$-OBzl	2,4-DNPO		77	DMF-Eth	210–211	−58	Ac	356a
Thr-Ala-Ala-Ala-OEt					205–206	−94	Me	507
Actinocinyl-bis[Thr-D-allo-Ile-Pro-Sar]	1+3 DCCI	MeCl	66	EtAc-Cy		−23	Me	77
N[2-Nitro-OBzl-4-me-bz] Thr-D-allo-Ile-Pro-Sar-OBzl	1+3 WRK	NMe	65				Me	77
Z-Phe-Thr-Ser Hydrazide	2+2 DCCI			Me	234–235	+1.4	DMSO	458
Z-Phe-Thr-Ser-OMe	1+3		73		199	−4	DMF	47
Z-Thr-Phe-Thr-Ser-OMe Hydrate	2,4-DNPO	DMF	85	Alc	198–200	−10.4	DMF	458
Pht-Thr-Phe-Thr-OBzl-Ser Z-hydrazide	2+2 DCCI	Aq-Acn	73	EtAc-Me	199	−4	DMF	47
Pht-Thr-Phe-Thr-bzl-Ser Z-hydrazide	2+2 A		84			−22	Me	728
Thr-Phe-Thr-OBzl-Ser Z-hydrazide	DCCI		77			−23	Me	728
Thr-Phe-Thr-Ser-OMe					164–167	−14	Me	728
								47
								47
Z-Thr-Pro-N$^\epsilon$-boc-Lys-Ala-OBu^t	1+3 DCCI		95		112–116	−39	DMF	536
Z-Thr-Pro-N^G-tos-Lys-Ala					99–104			761a
Z-Thr-Pro-N$^\epsilon$-tos-Lys-Ala-OMe	1+3 DCCI	Acn	72.4	EtAc-Pe	87–90			761a
	1+3 DCCI	MeCl	85	EtAc-Pe	82–100			308
Thr-Pro-Lys-Ala	1+3 A				oil			761a
Z-Thr-Pro-N$^\epsilon$-tos-Lys-OBu^t-Thr-OBu^t	1+3 DCCI	DMF-MeCl	89	Me-Eth	105–110	−31	DMF	408
Z-Thr-Pro-Phe-N^G-nitro-Arg-ONBzl	1+3 DCCI		68			−46	Ac	653
Boc-Thr-OBzl-Ser(Ala)$_2$-OBzl	EDCI	DMF	88	EtAc-He	168–171			356a
Boc-Thr-Ser-Met-Ala-OEt			9					594

Compound	Coupling	Solvent	Yield (%)	Solvent (recryst.)	m.p. (°C)	[α]	Solvent	Ref.
Nα-Z-Nγ-tos-Dbu-Thr-Nγ-tos-Dbu-Thr-Nγ-tos-Dbu-Nγ-tos-Dbu-D-Leu-Thr-Nγ-tos-Dbu-Nγ-pelargonyl-Dbu Hydrazide				Me-Aq	200–205	−24		486
Nα-Boc-Nγ-pelargonyl-Dbu-Nγ-Z-Dbu-Thr-Nγ-Z-Dbu-Thr-Nγ-Z-Dbu-Nγ-Z-Dbu-D-Leu-Ile-Nγ-Z-Dbu-OMe				DMF	225–227(dec)			485
Me-Nγ-Z-Nα-nps-Dbu-Thr-Nγ-Z-Dbu-Thr-Nγ-Z-Dbu-Nγ-Z-Dbu-D-Leu-Ile-Nγ-Z-Dbu				DMF-Aq	207–212(dec)			485
Me-Nα-Z-Nγ-tos-Dbu-Thr-Nγ-tos-Dbu-Thr-Nγ-tos-Dbu-Nγ-tos-Dbu-D-Leu-Ile-Nγ-tos-Dbu-Nγ-pelargonyl-Dbu				i-Pr	178–185			486
Me-Nps-Thr-Nγ-Z-Dbu-Thr-Nγ-Z-Dbu-Nγ-Z-Dbu-D-Leu-Ile-Nγ-Z-Dbu				DMF-Aq	205–210(dec)	−30		485
Me-Nγ-pelargonyl-Dbu-Nγ-Z-Dbu-Thr-Nγ-Z-Dbu-Thr-Nγ-Z-Dbu-Nγ-Z-Dbu-D-Leu-Ile-Nγ-Z-Dbu Trifluoroacetate				DMF-Aq	218–228(dec)			485
Nγ-Pelargonyl-Dbu-Nγ-Z-Dbu-Thr-Nγ-Z-Dbu-Thr-Nγ-Z-Dbu-Nγ-Z-Dbu-D-Leu-Ile-Nγ-Z-Dbu Hydrazide				DMF-Aq	220–225(dec)			485
Nγ-Tos-Dbu-Thr-Nγ-tos-Dbu-Thr-Nγ-tos-Dbu-Nγ-tos-Dbu-D-Leu-Ile-Nγ-tos-Dbu-Nγ-pelargonyl-Dbu Hydrazide				DMF-Aq	185–194(dec)			486
Nα-Z-Nγ-tos-Dbu-Thr-Nγ-tos-Dbu-Thr-Nγ-tos-Dbu-Nγ-tos-Dbu-D-Leu-OMe				i-Pr	120–135	−17		486
Tryptophan								
Z-Trp-Leu-Ala-Thr-OMe	1+3 DCCI	THF	80–90	Me-Eth	133–137			704
Trp-Leu-Ala-Thr-OMe								704
Boc-Trp-Leu-Asp-Phe Amide	1+3 2,4,5-OTCP	DMF		Alc	217(dec)	−46	DMF	323

255

Table 4 Tetrapeptides (continued)

Compound	Method	Solvent	% Yield	Solvent Crystallization	M.P. (°C)	$[\alpha]_D$	Solvent Rotation	Ref.
Trp-Leu-Asp-Phe Amide Hydrochloride				Me-Eth	201–203	−30	Me	323
Trp-Leu-Asp-Phe Amide Trifluoroacetate				Me	200–202	−21	Me	323
					229–			
Aoc-Trp-Met-Asp-Phe Amide	2+2 A	DMF-Di	76	Alc	230(dec)	−31	DMF	520
Z-Trp-Met-Asp-Phe Amide				EtO-Alc-Aq	237–238	−41	DMF	111
					202–			
Boc-D-Trp-D-Met-D-Asp-D-Phe Amide				Aq-Alc	210(dec)	+36	DMF	111
					201–			
Boc-Trp-D-Met-D-Asp-D-Phe Amide	1+3 OTCP	DMF-Aq	57	Aq-Me	202(dec)	+24	DMF	111
					206–			
Boc-D-Trp-Met-D-Asp-D-Phe Amide	1+3 OTCP	DMF-Aq	53	Me-EtAc	207(dec)	+50	DMF	111
					196–			
Boc-Trp-Met-D-Asp-D-Phe Amide	2+2 A	THF-DMF	52	Me-EtAc	197(dec)	+34	DMF	111
					208–			
Boc-D-Trp-D-Met-Asp-Phe Amide	1+3 OTCP	DMF-Aq	52	Aq-Me	209(dec)	−33	DMF	111
					209–			
Boc-Trp-Met-Asp-D-Phe Amide	2+2 A	THF-DMF	55	Me-EtAc-Pe	210(dec)	−19	DMF	111
					150–			
Boc-Trp-Met-D-Asp-Phe Amide	2+2 A	THF-DMF	34	Me-EtAc-Pe	151(dec)	−0.4	DMF	111
					207–			
Boc-D-Trp-Met-Asp-Phe Amide	1+3 OTCP	DMF-Aq	74	Aq-Alc	208(dec)	−52	DMF	111
					198–			
Boc-D-Trp-Met-Asp-Phe Amide	1+3 OTCP	DMF-Aq	59	Me-EtAc-Pe	200(dec)	−23	DMF	111
					209–			
Boc-Trp-Met-Asp-Phe Amide	1+3 OTCP	DMF	59	Aq-EtO-Alc	210(dec)	−35	DMF	111
	2+2 A	DMF-THF		Alc	209–210			9
Boc-Trp-Met-Asp-Phe-OMe	1+3 OTCP	DMF	50	i-Pr	168–170	−24	DMF	111
	2+2 A	MeCl-DMF	66	Aq-Me	167–169			9

Compound	Method	Solvent	Yield %	Recryst.	m.p.	[α]	Solv.	Ref.
Boc-Trp-Met-β-OBu^t-Asp-Phe Amide	1+3 OTCP	DMF			172–174			111
N-Carbamoyl-Trp-Met-Asp-Phe Amide				Aq-DMF	205–206(dec)			111
N-Nps-Trp-Met-β-OBu^t-Asp-Phe Amide	1+3 DCCI	Chf			183–184			487
Trp-Met-Asp-Phe Amide	1+3 OTCP	DMF			251–252 (dec)			111
Trp-Met-Asp-Phe Amide Hydrochloride				Me-Eth	215–216(dec)	−31	DMF	111
Trp-Met-Asp-Phe Amide Trifluoroacetate				EtAc	197(dec)	−26	DMF	111
Trp-Met-β-OBu^t-Asp-Phe Amide					167–168	−20	DMF	423
						+1.9	Me	
Tyrosine								
Z-Tyr-Ile-Gln-Asn Hydrazide	1+3 A	DMF	79	Aq-DMF	230–232			289
Z-Try-Ile-Gln-Asn-OMe	3+1 MCA		63	THF	236–238	−1.5	DMF	289
Z-Tyr-Ile-Gly-Lys-OMe	1+3 ONP	DMF	76		265			122
OBzl-Z-Tyr-Leu-β-bu^t-Asp-Ser-OMe	1+3 OTCP	EtAc		Aq-Me	174–176	−23	DMF	199
N,O-di-Z-Tyr-Leu-β-OBu^t-Asp-Ser-OMe	1+3 EDCI		68		163.5–165	−21	DMF	199
Z-Tyr-Leu-β-bu^t-Asp-Ser-OMe	1+3 EDCI	MeCl	21	An-Pe	159–160	−25	DMF	199
OBzl-Z-Tyr-Leu-Val-S-bzl-Cys Amide	1+3 ONP	DMF	82	Aq-Ac	263–264			307
Z-Tyr-Phe-Gln-Asn Hydrazide				Aq-DMF	228–230			289
Z-Tyr-Phe-Gln-Asn-OMe	1+3 A	DMF-Eth			234–236	−27	DMF	289
Valine								
N-Bzhoc-Val-S(N′-Z-Cys)Cys-Gly-OBzl					131–133	−118	DMF	225
Z-Val-Gln-Trp-Leu-OBu^t	1+3 SmA	Acn	90	Me-Aq	194–196	−60	Me	719
Val-Gln-Trp-Leu-OBu^t					188–189	−44	Alc	719
Z-Val-Glu-Trp-Leu-OMe	1+3 OTCP	DMF			243–245	−23	DMF	260
Val-Glu-Trp-Leu-OMe					200–201			260
Boc-Val-Gly-Leu-Met Amide	1+3 MCA			Ac	200–201	−35	Ac	394
Val-Gly-Leu-Met Amide Hydrochlorde				Aq	215–217	−30	Aq	394
Z-D-Val-D-His-D-Pro-D-Phe-OBu^t	2+2 A		85	Alc	102–105	+52	Alc	684

Table 4 Tetrapeptides (continued)

Compound	Method	Solvent	% Yield	Solvent Crystallization	M.P. (°C)	$[\alpha]_D$	Solvent Rotation	Ref.
Z-Val-His-Pro-Phe-OBu^t	2+2 A		88		75–80	−51	Alc	552
Val-His-Pro-Phe-OBu^t					75–80	−51	Alc	563
D-Val-D-His-D-Pro-D-Phe-OBu^t					92–96	−48	Alc	552
Z-Val-Tos-N$^\epsilon$-Lys-Leu-D-Phe Hydrazide				DMF-Aq	220–224	+46	Alc	684
Z-Val-tos-N$^\epsilon$-Lys-Leu-D-Phe-OMe	2+2 A		81	EtAc				130
Z-Val-N$^\epsilon$-boc-Lys-Tyr Amide	2+2 A		62		236–237(dec)	−18	DMF	644
Val-boc-Lys-Val-Tyr					248–250(dec)	−31	Ac	644
Z-Val-N$^\delta$-tos-Orn-Leu-Phe-OEt	1+3 ONP	EtAc	95.3		228–233.5	+22	DMF	129
Z-D-Val-Pro-Sar-N-me-Val-OBu^t	1+3 DCCI	Acn	95.3		oil	−75	Me	410
For-D-Val-Pro-Sar-N-me-Val-OMe	1+3 DCCI	MeCl	65		oil	−77	Me	76
D-Val-Pro-Sar-N-me-Val-OMe Hydrochloride						−91	Me	76

5

Pentapeptides

Selection of peptide bond-forming reagent and purification procedure becomes increasingly important from the pentapeptide stage onward. In this regard, ref. 313 outlines a particularly valuable series of experiments. As with the tetra- and larger peptides, the ONP, DCCI, MCA and A methods were generally favored. Again, in some cases, mixtures were encountered using DCCI.[225] The studies relating to a particular peptide synthesis using different reagents and points of coupling summarized in Table 5 emphasize importance of the experimental approach. The MCA (2+3, 77%) *vs* A (2+2, 20%) synthesis[776] of Nps-Ala-Gly-Val-S-Bz-Cys-Ser-OMe and ONP (1+4, 78%) *vs* A (1+4, 77%) for preparation[372] of N^{ϵ}-Tos-Z-Lys-N^{ϵ}-Tos-Lys-N^{G}-Tos-Arg-N^{G}-Tos-Arg-Trp-OBu^t are characteristic. Similarly, the choice of coupling site can be quite important. Here, the A (1+4, 75%) *vs* A (2+3, 16%) syntheses[747] of Z-Ser-Pro-Pro-N^{ϵ}-For-Lys-Asp and the OTcp (1+4, 98%) *vs* A (3+2, 31%) route[111] to Boc-β-Ala-Trp-Met-Asp-The amide are illustrative.

A majority of solvents appearing in the crystallization solvent column of Table 5 were employed for precipitations. Only a relatively small number of the pentapeptides were recrystallized. The solvents which yielded crystalline pentapeptides were ethyl acetate,[653,681,175] methanol,[94,375,746,737] propanol,[300] dimethylformamide-ether,[451,506,494] dimethylformamide-water,[279,744,768] dioxane-ether,[337,18] ethanol-water,[602,241] methanol-water,[300] dioxane-ether-ligroin,[431] and ethyl acetate-ether-ligroin.[338,375,403] The experimental difficulties which begin to be encountered in penta- and larger peptide syntheses can be in part appreciated from the following statement.[527] "From the pentapeptide level on upward from molecular weights greater than 700 elemental analyses no longer adequately characterized the product." At this stage, the use of various thin layer[527] and column (silica gel,[573] carboxymethylcellulose,[744,743,94] and Amberlite XE-64[375]) chromatographic techniques become quite important. A number of the pentapeptides were also purified by countercurrent distribution.[94,375,371,372,455,241,405] Isolation of Z-His-Phe-N^G-Tos-Arg-Try-Gly-OBu^t (from A, 1+4)[370] and γ-OBzl-Z-Glu-Ala-Leu-Tyr-Leu (from ONP, 1+4)[166] was realized in this manner. The latter countercurrent distribution was conducted with the commonly employed toluene-chloroform-methanol-water (5:5:8:2) system.

Recent advances in the area of pentapeptides include synthesis of Thr-Ala-Cys-His-Asp.[482]

Table 5 Pentapeptides

Compound	Method	Solvent	% Yield	Solvent Crystallization	M.P. (°C)	[α]$_D$	Solvent Rotation	Ref.
Alanine								
Ala-Ala-Ala-Ala-Ala								759
Z-Ala-Ala-Ala-Ala-Ala	2+3 MCA	DMF	63					759
Z-α-me-Ala-α-me-Ala-α-me-Ala-α-me-Ala-α-me-Ala				Aq-Me	254–256 (dec)			284
Z-α-me-Ala-α-me-Ala-α-me-Ala-α-me-Ala-α-me-Ala-OBu^t	4+1 O	Acn	86	EtAc-Pe	234–236 (dec)			284
Tos-α-me-Ala-α-me-Ala-α-me-Ala-α-me-Ala-α-me-Ala-OMe	2+3 O	Acn	19	Aq-Me	251–252.5			365
Ala-Gln-β-OBu^t-Asp-Phe-Val-OBu^t	4+1 O	Acn	91		251			
Z-Ala-Gln-β-OBu^t-OBu^t-Asp-Phe-Val-OBu^t	4+1 MCA	THF		Aq-Alc	210–211	−39	Me	727
Boc-Ala-Glu-Z-Lys-D-Ala-D-Ala-di-ONBzl	4+1 ONP	Me	83		206–208	−38	Aq-Ac	727
Z-Ala-Gly-Gly-Leu-Gly	3+2 SPh	Ac	58		172			662
Z-Ala-Gly-Gly-Leu-Gly-S-bzl				Alc	196–197	−11	DMF	700
Z-Ala-Gly-Val-S-bzl-Cys-Gly-OMe-OBzl	ONP	DMF-Ac	95	DMF-Eth	201–202	−19	DMF	700
Ala-Gly-Val-S-bzl-Cys-Ser-OMe Hydrochloride				Me	206–207	−33	DMF	619
Ala-Gly-Val-S-trt-Cys-Ser-OMe Hydrochloride				Me	202–203	−44	DMF	776
Nps-Ala-Gly-Val-S-bz-Cys-Ser-OMe	2+3 MCA	Chf	77	Acn	204–205	−32	Me	776
N-Trt-Ala-Gly-Val-S-trt-Cys-Ser-OMe	2+3 A		20		205–206	−71	DMF	776
Ala-Leu-Tyr-Leu-Val	2+3 DCCI	THF		Me	200–204	−69	DMF	756
Z-Ala-Leu-Tyr-Leu-Val	2+3 MCA	THF	70		227–228	−34	THF	756
Ala-N$^\delta$-Z-Orn-Leu-D-Phe-Pro Hydrochloride					258 (dec)			338
Z(OMe)-Ala-N$^\delta$-Z-Orn-Leu-D-Phe-Pro Hydrazide					108–110	−29	DMF	338
Z(OMe)-Ala-N$^\delta$-Z-Orn-Leu-D-Phe-Pro				Di-Eth-Pe	88–89	−36	DMF	338
Z(OMe)-Ala-N$^\delta$-Z-Orn-Leu-D-Phe-Pro-OEt					105–108	−33	DMF	338
Ala-Phe-Ile-Gly-Leu-ONBzl					184–185	−28	DMF	524
Ala-Phe-Ile-Gly-Leu-ONBzl Hydrobromide					153 (dec), 215 (dec)	−12	Aq-Ac	524

261

Table 5 Pentapeptides (continued)

Compound	Method	Solvent	% Yield	Solvent Crystallization	M.P.(°C)	$[\alpha]_D$	Solvent Rotation	Ref.
Z-Ala-Phe-Ile-Gly-Leu-ONBzl	2+3 A	DMF	65	Eth-THF	172 (dec)	-30; -22	Aq-Ac; DMF	524
Ala-Ser-Pro-Phe-N^G-nitro-Arg-OMe Hydrobromide	A	DMF-THF	70	Alc-Eth		-36	DMF	555
Z-Ala-Ser-Pro-Phe-N^G-nitro-Arg-OMe	1+4 ONP	DMF	67	DMF-Aq	227-228 (dec)	-42	DMF	555
Boc-β-Ala-Trp-Met-Asp-Phe Amide	1+4 OTCP	DMF	98	EtO-Alc-Aq	229-230 (dec)	-28	DMF	520
	3+2 A	DMF	31	EtO-Alc-Aq	229-230 (dec)	-28	DMF	111
Arginine								
N^G-Nitro-Z-Arg-Ala-Leu-Val-Gln-di-OEt	2+3 DCCI	DMF	45	Ac-Eth	199-202	-21	DMF	165
Arg-Arg-Ala-Gln-Asp-β-OBu^t Acetate Hydrobromide				Alc		-27; -10	Aq; Aq-Ac	726
Arg-Arg-Ala-Gln-Asp-β-OBu^t Dihydrobromide Ethanol Solvate	1+4 ONP	DMF	85	DMF-EtAc	230 (dec)	-26; -15	Aq; Aq-Ac	726
N^{α}, N^{δ}, N^{ω}-tris-Z-Arg-Arg-Ala-Gln-Asp-β-OBu^t	1+4 ONP	DMF		DMF-Eth	161-162	-15	Ac-Aq	726
N^{α}, N^{δ}, N^{ω}-tris-Z-Arg-Arg-Ala-Gln-Asp-β-OBu^t. α-OMe Acetate						-15	Ac-Aq	726
Arg-Arg-Pro-Val-N^{ϵ}-boc-Lys Amide Trihydrochloride						-58	Aq	644
N^G-Nitro-Z-Arg-Pro-Pro-Gly-Phe					134-137	-13	THF	605
N^G-Nitro-Z-Arg-Pro-Pro-Gly-Tyr					105-110	-28	THF	605
N^G-Nitro-Arg-Pro-Val-N^{ϵ}-tos-Lys-Val-OMe Hydrobromide				Alc-Eth		-50; -56	Ac; Alc	560

The following is a continuation of a tabulated list of peptide syntheses (conditions, yields, melting points, optical rotations, solvents and literature references). Because of the dense layout, some column alignments are approximate.

Compound	Method	Solv.	Yield (%)		mp (°C)	$[\alpha]$	Solv.	Ref.
N^G-Nitro-Z-Arg-Pro-Val-N^ϵ-tos-Lys-Val-OMe	2+3 MCA	DMF	91			−35; −57	DMF; Ac	560

Asparagine

Compound	Method	Solv.	Yield (%)		mp (°C)	$[\alpha]$	Solv.	Ref.
Z-Asn-S-bzl-Cys-Pro-Ala-Gly Amide	1+4 OTCP	DMF	74		239	−75; −43	Aq-Ac; DMF	275
Asn-S-bzl-Cys-Pro-N^G-tos-Arg-Gly Amide						−43	DMF	255
Z-Asn-S-bzl-Cys-Pro-N^G-tos-Arg-Gly Amide	1+4 OTCP	DMF	93	Me-Aq	155	−36	DMF	255
Z-Asn-S-btm-Cys-Pro-N^G-nitro-Arg-Gly Amide Hydrate	2+3 ONP	DMF	69		189-191	−51	DMF	103
	1+4 ONP	DMF	32		183-190	−51	DMF	
Z-Asn-S-bzl-Cys-Pro-Cit-Gly Amide	1+4 ONP	Py	86		225 (dec)	−48	Ac-Aq	61
Z-Asn-S-bzl-Cys-Pro-Gly-Gly Amide	1+4 OTCP	DMF	78		216	−45	DMF	275
Asn-S-bzl-Cys-Pro-Ile-Gly Amide								189
Z-Asn-S-bzl-Cys-Pro-Ile-Gly Amide	1+4 ONP	DMF-EtAc	73		212	−59	Ac-Aq	189
Asn-S-Eac-Cys-Pro-Leu-Gly Amide					188	−45	DMF	188
Z-Asn-S-bzl-Cys-Pro-Leu-Gly Amide					210.5-211.5	−68	DMF	628
Z-D-Asn-S-bzl-Cys-Pro-Leu-Gly Amide					230	−59	DMF	127
Z-Asn-S-Eac-Cys-Pro-Leu-Gly Amide	1+4 OTCP		81		228	−54	Ac-Aq	188
Z-Asn-Se-bzl-Cys-Pro-Leu-Gly Amide					209-211	−41	DMF	687
Z-Asn-S-bzl-Cys-Pro-N^ϵ-tos-Lys-Gly Amide	1+4 ONP	DMF	88		196-199	−49	DMF	62
Asn-S-bzl-Cys-Pro-N^δ-tos-Orn-Gly Amide					213-215	−48	Ac	254
Z-Asn-S-bzl-Cys-Pro-N^δ-Pht-Orn-Gly Amide	1+4 OTCP	DMF	84		173-174	−39	Ac	63
Z-Asn-S-bzl-Cys-Pro-N^δ-tos-Orn-Gly Amide					210-215	−31	DMF	254
β-OBu^t-Asp-Ala-Phe-Ile-Gly-OBu^t					227-228	−21	Ac	85
β-OBu^t-Z-Asp-Ala-Phe-Ile-Gly	1+4 ONP	Py	89			−22	DMF	25
β-OBu^t-Z-Asp-Ala-Phe-Ile-Gly-OBu^t	1+4 DCCI					−34	Ac-Aq	85
Asp-Ala-Phe-Ile-Met Amide Trifluoroacetate					255		Ac-Aq	524
Boc-Asp-Ala-Phe-Ile-Met Amide	4+1 A	DMF	64		235	−25	DMF	524

263

Table 5 Pentapeptides (continued)

Compound	Method	Solvent	% Yield	Solvent Crystallization	M.P. (°C)	$[\alpha]_D$	Solvent Rotation	Ref
Z-Asp-S-bzl-Cys-Pro-Ala-Gly Amide	1+4 ONP	DMF			237–239	–47	DMF	690
Asp-S-bzl-Cys-Pro-N$^\delta$-tos-Orn-Gly Amide						–49	Ac-Aq	254
β-OBu^t-Asp-Val-Glu-Tyr-Leu-OMe								260
β-OBu^t-Z-Asp-Val-Glu-Tyr-Leu-OMe	1+4 ONP	DMF	61		235–237	–29	DMF	260
Cysteine								
S-Bzl-Z-Cys-Ala-Gln-S-bzl-Cys-His Mono-hydrate	1+4 MCA	THF	67	Me	198–201	–30	DMF	746
S-Bzl-Cys-Ala-Gly-Ala-Gly	4+1 A	Aq	24	Ac	188–191	–9.7	HCl	631
S-Trt-Z-Cys-S-bzh-Cys-Gly-Phe-Gly	1+4 EDCI	DMF-MeCl		Aq-Ac	200 (dec)	–14	DMF	229
S-Trt-Z-Cys-S-bzh-Cys-Gly-Phe-Gly-OBu^t			42	DMF-Ac-Eth	240–242	–51	DMF	229
S-(N′-Z-Cys-Gly-OEt)-Z-Cys-Gly-Glu-OEt	EDCI	DMF-MeCl	50	Chf-Me-Eth	219–221	–123	DMF	227
S-(N′-Z-Cys-Gly-OEt)-Z-Cys-Gly-Ser-OMe	EDCI	DMF-MeCl	60	EtAc-He	133–135	–124	DMF	225
S-Bzl-Z-Cys-Gly-Gly-S-bzl-Cys-His-OBzl	4+1 A			EtAc-Eth	178	–54	Di	263
Cys-Gly-Gly-Cys-His								263
S-Bzl-N-Z-Cys-tri-Gly-Gly-OEt	3+2 A	Chf	76	Aq-Alc	159–161	–28	Aq-Py	279
S-Bzl-N-Z-Cys-tri-Gly-Gly Hydrazide				Glyme	209–211			279
S-Bzl-Z-Cys-Gly-Leu-Val-Glu-di-OBzl	2+3 A	THF	31	Chf-Pe	138			674
S-Bzl-Z-Cys-p-OMe-Phe-Ile-Gln-Asn	2+3 MCA	THF			232–236 (dec)	–22	DMF	357
S-Bzl-N-tos-Cys-Tyr-Ile-Gln-Asn	2+3 MCA	THF	65	Ac-EtAc	239–241 (dec)	+5.1	DMF	84
S-4,4′-di-OMe-diphenylmethyl-Z-Cys-Tyr-Ile-Gln-Asn	2+3 MCA	THF			240–244 (dec)	–21	DMF	200
N-Tos-S-bzl-Cys-Tyr-Ile-Gln-Asn	2+3 MCA	THF			226–228 (dec)	+5.0	DMF	72
S-Bzl-Z-Cys-Tyr-Ile-Gln-Asp					238–240 (dec)	–23	DMF	141
S-Bzl-Z-Cys-Tyr-Ile-Gly-Asp	2+3 MCA		71		198–203	–19	DMF	141

Glutamine

Compound	Method	Solvent	Yield (%)	Recryst. Solvent	M.p.	[α]	Solvent	Ref.
Z-Gln-Asn-S-bzl-Cys-Leu-Gly Amide	3+2 A	DMF	53	DMF-An	246-248	-36	DMF	276
Gln-Asn-S-bzl-Cys-Leu-Gly Amide				Tol-Alc	184 (dec)	-42	Ac-Aq	276
Z-Gln-Asn-S-bzl-Cys-Pro-Abu-Gly Amide	1+4 OTCP	DMF	91		250	-52	DMF	275
Z-Gln-Asn-S-bzl-Cys-Pro-Gly Amide	1+4 ONP	DMF	68	EtAc-Alc	228	-78	Ac	276
Z-Gln-Asn-S-bzl-Cys-Pro-Leu Amide	3+2 A	DMF	51	DMF-An	240-242	-38	DMF	276
Gln-Asn-S-bzl-Cys-Pro-Leu Amide					125 (dec)	-67	Ac-Aq	276
Z-Gln-Asn-S-bzl-penicillaminyl-Pro-Leu-Gly	1+4 ONP	DMF	77		113-116	-42	DMF	567
Boc-Gln-α'-hemicystathionyl-S-bzl-Cys-Ala-Gly-Val-α-hemicystathionine				DMF-Eth	255-258	-20	HMPA	290
Z-Gln-S-bzl-Cys-S-bzl-Cys-Ala-Gly-OEt	1+4 ONP	DMF	97	Aq-Ac	250-252 (dec)	-31	DMF	305
Z-Gln-S-bzl-Cys-S-bzl-Cys-Ala-Gly Hydrazide					244-245	-24	DMSO	316
Z-Gln-S-bzl-Cys-S-bzl-Cys-Ala-Gly-OMe	1+4 ONP	DMF	92		248-250	-34	DMF	314
Z-Gln-S-bzl-Cys-S-bzl-Cys-Ala-Gly-2,4,6-trimethyl-OBzl				Ac	241-242	-28	DMF	625
Gln-S-bzl-Cys-S-bzl-Cys-Ala-Gly				Aq-Me	231.5-232.5	-16	Ac	625
Z-Gln-S-bzl-Cys-S-bzl-Cys-Thr-Ser Hydrazide				DMSO-Aq	246-248 (dec)	-16	DMSO	313
Z-Gln-S-bzl-Cys-S-bzl-Cys-Thr-Ser-OMe	1+4 ONP	DMF	74	Ac-Aq	222-223	-26	DMF	317
Z-Gln-His-Leu-S-bzl-Cys-Gly	1+4 ONP	DMF	75		218-222	-34	Ac	758
Z-Gln-Leu-γ-OBu^t-Glu-Asn-Tyr-boc Hydrazide	1+4 ONP		68		229-234	-30	Ac	762
Z-Gln-Leu-Gly-Leu-Val Amide				Ac	267-270 (dec)	-35	Ac	367
Boc-Gln-Pro-Ser-N$^\epsilon$-boc-Lys-β-OBu^t-Asp					120	-34	DMF	90
Boc-Gln-Pro-Ser-N$^\epsilon$-boc-Lys-β-OBu^t-Asp-OMe					112-115	-56	Alc	90
γ-OBzl-Z-Gln-Thr-Ala-Ala-Ala-OEt	2+3 DCCI		46		201-202	-12	DMF	507

Table 5 Pentapeptides (continued)

Compound	Method	Solvent	% Yield	Solvent Crystallization	M.P. (°C)	$[\alpha]_D$	Solvent Rotation	Ref.
γ-OBzl-Gln-Thr-Ala-Ala-Ala-OEt	1+4 ONP	DMF	48	DMF-Eth	197–200	−27	DMF	507
γ-OBzl-Z-Glu-Ala-Leu-Tyr-Leu	1+4 ONP	DMF	47	Aq-Ac	218–219		DMF	166
γ-OBz-Z-Glu-Asn-Tyr-S-NBzl-Cys-Asn-ONBzl	1+4 ONP	DMF		Aq-DMF-Ac	186–187	−33	DMF	309
γ-OBzl-Z-Glu-Asn-O-tos-Tyr-S-bzl-Cys-Asn								625
γ-OBut-Z-Glu-γ-OBut-Glu-Ala-OBut-Tyr-Gly-OMe				Chf	198–199	−16	Chf	28
γ-OBut-Z-Glu-γ-OBut-Glu-Ala-Tyr-Gly-OMe	1+4 OTCP		74	EtAc	168–170	−16	DMF	28
γ-OBut-Glu-γ-OBut-Glu-Ala-Tyr-Gly-OMe	1+4 OTCP	DMF	95	EtAc	177–178	−17	DMF	423
Z-γ-OMe-Glu-γ-OMe-Glu-γ-OMe-Glu-OAc-Ser-γ-OMe-Glu-ONP Acetate Hydrate					204–210	−7.7	DMF	423
γ-OMe-Glu-γ-OMe-Glu-γ-OMe-Glu-OAc-Ser-γ-OMe-Glu-ONP Hydrobromide	1+4 MCA		90	Ac-Me	171–173	−26	DMF	620
Z(OMe)-γ-tetra-Glu-Gln-hexa-OBzl					314–316 (dec)			620
Z-di-(γ-OMe-Glu)-γ-OMe-D-Glu-γ-OMe-Glu-Glu-di-OMe	2+3 DCCI	Acn	35	THF	175–176	−19	DMF	694
Z-tetra-(γ-OMe-Glu)-di-Glu-OEt				EtAc	188–190	−13	Di	175
Pyro-Glu-Gly-Pro-Trp-Leu Hydrazide	1+4 ONP	DMF	78	Alc	196–200	−21	DCA	175
Pyro-Glu-Gly-Pro-Trp-Leu-OMe	1+4 OTCP		72	Chf-Eth	132–135	−76	Me	28
γ-OMe-boc-Glu-Gly-Pro-Trp-Met-OMe	3+2 DCCI	MeCl	85	Me-Eth	70–75	−69	Me	28
Pyro-Glu-Gly-Pro-Trp-Met Hydrazide				Me-Eth	120–125 (dec)			9
Pyro-Glu-Gly-Pro-Trp-Met-OMe	1+4 OTCP	DMF	72	Me-Eth	98–100 (dec)	−54	DMF	9
Z-Glu-Nim-bzl-His-Leu-S-bzl-Cys-Gly	1+4 ONP	DMF	75		225–227 (dec)	−64	DMF	764
OBzl-Z-Glu-Nim-His-Phe-Ala-Asn Amide	1+3 ONP	DMF	83		232–234	−12	DMF	436

Compound	Method	Solvent	Yield (%)	Cryst.	M.p. (°C)	[α]	Solv.	Ref.
Glu-His-Phe-Ala-Asn Amide				Me-Eth	119–121			436
OBu^t-Glu-His-Phe-Arg-Trp-OMe Diacetate				Me	206	−27	Me	575
γ-OBu^t-Z-Glu-His-Phe-Trp-Gly	2+3 A	DMF	70		175–180	−34	Me	573
γ-OBu^t-Z-Glu-His-Phe-Trp-Gly-OMe Acetate				Me				573
γ-OBzl-Boc-Glu-Leu-OBzl-Ser-N^G-nitro-Arg-Leu-Z-Hydrazide					220–221	−19	DMF	458
γ-OBzl-Boc-Glu-Leu-OBzl-Ser-N^G-nitro-Arg-Leu-OMe				Alc	184–186	−30	Me	458
Boc-Glu-Leu-Ser-Arg-Leu Hydrazide Dihydrate	1+4 ONP	Py	90	Me	191–193	−26	DMF	458
γ-OBu^t-Z-Glu-Thr-Ala-Ala-Ala-OEt	1+4 ONP	DMF	82	DMF-Eth	209–210	−13	DMF	506
γ-OBu^t-Glu-Thr-Ala-Ala-OEt				Eth	192–194	−12	DMF	506
γ-OBzl-Z-Glu-Asp-Tyr-S-bzl-Cys-Asp-ONBzl					219–222	−42	DMF	315
Glycine								
Z-Gly-Gly-β-chloro-Ala-Gly-Gly-OEt	2+3 DCCI		70		166	−5.6	DMF	708
Z-Gly-Gly-S-Ac-Cys-Gly-Gly-OEt	2+3 MCA	Chf	60	i-Pr	172	−17	DMF	708
Z-Gly-Gly-S-bzl-Cys-Tyr-OEt	2+3 A	EtAc-THF	70	i-Pr	137–140	−14	Di	300
Z-Gly-Gly-Gly-S-bzl-Cys-Tyr Hydrazide				Aq-Me	140–142			300
Tetra-Gly-S-bzl-Cys	2+3 MA	Py	62–77	Aq-DMF	216–217	−24	Ac	279
Tetra-Gly-S-bzl-Cys-OBzl Hydrobromide				Alc-Eth	152–154			279
Z-Gly-Gly-Gly-Gly-Leu	1+4 ONP				210			30
Gly-Gly-Gly-Leu Sesquihydrate				Alc-Aq		−11		30
Z-Gly-Gly-Leu-Gly-Gly				Me-Be	194–195			30
Gly-Gly-Leu-Gly-Gly-Gly Sesquihydrate				Aq-Alc				30
Z-Gly-Leu-Gly-Gly-Gly Hemihydrate	3+2 ONP		79	EtAc	128–129			30
Gly-Leu-Gly-Gly-Gly Sesquihydrate				Aq-Alc				30
Z-Gly-Leu-Leu-Gly-Gly					124–126			202
Z-Gly-Leu-Leu-Gly-Gly-OEt	2+3 MA		75	Aq-Alc	123.5–124.5			202

Table 5 Pentapeptides (continued)

Compound	Method	Solvent	% Yield	Solvent Crystallization	M.P. (°C)	$[\alpha]_D$	Solvent Rotation	Ref.
Z-Gly-D-Leu-Gly-Gly-OEt					120–123			202
Z-Gly-Leu-Gly-Gly-SNPh					115–120			202
Z-Gly-D-Leu-Gly-Gly-SNPh					116–119			202
Gly-Leu-D-Leu-Gly-Gly					106–108			202
Gly-Leu-Leu-Gly-Gly Hydrate								202
Gly-Leu-D-Leu-Gly-Gly Hydrate								202
Z-Gly-N^ϵ-boc-Lys-γ-OBu^t-Glu-Phe-Thr-OMe	1+4 ONP	DMF	62	Alc	206–207	−20	Ac-Aq	98
Gly-N^ϵ-Z-Lys-Gly-S-bzh-Cys-Gly-OBu^t								220
Gly-N^ϵ-Z-Lys-S-bzh-Cys-Gly-OBu^t Trifluoroacetate	3+2 DCCI		78	Me-Aq	130–134	+12	DMF	220
Z-Gly-N^ϵ-Z-Lys-γ-OBzl-Glu-Gly-OBzl	3+2 A	Chf	43	Me-Aq	176–178			754
Gly-Lys-Gly-Gly								754
Gly-N^δ-Z-Orn-Leu-D-Phe-Gly Hydrochloride					188–191	−7.6	DMF	337
Z(OMe)-Gly-N^δ-Z-Orn-Leu-D-Phe-Gly				Di-Eth	157–159			337
Z(OMe)-Gly-N^δ-Z-Orn-Leu-D-Phe-Gly-OEt	A	DMF	78	Me-Di-Eth	180–181	+1.0	DMF	337
Z(OMe)-Gly-N^δ-Z-Orn-Leu-D-Phe-Gly Hydrazide				Me-Eth	163–164	−2.5	DMF	337
Z(OMe)-Gly-N^δ-Z-Orn-Leu-D-Phe-Gly-ONp					119–121	−34	DMF	337
Gly-N^δ-Z-Orn-Leu-D-Phe-Pro-OEt Hydrochloride					92–95	−34	DMF	338
Gly-N^δ-Z-Orn-Leu-D-Phe-Pro Hydrochloride					97	−37	DMF	338
Z(OMe)-Gly-N^δ-Z-Orn-Leu-D-Phe-Pro				Di-Eth-Pe	94–96	−32	DMF	338
Z(OMe)-Gly-N^δ-Z-Orn-Leu-D-Phe-Pro-OEt	2+3 A	DMF	63	EtAc-Eth-Pe		−32	DMF	338
Z(OMe)-Gly-N^δ-Z-Orn-Leu-D-Phe-Pro Hydrazide					112–114			338
Z-Gly-Phe-Ser-Pro-Phe-OMe	1+4 ONP	EtAc		Me-Aq	106–108	−32	DMF	123
Z-Gly-D-Phe-D-Ser-D-Pro-D-Phe-OMe	4+1 A	EtAc	75		109–111	+31		681
Gly-D-Phe-D-Ser-D-Pro-D-Phe-OMe				Alc-Eth	148–150	+32		681
Boc-Gly-Sar-N^ϵ-Z-Lys-D-Val-Pro								75

Compound	Method	Solvent	Yield (%)	Recryst. solvent	m.p. (°C)	[α]	Solvent	Ref.
Boc-Gly-Sar-N^{ϵ}-Z-Lys-D-Val-Pro-OMe	4+1 DCCI							75
Boc-Gly-Sar-N^{ϵ}-Z-Lys-D-Val-Pro-ONp								75
Gly-Sar-N^{ϵ}-Z-Lys-D-Val-Pro-ONp								75
O-(Boc-Gly)-N-Z-Ser-D-allo-Ile-Pro-Sar-OBu^{t}	DCCI		75			−18	Alc	74
O-(Gly)-N-Z-Ser-D-allo-Ile-Pro-Sar Hydrochloride						−22	Alc	74
Histidine								
Z-His-Leu-Val-γ-OBu^{t}-Glu-Ala-OMe	1+4 A	Acn	95		212–214	−27	DMF	411
N^{im}-Bzl-Z-His-D-Phe-Arg-Trp-Gly-OMe	2+3 DCCI	DMF	61		115–119			544
N^{im}-Bzl-Z-His-Phe-Arg-Trp-Gly-ONBzl	3+2 DCCI	DMF	63		133–136			297
N^{im}-Bzl-Z-His-Phe-N^{G}-tos-Arg-Trp-Gly-OMe	2+3 ONP			Chf-Pe	144–146			371
N^{im}-Bzl-Z-His-D-Phe-N^{G}-tos-Arg-Trp-Gly-OMe				Me	148–150			544
Z-D-Phe-D-Phe-D-Arg-D-Trp-Gly	1+4 A	EtAc	69	Me-Aq	218–220	+26	Aq-Ac	744
Z-His-Phe-Arg-Trp-Gly Dihydrate	1+4 A		62		212–217			235
Z-His-Phe-Arg-Trp-Gly Dihydrochloride Dihydrate								235
Z-His-Phe-N^{G}-nitro-Arg-Trp-Gly	1+4 A	DMF	77	DMF-Aq	241–242	−29	DMF	240
Z-His-D-Phe-N^{G}-nitro-D-Arg-Trp-Gly					223 (dec)	+13	DMF	744
Z-D-His-D-Phe-N^{G}-nitro-D-Arg-Trp-Gly					215 (dec)	+12	DMF	744
Z-D-His-D-Phe-N^{G}-nitro-D-Arg-D-Trp-Gly					199–201	+25	DMF	742
Z-His-Phe-N^{G}-nitro-Arg-Trp-Gly Acetate Hydrate					226–228			162
Z-His-Phe-N^{G}-nitro-D-Arg-Trp-Gly Dihydrate					235 (dec)	−32	DMF	743
Z-D-His-Phe-N^{G}-nitro-D-Arg-Trp-Gly					165–170	−7.4	DMF	743
N^{α}-Z-His-D-Phe-N^{G}-nitro-Arg-D-Trp-Gly Dihydrate					170–175			743
Z-His-Phe-N^{G}-nitro-Arg-Trp-Gly Hydrate	1+4 A	DMF	73	DMF-Aq	246–249	+4.9	DMF	235
Z-D-His-D-Phe-N^{G}-nitro-D-Arg-D-Trp-Gly-OMe Hydrate	1+4 A	DMF	78.2	Me	178–180	+26	DMF	742
Z-His-Phe-N^{G}-nitro-Arg-Trp-Gly-OMe Hydrate	1+4 A	DMF	72.6		176–178			162
Z-His-Phe-N^{G}-tos-Arg-Trp-Gly					162–164		DMF-Eth	370

Table 5 Pentapeptides (continued)

Compound	Method	Solvent	% Yield	Solvent Crystallization	M.P.(°C)	$[\alpha]_D$	Solvent Rotation	Ref.
Z-His-Phe-N^G-tos-Arg-Trp-Gly-OBu^t	A	EtAc	78	Me-Aq	152–160 158–160			370 369
His-Phe-Arg-Trp-Gly								240
His-D-Phe-Arg-Trp-Gly						–20	1N HCl	745 544
His-D-Phe-D-Arg-Trp-Gly						–11	1N HCl	744
D-His-Phe-Arg-D-Trp-Gly						–16	1N HCl	745
D-His-D-Phe-Arg-Trp-Gly						–49	1N HCl	745
D-His-D-Phe-D-Arg-Trp-Gly						–25	1N HCl	744
His-D-Phe-D-Arg-D-Trp-Gly						+30	1N HCl	744
His-Phe-Arg-Trp-Gly Acetate Dihydrate				Me-Eth				162 235
D-His-Phe-D-Arg-Trp-Gly Acetate Tetrahydrate						–20	1N HCl	743
His-D-Phe-Arg-D-Trp-Gly Acetate Tetrahydrate								743
His-Phe-D-Arg-Trp-Gly Acetate Trihydrate						+26	1N HCl	743
His-Phe-Arg-Trp-Gly Hydrobromide						+24	1N HCl	63
D-His-D-Phe-D-Arg-D-Trp-Gly Monoacetate Pentahydrate						–11	1N HCl	742
His-Phe-N^G-tos-Arg-Trp-Gly-OBu^t						+12	1N HCl	369
Z-His-Phe-Cit-Trp-Gly								63
His-Phe-Cit-Trp-Gly						–9	Ac	63
Z-His-Phe-N$^\epsilon$-boc-Lys-Trp-Gly-OBu^t	1+4 A	DMF	78	Me	172–174	–32	Me	94
Z-His-Phe-N$^\epsilon$-for-Lys-Trp-Gly					202–204	–30	DMF	743
Z-His-Phe-N$^\epsilon$-for-Lys-Trp-Gly-OMe								743
Z-His-Phe-N$^\epsilon$-tos-Lys-Trp-Gly-OBu^t	2+3 A	DMF	84		161–163	–38	Me	94
His-Phe-Lys-Trp-Gly						–15	0.1 N Ac	94
His-Phe-Lys-Trp-Gly Acetate Monohydrate						–10	1N HCl	743

270

Compound	Method	Solvent	Yield (%)	Recryst.	m.p. (°C)	$[\alpha]$	Solvent	Ref.
N^{im}-Bzl-Z-His-Phe-N$^{\delta}$-Z-Orn-Trp-Gly-OBzl	DCCI	Di	43	EtAc-Me	160–162	−10	Ac	375
N^{im}-Bzl-Z-His-D-Phe-N$^{\delta}$-Z-Orn-Trp-Gly-OMe	2+3 DCCI	THF	51	EtAc-Pe	135–140	−7.5	DMF	375
Z-His-Phe-N$^{\delta}$-Z-Orn-Trp-Gly-OBzl	3+2 DCCI	DMF	59	Me	203–205	−22		375
Z-His-Phe-N$^{\delta}$-for-Orn-Trp-Gly Monohydrate	2+3 A	DMF	58	DMF-Aq	231(dec)			743
Z-His-Phe-Orn-Trp-Gly								63
Z-His-Phe-Orn-Trp-Gly-OBu^{t}								63
Z-His-Phe-N$^{\delta}$-Pht-Orn-Trp-Gly-OBu^{t}	1+4 ONP		71	DMF	169–174	−24	DMF	63
His-Phe-Orn-Trp-Gly						−13	Aq	375
His-Phe-Orn-Trp-Gly Acetate Hydrate						−20	1N HCl	63
His-Phe-Orn-Trp-Gly Diacetate Hydrate						−7.8	Aq	743
His-D-Phe-Orn-Trp-Gly Dihydrate					oil	+6.1	Aq	375
N^{im}-Bzl-Z-His-Pro-Phe-His-N^{im}-bzl-Leu-ONBzl								375
N^{im}-Bzl-His-Pro-Phe-His-N^{im}-bzl-Leu-ONBzl								15
N^{im}-Bzl-Z-His-Ser-S-bzl-Cys-Tyr-Phe Hydrazide	2+3 DCCI	Py-Acn	69		220			15
N^{im}-Bzl-Z-His-Ser-S-bzl-Cys-Tyr-Phe-OMe								192
Isoleucine								192
Z-Ile-S-bzl-Cys-Leu-β-OBz-Asp-β-OBz-D-Asp Amide	3+2 DCCI	MeCl		EtAc-Me-Pe	158–160			639
Z-Ile-Gly-Ala-D-Leu-Ala					215–216			527
Z-Ile-Gly-Ala-D-Leu-Ala-OMe	1+4 MCA		80					527
Leucine								
Z-D-Leu-Ala-D-Val-Val-D-Val-OMe	1+4 MCA	DMF	56		270–272(dec)	−35	Ac	527
D-Leu-Ala-D-Val-Val-D-Val-OMe Acetate					260–261(dec)			527
Z-Leu-Gln-Gly-Leu-Val Amide	1+4 ONP	DMF	93		228(dec)	−10	Ac	66
Leu-Gln-Gly-Leu-Val Amide								66
Leu-Gln-Gly-Leu-Val Amide Hydrobromide								66
Z-Leu-Gly-Gly-Gly								30
Leu-Gly-Gly-Gly Hydrate	2+3 ONP		75	Aq-Alc	196–197	+36	Aq	30

Table 5 Pentapeptides (continued)

Compound	Method	Solvent	% Yield	Solvent Crystallization	M.P. (°C)	[α]D	Solvent Rotation	Ref.
Z-Leu-Phe-Pro-Tyr-Phe-OMe	2+3 A		63			-67	Me	753
	1+4	DMF	84			-69	Me	753
Leu-Phe-Pro-Tyr-Phe-OMe Hydrochloride						-55	Me	753
Z-Leu-Pro-Val-Asn-Leu-OBu^t	1+4 ONP	DMF	75		157–159	-51	Me	641
Leu-Pro-Val-Asn-Leu-OBu^t					110–111	-53		641
Z-Leu-Tyr-Leu-Val-S-bzl-Cys Amide	1+4 ONP	DMF	96		248–250		Aq-Ac	307
Z-Leu-Val-S-bzl-Cys-Gly-Glu-di-OBzl	4+1 A		53	Chf-Pe	136			674
	2+3 DCCI	Chf-MeCl-Acn						
Z-Leu-Val-Cys-Gly-Glu-di-OBzl	2+3 MCA	Chf	10	Chf-Pe	135			674
			12	Chf-Pe	129			
Lysine								
N^{α},N^{ϵ}-di-Z-Lys-S-bzl-Cys-Ala-Gln-S-bzl-Cys	4+1 MCA	THF	64	Me	195–197	-24	DMF	746
N^{α}-N^{ϵ}-di-Z-Lys-S-bzl-Cys-Ala-Gln-S-bzl-Cys-OMe					203–204	-17	DMF	746
Lys-S-bzl-Cys-Ala-Gln-S-bzl-Cys Tetrahydrate				Aq-An	201–206	-34	Aq	746
N^{ϵ}-Z-N^{α}-for-Lys-di-Gly-γ-OBzl-Glu-Gly-OEt	3+2 MA	Py		DMF-Eth	190–192	-7.2	DMF	422
N^{ϵ}-Boc-Z-Lys-N^{ϵ}-boc-Lys-N^G-tos-Arg-N^G-tos-Arg-Pro Amide					118–120	-17	Me	492
N^{ϵ}-Boc-Z-Lys-N^{ϵ}-boc-Lys-N^G-tos-Arg-N^G-tos-Arg-Pro-OBu^t					105–110	-36	Me	372
N^{ϵ}-Boc-N^{α}-Z-Lys-N^{ϵ}-boc-Lys-N^G-tos-Arg-N^G-tos-Arg-Pro-OBu^t	1+4 ONP	Acn	72.4		105–110	-36.5	Me	372
N^{ϵ}-Boc-Lys-N^{ϵ}-boc-Lys-N^G-nitro-Arg-N^G-nitro-Arg-Pro-OBu^t								503
N^{ϵ}-Boc-Lys-N^{ϵ}-boc-Lys-N^G-nitro-Arg-N^G-nitro-Arg-Pro-OMe								298
Boc-Lys-boc-Lys-tos-Arg-tos-Arg-Pro					105–109	-21	Me	455
Boc-Lys-boc-Lys-tos-Arg-tos-Arg-Pro-OBu^t					108–115	-33	Me	372

Compound	Method	Solvent	Yield (%)	Recryst.	M.p. (°C)	[α]	Solvent	Ref.
Nε-Boc-Nα-trt-Lys-Nε-boc-Lys-NG-nitro Arg-NG-nitro-Arg-Pro-OBut	2+3 DCCI	Acn-DMF	60	An-Eth	128–155			503
Nε-Boc-Nα-trt-Lys-Nε-boc-Lys-NG-nitro Arg-NG-nitro-Arg-Pro-OMe	2+3 DCCI	Acn	81	An-Eth	134–136			298
	2+3 WRK				134–136			574
Lys-Lys-Arg-Arg-Pro Tetraacetate				Me-Aq	213–215(dec)			412
Tos-Nε-Z-Lys-tos-Nε-Lys-tos-NG-Arg-tos-NG-Arg-Pro	1+4 A	DMF-EtAc	77.1	Me-Eth	124–126			371
Nε-Tos-Z-Lys-Nε-tos-Lys-NG-tos-Arg-NG-tos-Arg-Pro-OBut	1+4 ONP	Acn	78.3		110–115	−28	Me	372
Tos-Nε-Z-Lys-tos-Nε-Lys-tos-NG-Arg-tos-NG-Arg-Pro-OMe				An-Eth	108–113			371
Nε-Tos-Lys-Nε-tos-Lys-NG-tos-Arg-NG-tos-Arg-Pro-OBut	1+4 DCCI	MeCl	85.5	An-Eth	104–110	−30	Me	372
Nε-Boc-Z-Lys-Nε-boc-Lys-Pro-Pro-Gly					101–104	−88	Me	722
Nε-Boc-Z-Lys-Pro-Val-Gly-Nε-boc-Lys-Lys-OMe						−56	Me	461
Nε-Boc-Z-Lys-Pro-Val-Nε-boc-Lys-Nε-boc-Lys Azide								664
Nε-Boc-Z-Lys-Pro-Val-Nε-boc-Lys-Nε-boc-Lys Hydrazide								664
Methionine								
Z-Met-Gln-His-Phe-Arg Monoacetate Hydrate	2+3 A	DMF	38		193–195	−15	Ac	240
Met-Gln-His-Phe-Arg Monoacetate Pentahydrate						−15	Aq	240
Ornithine								
Nδ-Z-Orn-Leu-Phe-Gly-Gly Trifluoroacetate				Me-Eth	183–184	+13	DMF	337
Z(OMe)Nδ-Z-Orn-Leu-D-Phe-Gly-Gly				Di-Eth	190–192	−0.7	DMF	337
Z(OMe)Nδ-Z-Orn-Leu-D-Phe-Gly-Gly-OEt				Me-Eth	172–174	+1.5	DMF	337
Z(OMe)Nδ-Z-Orn-Leu-D-Phe-Gly-Gly Hydrazide					201–202	−2.1	DMF	337
Z(OMe)Nδ-Z-Orn-Leu-D-Phe-Gly-Gly-ONp								337

Table 5 Pentapeptides (continued)

Compound	Method	Solvent	% Yield	Solvent Crystallization	M.P. (°C)	$[\alpha]_D$	Solvent Rotation	Ref.
Phenylalanine								
Z-Phe-β-Ala-Pro-Phe-N^G-nitro-Arg-ONBzl Dihydrate	1+4 ONP	DMF			94–100	−17	Ac	651
Z-Phe-β-OBu^t-Asp-Ala-β-OBu^t-Ser-Val-OBu^t	1+4 MCA	THF	62	Aq-Alc	206–208	−17	DMF	602
Phe-β-OBu^t-Asp-Ala-β-OBu^t-Ser-Val-OBu^t Hydrochloride				Alc-EtAc	197–199 (dec)	−7.9	DMF	602
Boc-Phe-γ-OBu^t-Glu-Arg-Glu-β-(pyrazoyl-1)Ala Amide	2+3 A	DMF	59			−21	DMF	232
Boc-Phe-γ-OBu^t-Glu-Arg-Glu-β-(pyrazoyl-3)Ala Amide Diacetate Dihydrate	2+3 A		68			−80	DMF	232
Phe-Glu-Arg-Glu-β(pyrazoyl-1)Ala Amide						−28	DMF	232
Phe-Glu-Arg-Glu-β(pyrazoyl-3)Ala Amide Trihydrate						−19	Ac	65
Z-Phe-Gly-Pro-Phe-N^G-nitro-Arg-OMe	1+4 ONP	DMF	66	EtAc	114–116	−2.7	Ac	649
Z-Phe-Gly-Pro-Phe-N^G-nitro-Arg-ONBzl	2+3 A	DMF	59		94–100	−60	Alc	555
Boc-Phe-Gly-Pro-Phe-N^G-nitro-Arg-OMe		DMF	53	Alc-Aq	188–190	−40	DMF	555
Phe-Gly-Pro-Phe-N^G-nitro-Arg-OMe Hydrobromide						−36	DMF	555
Z-Phe-His-Gly-Ser-Phe-OBzl	DCCI	DMF-THF	67	Alc-Eth				120
Phe-His-Gly-Ser-Phe Diacetate				Ac-Eth				120
Boc-Phe-Ile-Gly-Leu-Met Amide	OTCP	DMF	70		230–255	−29 / −23	Ac-Aq / DMF	524
Phe-Ile-Gly-Leu-Met Amide					160 (dec)	−16 / −16	Ac-Aq / DMF	524
Z-Phe-Leu-Gly-γ-OBzl-Glu-Phe-OBzl	3+2 MCA			EtAc	154–156	−15	Chf	120
Phe-Leu-Gly-Glu-Phe				Ac-Eth				120

274

Compound	Method	Solvent	Yield (%)	Recryst.	M.p. (°C)	[α]	Solvent	Ref.
(N-Carboxy-me-carbamyl)D-Phe-Leu-Gly D-Phe-Leu								56
Z-Phe-Leu-Gly-Ser-Tyr-OMe	3+2 MCA		85		188–190	−4.7	DMF	120
Phe-Leu-Gly-Ser-Tyr								120
Z-Phe-Leu-Pro-Phe-N^G-nitro-Arg-ONBzl	1+4 ONP	DMF	64	EtAc	132–134	−39	Ac	653
Z-Phe-Leu-Ser-γ-OBzl-Glu-Phe-OBzl	3+2 A		50	i-Pr	189–191	−13	Chf	120
Phe-Leu-Ser-Glu-Phe								120
Z(OMe)-Phe-D-Phe-Asn-Gln-Tyr-OEt	A	DMF	75	DMF-Eth	206–209	−10	DMF	451
Z(OMe)-Phe-D-Phe-Asn-Gln-Tyr Hydrazide					225–227(dec)	−26	DMF-Eth	451
Z-Phe-Ser-Ala-Phe-N^G-nitro-Arg-OMe	2+3 A		56			−32	Me	553
Phe-Ser-Ala-Phe-N^G-nitro-Arg-OMe Hydrobromide								553
Z-Phe-Ser-Gly-Phe-N^G-nitro-Arg-OMe	2+3 WRK	Acn	50	Acn-Aq	146–148	−8.2	DMF	65
Z-Phe-Ser-Pro-Ala-N^G-nitro-Arg-OMe	2+3 A		48			−36	DMF	553
Phe-Ser-Pro-Ala-N^G-nitro-Arg-OMe Hydrobromide								553
Z-Phe-Ser-Pro-Phe-Ala-OMe	2+3 A		54		189–190	−55	Me	553
Phe-Ser-Pro-Phe-Ala-OMe						−58	Alc	553
Aoc-Phe-Ser-Pro-Phe-N^G-nitro-Arg-OBzl	A	DMF-Chf	70	Me-Eth	100–115	−44	DMF	553
Z-OAc-Ser-Pro-Phe-N^G-nitro-Arg-OMe	1+4 ONP	DMF	50	DMF-Eth	215–216	−72	Aq	518
Z-OAc-Ser-Pro-Phe-N^G-nitro-Arg-ONBzl	1+4 ONP	DMF	45		208–211	−38	DMF	440
Z-Phe-Ser-Pro-p-fluoro-Phe-N^G-nitro-Arg-OMe	1+4 ONP	DMF	38	DMF	225–226			456
Z-Phe-Ser-Pro-p-fluoro-D-Phe-N^G-nitro-Arg-OMe			40		148–150	−36	Ac	652
Z-Phe-Ser-Pro-Phe-Arg-OMe	A		72	DMF-EtAc	130–133			438
Z-Phe-Ser-Pro-D-Phe-N^G-nitro-Arg-OMe	1+4 ONP	EtAc	76	EtAc-Pe	218–220			438
Z-Phe-Ser-Pro-Phe-Arg-OMe	1+4 ONP	DMF	50	Me	112–115	−57	DMF	61
Z-Phe-Ser-Pro-Phe-N^G-nitro-Arg-OMe	2+3 A		71	Me-EtAc-Eth	214–216	−42	DMF	438
Z-Phe-Ser-Pro-Phe-N^G-nitro-Arg-ONBzl	2+3 A	DMF	71	Acn-Eth	150–152			456
Nps-Phe-OBzl-Ser-Pro-Phe-N^G-nitro-Arg-ONBzl	1+4 ONP	DMF	83	EtAc-Pe	140			558
					89–99			70
								652
								137

Table 5 Pentapeptides (continued)

Compound	Method	Solvent	% Yield	Solvent Crystallization	M.P.(°C)	$[\alpha]_D$	Solvent Rotation	Ref.
Phe-Ser-Pro-Phe-N^G-nitro-Arg-OMe Hydrobromide						−30	DMF	558
Phe-Ser-Pro-Phe-N^G-nitro-Arg-ONBzl								70
Z-Phe-Ser-Pro-Phe-Cit-OMe	2+3 A		39	Me	149–152	−41	DMF	123
	1+4 ONP	DMF	58	Acn-Aq	206–208			456
Z-Phe-Ser-Pro-Phe-His-OMe	2+3 A							123
Boc-Ser-Pro-Phe-N^ϵ-Z-Lys-OBzl	DCCI	DMF						722
Phe-Ser-Pro-Phe-N^ϵ-Z-Lys-OBzl Toluenesulfonate					136–138	−36	Me	722
Z-Phe-Ser-Pro-Phe-N^δ-boc-Orn-OMe	2+3 A		64		160–161	−43	Ac	565
Phe-Ser-Pro-Phe-Orn-OMe					152–153	−58	Me	565
Z-Phe-Ser-Sar-Phe-N^G-nitro-Arg	A	DMF	53	Alc-Eth	151–155	−13	DMF	752
Z-Phe-Ser-Sar-Phe-N^G-nitro-Arg-OMe				Alc-Eth	121–123	−25	DMF	752
Phe-Ser-Sar-Phe-Arg Monoacetate Dihydrate						+1.7	Aq	752
Z-Phe-OAc-Thr-Pro-Phe-N^G-nitro-Arg-ONBzl	ONP	DMF		Ac-Aq	106–110	−46	Ac	653
Z-Phe-Val-Asn-Gln-His Hydrazide								543
Z-Phe-Val-Asn-Gln-His-OMe								543
Boc-Phe-Val-Asn-Gln-His-OMe								543
Coc-Phe-Val-Asn-Gln-His-OMe								543
Boc-Phe-Val-Gln-Trp-Leu-OBu^t	1+4 OSU	THF	90	DMF-Eth	219–220	−45	Me	718
N-Nps-Phe-Val-Gln-Trp-Leu					216–218 (dec)	+22	DMF	718
Phe-Val-Gln-Trp-Leu				DMF-Aq	228–229 (dec)			718
Pht-Phe-Val-Gln-Trp-Leu	1+4 SmA		85	Alc	198–200	−81	Me	719
Pht-Phe-Val-Gln-Trp-Leu-OBu^t	2+3 A	DMF	59		257	−83	Me	719
N-Pht-Phe-Val-Gln-Trp-Leu Boc-hydrazide						−44	DMF	719
Pht-Phe-Val-Gln-Trp-Leu Hydrate				Alc-Aq	202–205	−97	Me	719

Compound	Method	Solvent	Yield	Recryst. solvent	m.p.	[α]	Solvent	Ref.
N-Pht-Phe-Val-Gln-Trp-Leu Hydrazide-hydrochloride					218–220(dec)			719
Z-Phe-Val-Glu-Tyr-Leu-OMe	1+4 OTCP	DMF	88		253–255	−22	DMF	260
Phe-Val-Glu-Tyr-Leu-OMe								260
Proline								
Z-Pro-Ala-Gly-Pro-Ala-ONBzl					160–165			113
Dansyl-Pro-Leu-Gly-Pro-Arg								547
Dansyl-Pro-Leu-Gly-Pro-N^G-nitro-Arg								547
Pz-Pro-Leu-Gly-Pro-D-Arg-OMe Hydrochloride	4+1 DCCI	DMF	50.8	Pe-Eth	203–205	−66	DMF	721
Pro-Pro-Pro-Tyr-N^ε-boc-Lys	4+1 DCCI	DMF	72					573
Tri-Pro-Tyr-N^ε-boc-Lys-OMe	A		47					573
Serine								
OBu^t-Z-Ser-Gln-Gly-OBu^t-Thr-Phe	3+2 NHS-DCCI	DMF	93	Acn	155.5–157	+16	Me	736
OBu^t-Z-Ser-Gln-Gly-OBu^t-Thr-Phe-OMe				Me-Aq	178.5–181.5	+5.4	Me	736
OBu^t-Z-Ser-Gln-Gly-Thr-Phe	1+4 A		67	Me-Pr-Eth	174–176	−12	Me	566
OBu^t-Ser-Gln-Gly-OBu^t-Thr-Phe	DCCI		75		170–173	−13	Me	736
OBu^t-Ser-Gln-Gly-Thr-Phe-OMe					123–125	+7.3	Aq	556
OBu^t-N-trt-Ser-His-Leu-Val-Gln-γ-OBu^t Hydrazide				Alc-Aq	154–157	−34	Aq	329
OBu^t-N-trt-Ser-His-Leu-Val-Gln-γ-OBu^t α-OMe					122–125	−16	DMF	329
Z-Ser-N^{im}-bzl-His-Leu-Val-Glu-di-OEt	EDCI		40	Chf-Pe	188–190			594
Z-Ser-His-Leu-Val-Glu-di-OEt	1+4 A / EDCI	DMF	47 / 11	DMF / Me-Alc / Alc	219.5–220 / 210–213	−16	DMF	755 / 594
OBu^t-Z-Ser-Leu-Val-Glu-γ-OBu^t α-OMe	1+4 OSU / 1+4 A	THF / DMF	83 / 77	Alc-Aq / Alc-Aq	190–198 / 194–198	−22 / −23	DMF / DMF	594 / 329

277

Table 5 Pentapeptides (continued)

Compound	Method	Solvent	% Yield	Solvent Crystallization	M.P.(°C)	[α]$_D$	Solvent Rotation	Ref.
Ser-His-Leu-Val-Glu				Aq-Alc	228–231			755
Z-Ser-Leu-Tyr-Gln-Leu Hydrazide				Alc-Eth	240–243			311
Z-Ser-Leu-Tyr-Gln-Leu-OMe	1+4 A		52	Aq-Ac	232			311
Z-Ser-N$^\varepsilon$-boc-Lys-Asn-Ala-Phe-OMe	2+3 A				207–210	−4.8	Ac	392
Boc-Ser-N$^\varepsilon$-boc-Lys-Asn-Ala-Phe					191–192	−16	Ac	392
Boc-Ser-N$^\varepsilon$-boc-Lys-Asn-Ala-Phe-OMe	2+3 A				oil			392
Ser-N$^\varepsilon$-boc-Lys-Asn-Ala-Phe-OMe								392
OBu^t-Z-Ser-N$^\varepsilon$-boc-Lys-OBu^t-Tyr-Leu-β-OBu^t-Asp-OMe	1+4 DCCI	DMF-MeCl		Me	188.5–189.5	−19	Alc	737
OBu^t-Z-Ser-N$^\varepsilon$-boc-Lys-Tyr-Leu-β-OBu^t-Asp	1+4 ONP	Py	82		192–193	−15	Alc	730
OBu^t-Ser-N$^\varepsilon$-boc-Lys-OBu^t-Tyr-Leu-β-OBu^t-Asp-OMe	1+4 DCCI	Acn	78	EtAc-Eth	138–140	−28	Alc	737
OBu^t-Ser-N$^\varepsilon$-boc-Lys-Tyr-Leu-β-OBu^t-Asp-di-OBu^t	1+4 A	Aq	75		250	−24	DMF	730
Z-Ser-Pro-N$^\varepsilon$-boc-Lys-Asp-di-OBu^t	2+3 A	Aq	16		oil	−96	Me	573
Z-Ser-Pro-N$^\varepsilon$-for-Lys-Asp	2+3 MCA	Di-THF	34		88–90	−115	Me	747
Z-Ser-Pro-Pro-N$^\varepsilon$-for-Lys-Asp-di-OMe				Bu-EtAc		−114	Me	747
Ser-Pro-Pro-N$^\varepsilon$-boc-Lys-Asp-di-OBu^t				Me-EtAc		−74	Me	573
Ser-Pro-Pro-N$^\varepsilon$-for-Lys-Asp						−126	Aq	747
Ser-Pro-Pro-Lys-Asp								573
Z-Ser-Thr-Ser-Ala-Ala-OBu^t	2+3 A	DMF-EtAc	66		205–206	−3.9	DMF	398
Z-Ser-Thr-Ser-Ala-Ala-OEt	2+3 A	DMF	80		235–236	−1	DMF	399
Boc-OBzl-Ser-Thr-OBzl-Ser-(Ala)$_2$-OBzl	2+3 A		94		229–230	−1	DMF	507
				Glyme	187–189	−20	Ac	356a
N-Ac-Ser-OAc-Tyr-Ser-Met-Gln				Me-Aq	187–191	−20	DMF	241
N-Ac-Ser-Tyr-Ser-Met-Gln				Aq-Me	215–217	−39	Ac	241

Compound	Method	Solvent	Yield (%)	Recryst. solvent	M.p. (°C)	$[\alpha]$	Solvent	Ref.
N-Ac-Ser-Tyr-Ser-Met-Gln Hydrazide				Me-Aq	217–220 (dec)			241
N-Ac-Ser-Tyr-Ser-Met-Gln-OMe	2+3 A	Eth	35	Alc-Aq	204–209	−28	Me	241
Z-Ser-Tyr-Ser-Met-Gln				Me-Aq	164–170	−16	Ac	241
Z-Ser-Tyr-Ser-Met-Gln Hydrazide				Me-Aq	204 (dec)	−29	Me	241
Z-Ser-Tyr-Ser-Met-Gln-OMe				Aq-Alc	179–184	−19	2N HCl	241
Ser-Tyr-Ser-Met-Gln					214–217			241
Threonine								
Z-Thr-Ala-Leu-Leu-Gly-OMe					227–230	−24	Me	78
Z-Thr-Ala-Ser-N^{im}-bzl-His-Asp-ONBzl	2+3 EDCI				145 (dec)	−17	Aq	106
Thr-Ala-Ser-His-Asp					177 (dec)			106
Actinocinyl-bis-[Thr-D-allo-Ile-Pro-Sar-N-me-Val-OMe]								77
N-[2-Nitro-3-OBzl-4-me-bz]-Thr-D-allo-Ile-Pro-Sar-N-me-Val						−50	Me	76
N-[2-nitro-3-OBzl-4-me-bz]-Thr-D-allo-Ile-Pro-Sar-N-me-Val-OMe								76
Z-Thr-Pro-N^ϵ-tos-Lys-Ala-OBu^t	WRK	NMe	66		85–88	−59	Me	542
Z-Thr-Ser-Asp-Tyr-Ser-OMe	1+4 DCCI	DMF	85		215–216	−38	DMF	559
Z-Thr-D-Val-Pro-Sar-N-me-Val	2+3 A		35		oil	−87	Me	410
Z-Thr-D-Val-Pro-Sar-N-me-Val-OBu^t					oil	−86	Me	410
N-[2-Nitro-3-OBzl-4-me-bz]-Thr-D-Val-Pro-Sar-N-me-Val	1+3 A	EtAc	83			−47	Me	76
[2-Nitro-3-OBzl-4-me-bz]-Thr-D-Val-Pro-Sar-N-me-Val				Chf-Eth		−56	Me	410
N-[2-Nitro-3-OBzl-4-me-bz]-Thr-D-Val-Pro-Sar-N-me-Val-OMe	1+4 WRK	NMe	65			−54	Me	76
Tryptophan								
Z-Trp-D-Leu-Trp-D-Leu-Trp 2-Hydroxy-et-amide								527
Trp-D-Leu-Trp-D-Leu-Trp 2-Hydroxy-et-amide								527

Table 5 Pentapeptides (continued)

Compound	Method	Solvent	% Yield	Solvent Crystallization	M.P. (°C)	[α]D	Solvent Rotation	Ref.
Tyrosine								
Z-Tyr-Ile-Gly-N^ϵ-tos-Lys-Phe-OBzl	3+2 MCA		40	i-Pr	172–174			122
Di-Z-Tyr-Ile-N^{im}-bzl-His-Pro-Phe-OMe	DCCI	MeCl	72		96			405
Z-Tyr-Leu-Gly-γ-OBzl-Glu-Phe-OBzl	3+2 DCCI		70	EtAc-Pe				122
Z-Tyr-Leu-Gly-Glu-Tyr-OBzl	3+2 DCCI		72					122
Z-Tyr-Leu-Gly-N^ϵ-tos-Lys-Phe-OBzl	3+2 DCCI		65					122
Z-Tyr-Leu-Gly-Val-Phe	3+2 DCCI		46	EtAc-Pe	176–178			122
OBzl-Z-Tyr-Leu-Val-S-bzl-Cys-Gly-OEt	1+4 ONP		97		208	−24	Ac	310
Di-Z-Tyr-Leu-Val-S-bzl-Cys-Gly-OMe	1+4 ONP		98		221–222	−30	DMF	411
Z-Tyr-N^ϵ-tos-Lys-Gly-γ-OBzl-Glu-Phe-OBzl	DCCI		82	EtAc-Pe	151–153			122
3-Bzl-thiopropionyl-Tyr-Phe-Gln-Asn-S-bzl-Cys Hydrazide				DMF-Aq	266–268	−33	DMF	768
3-Bzl-thiopropionyl-Tyr-Phe-Gln-Asn-S-bzl-Cys-OMe								768
Z-Tyr-Ser-Pro-Phe-N^G-nitro-Arg-ONBzl	2+3 A		75	DMF-Aq	253–255	−29	DMF	565
Tyr-Ser-Pro-Phe-N^G-nitro-Arg-ONBzl Hydrobromide						−32	DMF	565
OBu^t-Z-Tyr-OBu^t-Thr-Pro-N^ϵ-boc-Lys-Ala-OBu^t						−35	Me	565
OBu^t-Z-Tyr-OBu^t-Thr-Pro-N^ϵ-tos-Lys-Ala-OBu^t				Eth-Pe	94	−43	Me	403
OBzl-Z-Tyr-Thr-Pro-N^ϵ-tos-Lys-Ala-OMe	1+4 ONP	DMF	96	EtAc-Pe	102–106	−18	DMF	403
Di-Z-Tyr-Thr-Pro-N^ϵ-boc-Lys-Ala-OBu^t	1+4 ONP	DMF	45	Me-EtAc-Pe	153			308
Di-Z-Tyr-Thr-Pro-N^ϵ-tos-Lys-Ala	1+4 ONP	DMF	88	EtAc-Eth	172–174	−37	DMF	536
Di-Z-Tyr-Thr-Pro-N^ϵ-tos-Lys-Ala-OBu^t	1+4 ONP		78		95–110	−32	DMF	539
Di-Z-Tyr-Thr-Pro-N^ϵ-tos-Lys-OBu^t-					185–187	−35	DMF	542
Thr-OBu^t	1+4 OSU		82			−31	DMF	408

Valine

Compound	Method	Solvent	Yield (%)	Recryst.	m.p.	[α]	Rot. solv.	Ref.
N-Z-Val-S-bzl-Cys-Pro-Leu-Gly Amide	1+4 ONP	DMF	60	DMF-Alc	174–176	−56	DMF	688
Z-Val-Gln-Ala-Ala-Tyr-OMe	1+4 ONP	DMF	60	Alc-Aq	247–249	−20	HMPA	98
Z-Val-γ-OMe-Glu-Ala-Leu-Tyr	2+3 ONP	DMF			208–210	−38	Me	319
Val-γ-OMe-Glu-Ala-Leu-Tyr				EtAc-Me-Pe	258(dec)	−6	Ac	319
Z-Val-Gly-Ala-D-Leu-Tyr					222–223			527
Z-Val-Gly-Ala-D-Leu-Ala-OMe	2+3 A		79	Aq-Alc	219–221.5			527
Z-Val-Lys-Leu-D-Phe-Pro-OMe				EtAc-Pe	142–143			130
Boc-Val-Nε-Z(OMe)-Lys-Leu-D-Phe-Pro			83	Me-Aq	168–169			580
Boc-Val-Nε-Z(OMe)-Lys-Leu-D-Phe-Pro-OMe								580
Boc-Val-Nε-Z(OMe)-Lys-Leu-D-Phe-Pro-ONp					164–168			580
Val-Nε-Z(OMe)-Lys-Leu-D-Phe-Pro-OMe								580
Val-Nε-tos-Lys-Leu-D-Phe-Pro-OMe								130
Z-Val-Nε-boc-Lys-Val-Tyr-Pro Amide	2+3 A	DMF	60		148–153	−52	Me	645
Z-Val-Nε-tos-Lys-Val-Tyr-Pro	2+3 A		75	EtAc	133–135			493
Z-Val-Nε-tos-Lys-Val-Tyr-Pro-OBzl					152.5–153.5			494
Pz-Val-Nε-boc-Lys-Val-Tyr-Pro-OBuᵗ	2+3 DCCI	DMF	50	Acn	158–159			298
Val-Nε-boc-Lys-Val-Tyr-Pro Amide	2+3 DCCI				174–179			578
Val-Nε-boc-Lys-Val-Tyr-Pro-OBuᵗ								645
Val-Lys-Val-Tyr-Pro								298
Val-Nε-tos-Lys-Val-Tyr-Pro Hydrate	2+3 A	DMF	80	Me-Aq	240–241 (dec)			494
Z(OMe)-Val-Nδ-Z-Orn-Leu-Gly-Pro				Me-Eth-Pe	144–147	−37	Ac	431
Z(OMe)-Val-Nδ-Z-Orn-Leu-Gly-Pro-OEt	2+3 A	DMF		Di-Eth-Pe	150–152	−48	Ac	431
Z(OMe)-Val-Nδ-Z-Orn-Leu-Gly-Pro Hydrazide					165–167	−52	Ac	431
Val-Nδ-Z-Orn-Leu-Gly-Pro Hydrochloride					160–162	−41	Ac	431
Z(OMe)-Val-Nδ-Z-Orn-Leu-D-Phe-Gly				Di-Eth	214–215	−21	Ac	18
Z(OMe)-Val-Nδ-Z-Orn-Leu-D-Phe-Gly-OEt	2+3 A	DMF		Di-Eth				18
Z(OMe)-Val-Nδ-Z-Orn-Leu-D-Phe-Gly Hydrazide				Me-EtAc-Eth	217–219	−20	Ac	18

Table 5 Pentapeptides (continued)

Compound	Method	Solvent	% Yield	Solvent Crystallization	M.P.(°C)	$[\alpha]_D$	Solvent Rotation	Ref.
Val-N^δ-Z-Orn-Leu-D-Phe-Gly	2+3 A				191–192	–4	Ac	18
Z-Val-N^δ-tos-Orn-Leu-Phe-Pro-OMe			71	Aq-Alc	174.5–176			129
Boc-Val-N^δ-Z-Orn-Leu-D-Phe-Pro	A	EtAc-DMF		EtAc-Eth-Pe	122–125	–39	DMF	451
Boc-Val-N^δ-Z-Orn-Leu-D-Phe-Pro-OEt			69	EtAc-Eth-Pe	167–170	–32	DMF	451
Val-N^δ-Z-Orn-D-Leu-Phe-Pro-OEt Hydrochloride				Alc-Eth	183–185	–19	DMF	451
Val-N^δ-Z-Orn-Leu-D-Phe-Pro Hydrochloride					195–200 (dec)	–22	DMF	451
Val-N^δ-tos-Orn-Leu-Phe-Pro-OMe Hydrochloride				oil				129
Z(OMe)-Val-N^δ-Z-Orn-Leu-D-Phe-Sar	2+3 A	DMF	75	Me-Eth-Pe	151–153	–26	Ac	16
Z(OMe)-Val-N^δ-Z-Orn-Leu-D-Phe-Sar-OEt				Me-Eth-Pe	143–146	–28	Ac	16
Z(OMe)-Val-N^δ-Z-Orn-Leu-D-Phe-Sar Hydrazide					172–175	–32	Ac	16
Val-N^δ-Z-Orn-Leu-D-Phe-Sar Hydrochloride					162	–15	Ac	16
N-[2-Nitro-3-OBzl-4-me-bz]-O-[Z-N-me-Val]-Thr-D-allo-Ile-Pro-Sar-OBzl	1+4 CDI	THF						77
Di-(Z-Val)-Cys-di-Ser-OMe				Me	224–225	–49	DMF	776

6

Hexapeptides

General comments pertaining to synthesis of pentapeptides (Table 5) apply also to the hexapeptides. At the reaction stage, aside from comparison (for example, see ref. 556, 89, and 506) of coupling reagents, two selective reactions should be mentioned. First, use of the azide (4+2, 43%) procedure for obtaining Z-Leu-Val-S-Bzl-Cys-Gly-γ-OEt-Glu-Arg-OMe without protecting the arginine quanidino group.[674] Secondly, the selective cleavage of a *t*-butyl ester in presence of a methyl ester using *p*-toluenesulfonic acid in dioxane.[422] The experimental summaries of ref. 422 and 517 were considered especially useful.

For washing (1*N* hydrochloric acid, 5% sodium carbonate, 5% sodium chloride[319] and 1*N* ammonium hydroxide, water, 1*N* hydrochloric acid, water)[648] crude products, thin layer[602, 207, 529] and column (cellulose[658] and Dowex 50 W-X2,[527] chromatography, and countercurrent distribution[677, 297, 371, 674, 539, 207, 405] of hexapeptides, consult the references indicated. Recrystallization of certain hexapeptides was achieved using methanol,[776, 28] water,[700] acetic acid-ether,[62] acetonitrile-ether,[123] acetonitrile-ethyl acetate,[461] dimethylformamide-acetone,[765] dimethylformamide-ether,[439] dimethylformamide-ethyl acetate,[632] ethanol-ether,[506,422] ethanol-water,[422] ethyl acetate-ethanol,[59] ethyl acetate-ligroin,[422, 284] 2-propanol-ethyl acetate,[87] methanol-ether,[582] methanol-water,[583, 701, 28] dioxane-methanol-ether,[301, 1] and methanol-dimethylformamide-water.[87]

Subsequent to July, 1968, synthesis of Val-Tyr-Val-His-Pro-Phe was reported.[463a]

Table 6 Hexapeptides

Compound	Method	Solvent	% Yield	Solvent Crystallization	M.P. (°C)	[α]$_D$	Solvent Rotation	Ref.
Alanines								
Ala-Ala-Ala-Ala-Ala-Ala								759
Z-Ala-Ala-Ala-Ala-Ala-Ala	2+4 MCA	DMF	67					759
Z-α-me-Ala-α-me-Ala-α-me-Ala-α-me-Ala-α-me-Ala				Aq-Me	243-245 (dec)			284
Z-α-me-Ala-α-me-Ala-α-me-Ala-α-me-Ala-α-me-Ala-α-me-Ala-OBu^t	1+5 O	Acn	84	EtAc-Pe	215-218			284
Ala-Ala-N$^\epsilon$-for-Lys-Phe-γ-OBu^t-Glu-OMe								535
Z-Ala-Ala-N$^\epsilon$-for-Lys-Phe-γ-OBu^t-Glu-OMe	3+3 A		60	Aq-Acn	239.5-240.5	-29	DMF	535
Ala-Ala-Gly-Phe-Gly-Gly Pentahydrate	1+5 ONP	DMF	78		193.5-196	-12	1N HCl	631
Z-β-Ala-Asn-S-bzl-Cys-Pro-Leu-Gly Amide					228-229	-77	DMF	397
Ala-Asp-S-bzl-Cys-Pro-Leu-Gly Amide	1+5 OTCP	DMF	76	Me-Eth	245			191
Z-Ala-Asp-S-bzl-Cys-Pro-Leu-Gly Amide					150-152	-11		191
Ala-Glu-His-Phe-Ala-Asn Amide	1+5 ONP	DMA	80	Aq-Acn	203-204	-23		436
Z-Ala-Glu-His-Phe-Ala-Asn Amide					210 (dec)	-40	1N HCl	436
Ala-Gly-Ala-Gly-S-bzl-Cys-Gly								631
Nps-Ala-Gly-Ala-Gly-Ser-Gly-OEt	2+4 ONP		78	DMF-EtAc	229-231	-28	DMF	632
Nps-Ala-Gly-Ala-Gly-Ser-Gly-ONp	2+4 MCA	DMF		DMF-EtAc	190.5-192	-25	DMF	632
Z-Ala-Gly-Gly-Ala-Gly-Gly	3+3 SPh	Ac	67	Aq	161-163	-4.6	DMF	700
Ala-D-Leu-Ala-D-Val-Val-D-Val-OMe Acetate								527
Z-Ala-D-Leu-Ala-D-Val-Val-D-Val-OMe								527
Ala-Leu-Ile-Ser-Trp-Ile-OBu^t	A	EtAc-DMF	84	Alc	253-254	-24	DMF	549
Z-Ala-Leu-Ile-Ser-Trp-Ile-OBu^t				Me	231-232	-26	DMF	549

Compound	Method	Solvent	Yield (%)	Recryst. solvent	m.p.	[α]	Solvent	Ref.
Z-Ala-Leu-Tyr-Leu-Val-S-bzl-Cys Amide Hydrate	1+5 ONP	DMF	90	Aq-Ac	259	−12	Aq-Me	307
Ala-Phe-Ala-Gly-Leu-Met Amide Hydrochloride					160–163 (dec)			168
Boc-Ala-Phe-Ala-Gly-Leu-Met Amide	4+2 DCCI	DMF			241–243 (dec)	−28	DMF	168
Z-β-Ala-Phe-β-Ala-Pro-Phe-N^G-nitro-Arg-ONBzl	1+5 ONP	DMF	62	Acn-Eth	95–110	−12	Ac	651
Ala-Phe-Ile-Gly-Leu-Ala Amide					271–272	−51	TFA	563
Ala-Phe-Ile-Gly-Leu-Met Amide					225 (dec)	−18	DMF	89
Ala-Phe-Ile-Gly-Leu-Met Amide Bromohydrate					250–255 (dec)	−21	Aq-Ac	395
Ala-Phe-Ile-Gly-Leu-Met Amide Hydrate					233–234	−35	DMF	89
Ala-Phe-Ile-Gly-Leu-Met Amide Trifluoroacetate					221–230	−25	DMF	563
Acp-Ala-Phe-Ile-Gly-Leu-Met Amide					243–245	−26	DMF	524
Z-Ala-Phe-Ile-Gly-Leu-Met Amide					242–244	−31	DMF	393
Boc-Ala-Phe-Ile-Gly-Leu-Met Amide	3+3 DCCI / 3+3 A / 2+4 A / 5+1 A	DMF / DMF / DMF	74, 77	Ac-Alc	250 (dec)	−29	DMF	89, 524, 395, 393
Boc-Acp-Ala-Phe-Ile-Gly-Leu-Met Amide	MCA		78	Me	248–250 (dec)	−33	DMF	393
Caproyl-Ala-Phe-Ile-Gly-Leu-Met Amide	MCA		89		247–248	−36	DMF	563
Ala-Phe-Leu-Gly-Leu-Met Amide Hydrate					230–232	−25	DMF	168
Ala-Phe-Leu-Gly-Leu-Met Amide Hydrochloride					195–198 (dec)	−20	Ac-Aq	168
Boc-Ala-Phe-Leu-Gly-Leu-Met Amide	2+4 DCCI	DMF			234–236 (dec)	−29	DMF	168
Ala-Phe-Phe-Gly-Leu-Met Amide Hydrate					284–286 (dec)	−20	Me-Aq	168
Boc-Ala-Phe-Phe-Gly-Leu-Met Amide	4+2 DCCI				250–252 (dec)	−43	DMF	168

Table 6 Hexapeptides (continued)

Compound	Method	Solvent	% Yield	Solvent Crystallization	M.P.(°C)	$[\alpha]_D$	Solvent Rotation	Ref.
Ala-Phe-Pro-Gly-Leu-Met Amide Hydrochloride	4+2 DCCI				157–159 (dec)	−44	Ac-Aq	168
Boc-Ala-Phe-Pro-Gly-Leu-Met Amide					155	−44	Alc	168
N-Bz-Ala-Phe-Ser-Gly-Leu-Val-OMe				Me-Aq	233–235	−58	Me	701
N-[p-Chloro-bz]-Ala-Phe-O-[2,2,2 trifluoro-1-Z-amino-et]-Ser-Gly Leu-Val-OMe				Me-Aq	220			701
Z-β-Ala-Phe-OAc-Ser-Pro-Phe-N^G-nitro-Arg-ONBzl	1+5 ONP	DMF	57	DMF-1N-NH$_4$OH	130–144	−32	Ac	651
Ala-Phe-Val-Gly-Leu-Met Amide					225–229	−52	TFA	563
Ala-Phe-Val-Gly-Leu-Met Amide Hydrochloride					285–288 (dec)	−22	Ac	168
Boc-Ala-Phe-Val-Gly-Leu-Met Amide	3+3 DCCI				254–257 (dec)	−33	DMF	168
Boc-Ala-Ser-N$^\epsilon$-boc-Lys-Asp-Ala-Phe-OMe	3+3 A	DMF	50		225	−26	Aq-Ac	524
Arginines								
Arg-Ala-Gln-β-OBu^t-Asp-Phe-Val-OBu^t Acetate Hydrobromide					173–175	−32	Me	727
Z-Arg-Ala-Gln-β-OBu^t-Asp-Phe-Val-OBu^t Hydrobromide	1+5 DCCI	Py	91	Me-EtAc	196.5–197	−38	Me	727
Arg-Arg-Pro-Val-N$^\epsilon$-boc-Lys-Val-OBu^t Triacetate						−76	Aq	644
N^g-Nitro-Z-D-Arg-D-Phe-D-Pro-D-Ser-D-Phe-Gly						+26		681
N^G-Nitro-Z-D-Arg-D-Phe-D-Pro-D-Ser-D-Phe-Gly-OMe						+25		681
N^G-Nitro-Z-Arg-Phe-Pro-Ser-Phe-Gly				Me-Eth				680
N^G-Nitro-Z-Arg-Phe-Pro-Ser-Phe-Gly-OMe	3+3 DCCI	DMF-Acn	52			−18	Me	680

Compound	Method	Solvent	Yield (%)	Recryst. solvent	mp (°C)	$[\alpha]$	Rotation solvent	Ref.
Arg-Val-Tyr-Ile-His-Phe								677
N^G-Nitro-Arg-Arg-Val-Tyr-Ile-His-Phe-OBzl					163–164			677
N^G-Nitro-Z-Arg-Val-Tyr-Ile-His-Phe-OBzl	1+5 MCA		47		205–207	−35	Ac	677
Asparagines								
Asn-Arg-Tyr-Val-His-Pro						−61	1N Ac	502
Z-Asn-Arg-Tyr-Val-His-Pro								502
Z-Asn-Gln-His-Leu-S-bzl-Cys-Gly	1+5 ONP				209–210	−37	Ac	758
Z-Asn-Ser-Gly-Pro-Tyr-N$^\varepsilon$-tos-Lys	3+3 MCA	THF	48	Alc	138–143	−31	DMF	269
Asp-Ala-Phe-Ile-Gly-Leu					200 (dec)	−2.8	Ac-Aq	524
Asp-Ala-Phe-Ile-Gly-Leu-ONBzl					222 (dec)	−29	Ac-Aq	524
Z-Asp-Ala-Phe-Ile-Gly-Leu-ONBzl					240 (dec)	−33	DMF	524
Z-Asp-Glu-N^{im}-bzl-His-Leu-S-bzl-Cys-Gly	1+5 ONP	DMF	70	DMF-Aq	205–208 (dec)	−29	Ac-Aq	764
Asp-Ser-Gly-Pro-Tyr-N$^\varepsilon$-tos-Lys	1+5 ONP	DMF	71	DMF-Me	198–201	−67	DMF	269
Cysteines								
S-Trt-Cys-Ala-Gly-Val-S-bz-Cys-Ser-OMe Hydrochloride	1+5 DCCI	DMF	50	Me	181–183	−36	DMF	776
S-Trt-N-Nps-Cys-Ala-Gly-Val-S-bz-Cys-Ser-OMe	4+2 DCCI		67	Me	208–209	−48	DMF	776
Z-Cys-Gly-Gly-Gly-S-bzl-Cys-Gly					202 (dec)	−43	DMF	220
Z-Cys-Gly-Gly-Gly-Gly-S-bzl-Cys-Gly-Gly-OBu^t					213.5–214 (dec)	−22	DMF	220
S-Trt-Z-Cys-Gly-Gly-Gly-S-bzl-Cys-Gly-OBu^t						−11	DMF	220
S-Trt-Z-Cys-Gly-N$^\varepsilon$-Z-Lys-Gly-S-bzl-Cys-Gly-OBu^t	1+5 DCCI		90		189–191	−7.4	DMF	220
S-Bzl-N-tos-Cys-Tyr-Phe-Asn-Asn-S-bzl-Cys Hydrazide				DMF-Alc	237–238	−22	DMF	765
S-Bzl-N-tos-Cys-Tyr-Phe-Asn-Asn-S-bzl-Cys-OMe	3+3 A	DMF	54–62	DMF-An	226–228	−12	DMF	765

Table 6 Hexapeptides (continued)

Compound	Method	Solvent	% Yield	Solvent Crystallization	M.P. (°C)	[α]D	Solvent Rotation	Ref.
S-Bzl-Z-Cys-Tyr-Phe-Gln-Asn-S-bzl-Cys-OMe	3+3 A	DMF	70		256–257			643
S-Bzl-Cys-Tyr-Phe-Gln-Asn-S-bzl-Cys Hydrazide					250–251			643
S-Bzl-N-tos-Cys-Tyr-Phe-Gln-Asn-S-bzl-Cys Hydrazide	3+3 MCA	DMF	67	Ac-Aq	261–262			643
S-Bzl-N-tos-Cys-Tyr-Phe-Gln-Asn-S-bzl-Cys-OMe	A		60		247–248 / 247–248			643
Tos-S-bzl-Cys-Tyr-Phe-Gln-Asn-S-bzl-Cys Hydrazide				DMF-Aq	264–265	−15	DMF	765
Tos-S-bzl-Cys-Tyr-Phe-Gln-Asn-S-bzl-Cys-OMe	3+3 A	DMF	85–89	Aq-DMF	245–250	−40	Ac	765
S-Bzl-Z-Cys-Tyr-Tyr-Tyr-Gln-Asn	4+2 MCA	Di-THF	67		198–203	−24	DMF	50
Glutamines								
Z-Gln-Asn-Ala-Pro-N^G-nitro-Arg-Gly Amide	4+2 OTCP		47		153–156	−74	Ac-Aq	259
Gln-Asn-Ala-Pro-N^G-nitro-Arg-Gly Amide					170	−67	Ac-Aq	259
Z-Gln-Asn-Ala-Pro-N^ε-boc-Lys-Gly Amide	4+2 OTCP	DMF	65		236	−72	Ac-Aq	259
Z-Gln-Asn-Cys-Pro-Ala-Gly Amide	1+5 OTCP	DMF	67		224	−74 / −39	Ac-Aq / DMF	275
Z-Gln-Asn-S-bzl-Cys-Pro-N^G-tos-Arg-Gly Amide	1+5 OTCP	DMF	99		190	−53	Ac-Aq	255
Gln-Asn-S-bzl-Cys-Pro-N^G-tos-Arg-Gly Amide						−34	DMF	255
Gln-Asn-S-bzl-Cys-Pro-N^G-tos-Arg-Gly Amide Hydrobromide								640
Z-Gln-Asn-S-bzl-Cys-Pro-Cit-Gly Amide	1+5 ONP	Py	86	EtAc	186–202 (dec)	−45	Ac-Aq	61

Peptide	Method	Solvent	Yield (%)	Solvent	M.p. (°C)	$[\alpha]_D$	Solvent	Ref.
Z-Gln-Asn-S-bzl-Cys-Pro-Cit-Gly Amide	1+5 OTCP	DMF	70		241–243	−53 / −35	Ac-Aq. / DMF	275 / 277
Z-Gln-Asn-S-bzl-Cys-Pro-Ile-Gly Amide	3+3 A	DMF	54	An-Eth	232 (dec)	−70 / −44	Ac-Aq / DMF	277 / 127
Gln-Asn-S-bzl-Cys-Pro-Ile-Gly Amide					160	−68	Ac_2O	127
Z-Gln-D-Asn-S-bzl-Cys-Pro-Leu-Gly Amide					238	−43	DMF	188
Z-D-Gln-D-Asn-S-bzl-Cys-Pro-Leu-Gly Amide					244	−45	DMF	143
Z-Gln-Asn-S-Eac-Cys-Pro-Leu-Gly Amide	1+5 OTCP	DMF	82		211	−76	Ac-Aq	687
Z-Gln-Asn-Se-Eac-Cys-Pro-Leu-Gly Amide					206–209	−77	Me	188
Gln-Asn-S-Eac-Cys-Pro-Leu-Gly Amide	4+2 A	DMF	69–75	THF-Aq / Ac-Alc / DMF-Aq	222–224	−56	DMF	62
Z-Gln-Asn-S-bzl-Cys-Pro-N^ϵ-tos-Lys-Gly Amide	1+5 ONP	DMF	91		203	−41	DMF	765
Gln-Asn-S-bzl-Cys-Pro-N^ϵ-tos-Lys-Gly Amide					165–175	−41	DMF	765
Z-Gln-Asn-S-bzl-Cys-Pro-N^δ-Pht-Orn-Gly-Amide Hydrate	1+5 OTCP	DMF	88		203–213	−37	DMF	63
Z-Gln-Asn-S-bzl-Cys-Pro-N^δ-tos-Orn-Gly Amide	3+3 A	DMF		An-Eth	193	−60	Ac	254
Gln-Asn-S-bzl-Cys-Pro-N^δ-tos-Orn-Gly Amide					223 (dec)	−38	DMF	254
Z-Gln-Asn-S-bzl-Cys-Pro-Val-Gly Amide	1+5 ONP	DMF	64		128 (dec)	−48	Ac	277
Gln-Asn-S-bzl-Cys-Pro-Val-Gly Amide					240–242	−37	Ac-Aq	277
Z-Gln-Asp-S-bzl-Cys-Pro-Ala-Gly Amide	2+4 DCCI	DMF			203–206	−66	Ac	690
Z-Gln-Gly-Thr-Phe-Thr-Ser-OMe				Me		−48	DMF	47
Z-Gln-His-Phe-Arg-Trp-Gly Acetate Hydrate	1+5 A	DMF	67	Me	206	−46	DMF	297
Z-Gln-His-Phe-Arg-Trp-Gly Acetate Trihydrate					200–202	−9	DMF	162

Table 6 Hexapeptides (continued)

Compound	Method	Solvent	% Yield	Solvent Crystallization	M.P. (°C)	[α]D	Solvent Rotation	Ref.
Z-Gln-His-Phe-Arg-Trp-Gly-OMe								297
Z-Gln-His-Phe-Arg-Trp-Gly-OMe Dihydrochloride	2+4 DCCI	DMF	60	DMF-EtAc				297
Z-Gln-His-Phe-Arg-Trp-Gly-ONBzl Hydrochloride Hydrate								297
Gln-His-Phe-Arg-Trp-Gly Acetate Trihydrate				Ac-Aq				162, 297
Z(OMe)-Gln-His-Phe-Arg-Trp-Gly-OMe Hydrochloride	2+4 DCCI	DMF	68	Alc	204–205	−16		297
N-Tfa-Gln-Trp-Leu-Met-Asn-OBu^t-Thr-OBu^t	3+3 A				231–234	−57	DMF	720
Z-Gln-Val-S-bzl-Cys-Pro-Leu-Gly Amide	1+5 ONP	DMF			217–218	−53	DMF	688
Z-Glu-Asp-S-bzl-Cys-Pro-N^G-tos-Arg-Gly Amide	3+3 A	DMF	65		184–186			257
Z-Glu-Asp-S-bzl-Cys-Pro-Leu-Gly Amide	2+4 DCCI		80		190–193			51
Glu-Asp-S-bzl-Cys-Pro-Leu-Gly Amide Hydrobromide					105–110 (dec)	−66	Ac	51
Z-Glu-Asp-S-bzl-Cys-Pro-N^G-tos-Orn-Gly Amide	1+5 OTCP		62	EtAc	193	−38	DMF	254
Z-Glu-Asp-S-bzl-Cys-Pro-N$^\delta$-tos-Orn-Gly Amide	3+3 A	EtAc	61	DMF-EtAc	176–178 (dec)			256
Glu-Asp-S-bzl-Cys-Pro-N$^\delta$-tos-Orn-Gly Amide						−48	Ac-Aq	254
Z-Glu-S-bzl-Cys-bzl-N^{im}-His-Thr-Val-Glu-di-OBzl	2+4 A		85	Aq-Me	195–196	−9.6	DMF	669
γ-OBu^t-Z-Glu-γ-OBu^t-Glu-γ-OBu^t-Glu-Ala-Tyr-Gly-OMe	1+5 OTCP	DMF	94		203–204	−20	DMF	28
					197–198 (dec)	−19	DMF	423

Compound	Coupling	Solvent	Yield	Recryst.	m.p. (°C)	[α]	Solvent	Ref.
γ-OBuᵗ-Glu-γ-OBuᵗ-Glu-γ-OBuᵗ-Glu-Ala-Tyr-Gly-OMe	1+5 OTCP	DMF		Me	212–214 (dec)	−13	DMF	423
Pyro-Glu-γ-OBuᵗ-Glu-γ-OBuᵗ-Glu-Ala-Tyr-Gly-OMe				Me	206–208	−14	DMF	28
γ-OBzl-N-Tfa-Glu-di-Gly-Nᵋ-Z-Lys-Gly-Gly-OBuᵗ	3+3 DCCI	Py		Alc-Eth	165–166	−8.2	DMF	422
Glu-di-Gly-Lys-Gly-Gly				Aq-Alc	178–182	−11	N HCl	422
					(dec)	−11	Ac	
γ-OMe-Z-Glu-di-Gly-Nᵋ-Tfa-Lys-Gly-Gly-OBuᵗ	3+3 DCCI	Py		Aq-Alc	139–141	−8.7	DMF	422
OBzl-Glu-His-Phe-Nᴳ-tos-Arg-Trp-Gly				Di-Aq	193–195			369
γ-OBzl-Z-Glu-His-Phe-Nᴳ-tos-Arg-Trp-Gly			77					371
γ-OBzl-boc-Glu-His-Phe-Nᴳ-tos-Arg-Trp-Gly-OBuᵗ	1+5 ONP	Acn		Me	165–168 (dec)			370
γ-OBzl-Glu-His-Phe-Nᴳ-tos-Arg-Trp-Gly Difluoroacetate				Me				370
Z-Glu-His-Phe-Nᴳ-nitro-Arg-Trp-Gly			63.5					575
γ-OBuᵗ-Z-Glu-His-Phe-Arg-Trp-Gly Acetate Trihydrate	1+5 A	DMF		Me	200–202			162
γ-OBuᵗ-Z-Glu-His-Phe-Nᴳ-nitro-Arg-Trp-Gly			68	Me	206			298
γ-OBuᵗ-Z-Glu-His-Phe-Nᴳ-nitro-Arg-Trp-Gly-OMe	2+4 A / 2+4 DCCI	Acn	72	Me-Eth	174–177			575
γ-OBuᵗ-Glu-His-Phe-Arg-Trp-Gly	2+4 A				155–165			575
γ-OBuᵗ-Glu-His-Phe-Arg-Trp-Gly Acetate					175–178			298
γ-OBuᵗ-Glu-His-Phe-Arg-Trp-Gly Acetate Dihydrate								298, 575, 162

Table 6 Hexapeptides (continued)

Compound	Method	Solvent	% Yield	Solvent Crystallization	M.P. (°C)	$[\alpha]_D$	Solvent Rotation	Ref
OBzl-N-boc-Glu-His-Phe-N^G-tos-Arg-Trp-Gly-OBu^t	1+5 ONP							369
Glu-His-Phe-Arg-Trp-Gly					162–164			370
Glu-His-Phe-Arg-Trp-Gly Hydrate					220–223			575
γ-OBzl-boc-Glu-His-Phe-N^ε-tos-Lys-Trp-Gly-OBu^t	1+5 ONP	DMF	70	Me	160–162	−27	DMF	94
Glycines								
Z-Gly-Asp-S-bzl-Cys-Pro-Leu-Gly Amide	1+5 ONP	DMF			203–205	−55	DMF	126
Boc-Gly-N^ε-boc-Gly-Asp-Gly-OBu^t-Lys-Gly-OBu^t	3+3 WRK		51		155	−13	Aq-Alc	559
Gly-N^ε-Gly-Asp-Gly-Lys-Gly						−21	Aq	559
Z-(aza-Gly-Gly)$_3$-OEt					194–195			154
Z-(aza-Gly-Gly)$_3$ Hydrazide					213–215			154
Z-hexa-Gly	3+3 SPh	Ac	87	DMF-Aq	267–270 (dec)			700
Z-Gly-Gly-Leu-Gly-Gly-Gly Anhydride	MCA	An		Alc-Pe	197–199			29
Z-Gly-Gly-Leu-Gly-Gly-Gly				Alc	194–197	−27		29
Gly-Gly-Leu-Gly-Gly-Gly Monohydrate	A	DMF	84	Di-Me-Eth-Pe	148–153	−11	DMF	30
Z-di-Gly-N^ε-Z-Lys-di-Gly-N^ε-Z-Lys-OBzl								1
Di-Gly-Lys-di-Gly-Lys Dihydrochloride								1
Boc-Gly-Ile-Gly-Ala-Val-Leu Hydrazide	A	DMF	86	EtAc-Alc	259–260	−42	DMSO	549
Boc-Gly-Ile-Gly-Ala-Val-Leu-OMe				Aq	222–223	−22	DMF	549
Z-Gly-Leu-Gly-Gly-Gly-Gly Monohydrate				Aq-Alc	172–173	−17	Aq	30
Gly-Leu-Gly-Gly-Gly-Gly Sesquihydrate						−17		30
Gly-N^ε-Z-Lys-di-Gly-N^ε-Z-Lys-Gly-ONp Trifluoroacetate								1
Z(OMe)-N^ε-Z-Lys-di-Gly-N^ε-Z-Lys-Gly				Di-Eth-Me	174–176	−8.3	DMF	1

Compound	Method	Solvent	Yield (%)	Recryst. solv.	mp (°C)	[α]	Solv.	Ref.
Z(OMe)-Gly-N^ϵ-Z-Lys-di-Gly-N^ϵ-Z-Lys-Gly-OBzl	MCA	DMF-THF	94	DMF-Eth	171-175	-10	DMF	1
Z(OMe)-Gly-N^ϵ-Z-Lys-di-Gly-N^ϵ-Z-Lys-Gly-ONp								1
Z-Gly-p-nitro-Phe-di-Gly-p-nitro-Phe-Gly-ONp	MCA			DMF-Eth	190 (dec)	-20	DMF	548
Z-Gly-p-nitro-Phe-di-Gly-Phe-Gly-ONp					210-212	-20	DMF	548
Z-Gly-Phe-Gly-Pro-Phe-N^G-nitro-Arg-ONBzl	1+5 ONP	DMF	66	Ac-Aq	96-103	-15	Ac	649
Z-D-Phe-Leu-Gly-D-Phe-Leu				Aq-Me	233-235			56
Z-Gly-Phe-Leu-Gly-D-Phe-Leu Hydrazide				DMF-Me-Aq	237-239	-9.4	DMF	87
Z-Gly-Phe-Leu-Gly-Phe-Leu Hydrazide								87
Z-Gly-D-Phe-Leu-Gly-Phe-Leu Hydrazide				Me-DMF-p-Aq	234-235	-17	DMF	87
Z-Gly-D-Phe-Leu-Gly-D-Phe-Leu Hydrazide Hydrate	3+3 A	Eth	72	Aq-Me	202-203	-3.5	DMF	87
Z-Gly-D-Phe-Leu-Gly-D-Phe-Leu-OMe	A	Eth-EtAc	83	EtAc-Me	200-201	-4.6	DMF	87
Z-Gly-Phe-Leu-Gly-Phe-Leu-OMe	A	Eth-EtAc	54	Me-EtAc-Pe	223-225	-22	DMF	87
Z-Gly-Phe-Leu-Gly-D-Phe-Leu-OMe	A	Eth-EtAc	73	Me-EtAc	223-225	-8.7	DMF	87
Z-Gly-D-Phe-Leu-Gly-Phe-Leu-OMe				i-Pr-EtAc	208-209	-16	DMF	87
Gly-D-Phe-Leu-Gly-Phe-Leu								56
Gly-Phe-Leu-Gly-Phe-Leu Hydrazide Dihydrobromide								87
Gly-Phe-Leu-Gly-D-Phe-Leu Hydrazide Dihydrobromide								87
Gly-D-Phe-Leu-Gly-D-Phe-Leu Hydrazide Dihydrobromide								87
Z-Gly-Phe-OAc-Ser-Pro-Phe-Arg-OMe	1+5 ONP	DMF	79	Me-Eth	222-224			440
Z-Gly-Phe-OAc-Ser-Pro-p-fluoro-Phe-N^G-nitro-Arg-OMe			69		226-228			438
Z-Gly-Phe-OAc-Ser-Pro-p-fluoro-D-Phe-N^G-nitro-Arg-OMe			87		110-120			438
Z-Gly-Phe-OAc-Ser-Pro-D-Phe-N^G-nitro-Arg-OMe	1+5 ONP	DMF	73.5	Me-Eth	118-122			438

Table 6 Hexapeptides (continued)

Compound	Method	Solvent	% Yield	Solvent Crystallization	M.P. (°C)	$[\alpha]_D$	Solvent Rotation	Ref.
Z-Gly-Phe-Ser-Pro-Phe-N^G-nitro-Arg-OMe	1+5 ONP	DMF	76	DMF-Eth	218–220	−52	DMF	439
	ONP		76	DMF-Eth	218–220			439
Nps-Gly-Phe-OBzl-Ser-Pro-Phe-N^G-nitro-Arg-ONBzl								137
Z-Gly-Pro-Ala-Gly-Pro-Ala					219–220 (dec)	−164	Me	59
Z-Gly-Pro-Ala-Gly-Pro-Ala-OMe	3+3 WRK	Acn	58	Me-EtAc	208–210	−198	Aq	59
Gly-Pro-Ala-Gly-Pro-Ala				Aq-Alc	215–216 (dec)			59
Gly-Pro-Ala-Gly-Pro-Ala-OMe Hydrochloride								59
Z-Gly-Pro-Gly-Gly-Pro-Ala	3+3 DCCI	Acn	84–88	Alc-Pe	170–174	−80	Alc	716
Z-Gly-Pro-Gly-Gly-Pro-Ala-OMe				Alc-Eth	203–205	−88	Alc	716
Z-Gly-Pro-Gly-Gly-Pro-Gly	3+3 WRK	Acn	62.8	EtAc-Alc	216–217	−80	Alc	59
Z-Gly-Pro-di-Gly-Pro-Gly				Alc-EtAc	161–163	−88	Alc	496
Z-Gly-Pro-di-Gly-Pro-Gly-OEt	3+3 ONP	Chf		Me-Aq	218–219			496
Z-Gly-Pro-di-Gly-Pro-Gly-ONp				Alc-Eth	163–164			496
Gly-Pro-Gly-Gly-Pro-Gly				Acn	187–188	−76	Ac	59
Gly-Pro-Gly-Gly-Pro-Gly-OEt Hydrochloride					220–222			59
Pz-Gly-Pro-Gly-Gly-Pro-Gly-OEt	3+3 A		79					570
Z-Gly-Tyr-Gly-Gly-N^{im}-bzl-His-Gly-ONBzl	3+3 EDCI	DMF	79	Alc	130–132	−79	DMF	278
Trt-Gly-Tyr-di-Gly-Tyr-Gly-OEt	3+3 DCCI	Alc	59	Alc-Aq	200–201			548
Histidine								
N^{im}-Bzl-Z-His-Phe-N^G-tos-Arg-Trp-Phe-Gly				DMF-Eth	144–148			371
His-Phe-β-OBu^t-Asp-Ala-β-OBu^t-Asp-Val-OBu^t				Aq-Me	188–191		Alc	602
N^{α},N^{im}-di-Z-His-Phe-β-OBu^t-Asp-Ala-OBu^t-Ser-Val-OBu^t	1+5 MCA	THF	63	Aq-Alc	181.5–182.5	−18	DMF	602

Compound	Method	Solv.	Yield (%)	Recrystn. solvent	M.p. (°C)	[α]	Solv.	Ref.
N$^\alpha$,N^{im}-Bis-Adoc-His-OBu^t-Ser-Gln-Gly-OBu^t-Thr-Phe	1+5 OSU	Py	71		203–205	+16	Me	736
Boc-His-OBu^t-Ser-Gln-Gly-Thr-Phe Hydrazide	2+4 A				193–194.5	−10	DMF	556
Boc-His-OBu^t-Ser-Gln-Gly-Thr-Phe-OMe	1+5 A					−1	DMF	556
Z-His-Ser-Glu-Gly-Thr-Phe Hydrazide	2+4 A		65		203–205	−16	Me	559
Z-His-Ser-Glu-Gly-Thr-Phe-OMe		DMF	85.4	Alc-Eth	205–207	−16	Me	559
Isoleucine								
Z-Ile-Gln-Asn-S-bzl-Cys-Pro-Abu-Gly Amide	6+1 OTCP	DMF	75		242	−79	Ac	275
Z-Ile-Phe-OAc-Ser-Pro-Phe-N^G-nitro-Arg-ONBzl	1+5 ONP		50	Me-Eth	138–144	−50	DMF	648
Z-Ile-Phe-OAc-Thr-Pro-Phe-N^G-nitro-Arg-ONBzl	1+5 ONP		65	Ac-Aq	104–124	−4	DMF	648
Leucine								
Z-Leu-Gln-Leu-Gly-Leu-Val Amide	1+5 ONP	DMF			283–285(dec)	−6	Ac	367
Leu-Gln-Leu-Gly-Leu-Val Amide					253–260(dec)	−47	Ac	367
Z-Leu-Leu-Gln-Gly-Leu-Val Amide	1+5 ONP	DMF			264–267(dec)	−35	Ac	66
Leu-Leu-Gln-Gly-Leu-Val Amide					239–241(dec)		Ac	66
Z-Leu-Phe-OAc-Ser-Pro-Phe-N^G-nitro-Arg-ONBzl	1+5 ONP		64	Ac-Aq	104–107	−47	Ac	652
Z-Leu-Phe-OAc-Thr-Pro-Phe-N^G-nitro-Arg-ONBzl			66	Ac-Aq	105–115	−28	Ac	648
Z-D-Leu-Trp-D-Leu-Trp 2-Hydroxyethylamide						−60		527
D-Leu-Trp-D-Leu-Trp-D-Leu-Trp 2-Hydroxyethylamide	ONP					−22		527
Z-Leu-Tyr-Leu-Val-S-bzl-Cys-Gly					240–243	−42	DMF	411
Z-Leu-Tyr-Leu-Val-S-bzl-Cys-Gly-OEt	1+5 ONP		80		236–238	−38	Ac	310
Z-Leu-Tyr-Leu-Val-S-bzl-Cys-Gly-OMe	1+5 ONP		90		249–251	−39	DMF	411

Table 6 Hexapeptides (continued)

Compound	Method	Solvent	% Yield	Solvent Crystallization	M.P.(°C)	$[\alpha]_D$	Solvent Rotation	Ref.
Leu-Tyr-Leu-Val-S-bzl-Cys-Gly Hydrobromide					265	−31	Aq	411
Z-Leu-Val-S-bzl-Cys-Gly-γ-OBzl-Glu-N^G-nitro-Arg-OBzl	4+2 A		38	Chf-Pe	162–164			674
Z-Leu-Val-S-bzl-Cys-Gly-γ-OEt-Glu-Arg-OMe Hydrochloride	4+2 A	DMF	43	Me-EtAc	128	−54		674
Z-Leu-Val-γ-OMe-Glu-Ala-Leu-Tyr-OEt	3+3 DCCI	THF-DMF	47	Me	260–262	−25	DMF	319
Lysine								
N$^\varepsilon$-Boc-N$^\alpha$-Z-Lys-Ala-γ-OBu^t-Glu-N$^\delta$-boc-Orn-Gln-His-OMe	A		46		205–207	−14	DMF	583
N$^\varepsilon$-Boc-N$^\alpha$-Z-Lys-β-OBu^t-Asp-Ala-Phe-Ile-Gly	1+5 ONP	DMF-Py	75.5		219–221	−23	A	25
N$^\varepsilon$,N$^\alpha$-di-Z-Lys-S-bzl-Cys-Ala-Gln-S-bzl-Cys-His Monohydrate	1+5 MCA	THF	98	DMF-Aq	209–213	−31	DMF	746
Lys-S-bzl-Cys-Ala-Gln-S-bzl-Cys-His Hexahydrate				Aq-An	160–165	−37	1N HCl	746
N$^\varepsilon$,N$^\alpha$-di-Z-Lys-Glu-Thr-Ala-Ala-Ala-OEt	1+5 ONP	Py	83	Alc-Eth	229–230	−24	DMF	507
N$^\varepsilon$,N$^\alpha$-di-Boc-Lys-γ-OBu^t-Glu-Thr-Ala-Ala-Ala-OEt	2+4 A	DMF-EtAc	70	Alc-Eth	203–204	−21	DMF	506
					198–200	−20	DMF	581
N$^\varepsilon$,N$^\alpha$-di-Boc-Lys-γ-OBu^t-Glu-Thr-Ala-Ala-Ala Hydrazide					226–228	−13	DMF	506
Lys-Di-Gly-Glu-Gly-Gly					190–192(dec)	+13	Ac	422
N$^\varepsilon$-Tfa-N$^\alpha$-Z-Lys-di-Gly-γ-OMe-Glu-Gly-Gly	1+3 DCCI	Py	55	Alc-Eth	93–95	−8.5	Ac	422
N$^\varepsilon$-Tfa-N$^\alpha$-Z-Lys-di-Gly-γ-OMe-Glu-Gly-Gly-OBu^t				EtAc-Pe	100	−8.0	Ac	422
					169–	−7.6	DMF	
N$^\varepsilon$-Tfa-Lys-di-Gly-γ-OMe-Glu-Gly-Gly				Me-Eth	171(dec)	+14	Ac	422

Compound	Method	Solvent	Yield (%)	Recryst. solvent	m.p. (°C)	[α]	Solvent	Ref.
N^ϵ-Boc-N^α-Z-Lys-Ile-γ-OBu^t-Glu-N^δ-boc-Orn-Glu-His-OMe	2+4 A	DMF-EtAc	60	Me-Aq	224–225	−15	DMF	583
N^ϵ-Boc-N^α-Z-Lys-Phe-γ-OBu^t-Glu-N^δ-Orn-Gln-His-OMe	2+4 A	DMF-EtAc	74		221–222	−19	DMF	400
N^ϵ-Boc-N^α-Z-Lys-Phe-γ-OBu^t-Glu-N^δ-boc-Orn-γ-OBu^t-Glu-His-OMe	2+4 A	DMF-EtAc	67	Me-Eth	205–206	−17	DMF	582
N^ϵ-Boc-N^α-Z-Lys-Phe-γ-OBu^t-Glu-Orn-Glu-His-OMe								581
N^ϵ,N^α-di-Aoc-Lys-Phe-Ile-Leu-Met Amide				DMF-Aq	233–234	−19	DMF	517
Lys-Phe-Ile-Gly-Leu-Met Amide Dihydrochloride Dihydrate					240–243(dec)	−26	DMF	517
N^ϵ,N^α-di-Boc-Lys-Phe-Phe-Gly-Leu-Met Amide	4+2 DCCI				233–235(dec)	−16	Ac	168
Lys-Phe-Phe-Gly-Leu-Met Amide Hydrochloride					165–170(dec)	−39	DMF	168
N^ϵ-Boc-Lys-Pro-Gly-N^ϵ-boc-Lys-N^ϵ-boc-Lys-OMe Toluenesulfonate				Acn-EtAc		−16	Me-Aq	577
N^ϵ-Boc-N^α-Z-Lys-Pro-Val-Gly-N^G-nitro-Arg-N^G-nitro-Arg-OBzl	4+2 DCCI	MeCl-DMF	92.8		114–115	−49	Me	461
N^ϵ-Boc-Lys-Pro-Val-Gly-Arg-Arg Diacetate						−50	Ac	461
N^ϵ-Boc-N^α-Z-Lys-Pro-Val-Gly-N^ϵ-boc-Lys-N^ϵ-boc-Lys Hydrazide	3+3 DCCI	Acn	81	Acn-Me	112–114			645
N^ϵ-Boc-N^α-Z-Lys-Pro-Val-Gly-N^ϵ-boc-Lys-N^ϵ-boc-Lys-OMe	4+2 MCA	THF	76		121–126			645, 577
N^ϵ-For-Z-Lys-Pro-Val-Gly-N^ϵ-for-Lys-N^ϵ-for-Lys Amide	4+2 CDI	DMF	64		174–179			247
N^ϵ-For-N^α-Z-Lys-Pro-Val-Gly-N^ϵ-for-Lys-N^ϵ-for-Lys-OMe					173–177			247
N^ϵ-For-Lys-Pro-Val-Gly-N^ϵ-for-Lys-N^ϵ-for-Lys Amide Hydrochloride Tetrahydrate								247

Table 6 Hexapeptides (continued)

Compound	Method	Solvent	% Yield	Solvent Crystallization	M.P.(°C)	$[\alpha]_D$	Solvent Rotation	Ref.
Ornithine								
N^δ-Boc-N^α-for-DL-Orn-N^δ-boc-DL-Orn-N^δ-boc-DL-Orn-DL-Ser-DL-Ser-DL-Ser-OMe	A	DMF-EtAc	53	Me	153-154			432
N^δ-Boc-Orn-Pro-Val-N^ϵ-boc-Lys-Val-Tyr-OBu^t						-87	Me	664
						-27	Ac-Aq	
N^δ-Boc-N^α-for-DL-Orn-DL-Ser-N^δ-boc-DL-Orn-DL-Ser-DL-Ser-N^δ-tos-DL-Orn-OMe	3+3 A	EtAc-DMF	50	Me	130-132			432
Phenylalanine								
Z-Phe-Gly-N^ϵ-boc-Lys-γ-OBu^t-Glu-Phe-Thr Hydrazide	1+5 ONP	DMF		Alc-Aq	240-242(dec)	-22	Ac-Aq	98
Z-Phe-Gly-N^ϵ-boc-Lys-γ-OBu^t-Glu-Phe-Thr-OMe	1+5 ONP			Alc	230	-21	Ac-Aq	98
Z-Phe-Gly-Pro-Phe-N^G-tos-Arg-N^ϵ-tos-Lys Hydrazide	3+3 DCCI		55	Di-Me-Eth	113-117	-32	DMF	409
Z(OMe)-D-Phe-D-Leu-N^δ-Z-Orn-Val-N^δ-Z-D-Orn-Pro	A	DMF	65	Di-Me-Eth	163	-15	Ac	301
Z(OMe)-D-Phe-D-Leu-N^δ-Z-Orn-Val-N^δ-Z-D-Orn-Pro-OEt	A	DMF	71	Di-Eth	168-170	-14	Ac	301
D-Phe-D-Leu-Orn-Val-D-Orn-Pro Diacetate	1+5 ONP	DMF	80		184-186	-47		301
Z-Phe-Leu-Pro-Val-Asn-Leu-OBu^t				Eth-Pe	98-100	-69		641
Phe-Leu-Pro-Val-Asn-Leu-OBu^t				Eth-Pe	110-112	-46		641
Z-Phe-OBu^t-Tyr-OBu^t-Thr-Pro-N^ϵ-boc-Lys-Ala-OBu^t	1+5 ONP					-38	Me	403
Z-Phe-Thr-Pro-N^ϵ-boc-Lys-Ala-OBu^t	1+5 ONP		85		155-158	-53	DMF	536
Z-Phe-Thr-Pro-N^ϵ-tos-Lys-Ala	1+5 ONP	DMF	73	Me	203-205	-42	DMF	539
Z-Phe-Thr-Pro-N^G-tos-Lys-Ala-OBu^t	1+5 ONP		82	Me-EtAc-Pe	165-167	-44	DMF	542
Z-Phe-Thr-Pro-N^ϵ-tos-Lys-Ala-OMe	1+5 ONP	DMF	76	Me	144-146	-45	DMF	308
Phe-Tyr-Thr-Pro-N^ϵ-tos-Lys-Ala								539

Compound	Coupling	Solvent	Yield (%)	Recryst. solvent	m.p. (°C)	$[\alpha]$	Rotn. solvent	Ref.
Z-Phe-Tyr-Thr-Pro-N^ϵ-tos-Lys-OBu^t-Thr-OBu^t	1+5 OSU		24	DMF-Alc	132–135	−50	Me	408
Z-Phe-Val-Asn-Gln-N^{im}-bzl-His-Leu-bzl-Cys-Gly	1+5 ONP	DMF	76		230–232(dec)			543

Proline

Compound	Coupling	Solvent	Yield (%)	Recryst. solvent	m.p. (°C)	$[\alpha]$	Rotn. solvent	Ref.
Z-Pro-Gly-Phe-Ser-Pro-Phe-OMe	1+5 ONP	DMF	79	Ac-Eth	153–155			123
Z-Pro-Gly-Phe-Ser-Pro-Phe-N^γ-tos-Dbu-OMe	4+2 DCCI	DMF	81					683
Pro-Gly-Phe-Ser-Pro-Phe-N^γ-tos-Dbu-OMe								683
Z-Pro-Gly-Phe-OAc-Ser-Sar-Phe-N^G-nitro-Arg-OMe	2+4 ONP	DMF	61	Di-Eth	136–140	−56	DMF	752
Z-Phe-Gly-Ser-Phe-N^G-nitro-Arg-ONBzl	2+4 DCCI	Acn	88		140(dec)	−31	Me	193
Pro-Phe-Gly-Ser-Phe-N^G-nitro-Arg-ONBzl					135(dec)	−27	DMF	193
Pro-Pro-Tyr-N^ϵ-boc-Lys-Met-OMe	5+1 DCCI	Acn	41	EtAc	172–174	−18	DMF	573
Boc-Pro-Ser-N^ϵ-boc-Lys-Asn-Ala-Phe Hydrate			48			−12	Ac-Aq	392
Boc-Pro-Ser-N^ϵ-boc-Lys-Asn-Ala-Phe-OMe	3+3 A	DMF	47	DMF-Alc	185–186	−60	DMF	392
Boc-Pro-Ser-N^ϵ-boc-Lys-Asp-Ala-Phe-OMe	1+5 ONP	DMF	67		198	−26	Ac	524
N-Z-Pro-Val-Gln-Ala-Ala-Tyr-OMe					287–289	−19	DMF	98
Z-Pro-Val-Gly-N^ϵ-tos-Lys-N^ϵ-tos-Lys-N^G-nitro-Arg	4+2 A	THF-EtAc	46	Ac-Eth		−42	Ac-Aq	560
Z-Pro-Val-Gly-N^ϵ-tos-Lys-N^ϵ-tos-Lys-N^G-nitro-Arg-OMe				Ac-Eth		−63	HMPA	560
Z-Pro-Val-tos-N^ϵ-Lys-Leu-D-Phe-Pro-OMe Hydrochloride	1+5 MCA	THF	60	An-Aq	157–159	−15	DMF	130
Pro-Val-tos-N^ϵ-Lys-Leu-D-Phe-Pro-OMe Hydrochloride						−35	Ac	130
Z-Pro-Val-N^ϵ-boc-Lys-Val-Tyr-Pro-OBu^t	1+5 ONP	DHF	87	Me-Eth	156–180	−94	Me	664
Z-Pro-Val-N^δ-tos-Orn-Leu-Phe-Pro-OMe	1+5 MCA	THF			175–178			129

Table 6 Hexapeptides (continued)

Compound	Method	Solvent	% Yield	Solvent Crystallization	M.P.(°C)	[α]D	Solvent Rotation	Ref.
Pro-Val-N$^\delta$-tos-Orn-Leu-Phe-Pro-OMe Hydrochloride				Me-EtAc				129
Serine								
OBu^t-N-Pht-Ser-Arg-Arg-Ala-Gln-Asn-β-OBu^t Hydrobromide	1+5 ONP	DMF	88	Alc	175(dec)	-22	Me	726
OBu^t-N-Pht-Ser-Arg-Arg-Ala-Gln-Asn-β-OBu^t Dihydrobromide					115(dec)	-20	Me	726
OBu^t-Nps-Ser-Arg-Arg-Ala-Gln-β-OBu^t-Asp Hydrobromide	1+5 ONP	DMF		Me-Alc	170(dec)	-31	DMF	725
Ser-Asn-S-bzl-Cys-Pro-Ile-Gly Amide					160			189
N-Trt-Ser-Asn-S-bzl-Cys-Pro-Ile-Gly Amide								189
Z-Ser-Asp-S-bzl-Cys-Pro-Leu-Gly Amide	DCCI	DMF-Acn	76	EtAc-Eth	179			191
Ser-Asp-S-bzl-Cys-Pro-Leu-Gly Amide	1+5 DCCI	Acn	61		152(dec)			191
Boc-Ser-Gly-Gly-Pro-Leu-Val-OMe	1+5 OSU			Me	85-90	-70		356
Z-Ser-His-Leu-Val-γ-OBu^t-Glu-Ala Hydrazide	1+5 A		70		221-223	-25	DMF	411
Z-Ser-His-Leu-Val-γ-OBu^t-Glu-Ala-OMe					230-232	-32	DMF	411
Z-OBu^t-Ser-N^{im}-bzl-His-Leu-Val-Glu-γ-OBu^t-Ala Hydrazide					222-224	-15	DMF	534
Z-OBu^t-Ser-N^{im}-bzl-His-Leu-Val-Glu-γ-OBu^t-Ala-OMe	2+4 A		16	Alc	209-211	-17	DMF	534
Z-OBu^t-Ser-His-Leu-Val-γ-OBu^t-Glu-Ala-OMe	1+5 NHS-DCCI	THF	70		237-239	-30	DMF	534
OBu^t-Z-Ser-N^{im}-bzl-His-Leu-Val-γ-OBu^t-Glu-Ala Hydrazide					222-224	-15	DMF	534
OBu^t-Z-Ser-N^{im}-bzl-His-Leu-Val-γ-OBu^t-Glu-Ala-OMe	2+4 A		16	Alc	209-211	-17	DMF	534

Compound	Method	Solvent	Yield (%)	Recrystn. solvent	M.p. (°C)	[α]	Solvent	Ref.
OBu^t-Z-Ser-His-Leu-Val-OBu^t-Glu-Ala Hydrazide	2+4 A			DMF-Alc	231–233	−27	Ac	534
OBu^t-Z-Ser-His-Leu-Val-γ-OBu^t-Glu-Ala-OMe					210(dec)	−58	Ac-Aq	534
Boc-Ser-N$^\varepsilon$-boc-Lys-Gly-Ile-Leu-Met Amide	3+3 A	DMF	61		168–169			524
N-Boc-DL-Ser-N$^\delta$-boc-DL-Orn-N$^\delta$-boc-DL-Orn-DL-Ser-N$^\delta$-tos-DL-Orn-OMe	A		57		110–112			432
N-Boc-DL-Ser-N$^\delta$-boc-DL-Orn-DL-Ser-N$^\delta$-boc-DL-Orn-DL-Ser-N$^\delta$-boc-DL-Orn-DL-Ser-N$^\delta$-boc-DL-Orn-OMe	3+3 A		53					432
Z-Ser-Phe-Gly-Pro-Pro-N^G-nitro-Arg-OMe	1+5		76					354
Z-Ser-Ser-Thr-Ser-Ala-Ala-OBu^t			51	Me-DMF	235–236 (dec)	−3.5	DMF	398
Boc-(Ser)$_2$-Thr-OBzl-Ser-(Ala)$_2$-OBzl	2,4-DNPO	DMF	79	EtAc-He	202–204			356a
Tyrosine								
Z-Tyr-Gly-Gly-bzl-N^{im}-His-Gly-ONBzl	3+3 WRK	DMF	74	Alc				341
Tyr-Gly-Gly-Gly-bzl-N^{im}-His-Gly Hydrate								341
Tyr-Gly-Gly-Gly-bzl-N^{im}-His-Gly Hydrobromide								341
OBu^t-N$^\alpha$-Z-Tyr-OBu^t-Ser-N$^\varepsilon$-boc-Lys-OBu^t-Tyr-Leu-Asp-β-OBu^t				Me	200–201 (dec)			737
OBu^t-N$^\alpha$-Z-Tyr-OBu^t-Ser-N$^\varepsilon$-boc-Lys-OBu^t-Tyr-Leu-β-OBu^t-Asp-OMe								737
OBu^t-Z-Tyr-OBu^t-Ser-N$^\varepsilon$-boc-Lys-Tyr-Leu-β-OBu^t-Asp	1+5 DCCI	DMF		Alc-Aq	205–206.5	−19	Alc	730
OBu^t-Tyr-OBu^t-Ser-N$^\varepsilon$-boc-Lys-OBu^t-Tyr-Leu-Asp-β-OBu^t	1+5 MCA		82		181	−14	Alc	737
OBu^t-N$^\alpha$-Tyr-OBu^t-Ser-N$^\varepsilon$-boc-Lys-Tyr-Leu-β-OBu^t-Asp					250	+16	Ac	730
Valine								
Z-Val-Ala-Ile-His-Pro-Phe-ONp	2+4 A		74.7	Me-Eth	163–166	−21	DMF	588

Table 6 Hexapeptides (continued)

Compound	Method	Solvent	% Yield	Solvent Crystallization	M.P.(°C)	$[\alpha]_D$	Solvent Rotation	Ref.
Val-Ala-Ile-His-Pro-Phe-ONp Dihydrobromide				THF-Me-Eth	171–174			588
Z-Val-Gly-Leu-Gly-Ala-N^G-nitro-Arg-ONBzl	1+5 ONP	DMF	53	Ac-Aq	151–153	−17	Ac	646
Val-Gly-Leu-Gly-Ala-Arg Diacetate	3+3 DCCI	MeCl-Acn				−15	Aq	646
Z-Val-His-Pro-Phe-His-Leu-ONBzl	1+5 DCCI		65	EtAc-Pe	155–160	−16	Me	190
	3+3 A	EtAc	31			−55	Me	
						−27	DMF	
Val-His-Pro-D-Phe-His-Leu				Chf-Eth	150(dec)	−22	Me	190
Val-His-Pro-D-Phe-His-Leu-ONBzl						−18	DMF	190
Val-His-Pro-Phe-His-Leu-ONBzl				Chf-Eth	160(dec)	−45	Me	190
						−47	DMF	
Z(OMe)-Val-N^δ-Z-Orn-Leu-D-Phe-Pro-Gly	A	DMF	72	An-Eth	154–158	−39	DMF	302
Z(OMe)-Val-N^δ-Z-Orn-Leu-D-Phe-Pro-Gly-OEt				Di-Eth	125–129	−33	DMF	302
Z(OMe)-Val-N^δ-Z-Orn-Leu-D-Phe-Pro-Gly-ONp								302
Z-Val-Phe-OAc-Ser-Pro-Phe-N^G-nitro-Arg-ONBzl	ONP	An-Eth	57	An-Eth	103–109	−30	DMF	648
Z-Val-Phe-OAc-Thr-Pro-Phe-N^G-nitro-Arg-ONBzl	1+5 ONP	DMF	56		115–121	−33	Ac	648
Z-Val-Phe-Val-His-Pro-Phe-OMe	2+4 DCCI				170–175	−67	Me	499
Val-Phe-Val-His-Pro-Phe-OMe				Me-Eth	130–135	−54	Me	499
Val-Tyr-Ile-N^{im}-bzl-His-Pro-Ala-ONBzl	2+4 A	EtAc	43	DMF-Me-Ac-Aq	192–196	−53	Me	468
Z-Val-Tyr-Ile-N^{im}-bzl-His-Pro-Phe-OMe	1+5 DCCI	MeCl	66	Me-Eth	188–191	−21		405
Z-Val-Tyr-Ile-His-hydroxy-Pro-Phe-ONBzl	2+4 A	DMF-EtAc	92		162–166		DMF	606
Z-Val-Tyr-Ile-His-Pro-Phe-OBzl	2+4 DCCI		68		160–162	−27	DMF	531
Z-Val-Tyr-Ile-His-Pro-Phe-ONBzl	2+4 A	EtAc	91	Me-Eth		−60	Me	19

Compound	Method	Solvent	Yield (%)	Recrystn. solvent	M.p. (°C)	[α]	Solv.	Ref.
δ-Guanidinovaleroyl-Val-Tyr-Ile-His-Pro-Phe								207
ε-Tri-me-acap-Val-Tyr-Ile-His-Pro-Phe								207
ε-Tri-me-acap-Val-Tyr-Ile-His-Pro-Phe-OBzl					167–168 (dec)	−29	Ac	207
δ-Nitro-guanidinovaleroyl-Val-Tyr-Ile-His-Pro-Phe								207
δ-Nitro-guanidinovaleroyl-Val-Tyr-Ile-His-Pro-Phe-OBzl				DMF-Aq	180–182 (dec)	−34	Ac	207
Val-Tyr-Ile-His-Pro-Phe-OBzl					135–139 (dec)	−55	Me	531
Val-Tyr-Ile-His-hydroxy-Pro-Phe-ONBzl Dihydrobromide				Alc-Eth	174–179	+12	DMF	606
Val-Tyr-Ile-His-Pro-Phe-ONBzl Dihydrobromide	2+4 A		87	Me-EtAc	193–199	−36	Me	19
Z-Val-Tyr-Ile-His-Pro-Tyr-OMe				Alc-Eth	164–168	−25	DMF	606
Val-Tyr-Ile-His-Pro-Tyr-OMe Dihydrobromide	2+4 A		73		181–185	+13	DMF	606
Z-D-Val-D-Tyr-D-Val-D-His-D-Pro-D-Phe-OBu^t	2+4 A		90		164–165	+35	DMF	684
Z-Val-Tyr-Val-His-Pro-Phe-OBu^t			90		165–168	−36	DMF	552
Z-Val-Tyr-Val-His-Pro-Phe-OMe	3+3 CMCl	DMF			165–168	−36	DMF	563
					152–156	−55	Me	216
Val-Tyr-Val-His-Pro-Phe Amide			80		147–150	−54	Me	216
Val-Tyr-Val-His-Pro-Phe-OBu^t					150–153	−35	DMF	552
					150–153	−35	DMF	563
D-Val-D-Tyr-D-Val-D-His-D-Pro-D-Phe-OBu^t					149–154	+35	DMF	684

7

Heptapeptides

Only a few examples of coupling method studies appear among the heptapeptides of Table 7. These studies involve MCA *vs* A[166] ONP *vs* A and MCA,[539] and A (2+5) *vs* A (2+3).[753] Thin layer chromatography,[28,688,207,461,681,602] and countercurrent distribution[677,529,405,95,529,269,530,71,295,207,493] techniques received greater attention in heptapeptide purification. Column chromatography on carboxymethyl-cellulose,[646,748] and on acid washed alumina[691] was also employed. From the hepta- to larger peptides, examples of recrystallization rapidly diminish. Crystalline heptapeptides were successfully obtained from acetic acid,[776] acetonitrile,[737] ethanol,[19] acetic acid-ethanol,[62] acetic acid-water,[295,328] dimethylformamide-ether,[694] dimethylformamide-methanol,[776] dimethylformamide-water,[128,328] ether-ligroin,[403] ethanol-water,[602,279] formic acid-water,[166] hexamethylphosphotriamide-ether,[328] methanol-ethylacetate,[439] methanol-water,[128,28] pyridine-ligroin,[398] and tetrahydrofuranethyl acetate.[319]

Table 7 Heptapeptides

Compound	Method	Solvent	% Yield	Solvent Crystallization	M.P.(°C)	$[\alpha]_D$	Solvent Rotation	Ref.
Alanine								
Ala-Ala-Ala-Ala-Ala-Ala-Ala	2+5 MCA	DMF	57					759
Z-Ala-Ala-Ala-Ala-Ala-Ala	1+6 ONP	DMF-EtAc	68					759
Z-di-et-Ala-Gln-Asn-S-bzl-Cys-Pro-Leu-Gly Amide				Aq-Ac	229-231	-48	DMF	128
Di-Et-Ala-Gln-Asn-S-bzl-Cys-Pro-Leu-Gly Amide				EtAc-i-Pr				128
Z-Ala-Gly-Phe-Gly-Pro-Phe-N^G-nitro-Arg-ONBzl					112-118	-17	Ac	649
Ala-Gly-Phe-Ser-Pro-Phe-N^G-nitro-Arg-OMe Hydrobromide						-31	DMF	553
Ala-Leu-OBu^t-Tyr-Leu-Val-S-bzl-Cys-Gly				HMPA-Eth	239-244 (dec)	-44	HMPA	328
Z-Ala-Leu-OBu^t-Tyr-Leu-Val-S-bzl-Cys-Gly-OMe	3+4 A	DMF	99	DMF-Aq	258-261	-44	DMF	328
Z-Ala-Leu-Tyr-Leu-Val-S-bzl-Cys-Gly	A	DMF	65		244	-43	Ac	310
	1+6 ONP	DMF	80.5		285-290	-57	Fm	166
Z-Ala-Leu-Tyr-Leu-Val-S-bzl-Cys-Gly-OEt	MCA	DMF	69	Me	248-250	-47	Ac	310
Z-Ala-Leu-Tyr-Leu-Val-S-bzl-Cys-Gly-OMe	1+5 A	DMF		Fm-Aq	259-260	-54	Fm	166
				Ac-Aq	258-260	-59	Fm	328
Trt-Ala-Leu-OBu^t-Tyr-Leu-Val-S-bzl-Cys-Gly	3+3 A	DMF	82	DMF-Eth	257-258	-59	Fm	328
					210-220 (dec)	-34	DMF	328
Arginine								
Arg-Arg-Ala-Gln-β-OBu^t-Asp-Phe-Val-OBu^t Acetate Dihydrobromide				Me-Eth	174-175	-32	Me	727
						-27	Ac-Aq	

305

Table 7 Heptapeptides (continued)

Compound	Method	Solvent	% Yield	Solvent Crystallization	M.P. (°C)	$[\alpha]_D$	Solvent Rotation	Ref.
$N^\alpha,N^\delta,N^\omega$-tris-Z-Arg-Arg-Ala-Gln-$\beta$-OBu^t-Asp-Phe-Val-OBu^t Hydrobromide	1+6 ONP	DMF	95.5		189-190	-26	Ac-Aq	727
Arg-Arg-Pro-Val-N^ϵ-boc-Lys-Val-Tyr Amide Hydrochloride Hexahydrate						-68	Aq	644
N^G-Nitro-Z-Arg-N^G-nitro-Arg-Pro-Val-N^ϵ-boc-Lys-Val-Tyr Amide					213-215 (dec)	-28	DMF	644
Z-Arg-Arg-Pro-Val-(N^ϵ-boc)-Val-Tyr-Pro Dihydrochloride	1+6 2,4-DNPO							579
N^G-Nitro-Z-Arg-Leu-Gln-Gly-Leu-Val Amide		DMF		Aq-Alc	252 (dec)	-40	Ac	66
Arg-Pro-Gly-Phe-Ser-Phe-Arg Triacetate						-26	Ac	193
N^G-Nitro-Z-Arg-Pro-Gly-Phe-Ser-Phe-N^G-nitro-Arg-ONBzl	3+4 ONP	DMF			100 (dec)	-21	Me	193
Arg-Sar-Sar-Gly-Phe-Ser-Pro-Phe-Arg Diacetate Pentahydrate						-17 -22 -35	DMF Ac-Aq Aq	752
N^G-Nitro-Arg-Val-Ala-Ile-His-Pro-Phe-ONp	1+6 MCA	DMF	62.7	Me-Eth	149-158			588
N^G-Nitro-Z-Arg-Val-Ala-Ile-His-Pro-Phe-ONp				Me-EtAc	203-206			588
D-Arg-Val-Tyr-Ile-His-Pro-Phe								677
Arg-Val-Tyr-Ile-His-Pro-Phe-OBzl								677
Arg-Val-Tyr-Ile-His-Pro-Phe Succinate Salt				Aq-Ac	215-224			20
Z-nitro-Arg-Val-Tyr-Ile-His-Pro-Phe-ONBzl	1+6 MCA	THF-DMF		Alc-Aq	202-206	-59	Me	19
D-Homo-Arg-Val-Tyr-Ile-His-Pro-Phe						-31	Py	677
Homo-Arg-Val-Tyr-Ile-His-Pro-Phe-OBzl								677

Compound	Method	Solvent	Yield (%)	Recryst. solvent	M.p. (°C)	[α]	Solvent	Ref.
N^G-Nitro-Arg-Val-Tyr-Ile-His-Pro-Phe								529
N^G-Nitro-D-Arg-Val-Tyr-Ile-His-Pro-Phe								529
N^G-Nitro-Arg-Val-Tyr-Ile-His-Pro-Phe-OBzl								677
N^G-Nitro-D-Arg-Val-Tyr-Ile-His-Pro-Phe-OBzl								677
N^G-Nitro-Arg-Val-Tyr-Ile-His-Pro-Phe-ONBzl Dihydrobromide				Alc-EtAc	163-164 / 166-168			19
N^G-Nitro-Z-Arg-Val-Tyr-Ile-N^{im}-bzl-His-Pro-Phe-OMe	DCCI	DMF	98		220-221			405
N^G-Nitro-Z-Arg-Val-Tyr-Ile-His-Pro-Phe-OBzl	1+6 MCA		47		205-207 (dec)	-35	Ac	677
N^G-Nitro-Z-D-Arg-Val-Tyr-Ile-His-Pro-Phe-OBzl	1+6 MCA		65		148-150 (dec)	-24	Ac	677
N^G-Nitro-Z-homo-Arg-Val-Tyr-Ile-His-Pro-Phe-OBzl	MCA	DMF	40	i-Pr-Aq	175-177	-34	Ac	677
N^G-Nitro-Z-D-homo-Arg-Val-Tyr-Ile-His-Pro-Phe-OBzl	1+6 MCA	DMF	45	Me-Eth	135-140 (dec)	-25	Ac	677
N^G-Nitro-Z-Arg-Val-Tyr-Ile-His-Pro-Tyr-OMe				Me-Eth	174-179	-28	DMF	606
N^G-Nitro-Z-Arg-Val-Tyr-Ile-His-Pro-Tyr-OMe	1+6 MCA	DMF	89.9	Me-Eth	203-205	-19	DMF	606
Arg-Val-Tyr-Val-His-Pro-Phe					200 (dec)			95
Arg-Val-Tyr-Val-His-Pro-Phe-OMe								502
Z-Arg-Val-Tyr-Val-His-Pro-Phe-OMe	1+6 DCCI	DMF		Alc-Eth				95
N^G-Nitro-Arg-Val-Tyr-Val-His-Pro-Phe						-3.2	Ac	551
N^G-Nitro-Arg-Val-Tyr-Val-His-Pro-Phe Amide						-52	Me	216
N^G-Nitro-Z-Arg-Val-Tyr-Val-His-Pro-Phe Amide	1+6 DCCI		90		154-157			216
N^G-Nitro-Z-Arg-Val-Tyr-Val-His-Pro-Phe-OMe	1+6 DCCI		20		151-154	-57	Me	502
N^G-Nitro-boc-Arg-Val-Tyr-Val-His-Pro-Phe-OBu^t	DCCI	DMF-Acn	75	Alc-Eth	187-188	-36	DMF	551

Table 7 Heptapeptides (continued)

Compound	Method	Solvent	% Yield	Solvent Crystallization	M.P. (°C)	$[\alpha]_D$	Solvent Rotation	Ref.
Asn-Ala-Phe-Ile-Gly-Leu-Ala Amide Trifluoroacetate Hydrate					270	-57	TFA	563
Asn-Ala-Phe-Ile-Gly-Leu-Met Amide Ditrifluoroacetate					215-240	-22	DMF	563
Boc-Asn-Ala-α-hydrazino-β-phenyl-Pro-Ile-Gly-Leu-Met Amide				DMF-Eth	225-227	-42	DMF	185
Asn-Arg-Val-Tyr-Ile-His-Pro-Phe					200-203 (dec)	-30	Ac	677
Z-Asn-N^G-nitro-Arg-Val-Tyr-Ile-His-Pro-Phe-OBzl	1+6 ONP	DMF	56			-31	DMF	677
Z-Asn-Ser-Gly-Pro-Tyr-N^ϵ-tos-Lys-Met	3+4 MCA	DMF	31		179-183	-31	Ac	269
Asp-Ala-Phe-Ile-Gly-Leu-Ala Amide Hydrochloride Hydrate					212-215	-34	Ac	563
Asp-Ala-Phe-Ile-Gly-Leu-Met Amide					214-220	-19	TFA	395
Asp-Ala-Phe-Ile-Gly-Leu-Met Amide Trifluoroacetate					217-220	-16	DMF	563
β-OBzl-Z-Asp-Ala-Phe-Ile-Gly-Leu-Met Amide	1+6 DCCI	DMF		Ac-Alc	210-215			89
β-OBu^t-boc-Asp-Ala-Phe-Ile-Gly-Leu-Met Amide	1+6 MCA		64		237-239 (dec)	-42	Ac	395
Asp-Ala-Phe-Leu-Gly-Leu-Met Amide Trifluoroacetate					233-243	-77	TFA	563
Asp-Ala-Phe-Leu-Gly-Leu-Met Amide					196-200	-25	DMF	563
β-OBu^t-boc-Asp-Ser-Gly-Pro-Tyr-N^G-boc-Lys-Met-OMe	DCCI	DMF-Acn	82	EtAc-Eth	123-130	-48	Me	573
β-OBu^t-Z-Asp-Ser-Thr-Ser-Ala-Ala-OBu^t	1+6 ONP	Py	64	Py-Pe	213	-15	DMF	398
Boc-β-OBzl-Asp-OBzl-(Ser)$_2$-Thr-OBzl-Ser-(Ala)$_2$-OBzl			84	EtAc-He	218-219			356a

β-OBu^t-Asp-OBu^t-Tyr-OBu^t-Ser-N$^\epsilon$-boc-Lys-OBu^t-Tyr-Leu-β-OBu^t-Asp	1+6 OSU	DMF	93	Acn	198–200	+3.5	Ac-Aq	735
β-OBu^t-Z-Asp-OBu^t-Tyr-OBu^t-Ser-N$^\epsilon$-boc-Lys-OBu^t-Tyr-Leu-β-OBu^t-Asp	1+6 OSU	Di-DMF	82		203–205	−17	Alc	737
β-OBu^t-Z-Asp-OBu^t-Tyr-OBu^t-Ser-N$^\epsilon$-boc-Lys-Tyr-Leu-β-OBu^t-Asp						−19	Alc	730
Citrullene								
Z-D-Cit-Val-Tyr-Ile-His-Pro-Phe-OBzl					185–187 (dec)	−27	Ac	207
Z-Cit-Val-Tyr-Ile-His-Pro-Phe-OBzl	1+6 ONP	DMF-Acn	46		221–222 (dec)	−33	Ac	530
Cit-Val-Tyr-Ile-His-Pro-Phe					170–175 (dec)			530
Cit-Val-Tyr-Ile-His-Pro-Phe-OBzl								529
Cysteine								
S-Bz-N-Nps-Cys-S-trt-Cys-Ala-Gly-Val-S-bz-Cys-Ser-OMe	1+6 DCCI	DMF	75		221 (dec)	−25	DMF	776
Z-Cys-S-bzh-Cys-Ala-Gly-Val-Cys-Ser-OMe				Me	225–228 (dec)	−26	DMF	776
S-S′,N-Z-hemi-Cys-S-bzh-Cys-Ala-Gly-Val-hemi-Cys-Ser-OMe				Ac	235–240 (dec)	+8.5	DMF	776
N-Boc-Cys-S-bzh-Cys-Ala-Gly-Val-Cys-Ser-OMe					223 (dec)	−27	DMF	776
S-S′,N-Boc-hemi-Cys-S-bzh-Cys-Ala-Gly-Val-hemi-Cys-Ser-OMe					218 (dec)	+10	DMF	776
S-Chloromercuri-N-Z-Cys-S-bzh-Cys-Ala-Gly-Val-S-chloromercuri-Cys-Ser-OMe					210–215 (dec)			776
S-Chloromercuri-N-boc-Cys-S-bzh-Cys-Ala-Gly-Val-S-chloromercuri-Cys-Ser-OMe					192 (dec)			776
S-S′,Hemi-Cys-S-bzh-Cys-Ala-Gly-Val-hemi-Cys-Ser-OMe Hydrochloride					205–208 (dec)	+10	Me	776

Table 7   Heptapeptides (continued)

Compound	Method	Solvent	% Yield	Solvent Crystallization	M.P.(°C)	[α]D	Solvent Rotation	Ref.
S-S', Hemi-Cys-S-trt-Cys-Ala-Gly-Val-hemi-Cys-Ser-OMe Hydrochloride					210 (dec)	+4.2	DMF	776
N-Nps-Cys-S-trt-Cys-Ala-Gly-Val-Cys-Ser-OMe				DMF-Me	195-198 (dec)	-41	DMF	776
S-S',N-Nps-hemi-Cys-S-trt-Cys-Ala-Gly-Val-hemi-Cys-Ser-OMe				DMF-Me	215-218 (dec)	-71	DMF	776
S-Trt-N-Z-Cys-S-bzh-Cys-Ala-Gly-Val-S-trt-Cys-Ser-OMe				Ac	228-228.5 (dec)	-18	DMF	776
S-Trt-N-boc-Cys-S-bzh-Cys-Ala-Gly-Val-S-trt-Cys-Ser-OMe				Ac	225-226	-18	DMF	776
S-Bzl-N-Z-Cys-penta-Gly-S-bzl-Cys-OBzl	4+3 A	Chf	50	Aq-Alc	225-226 (dec)	-32	Aq-Py	279
Cys-penta-Gly-Cys						-25	Ac	279
Dehydro-Cys-penta-Gly-Cys								279
S,S'-N-Z-hemi-Cys-Val-Ala-Gly-Val-hemi-Cys-Gly-OBzl	EDCI	DMF-MeCl	55	DMF-Eth	261-263	-26	DMF	227
Glutamine								
Gln-Ala-Phe-Ile-Gly-Leu-Met Amide					245-248	-68	TFA	563
Gln-Ala-Phe-Leu-Gly-Leu-Met Amide					214-220	-62	TFA	563
γ-OBzl-Z-Glu-Ala-Leu-Tyr-Leu-Val-S-bzl-Cys Amide	1+6 ONP	DMF	97	Ac-Aq	254-260		Ac	307
Pyro-Glu-Ala-Phe-Leu-Gly-Leu-Met Amide Hydrate					279-281	-54	Ac	563
Z-Glu-β-OBu^t-Asp-Phe-Val-Glu-Trp-Leu-OMe	1+6 OTCP	DMF	43	Aq-Me	239-240	-32	DMF	260
γ-OBu^t-Z-Glu-γ-OBu^t-Glu-γ-OBu^t-Glu-γ-OBu^t-Glu-Ala-Tyr-Gly-OMe					222-223	-19	DMF	28

Compound	Method	Solvent	Yield (%)	Recrystn. solvent	m.p. (°C)	[α]	Solvent	Ref.
γ-OBu^t-Z-Glu-γ-OBu^t-Glu-γ-OBu^t-Glu-γ-OBu^t-Glu-Ala-Tyr-Gly-OMe	1+6 OTCP	DMF	92		220–221 (dec)	−21	DMF	423
γ-OBu^t-boc-Glu-γ-OBu^t-Glu-γ-OBu^t-Glu-γ-OBu^t-Glu-Ala-Tyr-Gly						−19	DMF	28
γ-OBu^t-boc-Glu-γ-OBu^t-Glu-γ-OBu^t-Glu-γ-OBu^t-Glu-Ala-Tyr-Gly-OMe	1+6 OTCP		91	Aq-Me	230–232	−18	DMF	28
γ-OBu^t-Glu-γ-OBu^t-Glu-γ-OBu^t-Glu-γ-OBu^t-Glu-Ala-Tyr-Gly-OMe Acetate Hydrate					235–237 (dec)	−19	DMF	423
Z(OMe)-γ-hexa-Glu-Gln-octa-OBzl	2+5 DCCI	DMF	49	DMF-Eth	189–191			694
Pyro-Glu-Pro-Ser-N^ε-boc-Lys-Asn-Ala-Phe						−41	Me	392
Pyro-Glu-Pro-Ser-N^ε-boc-Lys-Asn-Ala-Phe-OMe								392
Pyro-Glu-Pro-Ser-N^ε-boc-Lys-γ-OBu^t-Glu-Ala-Phe	4+3 DCCI		70		165–167	−52	Me	395
Pyro-Glu-Pro-Ser-N^ε-boc-Lys-γ-OBu^t-Glu-Ala-Phe-OMe								395
Glycine								
Boc-Gly-Ala-Phe-Ile-Gly-Leu-Met Amide	3+4 A		83		253–255	−27	DMF	394
Gly-Ala-Phe-Ile-Gly-Leu-Met Amide Hydrochloride					240–260	−45	Ac	394
Gly-Ala-Phe-Ile-Gly-Leu-Met Amide Trifluoroacetate					230–250	−41	Ac	563
Boc-Gly-Ala-Phe-Leu-Gly-Leu-Met	3+4 A		80		227–229	−32	DMF	394
Gly-Ala-Phe-Leu-Gly-Leu-Met Amide Hydrochloride					240–280	−46	Ac	394
					240–285	−46	Ac	563
Boc-Gly-Ala-Phe-Val-Gly-Leu-Met Amide	3+4 A		87		255–258	−28	DMF	394
Gly-Ala-Phe-Val-Gly-Leu-Met Amide					240–246	−45	Ac	394
					240–246	−45	Ac	563
Z-Gly-Glu-Asp-S-bzl-Cys-Pro-Leu-Gly Amide	1+6 ONP	DMF	80		202–204	−50	DMF	126
Gly-Glu-Asp-S-bzl-Cys-Pro-Leu-Gly Amide					214–216	−51	DMF	126

Table 7 Heptapeptides (continued)

Compound	Method	Solvent	% Yield	Solvent Crystallization	M.P.(°C)	$[\alpha]_D$	Solvent Rotation	Ref.
Z-Gly-Gly-Gly-Gly-Gly-Gly-N^G-nitro-Arg-OMe	3+4 ONP	DMF	61	Aq	231–234			65
Z-Gly-Gly-Phe-OAc-Ser-Pro-Phe-N^ω-nitro-Arg-ONBzl	2+5 ONP	DMF	67	Ac-Aq	104–112	0.0	Ac	649
Gly-Lys-Lys-Arg-Arg-Pro-Val-OMe Dihydrochloride				Me	170			71
N-Trt-Gly-N^ϵ-Z-Lys-N^ϵ-Z-Lys-Arg-Arg-Pro-Val-OMe	3+4 DCCI	DMF	51					71
N-Trt-Gly-Lys-Lys-Arg-Arg-Pro-Val-OMe Dihydrochloride					150 (dec)			71
Z(NO$_2$)-Gly-Phe-Phe-Tyr-Thr-Pro-N^ϵ-Z(NO$_2$)-Lys-ONBzl	4+3 A	THF		EtAc-Alc	122–124			600
Gly-Phe-Phe-Tyr-Thr-Pro-Lys Acetate				Alc	185–188			600
Histidine								
Boc-His-Ser-Gln-Thr-Phe-Thr-Ser Hydrazide					190.5	−27	Ac-Aq	731
Isoleucine								
Z-Ile-β-Ala-Asn-S-bzl-Cys-Pro-Leu-Gly Amide	1+6 ONP	DMF			231–232	−67	DMF	397
Z-Ile-Gln-Asn-S-bzl-Cys-Pro-Cit-Gly Amide	1+6 ONP	DMF	64	Ac-Alc	229–232 235 (dec)			61
Z-Ile-Gln-Asn-S-bzl-Cys-Pro-Leu-Gly Amide	1+6 ONP	DMF	68	Aq-Ac	227–229	−46	DMF	295
	2+5 ONP	DMF	74		230–231.5	−48	DMF	628
Z-Ile-Gln-Asn-S-Eac-Cys-Pro-Leu-Gly Amide					229	−77 −40	Ac-Aq DMF	188
Z-Ile-Gln-Asn-Se-Bzl-Cys-Pro-Leu-Gly Amide	1+6 ONP	DMF		THF-Aq	248–250	−46	DMF	687

Compound	Method	Solvent	Yield (%)	Recryst.	m.p. (°C)	$[\alpha]$	Solvent	
Ile-Gln-Asn-S-bzl-Cys-Pro-Leu-Gly Amide				DMF-EtAc				295
Ile-Gln-Asn-S-Eac-Cys-Pro-Leu-Gly Amide	1+6 ONP		83					188
Z-Ile-Gln-Asn-S-bzl-Cys-Pro-N^δ-Pht-Orn-Gly Amide	1+6 OTCP		54		230–232	−56	Ac	63
Z-Ile-Gln-Asn-S-bzl-Cys-Pro-N^δ-tos-Orn-Gly Amide					222–225	−36	DMF	253
Ile-Gln-Asn-S-bzl-Cys-Pro-N^δ-tos-Orn-Gly Amide					163–168	−44	Ac-Aq	253
Z-Ile-Gln-Asp-S-bzl-Cys-Pro-Ala-Gly Amide	1+6 ONP	DMF			233–234	−42	DMF	690
Z-Ile-Gln-Val-S-bzl-Cys-Pro-Leu-Gly Amide	1+6 ONP	DMF			228–231 (dec)	−55	DMF	688
Z-Ile-Glu-Asp-S-bzl-Cys-D-Pro-Leu-Gly Amide	ONP	DMF	85		214–217	−30	DMF	136
Z-Ile-Gly-Asp-S-bzl-Cys-Pro-Leu-Gly Amide	1+6 ONP	DMF	80		213–215	−52	DMF	126
Ile-Gly-Asp-Cys-Pro-Leu-Gly Amide					181–182	−57	DMF	126
Leucine								
Boc-nor-Leu-Ala-Phe-Ile-Gly-Leu-Met Amide	1+6 MCA		89.5		240–275	−30	DMF	393
Nor-Leu-Ala-Phe-Ile-Gly-Leu-Met Amide Hydrochloride						−20	DMF	393
Z-Leu-Val-S-bzl-Cys-Gly-γ-OMe-Glu-N^G-nitro-Arg-Gly	4+3 ONP	DMF		DMF-Di-Aq	198–202	−28	DMF	351
N^α-Z-ϵ-tri-me-amine-nor-Leu-Val-Tyr-Ile-His-Pro-Phe-OBzl	1+6 CDI		35	Me-Eth	198–200	−25	Ac	207
Lysine								
N^ϵ-Ac-boc-Lys-Ala-Phe-Ile-Gly-Leu-Met Amide	1+6 ONP	DMF	48		239–260	−44	Ac	393
N^α-Ac-Lys-Ala-Phe-Ile-Gly-Leu-Met Amide					225–245	−42	Ac	393
N^ϵ-Ac-Lys-Ala-Phe-Ile-Gly-Leu-Met Amide					230	−27	Ac	393
N^ϵ-N^α-di-Ac-Lys-Ala-Phe-Ile-Gly-Leu-Met Amide					260–266	−44	Ac	393

Table 7 Heptapeptides (continued)

Compound	Method	Solvent	% Yield	Solvent Crystallization	M.P.(°C)	$[\alpha]_D$	Solvent Rotation	Ref.
N^ϵ-Boc-N^α-ac-Lys-Ala-Phe-Ile-Gly-Leu-Met Amide	1+6 A		61.5		249-254	-40	Ac	393
N^ϵ-N^α-di-Boc-Lys-Ala-Phe-Ile-Gly-Leu-Met Amide	1+6 ONP	DMF	93		234-235	-37	Ac	393
Lys-Ala-Phe-Ile-Gly-Leu-Met Amide	1+6 MCA	THF	87	Ac-Eth	232-234	-59	Aq	393
N^ϵ-Tos-Z-Lys-N^G-nitro-Arg-N^G-nitro-Arg-Pro-Val-N^ϵ-tos-Lys-Val-OMe						-38	Ac	560
N^ϵ-Tos-Lys-N^G-nitro-Arg-N^G-nitro-Arg-Val-N^ϵ-tos-Lys-Val-OMe Hydrobromide				Alc-Eth		-37 / -21	Alc / DMF	560
N^α-N^β-bis-Boc-Lys-Asn-Ala-α-hydrazine-β-phenyl-propionyl-Ile-Gly-Leu-Met Amide	ONP	DMF		DMF-Eth	244-246	-31	DMF	185
N^β-[Lys-Asn-Ala-Phe-Ile]-hydrazino-ac-Leu-Met Amide Acetate Hydrate								443
N^ϵ-Z-N^α-boc-Lys-Gly-Phe-OAc-Ser-Pro-Phe-N^G-nitro-Arg-ONBzl Hydrate	1+6 ONP	DMF	71		98-104	-29	DMF	650
N^ϵ-Boc-N^α-Z-Lys-Pro-Val-Gly-N^ϵ-boc-Lys-N^G-nitro-Arg-N^G-nitro-Arg Amide	5+2 A	THF	65.6	Bu	133-135	-40	Me	461
N^ϵ-Boc-Lys-Pro-Val-Gly-N^ϵ-boc-Lys-Arg-Arg Amide Triacetate	4+3 WRK					-44	Ac-Aq	461
N^ϵ-Boc-N^α-Z-Lys-Pro-Val-Gly-N^ϵ-boc-Lys-N^ϵ-boc-Lys-N^G-tos-Arg Amide	4+3 WRK		71		172-174	-38	Me	492
Boc-Lys-Pro-Val-Gly-N^ϵ-boc-Lys-boc-Lys-tos-Arg Amide					128-134	-32	Me	492
N^ϵ-Tos-N^α-boc-Lys-Pro-Val-Gly-N^ϵ-tos-Lys-N^ϵ-tos-Lys-N^G-tos-Arg-OBzl	4+3 WRK		78		120-125	-33	Me	369
	4+3 DCCI		63			-32	Me	373

314

	Method	Solvent	Yield	Recryst.	m.p.	$[\alpha]$	Solvent	Ref.
N^ϵ-Tos-Lys-Pro-Val-Gly-N^ϵ-tos-Lys-N^ϵ-tos-Lys-N^G-tos-Arg					118–122			369
N^ϵ-Tos-Lys-Pro-Val-Gly-N^ϵ-tos-Lys-N^ϵ-tos-Lys-N^G-tos-Arg-OBzl					100–105	−28	Me	373
N^ϵ-Z-N^α-boc-Lys-Val-Gly-Leu-Gly-Ala-N^G-nitro-Arg-ONBzl	1+6 ONP	DMF	86	Me-Eth	175			646
Lys-Val-Gly-Leu-Gly-Ala-Arg Triacetate						−26	Aq	646
N^ϵ-N^α-di-Z-Lys-Val-Tyr-Ile-His-Pro-Phe-OBzl	1+6 ONP	DMF	75		156–158 (dec)	−32	Ac	530
N^ϵ-N^α-di-Z-D-Lys-Val-Tyr-Ile-His-Pro-Phe-OBzl	1+6 ONP	DMF	65		149–150	−24	Ac	530
Lys-Val-Tyr-Ile-His-Pro-Phe								530
D-Lys-Val-Tyr-Ile-His-Pro-Phe								530
Ornithine								
N^δ-Pht-N^α-Z-Orn-Arg-Ala-Gln-Asp-β-OBu^t-Phe-Val-OBu^t Hydrobromide	1+6 ONP	DMF	90	DMF-Aq	204–205	−21	DMF-Ac	727
N^δ-Pht-Orn-Arg-Ala-Gln-Asp-β-OBu^t-Phe-Val-OBu^t Acetate Hydrobromide					145–170 (dec)			727
N^δ-Pht-Orn-Arg-Ala-Gln-Asp-β-OBu^t-Phe-Val-OBu^t Hydrobromide				Alc-Eth	175–180 (dec)			727
N^δ-Boc-N^α-Z-Orn-Pro-Val-N^ϵ-boc-Lys-Val-Tyr-Pro-OBu^t	1+6 ONP	DMF	90		142–145	−38	DMF	664
N^δ,N^α-di-Z-D-Orn-Val-Tyr-Ile-His-Pro-Phe OBzl					142–146 (dec)	−90	Me	207
N^δ,N^α-di-Z-Orn-Val-Tyr-Ile-His-Pro-Phe-OBzl	1+6 ONP	DMF-Acn	48			−24	Ac	530
Orn-Val-Tyr-Ile-His-Pro-Phe								530
D-Orn-Val-Tyr-Ile-His-Pro-Phe Acetate					198–200 (dec)	−296	Ac	207
Phenylalanine								
Phe-Arg-Trp-Gly-N^ϵ-for-Lys-Pro-Val Amide	3+4 DCCI	DMF	36			−35	Aq	748

315

Table 7 Heptapeptides (continued)

Compound	Method	Solvent	% Yield	Solvent Crystallization	M.P.(°C)	$[\alpha]_D$	Solvent Rotation	Ref.
Phe-Arg-Trp-Gly-Lys-Pro-Val Amide						-29	Aq	748
N-Ac-Phe-Arg-Trp-Gly-Ser-Pro-Pro						-42	Aq	748
Phe-Arg-Trp-Gly-Ser-Pro-Pro						-64	Aq	748
Z-Phe-Gln-Asn-S-bzl-Cys-Pro-Cit-Gly Amide	1+6 ONP	Py				-39	DMF	61
Z-Phe-Gln-Asn-S-bzl-Cys-Pro-N^ϵ-tos-Lys-Gly Amide				Ac-Alc	205		DMF	62
Z-Phe-$[^{14}C]$-Gln-Asn-S-bzl-Cys-Pro-N^ϵ-tos-Lys-Gly Amide	1+6 WRK	Acn	87		182-188			671
Z-Phe-Gln-Asn-S-bzl-Cys-Pro-N^ϵ-tos-Lys-Gly Amide Hydrate	1+6 MCA	Chf-DMF	80-85	Aq-DMF	208-210	-40	DMF	765
Phe-Gln-Asn-S-bzl-Cys-Pro-N^ϵ-tos-Lys-Gly Amide					130-135			765
Phe-$[^{14}C]$-Gln-Asn-S-bzl-Cys-Pro-N^ϵ-tos-Lys-Gly Amide			100					671
Z-Gln-Asn-S-bzl-Cys-Pro-N^δ-Pht-Orn-Gly Amide	1+6 ONP				214-220	-47	Ac	63
Z-Phe-Glu-Asp-S-bzl-Cys-Pro-Ala-Gly Amide	1+6 ONP				205	-50	DMF	690
Z(OMe)-D-Phe-D-Leu-δ-Z-Orn-Val-N^δ-Z-D-Orn-Pro-ONp								301
Z-Phe-Phe-OBu^t-Tyr-OBu^t-Thr-Pro-N^G-boc-Lys-Ala-OBu^t	A	DMF-THF	85	Eth-Pe	119-122	-46	Me	403
Z-Phe-Phe-OBu^t-Tyr-OBu^t-Thr-Pro-N^ϵ-tos-Lys-Ala-OBu^t				Eth-Pe	133-135	-32	DMF	403
Z-Phe-Phe-Tyr-Thr-Pro-N^ϵ-boc-Lys-Ala-OBu^t	1+6 ONP	DMF	75		210-211	-45	DMF	536
Z-Phe-Tyr-Thr-Pro-Lys-Ala-OMe	1+6 ONP	DMF	72		172-175	-37	DMF	308
Z-Phe-Tyr-Thr-Pro-ϵ-tos-Lys-Ala	1+6 ONP	EtAc	69	Di-Aq	172-176	-37	DMF	539
	A		74	DMF-EtAc-Alc	164-170	-37	DMF	
	MCA		58	Di-Aq	173-176		DMF	
Z-Phe-Phe-Tyr-Thr-Pro-N^ϵ-tos-Lys-Ala-OBu^t	1+6 ONP	DMF	90		210-212	-45	DMF	542

Compound	Method	Solvent	Yield (%)	Recryst.	M.p. (°C)	$[\alpha]$	Solv.	Ref.
Z-Phe-Phe-Tyr-Thr-Pro-N^ϵ-tos-Lys-Ala-OMe	4+3 DCCI	DMF-THF Acn	44	THF-EtAc	182–184	–43	DMF	351
Phe-Phe-Tyr-Thr-Pro-N^ϵ-boc-Lys-Ala-OBu^t	3+4 DCCI		21	EtAc-Me	199–203			761a 536 308
Phe-Phe-Tyr-Thr-Pro-Lys-Ala-OMe Hydrochloride Hydrate								
Phe-Phe-Tyr-Thr-Pro-N^ϵ-tos-Lys-Ala	1+6 OSU		73	Aq-Me	152–154	–48	DMF	539
Z-Phe-Phe-Tyr-Thr-Pro-Lys-OBu^t-Thr-OBu^t					155–158	–45	Alc	408

Proline

Compound	Method	Solvent	Yield (%)	Recryst.	M.p. (°C)	$[\alpha]$	Solv.	Ref.
Z-Pro-β-Ala-Phe-β-Ala-Pro-Phe-N^G-nitro-Arg-ONBzl	1+6 ONP	DMF	67	An-Eth	106–124	–87	Ac	651
Z-Pro-β-Ala-Phe-OAc-Ser-Pro-Phe-N^G-nitro-Arg-ONBzl	1+6 ONP	DMF	66	An-Eth	159–164	–40	Ac	651
Z-Pro-Ala-Phe-Ser-Pro-Phe-N^G-nitro-Arg-ONBzl	2+5 A		71			–42	DMF	565
Pro-Ala-Phe-Ser-Pro-Phe-N^G-nitro-Arg-ONBzl Hydrobromide								565
Z-Pro-Gly-Phe-β-Ala-Pro-Phe-N^ω-nitro-Arg-ONBzl Hydrate	2+5 ONP	DMF	51	Ac-Aq	108–114	–31	Ac	651
Z-Pro-Gly-Phe-Gly-Pro-Phe-N^G-nitro-Arg-OMe	2+5 ONP	DMF	82	Me-Eth	126–134			65
Z-Pro-Gly-Phe-Leu-Pro-Phe-N^G-nitro-Arg-ONBzl	2+5 ONP	DMF			109–112	–12	Ac	653
Z-Pro-Gly-Phe-OAc-Ser-Pro-p-fluoro-Phe-N^G-nitro-Arg-OMe			78		195–197			438
Z-Pro-Gly-Phe-OAc-Ser-Pro-p-fluoro-D-Phe-N^G-nitro-Arg-OMe			51		120–125			438
Z-Pro-Gly-Phe-OAc-Ser-Gly-Phe-N^G-nitro-Arg-OMe	2+5 ONP	DMF	42	Alc	168–170			456
Z-Pro-Gly-Phe-OAc-Ser-Pro-Phe-N^G-nitro-Arg-OMe	2+5 ONP	DMF	83	Me-EtAc-Eth	193–196			456
Z-Pro-Gly-Phe-OAc-Ser-Pro-D-Phe-N^G-nitro-Arg-OMe	1+6 ONP	DMF	50	Me-EtAc-Eth	121–126			438

Table 7 Heptapeptides (continued)

Compound	Method	Solvent	% Yield	Solvent Crystallization	M.P.(°C)	[α]$_D$	Solvent Rotation	Ref.
Z-Pro-Gly-Phe-OAc-Ser-Pro-Phe-N^G-nitro-Arg-ONBzl	2+5 ONP	DMF	72	Ac-Aq	119-125	-48	Ac	652
Z-Pro-Gly-Phe-Ser-Pro-Phe-N^G-nitro-Arg-OMe	2+5 DCCI	THF-DMF	75.2	Alc-Eth	196-197	-60	Ac	558
						-51	DMF	439
Z-Pro-Gly-Phe-Ser-Pro-Phe-N^G-nitro-Arg-OMe Pro-Gly-Phe-Ser-Pro-Phe-N^G-nitro-Arg-OMe	1+6 ONP	DMF	81	Me-EtAc	196-197	-65	DMF	558
Z-Pro-Gly-Phe-OAc-Ser-Pro-Phe-Cit-OMe	2+5 ONP	DMF	86	Alc	214-216	-35	DMF	456
Z-Pro-Gly-Phe-OAc-Ser-Pro-Phe-His-OMe	2+5 ONP	DMF	68	Me-Aq	210-212	-59	DMF	123
Z-Pro-Gly-Phe-OAc-Thr-Pro-Phe-N^G-nitro-Arg-ONBzl	2+5 ONP	DMF	62		132-134	-55	DMF	123
			77		118-122	-40	Ac	653
Z-Pro-Ile-Phe-OAc-Ser-Pro-Phe-N^ω-nitro-Arg-ONBzl Monohydrate	1+6 ONP		63	An-Eth	125-134	-19	DMF	648
Z-Pro-Ile-Phe-OAc-Thr-Pro-Phe-N^G-nitro-Arg-ONBzl Hydrate	1+6 ONP		69	An-Eth	108-115	-43	DMF	648
Z-Pro-Leu-Phe-OAc-Ser-Pro-Phe-N^G-nitro-Arg-ONBzl	1+6 ONP	DMF	61	Ac-Aq	106-110	-48	Ac	652
Z-Pro-Leu-Phe-OAc-Thr-Pro-Phe-N^ω-nitro-Arg-ONBzl Hydrate	1+6 ONP		59	Ac-Aq	104-115	-41	Ac	648
Z-Pro-Pro-Gly-Phe-OAc-Ser-Pro-N^G-nitro-Arg-OMe	1+6 ONP			Me-Aq	131-135			456
N^γ,N^α-di-Z-Dbu-Pro-Pro-Gly-Phe-Ser-Pro-Phe-N^γ-tos-Dbu						-56	DMF	683
N^γ,N^α-di-Z-Dbu-Pro-Pro-Gly-Phe-Ser-Pro-Phe-N^γ-tos-Dbu-OMe						-54	DMF	683
Z-D-Pro-D-Pro-Gly-D-Phe-D-Ser-D-Pro-D-Phe-OMe	3+4 CDI	THF	52			+54		681
Z-D-Pro-D-Pro-Gly-D-Phe-D-Ser-D-Pro-D-Phe-OMe	2+5 CDI	DMF	80			+53		681

Compound								
Dbu-Pro-Pro-Gly-Phe-Ser-Pro-Phe-Dbu								683
Dbu-Pro-Pro-Gly-Phe-Ser-Pro-Phe-Dbu Trihydrochloride								683
D-Pro-D-Pro-Gly-D-Phe-D-Ser-D-Pro				Alc-Aq	248–250	−87	Ac-Aq	681
Z-Pro-Pro-Val-Gln-Ala-Ala-Tyr-OMe	1+6 ONP	DMF	74			−67	DMF	98
Z-Pro-Ser-Phe-Gly-Pro-Phe-N^G-nitro-Arg-OMe	2+5 A		65			−43	DMF	565
Pro-Ser-Phe-Gly-Pro-Phe-Arg-OMe Hydrobromide				An-Eth	104–109	−26	DMF	565
Z-Pro-Val-Phe-OAc-Ser-Pro-Phe-N^G-nitro-Arg-ONBzl	1+6 ONP		65	Ac-Aq	106–112	−36	Ac	648
Z-Pro-Val-Phe-OAc-Thr-Pro-Phe-N^G-nitro-Arg-ONBzl Dihydrate	1+6 ONP		77					648
Sarcosine								
Z-Sar-Gly-Phe-Gly-Pro-Phe-N^G-nitro-Arg-ONBzl Hemihydrate	1+6 ONP	DMF	97	Ac-Aq	103–108	−65	Ac	649
Z-Sar-Gly-Phe-OAc-Ser-Pro-Phe-N^G-nitro-Arg-OMe				Aq-Alc	209–210	−10	DMF	752
Z-Sar-Gly-Phe-OAc-Ser-Ser-Phe-N^G-nitro-Arg-OMe	2+5 ONP	DMF	66	Alc-Eth	122–129		DMF	752
Serine								
OBzl-N-boc-Ser-Gln-Gly-Thr-Phe-Thr-OBzl-Ser-Z-Hydrazide	3+4 MCA		71		220	−22	Ac-Aq	731
OBzl-Ser-Gln-Gly-Thr-Phe-Thr-OBzl-Ser-Z-Hydrazide					205	−18	Ac-Aq	731
Ser-Gly-Ala-Gly-Ala-Gly-Tyr	3+4 A		19		180–190			540
Z-Ser-Gly-Ala-Gly-Ala-Gly-Tyr-OBzl	1+6 A	Py-DMF	88		199–202			540
Z-Ser-N^ε-boc-Lys-β-OBu^t-Asp-Ala-Phe-Ile-Gly					207–209	−27	Ac	25
Z-Ser-Phe-Leu-Pro-Val-Asn-Leu					185–190	−47		641
Z-Ser-Phe-Leu-Pro-Val-Asn-Leu-OBu^t	1+6 A	DMF	62		189–190	−45		641

319

Table 7 Heptapeptides (continued)

Compound	Method	Solvent	% Yield	Solvent Crystallization	M.P. (°C)	$[\alpha]_D$	Solvent Rotation	Ref.
Z-Ser-Phe-Leu-Pro-Val-Asn-Leu-ONp								641
Ser-Phe-Leu-Pro-Val-Asn-Leu-ONp Hydrobromide								641
Z-Ser-Tyr-Ser-Met-Glu-His-Phe Hydrazide	4+3 A				214–215			407
Z-Ser-Tyr-Ser-Met-Glu-His-Phe-OMe			76		167–173	–15	Ac	407
Threonine								
Z(OMe)-Thr-S-bzl-Cys-Gly-Ser-Asn-S-bzl-Cys-Tyr-OEt	A	DMF	72	DMF-Eth	210–212 (dec)	–21	DMF	452
Thr-S-bzl-Cys-Gly-Ser-Asn-S-bzl-Cys-Tyr-OEt Trifluoroacetate					174–176	–20	DMF	452
Tryptophan								
Z-Trp-D-Leu-Trp-D-Leu-Trp-D-Leu-Trp 2-Hydroxyethylamide								527
Trp-D-Leu-Trp-D-Leu-Trp-D-Leu-Trp 2-Hydroxyethylamide								527
Tyrosine								
O,N-di-Z-Tyr-Ile-Gln-Asn-S-Bzl-Cys-Pro-Abu-Gly Amide	1+6 OTCP		74		248	–59 –35	Ac DMF	275
OBzl-N-Z-Tyr-Ile-Gln-Asn-S-bzl-penicillaminyl-Pro-Leu-Gly Amide				THF-Aq	201–206	–35	DMF	567
Z-Tyr-Ile-Gln-Asn-α-aminosuberyl-Pro-Leu-Gly Amide OMe	A	DMF	82	Aq-DMF	213–215	–28	DMF	291
Tyr-Ile-Gln-Asn-α-aminosuberyl-Pro-Leu-Gly Amide				Me-Eth	150–155			291
3-Benzylthiopropionyl-Tyr-Phe-Gln-Asn-S-bzl-Cys-Pro-Nγ-tos-D-Dbu-Gly Amide					238–240	–22	DMF	768

Valine

Compound	Method	Solvent	Yield	Recryst.	M.p.	[α]	Solvent	Ref.
Z-Val-Asn-Gln-His-Leu-S-bzl-Cys-Gly	1+6 ONP		81	DMF-Eth	215–217	–43	Ac	758
Z-Val-Asp-Glu-N^{im}-bzl-His-Leu-S-bzl-Cys-Gly	1+6 ONP	DMF	74.7		221–223 (dec)	–68	DMF	764
N-Bzhoc-Val-S-(N'-Z-Cys-Val-Ala-Gly-OBzh)-Cys-Gly-OBzl	EDCI	MeCl	74	Ac-Eth	239–240	–60	DMF	227
Val-S-(N'-Z-Cys-Val-Ala-Gly)-Cys-Gly-OBzl				Aq-DMF	207–208	–20	DMF	227
Z-Val-His-Phe-β-OBu^t-Asp-Ala-β-OBu^t-Ser-Val-OBu^t	1+6 ONP	DMF	72	Alc-Aq	218–220	–74	Aq	602
Val-His-Phe-Asp-Ala-Ser-Val								602
Z-Val-N$^\varepsilon$-tos-Lys-Val-Tyr-Pro-β-OBu^t-Asp-Gly-OBu^t					211–213	–37	DMF	493
Val-N$^\varepsilon$-tos-Lys-Val-Tyr-Pro-β-OBu^t-Asp-Gly-OBu^t					108–112	–62	Me	493
Z-Val-N$^\delta$-tos-Orn-Leu-Phe-Pro-Tyr-Phe-OMe	4+3 A; 2+5 A; 3+4 DCCI	EtAc	22; 55.5		138–140; 138–140	–38; –38	DMF; Me	357
Z-Val-Tyr-Tyr-Ile-His-Pro-Phe-OMe				An-Aq	205–210			691
Val-Tyr-Tyr-Ile-His-Pro-Phe-OMe Dihydrochloride								691
Z-Val-Tyr-Tyr-Val-His-Pro-Phe-OMe	3+4 DCCI				160–170	–57	Me	502
Val-Tyr-Tyr-Val-His-Pro-Phe-OMe								502

8

Octapeptides

The synthetic octapeptides listed in Table 8 were generally obtained by the A, MCA, or ONP coupling methods. A small number of coupling reagent and coupling position studies appear in Table 8 and give a tantilizing view of the necessity for such additional information. In one octapeptide synthesis,[681] the crude product in chloroform was washed successively with 1N hydrochloric acid, water, 5% sodium bicarbonate and water. Thin layer chromatography,[28,454,461,529] column chromatography (using cellulose,[19,240,651] carboxymethylcellulose,[468,551,606,645,649,651,653] Sephadex G-25,[398] amberlite CG-50)[398] and countercurrent distribution[85,193,207,216,239,240,371,454,466,492, 529,677] have been of greater service for octapeptide purification.

In Table 8, the solvent of crystallization column again primarily lists solvents used for precipitation. Those solvents whose application led to crystalline octapeptides were acetic acid,[166,279] methanol,[529,727] acetic acid-ethanol,[62] acetic acid-water,[289] dimethylformamide-ether,[229,398] dimethylformamide-ethyl acetate,[551] dimethylformamide-water,[289,291,771] dioxane-ether,[16] ethanol-ethyl acetate,[356] methanol-ethyl acetate,[439] methanol-water,[28] pyridine-water,[229,279] tetrahydrofuran-water,[579] and dimethylformamide-pyridine-acetone.[229]

Recent literature concerned with synthesis of octapeptides includes two new studies of angiotensin II analogs.[10,288]

Table 8   Octapeptides

Compound	Method	Solvent	% Yield	Solvent Crystallization	M.P. (°C)	$[\alpha]_D$	Solvent Rotation	Ref.
Arginine								
Arg-Arg-Pro-Val-N^ϵ-boc-Lys-Val-Tyr-Pro Amide								645
Z-Arg-Arg-Pro-Val-N^ϵ-boc-Lys-Val-Tyr-Pro Sulfate				THF-Aq	238			579
N^G-Nitro-Z-Arg-N^G-nitro-Arg-Pro-Val-N^ϵ-boc-Lys-Val-Tyr-Pro Amide	2+6 MCA	Di-DMF	77		147			645
N^G-Nitro-Z-Arg-N^G-nitro-Arg-Val-Tyr-Ile-His-Pro-Phe-ONBzl	1+7 MCA	THF-DMF	49.1	Me-Di-EtAc	173-180	-34	Py	19
Arg-Pro-Gly-Phe-Leu-Pro-Phe-Arg Triacetate						-85	Aq	653
Arg-Pro-Gly-Phe-Ser-Pro-Phe-Arg				Me-Eth		-48	Ac	193
N^G-Nitro-Z-Arg-Pro-Gly-Phe-Ser-Pro-Phe-N^G-nitro-Arg-ONBzl	3+5 DCCI	Py-Acn	81	i-Pr-Eth	160 (dec)	-42	Ac	193
Arg-Pro-Gly-Pro-Phe-Ser-Phe-Arg				Me-Eth		-58	Ac	193
N^G-Nitro-Z-Arg-Pro-Gly-Pro-Phe-Ser-Phe-N^G-nitro-Arg-ONBzl	4+4 DCCI	DMF	63		171 (dec)	-52	DMF	193
Arg-Pro-Pro-Gly-Phe-Ser-Pro-Phe						-54	Ac	123
N^G-Nitro-Z-Arg-Pro-Pro-Gly-Phe-Ser-OAc-Ser-Pro-Phe-OMe	2+6 ONP	DMF			85-90	-80	Ac	123
N^G-Nitro-Z-D-Arg-D-Pro-D-Pro-Gly-D-Phe-D-Ser-D-Pro-D-Phe						+53		681
N^G-Nitro-Z-Arg-Pro-Pro-Gly-Phe-Ser-Pro-Phe-Ser-D-Pro-D-Phe					75-78	-46		123
N^G-Nitro-Z-D-Arg-D-Pro-D-Pro-Gly-D-Phe-D-Ser-D-Pro-D-Phe-OMe	1+7 DCCI	DMF	71					681
Arg-Pro-Leu-Phe-Ser-Phe-Arg Triacetate Salt						-91	Aq	652

323

Table 8 Octapeptides (continued)

Compound	Method	Solvent	% Yield	Solvent Crystallization	M.P. (°C)	[α]D	Solvent Rotation	Ref.
Arg-Pro-Pro-Phe-Gly-Ser-Phe-Arg N^G-Nitro-Z-Arg-Pro-Pro-Phe-Gly-Ser-Phe-N^G-nitro-Arg-ONBzl	2+6 ONP	Di-DMF	87	Me-Eth	160 (dec)	−49	Me	193
	2+6 DCCI	DMF-Acn	79	i-Pr		−31	DMF	193
Asparagine								
Asn-Arg-Val-Phe-Val-His-Pro-Phe						−68	1N Ac	499
Asn-Arg-Val-Phe-Val-His-Pro-Phe-OMe								499
Z-Asn-N^G-nitro-Arg-Val-Phe-Val-His-Pro-Phe-OMe	2+6 DCCI							499
Asn-Arg-Val-Tyr-Ile-His-Pro-Phe								466
Asn-D-Arg-Val-Tyr-Ile-His-Pro-Phe								677
D-Asn-D-Arg-Val-Tyr-Ile-His-Pro-Phe								529
D-Asn-Arg-Val-Tyr-Ile-His-Pro-Phe								529
Z-Asn-D-Arg-Val-Tyr-Ile-His-Pro-Phe-OBzl	1+7 MCA		30		225–227			677
Z-Asn-N^G-nitro-Arg-Val-Tyr-Ile-His-Pro-Phe-OBzl	1+7 ONP	DMF	56		225–227	−21	Ac	677
	1+7 ONP	DMF Acn	30					677
Z-D-Asn-N^G-nitro-D-Arg-Val-Tyr-Ile-His-Pro-Phe-OBzl					146–149 (dec)	−24	Ac	529
Z-D-Asn-N^G-nitro-Arg-Val-Tyr-Ile-His-Pro-Phe-OBzl	ONP	DMF-Acn	32		201–204 (dec)	−29	Ac	529

Peptide	Coupling method	Solvent	Yield (%)	Recryst. solvent	mp (°C)	[α]	Rotation solvent	M
Z-Asn-N^G-nitro-Arg-Val-Tyr-Ile-His-Pro-Phe-OMe	4+4 CDI	DMF	45		221–222.5			466
D-Asn-Arg-Val-Tyr-Val-His-Pro-Phe						−68	Aq	551
D-Asn-D-Arg-D-Tyr-D-Val-D-His-D-Pro-D-Phe Acetate Hydrate						+59 / −59	Aq	563
Asn-Arg-Val-Tyr-Val-His-Pro-Phe Amide			90	Alc-DMF-Eth	156–158	−65	1N Ac	500
D-Asn-Arg-Val-Tyr-Val-His-Pro-Phe-OBu^t			94			−28	DMF	551
D-Asn-D-Arg-D-Val-D-Tyr-D-Val-D-His-D-Pro-D-Phe-OBu^t Acetate Hydrate		DMF			176–177 / 178–179	+28 / −32	DMF	563
D-Asn-D-Arg-D-Val-D-Tyr-D-Val-D-His-D-Pro-D-Phe Hydrate			70			+61 / −61	Aq / 1N Ac	684 / 500
Asn-N^G-nitro-Arg-Val-Tyr-Val-His-Pro-Phe					216–218	+20	DMF	684
Z-D-Asn-N^G-nitro-Arg-D-Val-D-Tyr-D-Val-D-His-Pro-Phe-OBu^t	2+6 MCA	DMF-THF	71	DMF-TEA-Aq	207	−29	DMF	551
Z-D-Asn-N^G-nitro-Arg-Val-Tyr-Val-His-Pro-D-Phe			48		206–208	+31	DMF	684
Z-D-Asn-N^G-nitro-D-Arg-D-Val-D-Tyr-D-Val-D-His-D-Pro-D-Phe-OBu^t	2+6 DCCI		74 / 82		208–209 / 208–209	+29 / −30	DMF	563
Asn-Cit-Val-Tyr-Ile-His-Pro-Phe	1+7 ONP	DMF-Acn			222–224 (dec)	−29	Ac	529
Z-Asn-Cit-Val-Tyr-Ile-His-Pro-Phe-OBzl								529
Asn-N$^\epsilon$-Boc-Lys-Val-Tyr-Val-His-Pro-Phe-OBu^t					230–232	−26 / −78	Ac / 1N Ac	552
Asn-Lys-Val-Tyr-Val-His-Pro-Phe-OBu^t								552

Table 8 Octapeptides (continued)

Compound	Method	Solvent	% Yield	Solvent Crystallization	M.P. (°C)	$[\alpha]_D$	Solvent Rotation	Ref.
Z-Asn-N$^\epsilon$-boc-Lys-Val-Tyr-Val-His-Pro-Phe-OBu^t	2+6 A		57.5		232–234.5	–36	DMF	552
Asn-Orn-Val-Tyr-Val-His-Pro-Phe	2+6							499
Z-Asn-N$^\delta$-Z-Orn-Val-Tyr-Val-His-Pro-Phe-OMe	DCCI				227–228			499
Asp-Arg-Ala-Tyr-Ile-His-Pro-Phe					203–206 (dec)	–69	1N Ac	325
Asp-Arg-Val-Ala-Ile-His-Pro-Phe	1+7 MCA			Aq-An	230–260			588
β-OBzl-Z-Asp-N^G-nitro-Arg-Val-Ala-Ile-His-Pro-Phe-ONp		DMF	90.9	Me-Eth	195–200			588
Asp-Arg-Val-Tyr-Ile-His-Pro-Ala Monoacetate	2+6 MCA	THF-DMF	74	Me-EtAc-Eth	230 (dec)	–83	Ac-Aq	468
β-OBzl-Z-Asp-N^G-nitro-Arg-Val-Tyr-Ile-N^{im}-bzl-His-Pro-Ala-ONBzl					182–186	–32	Py	468
Asp-Arg-Val-Tyr-Ile-His-Pro-Phe Monoacetate	1+7 DCCI	DMF		Alc-Aq	230–247 (dec)	–65	1N-HCl	19
β-OBzl-Z-Asp-N^G-nitro-Arg-Val-Tyr-Ile-N^{im}-bzl-His-Pro-Phe-OMe	1+7 MCA	THF-DMF						405
β-OBzl-Z-Asp-N^G-nitro-Arg-Val-Tyr-Ile-His-Pro-Phe-ONBzl	2+6 MCA	THF-DMF-EtAc	76	Me-Di-EtAc	180–184	–29	Py	19
Asp-Arg-Val-Tyr-Ile-His-Pro-Tyr			54.3	Alc	188.5–191 247–254 (dec)	–28 –58	Py Ac-Aq	606
Asp-Arg-Val-Tyr-Ile-His-Pro-Tyr-OMe	1+7 MCA			Ac-Eth	202–207			606
β-OBzl-Z-Asp-Arg-Val-Tyr-Ile-His-Pro-Tyr-OMe		DMF	78–86	Me-Eth	172–176	–60	Aq	606
Asp-Arg-Val-Tyr-Val-His-Pro-Phe								551

Compound	Method	Solvent	Yield	Recryst.	m.p.	[α]	Solvent	No.
Asp-Arg-Val-Tyr-Val-His-Pro-Phe Amide	1+7 DCCI				149–155	−47	Me	216
β-OBzl-Z-D-Asp-N^G-nitro-Arg-Val-Tyr-Val-His-Pro-Phe Amide					171–173	−59	Me	216
β-OBu^t-Asp-Arg-Val-Tyr-Val-His-Pro-Phe-OBu^t	2+6 MCA	THF-DMF	90	Alc-Eth	162–163	−35	DMF	551
β-OBu^t-Z-Asp-N^G-nitro-Arg-Val-Tyr-Val-His-Pro-Phe-OBu^t Hydrate		DMF	60	Alc-TEA-Aq		−31	DMF	551
Cysteine								
S-Bzl-N-tos-Cys-Ala-Glu-S-bzl-Cys-bzl-N^{im}-His-Thr-Val-Glu-di-OBzl	2+6 A				180	−35	Ac	669
S,S'-N-Z-hemi-Cys-S-bzh-Cys-Gly-Phe-Gly-S-trt-Cys-Gly-Val			40	Chf-He	168	+9	DMF	226
S,S'-N-Z-hemi-Cys-S-bzh-Cys-Gly-Phe-Gly-hemi-Cys-Phe-Gly-OBu^t					234–238	+30	DMF	226
S-Trt-Z-Cys-S-bzh-Cys-Gly-Phe-Gly-S-trt-Cys-Phe-Gly				DMF-Eth	228–229	−17	DMF	229
S-Trt-Z-Cys-S-bzh-Cys-Gly-Phe-Gly-S-trt-Cys-Phe-Gly-OBu^t				Py-Aq	235–236	−16	DMF	229
S-Bzl-Z-Cys-hexa-Gly-S-bzl-Cys-OBzl	4+4 WRK / 5+3 EDCI / DCCI / 3+5 A	Acn-DMF / MeCl- / DMF / Py / EtAc	51.8 / 54.5 / 85–91 / 45	DMF-Py-An / Ac	234–236 / 235–236 / 244–246 (dec)	−16 / −16 / −30	DMF / DMF / Py-Aq	279
Dehydro-Cys-hexa-Gly-Cys	3+5 A	Chf	67	Aq-Py	246–247 (dec)	−20	Ac	279
S-Bzl-Z-Cys-Ile-Gln-Asn-S-bzl-Cys-Pro-Cit-Gly Amide	1+7 ONP	DMF	68	Ac-Alc	245–248			61
S-Bzl-N-tos-Cys-p-et-Phe-Ile-Gln-Asn-S-bzl-Cys-Pro-Leu-Gly Amide	1+7 A	THF	82	DMF-Aq	218–220	−30	DMF	778

Table 8 Octapeptides (continued)

Compound	Method	Solvent	% Yield	Solvent Crystallization	M.P. (°C)	$[\alpha]_D$	Solvent Rotation	Ref.
S-Bzl-N-tos-Cys-Tyr-Ile-Gln-Asn-S-bzl-Cys-Leu-Gly	3+5 A	DMF	56		259–260 (dec)	−21	DMF	276
S-Bzl-N-tos-Cys-Tyr-Ile-Gln-Asn-S-bzl-Cys-Pro-Gly Amide	3+5 ONP	DMF	56		248	−23	DMF	276
S-Bzl-N-tos-Cys-Tyr-Ile-Gln-Asn-S-bzl-Cys-Pro-Leu Amide	3+5 A	DMF	56 95		270–272	−65 −28	Ac DMF	276
S-Bzl-N-tos-Cys-Tyr-Ile-Gln-Asn-S-bzl-Cys-Pro-Leu-me Amide	5+3 DCCI	DMF		DMF-Aq	255–257 (dec)	−31	DMF	72
S-Bzl-N-tos-Cys-Tyr-Ile-Gln-Asn-S-bzl-Cys-Pro-Leu Sarcosinamide					236–239 (dec)	−37	DMF	84
S-Bzl-Z-Cys-Tyr-Ile-Gln-Asn-S-bzl-penicillaminyl-Pro-Leu-Gly Amide				THF-Aq	191–195	−45	DMF	567
S-Bzl-N-tos-Cys-Tyr-Phe-Gln-Asn-S-bzl-Cys-Pro-N-tos-Dbu-Gly Amide				DMF-Aq	217–220	−19	DMF	771
S-Bzl-N-tos-Cys-Tyr-Phe-Gln-Asn-S-bzl-Cys-Pro-N$^\epsilon$-tos-Lys-N-(β-tos-amino)et Amide	6+2 A	DMF	71	DMF-Aq	210–215	−11	DMF	767
Glutamine								
Z-Gln-N^G-nitro-Arg-Leu-Gln-Gly-Leu-Val Amide	1+7 ONP	DMF		Alc-Aq	250 (dec)	−32	DMSO	66
Z-Gln-N^G-nitro-Arg-Val-Tyr-Val-His-Pro-Phe-OBu^t	2+6 MCA	DMF	71	DMF-EtAc	218–219	−30	DMF	551
Gln-Arg-Val-Tyr-Val-His-Pro-Phe				Alc-Eth		−73	Aq	551
Gln-Arg-Val-Tyr-Val-His-Pro-Phe-OBu^t								551

Compound	Method	Solvent	Yield (%)	Recryst. solvent	M.p. (°C)	[α]	Rot. solvent	Ref.
γ-OBzl-Z-Glu-Ala-Leu-Tyr-Leu-Val-S-bzl-Cys-Gly	MCA	DMF	100	Ac	285 (dec)	−56	Fm	166
	1+7 ONP	DMF	78		248−250	−38	Ac	310
Z-Pyro-Glu-N^G-nitro-Arg-Val-Tyr-Val-His-Pro-Phe	1+7 ONP	DMF		Alc-DMF-Eth		−35	DMF	551
γ-OBu^t-Z-Glu-N^G-nitro-Arg-Val-Tyr-Val-His-Pro-Phe-OBu^t					174−178	−32	DMF	551
γ-OBu^t-Glu-Arg-Val-Tyr-Val-His-Pro-Phe-OBu^t				Alc-Eth		−31	DMF	551
Pyro-Glu-Arg-Val-Tyr-Val-His-Pro-Phe						−73	Aq	551
γ-OBu^t-Z-Glu-γ-OBu^t-Glu-γ-OBu^t-Glu-γ-OBu^t-Glu-γ-OBu^t-Glu-Ala-Tyr-Gly-OMe	1+7 OTCP	DMF	91		240−242 (dec)	−17	DMF	423
γ-OBu^t-boc-Glu-γ-OBu^t-Glu-γ-OBu^t-Glu-γ-OBu^t-Glu-γ-OBu^t-Glu-Ala-Tyr-Gly-OMe					237−238 (dec)	−18	DMF	28
γ-OBu^t-Glu-γ-OBu^t-Glu-γ-OBu^t-Glu-Ala-Tyr-Gly-OMe Acetate				Aq-Me	229−231 (dec)	−14	DMF	423
Pyro-Glu-Pro-Ser-N^ε-boc-Lys-Asp-Ala-Phe-Ile								85
Pyro-Glu-Pro-Ser-N^ε-boc-Lys-Asp-Ala-Phe-Ile-OMe	4+4 A	DMF			172−175	−40	DMF	85
Pyro-Glu-Pro-Ser-Lys-Asp-Ala-Phe-Ile					140 (dec)	−61	Ac-Aq	85
Glycine								
Z-Gly-N^G-nitro-D-Arg-Val-Tyr-Ile-His-Pro-Phe-OBzl	1+7 ONP		45	Me	176−178 (dec)	−22	Ac	529
Z-Gly-N^G-nitro-Arg-Val-Tyr-Ile-His-Pro-Phe-OBzl	1+7 ONP	DMF	50		208−210 (dec)	−33	Ac	677
Gly-Arg-Val-Tyr-Ile-His-Pro-Phe	1+7 ONP	DMF-Acn	50		208−210 (dec)	−33		677
Gly-D-Arg-Val-Tyr-Ile-His-Pro-Phe								677
								529

Table 8 Octapeptides (continued)

Compound	Method	Solvent	% Yield	Solvent Crystallization	M.P. (°C)	[α] D	Solvent Rotation	Ref.
Z-Gly-N^G-nitro-Arg-Val-Tyr-Val-His-Pro-Phe-OMe	2+6 DCCI		70		160			499
Gly-Arg-Val-Tyr-Val-His-Pro-Phe					220			499
Gly-Arg-Val-Tyr-Val-His-Pro-Phe-OMe								499
Boc-Gly-β-OBzl-Asp-Ser-bzl-Gly-Gly-Pro-Leu-Val-OMe	1+7 OSU		77	He-Alc	130–133	−62	Me	356
N-For-Gly-Asp-Ser-Gly-Gly-Pro-Leu-Val-OMe					192–193	−84		88
N-For-Gly-β-OBzl-Asp-OBzl-Ser-Gly-Gly-Pro-Leu-Val-OMe					oil			88
Gly-Asp-Ser-Gly-Gly-Pro-Leu-Val-OMe Hydrochloride				Alc-EtAc	158–160	−106	Aq	356
Z-(Aza-Gly-Gly)$_4$-OEt					211			154
Z-Gly-Gly-Phe-Gly-Pro-Phe-N^G-nitro-Arg-ONBzl	2+6 ONP	DMF	78	Ac-Aq	100–110	0.0	Ac	649
Z-Gly-Ile-Glu-Asp-S-bzl-Cys-Pro-Leu-Gly Amide	1+7 ONP	DMF			229–231	−49	DMF	126
Z-Gly-Phe-Phe-Tyr-Thr-Pro-N^ϵ-tos-Lys-Ala-OMe								350
Z-Gly-Phe-Phe-Tyr-Thr-Pro-N^ϵ-tos-Lys-Ala-OMe Hydrate	1+7 ONP	DMF	80	Aq-Me	182–185			306
Histidine								
His-Phe-Arg-Trp-Gly-N^ϵ-tos-Lys-Pro-Val Amide Diacetate Dihydrate								240
His-Phe-Arg-Trp-Gly-N^ϵ-tos-Lys-Pro-Val Diacetate Tetrahydrate	5+3 DCCI	DMF	51					239
N^{im}-Bzl-Z-His-Ser-Gln-Gly-Thr-Phe-Thr-Ser					195–197	−3	DMF	47
N^{im}-Bzl-Z-His-Ser-Gln-Gly-Thr-Phe-Thr-Ser-OMe	4+4 DCCI		30		212–214	−6	DMF	47

Compound	Method	Solvent	Yield (%)	Solvent	M.p. (°C)	[α]	Solvent	Ref.
Boc-His-OBzl-Ser-Gln-Gly-Thr-Phe-Thr-OBzl-Ser-Z-Hydrazide	1+7 A		84		213	−20	Ac-Aq	731
	4+4 DCCI		77		211	−20	Ac-Aq	731
His-Ser-Gln-Gly-Thr-Phe-Thr-Ser-OMe					170	−14	DMF	47
Leucine								
Z-Leu-Gly-Gly-Leu-Gly-Gly-Gly								29
Leu-Gly-Gly-Gly-Leu-Glu-Gly-Gly								29
ε-Trimethylamino-n-Leu-Lys-Val-Tyr-Ile-His-Pro-Phe				Me-Aq	190–192			207
Lysine								
N^{ϵ}, N^{α}- di-boc-Lys-Asn-Ala-Phe-Ile-Gly-Leu-Met Amide	4+4 DCCI	DMF	70		239–240	−26	Ac	392
	4+4 A	DMF	20		234–245			443
	4+4 DCCI		40					
	4+4 NHS							
Lys-Gly-Glu-Gly-Lys-Gly-Glu-Gly					189–191 (dec)	+10	Ac	422
Lys-Asn-Ala-Phe-Ile-Gly-Leu-Met Amide	4+4 DCCI	Py	47	Alc-Eth	147–149	−15		392
	4+4 PPP	Py	38					
N^{ϵ}-Tfa-N^{α}-Z-Lys-Gly-γ-OMe-Glu-Gly-N^{ϵ}-tfa-Lys-Gly-γ-OMe-Glu-Gly-OBu^t				Alc-Eth	138–140	−13		422
N^{ϵ}-Tfa-Lys-Gly-Glu-Gly-Lys-Gly-Glu-Gly-OBu^t Hydrochloride				Alc-Eth	135–137	+15	Ac	422
N^{ϵ}-Tfa-Lys-Gly-γ-me-Glu-Gly-ε-N-tfa-Lys-Gly-γ-me-Glu-Gly					171–173 (dec)	+7	Ac	422

Table 8 Octapeptides (continued)

Compound	Method	Solvent	% Yield	Solvent Crystallization	M.P.(°C)	$[\alpha]_D$	Solvent Rotation	Ref.
Z-N^ϵ-Boc-Lys-Pro-Val-Gly-N^ϵ-boc-Lys-N^ϵ-boc-Lys-N^G-tos-Arg-N^G-tos-Arg Amide	6+2				165–167	−24	DMF	492
N^ϵ-Boc-N^α-Z-Lys-Pro-Val-Gly-N^ϵ-boc-Lys-N^ϵ-boc-Lys-Arg-Arg Acetate	A	THF-Aq	52.8			−46	Ac-Aq	461
N^ϵ-Boc-N^α-Z-Lys-Pro-Val-Gly-N^ϵ-boc-Lys-N^ϵ-boc-Lys-Arg-Arg Amide	5+3 A	Aq-THF	84.2			−43	Ac-Aq	461
N^ϵ-Boc-N^α-Z-Lys-Pro-Val-Gly-N^ϵ-boc-Lys-N^ϵ-boc-Lys-N^G-tos-Arg-N^G-tos-Arg-δ-aminovaleryl OMe	4+4 WRK	Acn	83		152–154	−26	Me	454
N^ϵ-Boc-Lys-Pro-Val-Gly-N^ϵ-boc-Lys-N^ϵ-boc-Lys-Arg-Arg Acetate						−41	Ac-Aq	461
N^ϵ-Boc-Lys-Pro-Val-Gly-N^ϵ-boc-Lys-N^ϵ-boc-Lys-Arg-Arg Amide Triacetate						−41	Ac-Aq	461
N^G-Tos-N^α-Z-Lys-Pro-Val-Gly-N^ϵ-tos-Lys-N^ϵ-tos-Lys-N^G-tos-Arg-N^G-tos-Arg-OMe	4+4 ONP 4+4 MCA	Acn	96 88		119–121 120–124			371
N^ϵ-Boc-Z-Lys-Val-Leu-Thr-Thr-Gly-Leu-Pro Hydrazide				Alc	185–187	−29	DMF	549
N^ϵ, N^α-di-boc-Lys-Val-Leu-Thr-Thr-Gly-Leu-Pro Hydrazide						−64	Ac	549
N^ϵ, N^α-di-boc-Lys-Val-Leu-Thr-Thr-Gly-Leu-Pro-OMe	3+5 A	DMF-THF		Bu-Pe	193–195	−67	Ac	549
Methionine								
Boc-Met-Asp-Ser-Ser-Thr-Ser-Ala-Ala-OBu^t					219–224	−11	DMF	581
Boc-Met-β-OBzl-Asp-OBzl-(Ser)$_2$-Thr-OBzl-Ser-(Ala)$_2$-OBzl			57					356a
Boc-Met-β-OBu^t-Asp-Ser-Ser-Thr-Ser-Ala-Ala-OBu^t	1+7 ONP	Py	77	DMF-Eth	212–213	−11	DMF	398

Compound	Coupling	Solvent	Yield (%)	M.p. (°C)	[α]	Solvent	Page
Met-Asp-Ser-Thr-Ser-Ala-Ala Acetate Trihydrate					−65	Aq	398
Ornithine							
N^{δ}-Boc-Z-Orn-N^{δ}-boc-Orn-Pro-Val-N^{ϵ}-boc-Lys-Val-Tyr-Pro-OBu^t	1+7 ONP	DMF		152–154	−83	Me	664
N^{δ}-Boc-Orn-N^{δ}-boc-Orn-Pro-Val-N^{ϵ}-boc-Lys-Val-Tyr-Pro-OBu^t					−51 / −87	DMF / Me	664
Phenylalanine							
Z-Phe-Ile-Gln-Asn-S-bzl-Cys-Pro-N^{δ}-tos-Orn-Gly Amide	1+7 OTCP		67	237–238	−51	Ac-Aq	253
β-S-Bzl-propionyl-Phe-Ile-Gln-Asn-S-bzl-Cys-Pro-N^{δ}-tos-Orn-Gly Amide				239–240	−35	DMF	253
Phe-Ile-Gln-Asn-S-bzl-Cys-Pro-N^{δ}-tos-Orn-Gly Amide				195–198	−52	Ac-Aq	253
β-S-Bzl-propionyl-Phe-Phe-Gln-Asn-S-bzl-Cys-Pro-N^{G}-tos-Arg-Gly-Amide	2+6 A		69	222–224	−38	DMF	255
Z-Phe-Phe-Gln-Asn-S-bzl-Cys-Pro-N^{ϵ}-tos-Lys-Gly Amide	1+7 ONP	DMF		222 (dec)		DMF-Alc	413
β-S-Bzl-propionyl-Phe-Phe-Gln-Asn-S-bzl-Cys-Pro-N^{δ}-tos-Orn-Gly Amide	2+6 A		57	246–247	−37	DMF	253
Z-Phe-Val-Asn-Gln-His-Leu-S-bzl-Cys-Gly	1+7 ONP		76	238–241	−45	Fm	758
Z-Phe-Val-Asp-Glu-N^{im}-bzl-His-Leu-S-bzl-Cys-Gly	1+7 ONP	DMF	86	215–218 (dec)		DMF-Eth	764
Nps-Phe-Val-Gln-Trp-Leu-Met-Asn-OBu^t-Thr-OBu^t	5+3 NHS-DCCI	DMF	87	231–235 (dec)		DMF-Eth	718
N-Pht-Phe-Val-Gln-Trp-Leu-Met-Asn-OBu^t-Thr-OBu^t	5+3 DCCI NHS-	Acn-DMF	31	223–224 (dec)	−34	DMF	719

Table 8 Octapeptides (continued)

Compound	Method	Solvent	% Yield	Solvent Crystallization	M.P. (°C)	[α]D	Solvent Rotation	Ref.
N-Pht-Phe-Val-Gln-Trp-Leu-Met-Asn-OBu^t-Thr-OBu^t (continued)	DCCI	DMF	75	Alc-Aq	226–227 (dec)	-31	DMF	
	5+3 A	EtAc	31	Alc-Aq	224–225 (dec)	-31	DMF	
Phe-Val-Gln-Trp-Leu-Met-Asn-OBu^t-Thr-OBu^t					243–244 (dec)	-26	Ac-Aq	718
Proline								
Aoc-Pro-Pro-Gly-Phe-Ser-Pro-Phe-N^G-nitro-Arg-OBzl				EtAc-Eth	125–130	-46	DMF	518
Z-Pro-Pro-Gly-Phe-OAc-Ser-Pro-p-fluoro-Phe-N^G-nitro-Arg-OMe			76		166–168			438
Z-Pro-Pro-Gly-Phe-OAc-Ser-Pro-p-fluoro-D-Phe-N^G-nitro-Arg-OMe			60		140–150			438
Z-Pro-Pro-Gly-Phe-OAc-Ser-Pro-D-Phe-N^G-nitro-Arg-OMe	ONP	DMF	50	Me-EtAc-Eth	123–126			438
Z-Pro-Pro-Gly-Phe-Ser-Pro-Phe-N^G-nitro-Arg-OMe	ONP	DMF	75	Me-EtAc	150–152	-64	DMF	439
	1+7 ONP	DMF	75	Me-EtAc	150–152			439
Nps-Pro-Gly-Phe-OBzl-Ser-Pro-Phe-N^G-nitro-Arg-ONBzl	1+7 ONP	DMF	76		182–184			137
Z-Pro-Pro-Gly-Phe-OAc-Ser-Pro-Phe-Cit-OMe								456
Serine								
OBu^t-Z-Ser-Arg-Arg-Ala-Gln-β-OBu^t-Asp-Phe-Val-OBu^t Dihydrobromide	1+7 ONP	DMF	90.1		179–180	-32	Me	727
OBu^t-Ser-Arg-Arg-Ala-Gln-Asp-β-OBu^t-Phe-Val-OBu^t Dihydrobromide						-38	Me	727

Compound	Method	Solvent	Yield	Recryst. solvent	M.p. (°C)	[α]	Solvent	Ref.
OBu^t-Z-Ser-β-OBu^t-Asp-OBu^t-Tyr-OBu^t-Ser-N$^\varepsilon$ Boc-Lys-OBu^t-Tyr-Leu-β-OBu^t-Asp	1+7 ONP	DMF	88	Me-Aq	208–209	−12	Me	735
	1+7 OSU	DMF	97.5		203–205	−12	Me	735
OBu^t-N-Nps-Ser-β-OBu^t-Asp-OBu^t-Tyr-OBu^t-Ser-N$^\varepsilon$-boc-Lys-OBu^t-Tyr-Leu-β-OBu^t-Asp	1+7 OSU	DMF	77.5		227 (dec)			735
OBu^t-Ser-β-OBu^t-Asp-OBu^t-Tyr-OBu^t-Ser-N$^\varepsilon$-boc-Lys-OBu^t-Tyr-Leu-β-OBu^t-Asp	3+5 A	DMF	70		250	−3	Ac-Aq	319
Z-Ser-N^{im}-bzl-His-Leu-Val-γ-OMe-Glu-Ala-Leu-Tyr				DMF-Aq	253–255	−20	DMF	319
Z-Ser-N^{im}-bzl-His-Leu-Val-γ-OMe-Glu-Ala-Leu-Tyr-OEt	1+7 A	THF	75	DMF-Me	240–242	−25	DMF	329
OBu^t-N-trt-Ser-His-Leu-Val-Glu-γ-OBu^t-Ala-Leu-OBu^t-Tyr Hydrazide					230–235 (dec)	−18	DMF	329
OBu^t-N-trt-Ser-His-Leu-Val-Glu-γ-OBu^t-Ala-Leu-OBu^t-Tyr-OMe	5+3 A	DMF	64	Chf-Pe	209–227	−15	DMF	
Z-Ser-Met-Gln-His-Phe-Arg-Trp-Gly Acetate Dihydrate	5+3 A	DMF	49			−29	Alc	240
Ser-Met-Gln-His-Phe-Arg-Trp-Gly								240
OBu^t-Z-Ser-N$^\delta$-Pht-Orn-Arg-Ala-Gln-β-OBu^t-Asp-Phe-Val-OBu^t Citrate	1+7 ONP	DMF	73.7	Me	220–221	−20	DMF	727
OBu^t-Z-Ser-N$^\delta$-Pht-Orn-Arg-Ala-Gln-β-OBu^t-Asp-Phe-Val-OBu^t Hydrobromide					185 (dec)	−24	1N HCl	727
Ser-Tyr-Ser-Met-Gln-His-His-Phe-Arg								240

Tyrosine

Compound	Method	Solvent	Yield	Recryst. solvent	M.p. (°C)	[α]	Solvent	Ref.
OBzl-Z-Tyr-Ile-β-Ala-Asn-S-bzl-Cys-Pro-Leu-Gly Amide	1+7 ONP	DMF			235–237	−60	DMF	397
OBzl-Z-Tyr-Ile-Gln-Asn-Se-bzl-Cys-Pro-Leu-Gly Amide	1+7 ONP	DMF			249–251 (dec)	−39	DMF	687
S-Bzl-β-mercaptopropionyl-OBzl-Tyr-Ile-Gln-Asn-S-bzl-Cys-Pro-Leu-Gly Amide				DMF-Aq	238–240	−37	DMF	657

Table 8 Octapeptides (continued)

Compound	Method	Solvent	% Yield	Solvent Crystallization	M.P. (°C)	[α] D	Solvent Rotation	Ref.
N-Z-S-bzl-penicillaminyl-Tyr-Ile-Gln-Asn-S-bzl-Cys-Pro-Leu-Gly Amide				THF-Aq	224–228	−44	DMF	568
O, N-Di-Z-N-me-Tyr-Ile-Gln-Asn-S-bzl-Cys-Pro-Leu-Gly Amide	1+7 ONP	DMF	73		211–214	−28	DMF	258
Z-Tyr-Ile-Gln-Asn-S-bzl-Cys-Pro-Leu-Gly Amide	1+7 A	THF EtAc-DMF	88	Aq-DMF	216–217	−36	DMF	291
	4+4 A	DMF	79	Aq-Ac	222–224	−34	DMF	289
O, N^α-di-Z-Tyr-Ile-Gln-Asn-S-Eac-Cys-Pro-Leu-Gly Amide	1+7 OTCP	DMF	81		236	−66 −41	Ac-Aq DMF	188
S-Bzl-β-propionyl-Tyr-Ile-Gln-Asn-Se-bzl-Cys-Pro-Leu-Gly Amide					244–248	−45	DMF	687
N-Me-Tyr-Ile-Gln-Asn-S-bzl-Cys-Pro-Leu-Gly Amide				Me	255–257 (dec)	−66	Ac	258
Se-bzl-β-selenopropionyl-Tyr-Ile-Gln-Asn-S-bzl-Cys-Pro-Leu-Gly Amide					239–241 (dec)	−38	DMF	687
O-Tos-N-Z-N-me-Tyr-Ile-Gln-Asn-S-bzl-Cys-Pro-Leu-Gly Amide	1+7 ONP	DMF	55		190–200	−63	Ac-Aq	258
O-Tos-N-me-Tyr-Ile-Gln-Asn-S-bzl-Cys-Pro-Leu-Gly Amide					204–210	−50	Ac-Aq	258
Tyr-Ile-Gln-Asn-S-(3-carboxypropyl)-Cys-Pro-Leu-Gly Amide				Me-Eth	145–147	−69	Ac-Aq	291
Tyr-Ile-Gln-Asn-S-Eac-Cys-Pro-Leu-Gly Amide					275 (dec)	−58	DMF	188

Compound	Synthesis	Solvent	Yield (%)	Recryst.	M.p. (°C)	[α]	Solvent	Ref.
OBzl-Z-Tyr-Ile-Gln-Asn-Cys-Pro-N^δ-Pht-Orn-Gly Amide	1+7 ONP				240–245	−42	Ac	63
O,N-di-Z-Tyr-Ile-Gln-Asn-S-bzl-Cys-Pro-Orn-Gly Amide	1+7 OTCP		95		224–226	−44	Ac-Aq	253
β-S-Bzl-propionyl-Tyr-Ile-Gln-Asn-S-bzl-Cys-Pro-N^δ-tos-Orn-Gly Amide					236–238	−34	DMF	253
Tyr-Ile-Gln-Asn-S-bzl-Cys-Pro-Orn-Gly						−48	Ac-Aq	253
OBzl-Z-Tyr-Ile-Gln-Asp-S-bzl-Cys-Pro-Ala-Gly Amide	1+7 ONP	DMF			244–246 (dec)	−34	DMF	690
OBzl-Z-Tyr-Ile-Gln-Val-S-bzl-Cys-Pro-Leu-Gly Amide	1+7 ONP	DMF			259–261	−65	Fm	688
S-Bzl-β-mercaptopropionyl-Tyr-Ile-Gln-Val-S-bzl-Cys-Pro-Leu-Gly Amide	1+7 ONP	DMF	85	THF	230–231	−68	Fm	688
OBzl-Z-Tyr-Ile-Gly-Asp-S-bzl-Cys-Pro-Leu-Gly Amide	1+7 ONP	DMF			227–229	−40	DMF	126
Propionyl-Tyr-Phe-Gln-Asn-Ala-Pro-Arg-Gly Amide						−89	0.1N Ac	259
Propionyl-Tyr-Phe-Gln-Asn-Ala-Pro-N^G-nitro-Arg-Glu Amide	2+6 A		50		235–237 (dec)	−43	DMF	259
Propionyl-Tyr-Phe-Gln-Asn-Ala-Pro-N^ϵ-boc-Lys-Gly Amide	2+6 A		64		237–238 (dec)	−45	DMF	259
Propionyl-Tyr-Phe-Gln-Asn-Ala-Pro-Lys-Gly Amide					205–207	−93	0.1N Ac	259
β-S-Bzl-propionyl-Tyr-Phe-Gln-Asn-S-bzl-Cys-Pro-N^G-tos-Arg-Gly Amide	2+6 A	DMF	52			−38	DMF	255
3-Benzylthio-propionyl-Tyr-Phe-Gln-Asn-S-bzl-Cys-Pro-N^G-D-Arg-Gly Amide					223–225			768
OBzl-Z-Tyr-Phe-Gln-Asn-S-bzl-Cys-Pro-Cit-Gly Amide	1+7 ONP	DMF	62	Ac-EtAc	242–245			61

Table 8 Octapeptides (continued)

Compound	Method	Solvent	% Yield	Solvent Crystallization	M.P. (°C)	$[\alpha]_D$	Solvent Rotation	Ref.
OBzl-Z-Tyr-Phe-Gln-Asn-S-bzl-Cys-Pro-N$^\epsilon$-tos-Lys-Gly Amide				Ac-Alc	228–231	−39	DMF	62
Z-Tyr-Phe-Gln-Asn-S-bzl-Cys-Pro-N$^\epsilon$-tos-Lys-Gly Amide	4+4 A	DMF	54	Aq-DMF	197–200	−32	DMF	289
3-Benzylthio-propionyl-Tyr-Phe-Gln-Asn-S-bzl-Cys-Pro-N$^\epsilon$-tos-D-Lys-Gly Amide					232–236	−18	DMF	768
OBzl-Z-Tyr-Phe-Gln-Asn-S-bzl-Cys-Pro-N$^\delta$-Pht-Orn-Gly Amide	1+7 ONP		94		232–236	−39	Ac	63
3-Benzylthio-propionyl-Tyr-Phe-Gln-Asn-S-bzl-Cys-Pro-N-tos-Orn-Gly Amide	2+6 A				233–237 (dec)	−40	DMF	253
OBzl-Z-Tyr-Phe-Glu-Asp-S-bzl-Cys-Pro-Ala-Gly Amide	1+7 ONP	DMF			257–258 (dec)	−39	DMF	690
Valine								
Z-Val-Gly-Ala-D-Leu-Ala-D-Val-Val-D-Val-OMe	2+6 MCA							527
For-Val-Gly-Ala-D-Leu-Ala-D-Val-Val-D-Val-OMe	2+6 MCA	THF-Acn	74					527
D-Val-Trp-D-Leu-Trp-D-Leu-Trp-D-Leu-Trp 2-Hydroxyethylamide	1+7 MCA		81					527
Z-Val-Tyr-Ile-N^{im}-bzl-His-Pro-Phe-N^{im}-bzl-His-Leu-ONBzl	A	DMF	34	Alc-Eth-Pe	125–134	−41	Ac	15
Val-Tyr-Ile-N^{im}-bzl-His-Pro-Phe-N^{im}-bzl-His-Leu-ONBzl Trihydrobromide					oil			15

9

Nonapeptides

The Table 9 of nonapeptides includes separate sections for bradykinin, oxytocin and vasopressin analogs. However, ten amino acid unit analogs of oxytocin and vasopressin were placed among the decapeptides of Table 10. Similarly, an eleven unit analog of vasopressin[300] appears in the Table (11) of unadecapeptides. Otherwise, the organization of Table 9 follows the form of Tables 3-8. Observations made in the introduction to Table 8 in regard to experimental methods also apply here. Partial purification of a nonapeptide by acid-base washing was noted only once[15] and no application of thin layer chromatography was uncovered. A number of bradykinin analogs were purified by column chromatography on carboxymethylcellulose.[648,649,651,553,65,456] Other examples of column chromatography were conducted using Amberlite IRC-50,[413,640] Sephadex G-25,[763] and silica gel.[298] Countercurrent distribution separations were performed primarily with bradykinin[680,354,70,456] and oxytocin[254,50,251,189,690] derivatives. Four other purification problems with nonapeptides were also solved using countercurrent distribution.[683,455,368,392] Approximately ten of the nonapeptides summarized in Table 9 were recrystallized from either methanol,[368,439] dimethylformamide-water,[336,289,215,766] dimethylformamide-ethanol,[765] dimethylformamide-formic acid[414] or dimethylformamide-ethyl acetate-ether.[18]

Literature concerning nonapeptide syntheses received too late for tabulation include synthesis of peptidyl-bradykinin,[647] a new synthesis of bradykinin using hydrogen fluoride for removing protecting groups,[521] syntheses of 7-Gly-oxytocin,[60] 1-(N-Me-Hemi-Cys-oxytocin),[749] Orn[4]-and Orn[5]-oxytocin,[209] Pro[4]-Ile[8]- and Leu[4]-Ile[8]-oxytocin,[512] Leu[2]- and Val[2]-oxytocin,[252] NVal[4]- and NLeu[4]-oxytocin,[676b] deamino-oxytocinoic acid dimethylamide,[656a] and syntheses of Ile[2]-Lys[8]-vasopressin[210] and acetone-Lys-vasopressin.[211]

Table 9 Nonapeptides

Compound	Method	Solvent	% Yield	Solvent Crystallization	M.P.(°)	[α] D	Solvent Rotation	Ref.
Alanine								
Ala-Tyr-Phe-Gln-Asn-Ala-Pro-Arg-Gly Amide	3+6 A					−79	1N Ac	259
Z-Ala-Tyr-Phe-Gln-Asn-Ala-Pro-NG-nitro-Arg-Gly Amide			37		237(dec)	−41	DMF	259
Ala-Tyr-Phe-Gln-Asn-Ala-Pro-Nε-boc-Lys-Gly Amide						−87	1N Ac	259
Z-Ala-Tyr-Phe-Gln-Asn-Ala-Pro-Nε-boc-Lys-Gly Amide			52		235(dec)	−43	DMF	259
Arginine								
Arg-Ala-Pro-Gly-Phe-Ser-Pro-Phe-Arg						−58	Aq	553
NG-Nitro-Z-Arg-Ala-Pro-Gly-Phe-Ser-Pro-Phe-NG-nitro-Arg-ONBzl	2+7 DCCI		72			−36	DMF	553
Arg-Gly-Gly-Gly-Gly-Gly-Gly-Gly-Arg								65
NG-Nitro-Z-Arg-Gly-Gly-Gly-Gly-Gly-Gly-Gly-NG-nitro-Arg-OMe	2+7 ONP	DMF	89		195–200 (dec)			65
Arg-Gly-Phe-Phe-Tyr-Thr-Pro-Nε-tos-Lys-Ala-OMe Dihydrochloride Hydrate								306
Tri-Z-Arg-Gly-Phe-Phe-Tyr-Thr-Pro-Nε-tos-Lys-Ala-OMe Hydrate	DCCI	DMF	44		188–190			306
NG-Nitro-Z-Arg-Gly-Phe-Phe-Tyr-Thr-Pro-Nε-tos-Lys-Ala-OMe	2+7 ONP	DMF	67		185–195			308
NG-Tos-Z-Arg-Gly-Phe-Phe-Tyr-Thr-Pro-Nε-tos-Lys-Ala-OMe Hydrate	1+8 WRK	DMF-Acn	87	Me-Eth				306
Arg-Phe-Pro-Ser-Phe-Gly-Pro-Pro-Arg								354 680
D-Arg-D-Phe-D-Pro-D-Ser-D-Phe-Gly-D-Pro-D-Pro-D-Arg Trihydrochloride								681

Compound	Method	Solvent	Yield (%)	Recryst. solvent	m.p. (°C)	$[\alpha]_D$	Solvent	Ref.
N^{G}-Nitro-Z-Arg-Phe-Pro-Ser-Phe-Gly-Pro-Pro-N^{G}-nitro-Arg-OMe	3+6 ONP		30				Aq	354
N^{G}-Nitro-Z-D-Arg-D-Phe-D-Pro-D-Ser-D-Phe-Gly-D-Pro-D-Pro-N^{G}-nitro-D-Arg-ONBzl							Ac	681
Arg-Pro-Ala-Gly-Phe-Gly-Pro-Phe-Arg Triacetate						−54	Aq	649
N^{G}-Nitro-Z-Arg-Pro-Ala-Gly-Phe-Gly-Pro-Phe-N^{G}-nitro-Arg-ONBzl	2+7 ONP	DMF	49	Ac-Aq	128–134	−71	Ac	649
Arg-Pro-Gly-Gly-Phe-Gly-Pro-Phe-Arg Triacetate						−43	Aq	649
N^{G}-Nitro-Z-Arg-Pro-Gly-Gly-Phe-Gly-Pro-Phe-N^{G}-nitro-Arg-ONBzl	2+7 ONP	DMF	62	Ac-Aq	124–129	−20	Ac	250
Arg-Pro-Gly-Gly-Phe-OAc-Ser-Pro-Phe-Arg Triacetate						−30	Aq	649
Arg-Pro-Gly-Gly-Phe-Ser-Pro-Phe-Arg Triacetate						−41	Aq	649
N^{G}-Nitro-Z-Arg-Pro-Gly-Gly-Phe-OAc-Ser-Pro-Phe-N^{G}-nitro-Arg-ONBzl	2+7 ONP	DMF	45	Ac-Aq	124–132	0.0	Ac	649
Arg-Pro-Lys-Gly-Phe-OAc-Ser-Pro-Phe-Arg Tetraacetate						−23	Aq	649
Arg-Pro-Lys-Gly-Phe-Ser-Pro-Phe-Arg Tetraacetate						−18	Aq	650
N^{G}-Nitro-Z-Arg-Pro-N^{ε}-Z-Lys-Gly-Phe-OAc-Ser-Pro-Phe-N^{G}-nitro-Arg-ONBzl Dihydrate	2+7 ONP	DMF	67	Ac-Aq	110–117	−7.6	DMF	650
Arg-Pro-Lys-Val-Gly-Leu-Gly-Ala-Arg Tetraacetate						−48	Aq	650
N^{G}-Nitro-Z-Arg-Pro-N^{ε}-Z-Lys-Val-Gly-Leu-Gly-Ala-N^{G}-nitro-Arg-ONBzl	2+7 ONP	DMF	70	Me-Eth	124–131	−53	Ac	646
Arg-Pro-Pro-β-Ala-Phe-β-Ala-Pro-Phe-Arg Triacetate						−81	Aq	646
N^{G}-Nitro-Z-Arg-Pro-Pro-β-Ala-Phe-β-Ala-Pro-Phe-N^{G}-nitro-Arg-ONBzl Trihydrate	2+7 ONP	DMF	65	Me-Eth	135–138	−64	Ac	651

Table 9 Nonapeptides (continued)

Compound	Method	Solvent	% Yield	Solvent Crystallization	M.P.(°C)	[α]$_D$	Solvent Rotation	Ref.
Bradykinins								
Arg-Pro-Pro-β-Ala-Phe-OAc-Ser-Pro-Phe-Arg Triacetate						-59	Aq	651
Arg-Pro-Pro-Ala-Phe-Ser-Pro-Phe-Arg						-99	Aq	565
Arg-Pro-Pro-β-Ala-Phe-Ser-Pro-Phe-Arg Triacetate						-80	Aq	651
N^G-Nitro-Z-Arg-Pro-Pro-β-Ala-Phe-OAc-Ser-Pro-Phe-N^G-nitro-Arg-ONBzl Dihydrate	2+7 ONP	DMF	38		130–137	-75	Ac	651
N^G-Nitro-Z-Arg-Pro-Pro-Ala-Phe-Ser-Pro-Phe-N^G-nitro-Arg-ONBzl	4+5 A		73			-55	DMF	565
Arg-Pro-Pro-Gly-Ala-Ser-Pro-Phe-Arg						-101	Aq	
						-116	Ac	555
N^G-Nitro-Z-Arg-Pro-Pro-Gly-Ala-Ser-Pro-Phe-N^G-nitro-Arg						-74	Alc	
						-55	DMF	555
N^G-Nitro-Z-Arg-Pro-Pro-Gly-Ala-Ser-Pro-Phe-N^G-nitro-Arg-OMe	4+4 A	DMF-THF	58			-76	Alc	555
Arg-Pro-Pro-Gly-Phe-Ala-Pro-Phe-Arg						-92	Aq	553
Arg-Pro-Pro-Gly-Phe-β-Ala-Pro-Phe-Arg Triacetate						-50	Aq	651
N^G-Nitro-Z-Arg-Pro-Pro-Gly-Phe-Ala-Pro-Phe-N^G-nitro-Arg-ONBzl	4+5 A	DMF	41	Ac-Aq	123–129	-61	DMF	553
N^G-Nitro-Z-Arg-Pro-Pro-Gly-Phe-β-Ala-Pro-Phe-N^G-nitro-Arg-ONBzl	2+7 ONP					-46	Ac	651
Arg-Pro-Pro-Gly-Phe-Gly-Pro-Phe-Arg						-79	Aq	65
						-85	Ac	555
N^G-Nitro-Z-Arg-Pro-Pro-Gly-Phe-Gly-Pro-Phe-N^G-nitro-Arg						-57	DMF	555

Compound	Coupling	Solvent	Yield (%)	Recryst.	m.p.	[α]	Solvent	Ref.
N^G-Nitro-Z-Arg-Pro-Pro-Gly-Phe-Gly-Pro-Phe-N^G-nitro-Arg-OMe	2+7 ONP	DMF		Me	155–170			65
N^G-Nitro-Z-Arg-Pro-Pro-Gly-Phe-Gly-Pro-Phe-N^G-nitro-Arg-OMe	A			Me-EtAc	135–150	−61	DMF	65
N^G-Nitro-Z-Arg-Pro-Pro-Gly-Phe-Leu-Pro-Phe-N^G-nitro-Arg-ONBzl	ONP	DMF	50			−38	Ac	555
Arg-Pro-Pro-Gly-Phe-Ser-Ala-Phe-Arg				Ac-Aq-AcONH$_4$	128–131	−67	Aq	653
N^G-Nitro-Z-Arg-Pro-Pro-Gly-Phe-Ser-Ala-Phe-N^G-nitro-Arg			44			−39	DMF	553
N^G-Nitro-Z-Arg-Pro-Pro-Gly-Phe-Ser-Ala-Phe-N^G-nitro-Arg-OMe	A					−42	DMF	553
Arg-Pro-Pro-Gly-Phe-Ser-Gly-Phe-Arg			61					553
N^G-Nitro-Z-Arg-Pro-Pro-Gly-Phe-OAc-Ser-Gly-Phe-N^G-nitro-Arg-OMe	2+7 ONP	DMF	54		155–170	−110	Aq	65
Arg-Pro-Pro-Gly-Phe-Ser-Pro-Ala-Arg						−54	DMF	553
N^G-Nitro-Z-Arg-Pro-Pro-Gly-Phe-Ser-Pro-Ala-N^G-nitro-Arg						−54	DMF	553
N^G-Nitro-Z-Arg-Pro-Pro-Gly-Phe-Ser-Pro-Ala-N^G-nitro-Arg-OMe	4+5 A		65			−95	Aq	553
Arg-Pro-Pro-Gly-Phe-Ser-Pro-Phe-Ala Acetate Hydrate						−57	DMF	553
N^G-Nitro-Z-Arg-Pro-Pro-Gly-Phe-Ser-Pro-Phe-Ala						−59	DMF	553
N^G-Nitro-Z-Arg-Pro-Pro-Gly-Phe-Ser-Pro-Phe-Ala-OMe	4+5 A		46			−80	Aq	553
Bradykinin						−76	1N Ac	553 433 137 605
Bradykinin Triacetate								416 518
Tyr^5-Bradykinin								605

Table 9 Nonapeptides (continued)

Compound	Method	Solvent	% Yield	Solvent Crystallization	M.P.(°C)	$[\alpha]_D$	Solvent Rotation	Ref.
Arg-Pro-Gly-Phe-OAc-Ser-Pro-Phe-Arg Triacetate								652
Arg-Pro-Gly-Phe-Ser-Pro-Phe-Arg					155–168	−107	Aq	438 605 416
D-Arg-D-Pro-D-Pro-Gly-D-Phe-D-Ser-D-Pro-D-Phe-D-Arg								681
Arg-Pro-Pro-Gly-Phe-Ser-Pro-Phe-Arg Diacetate						−83	Aq	555
Arg-Pro-Pro-Gly-Phe-Ser-Pro-Phe-Arg Dihydrochloride								70
Arg-Pro-Pro-Gly-Phe-Ser-Pro-Phe-Arg Triacetate					150–160	−82 −90	Aq Aq	439 652
Arg-Pro-Pro-Gly-Phe-Ser-Pro-Phe-N^G-nitro-Arg Triacetate					150–160			439
Tri-Z-Arg-Pro-Pro-Gly-Phe-OAc-Ser-Pro-Phe-N^G-nitro-Arg-OMe	1+8 ONP	DMF	52					438
Di-Z-Arg-Pro-Pro-Gly-Phe-Ser-Pro-Phe-N^G-Arg				Me	204–205	−52	DMF	439
Di-Z-Arg-Pro-Pro-Gly-Phe-Ser-Pro-Phe-N^G-nitro-Arg				Me-Eth	170–175 204–205			438 439
Tri-Z-Arg-Pro-Pro-Gly-Phe-Ser-Pro-Phe-nitro-Arg-OMe Hydrate	1+8 ONP	DMF		Me	156–158	−53	DMF	439
Tri-Z-Arg-Pro-Pro-Gly-Phe-Ser-Pro-Phe-N^G-nitro-OMe				Acn-EtAc	135–150			439
N^G-Nitro-Arg-Pro-Pro-Gly-Phe-Ser-Pro-Phe-N^G-nitro-Arg								416

Compound	Method	Solvent	Yield (%)	Recryst.	M.p. (°C)	$[\alpha]$	Solvent	Ref.
N^G-Nitro-Z-Arg-Pro-Gly-Phe-OAc-Ser-Pro-Phe-N^G-nitro-Arg-ONBzl	2+7 ONP	DMF	52	An-Eth	134–138	−68	Ac	652
N^G-Nitro-Z-Arg-Pro-Gly-Phe-OBzl-Ser-Pro-Phe-N^G-nitro-Arg-ONBzl				Acn-Eth	110–125	−54	DMF	137
N^G-Nitro-Z-Arg-Pro-Gly-Phe-Ser-Pro-Phe-N^G-nitro-Arg						−71	Alc	555
N^G-Nitro-Z-Arg-Pro-Gly-Phe-Ser-Pro-Phe-N^G-nitro-Arg-OMe	2+7 DCCI		50			−82	Alc	555
N^G-Nitro-Z-Arg-Pro-Gly-Phe-Ser-Pro-Phe-N^G-nitro-Arg-ONBzl					185(dec)		DMF	70
					155–160	−42		605
N^G-Nitro-Z-D-Arg-D-Pro-Gly-D-Phe-D-Ser-D-Pro-D-Phe-N^G-nitro-D-Arg-ONBzl	8+1 DCCI	DMF	80			−79	1N Ac	681
Arg-Pro-Gly-Phe-Ser-Pro-Phe-Cit						−88	1N Ac	123
								456
N^G-Nitro-Z-Arg-Pro-Gly-Phe-OAc-Ser-Pro-Phe-Cit-OMe	2+7 ONP	DMF	48	Acn-Me	118–120	−54	DMF	456
N^G-Nitro-Z-Arg-Pro-Gly-Phe-OAc-Ser-Pro-Phe-Cit-OMe Hydrobromide					125–130			123
N^G-Nitro-Z-Arg-Pro-Gly-Phe-Ser-Pro-Phe-Cit	2+7 ONP	DMF						123
Arg-Pro-Gly-Phe-Ser-Pro-Phe-His								123
N^G-Nitro-Z-Arg-Pro-Gly-Phe-OAc-Ser-Pro-Phe-His-OMe	1+8 DCCI	DMF			85–90	−32		123
N^G-Nitro-Z-Arg-Pro-Gly-Phe-Ser-Pro-Phe-His					140			123
Arg-Pro-Gly-Phe-Ser-Phe-Arg Diacetate Heptahydrate						−57	Aq	752
N^G-Nitro-Z-Arg-Pro-Gly-Phe-OAc-Ser-Sar-Phe-N^ω-nitro-Arg-OMe Hydrate	2+7 ONP	DMF	52	Alc	148–155	−46	DMF	752
N^G-Nitro-Z-Arg-Pro-Gly-Phe-Ser-Pro-Sar-Phe-N^G-nitro-Arg Dihydrate				Alc	165–174	−50	DMF	752

Table 9 Nonapeptides (continued)

Compound	Method	Solvent	% Yield	Solvent Crystallization	M.P.(°C)	$[\alpha]_D$	Solvent Rotation	Ref.
Arg-Pro-Gly-Phe-OAc-Thr-Pro-Phe-Arg Triacetate					172–182	−76	Aq	653
Arg-Pro-Gly-Phe-Thr-Pro-Phe-Arg Triacetate						−78	Aq	653
N^G-Nitro-Z-Arg-Pro-Gly-Phe-OAc-Thr-Pro-Phe-N^G-nitro-Arg-ONBzl	ONP	DMF	57	DMF-Aq	116–128	−57	Ac	653
Arg-Pro-Gly-Tyr-Ser-Pro-Phe-Arg Diacetate Hydrate						−76	Aq	565
N^G-Nitro-Z-Arg-Pro-Pro-Gly-Tyr-Ser-Pro-Phe-N^G-nitro-Arg-ONBzl	4+5 A				119–120 (dec)	−46	DMF	565
	4+5 DCCl	THF	66			−40		605
Arg-Pro-Ile-Phe-OAc-Ser-Pro-Phe-Arg Triacetate						−90	Aq	648
Arg-Pro-Ile-Phe-Ser-Pro-Phe-Arg Triacetate						−93	Aq	648
N^G-Nitro-Z-Arg-Pro-Pro-Ile-Phe-OAc-Ser-Pro-Phe-N^G-nitro-Arg-ONBzl Dihydrate	2+7 ONP	DMF	54	An-Eth	123–130	−7.5	DMF	648
Arg-Pro-Ile-Phe-OAc-Thr-Pro-Phe-Arg Triacetate						−54	Aq	648
Arg-Pro-Ile-Phe-Thr-Pro-Phe-Arg Triacetate						−89	Aq	648
N^G-Nitro-Z-Arg-Pro-Pro-Ile-Phe-OAc-Thr-Pro-Phe-N^G-nitro-Arg-ONBzl Dihydrate	2+7 ONP	DMF	64	Me-Eth	124–133	−48	DMF	648
Arg-Pro-Leu-Phe-OAc-Ser-Pro-Phe-Arg Triacetate						−54	Aq	652
N^G-Nitro-Z-Arg-Pro-Pro-Leu-Phe-OAc-Ser-Pro-Phe-N^G-nitro-Arg-ONBzl Dihydrate	ONP	DMF	76	Di-Eth	117	−87	Ac	652

Compound	Method	Solvent	Yield (%)	Recryst.	m.p. (°C)	[α]	Solvent	λ
Arg-Pro-Pro-Leu-Phe-OAc-Thr-Pro-Phe-Arg Triacetate						−83	Aq	648
Arg-Pro-Pro-Leu-Phe-Thr-Pro-Phe-Arg Triacetate						−98	Aq	648
N^G-Nitro-Z-Arg-Pro-Pro-Leu-Phe-OAc-Thr-Pro-Phe-N^G-nitro-Arg-ONBzl Dihydrate	2+7 ONP	DMF	53	Ac-Aq	117–124	−78	Ac	648
Arg-Pro-Ser-Phe-Gly-Pro-Phe-Arg Acetate Tetrahydrate						−96	Aq	565
N^G-Nitro-Z-Arg-Pro-Pro-Ser-Phe-Gly-Pro-Phe-N^G-nitro-Arg						−61	DMF	565
N^G-Nitro-Z-Arg-Pro-Pro-Ser-Phe-Gly-Pro-Phe-N^G-nitro-Arg-OMe	2+7 DCCI		46			−59	DMF	565
Arg-Pro-Pro-Val-Phe-OAc-Ser-Pro-Phe-Arg Triacetate						−59	Aq	648
Arg-Pro-Pro-Val-Phe-Ser-Pro-Phe-Arg Triacetate						−87	Aq	648
N^G-Nitro-Z-Arg-Pro-Pro-Val-Phe-OAc-Ser-Pro-Phe-N^G-nitro-Arg-ONBzl	2+7 ONP	DMF	65	Ac-Aq	112–118	−33	DMF	648
Arg-Pro-Pro-Val-Phe-OAc-Thr-Pro-Phe-Arg Triacetate						−40	Aq	648
Arg-Pro-Pro-Val-Phe-Thr-Pro-Phe-Arg Triacetate						−78	Aq	648
N^G-Nitro-Z-Arg-Pro-Pro-Val-Phe-OAc-Thr-Pro-Phe-N^G-nitro-Arg-ONBzl Hydrate	2+7 ONP	DMF	51	Ac-Aq	115–120	−25	Ac	648
Arg-Pro-Sar-Gly-Phe-Gly-Pro-Phe-Arg Triacetate						−21	Aq	649
N^G-Nitro-Z-Arg-Pro-Sar-Gly-Phe-Gly-Pro-Phe-N^G-nitro-Arg-ONBzl Hydrate	2+7 ONP	DMF	42		123–128	−17	Ac	649
Arg-Pro-Sar-Gly-Phe-Ser-Pro-Phe-Arg Diacetate Hexahydrate						−50	Aq	752

Table 9 Nonapeptides (continued)

Compound	Method	Solvent	% Yield	Solvent Crystallization	M.P.(°)	$[\alpha]_D$	Solvent Rotation	Ref.
N^G-Nitro-Z-Arg-Pro-Sar-Gly-Phe-OAc-Ser-Pro-Phe-N^G-nitro-Arg-OMe Monohydrate	2+7 ONP	DMF	50	Alc	145–149	−51	DMF	752
N^G-Nitro-Z-Arg-Pro-Sar-Gly-Phe-Ser-Pro-Phe-N^G-nitro-Arg Dihydrate				Alc	168–172	−60	DMF	752
Arg-Sar-Pro-Gly-Phe-Ser-Pro-Phe-Arg Diacetate Heptahydrate						−60	Aq	752
N^G-Nitro-Z-Arg-Sar-Pro-Gly-Phe-OAc-Ser-Pro-Phe-N^G-nitro-Arg-OMe Hydrate	2+7 ONP		63	Alc	146–152	−57	DMF	752
N^G-Nitro-Z-Arg-Sar-Pro-Gly-Phe-Ser-Pro-Phe-N^G-nitro-Arg Dihydrate				Alc	155–159	−60	DMF	752
N^G-Nitro-Z-Arg-Sar-Gly-Phe-OAc-Ser-Pro-Phe-N^G-nitro-Arg-OMe Monohydrate	1+8 ONP	DMF	53	Alc	146–151	−34	DMF	752
N^G-Nitro-Z-Arg-Sar-Gly-Phe-Ser-Pro-Phe-N^G-nitro-Arg Dihydrate				Alc	158–165	−46	DMF	752
Z-N^G-nitro-Arg-Sar-Gly-Phe-OAc-Ser-Sar-Phe-N^G-nitro-Arg-OMe Dihydrate	2+7 ONP	DMF	54	Alc	138–145	−26	DMF	752
Z-N^G-nitro-Arg-Sar-Gly-Phe-Ser-Sar-Phe-N^G-nitro-Arg Dihydrate				Alc	158–169	−27	DMF	752
N^G-Nitro-Z-Arg-Val-Trp-Ile-N^im-bzl-His-Pro-Phe-N^im-bzl-His-Leu-ONBzl	1+8 MCA	DMF-THF	78	Alc-Eth	135–142	−32	Ac	15
N^G-Nitro-Z-Arg-Val-Trp-Ile-N^im-bzl-His-Pro-Phe-N^im-bzl-His-Leu-ONBzl Trihydrobromide								15
Asparagine								
Asn-Arg-Tyr-Val-His-Pro-Phe-OMe								502
Z-Asn-N^G-nitro-Arg-Val-Tyr-Val-His-Pro-Phe-OMe	2+7 DCCI		60		210–215 (dec)			502

Citrulline

Z-Cit-Pro-Pro-Gly-Phe-OAc-Ser-Pro-Phe-N^G-nitro-Arg-OMe	1+8 ONP	DMF	55		132–140			456
Cit-Pro-Pro-Gly-Phe-Ser-Pro-Phe-Arg								456
Z-Cit-Pro-Pro-Gly-Phe-OAc-Ser-Pro-Phe-Cti-OMe	1+8 ONP	DMF	50		128–130			456
Cit-Pro-Pro-Gly-Phe-Ser-Pro-Phe-Cit								456

Cysteine

S-Bzl-Z-Cys-Gly-Ile-Glu-Asp-S-bzl-Cys-Pro-Leu-Gly Amide	1+8 ONP	DMF			229–232	−71	Ac	126
S-Bzl-N-tos-Cys-Leu-Ile-Gln-Asp-S-bzl-Cys-Pro-Leu-Gly Amide	1+8 A	DMF		DMF-Aq	232–235			295
S-Bzl-Z-Cys-p-OMe-Phe-Ile-Gln-Asn-S-bzl-Cys-Pro-Leu-Gly Amide	5+4 DCCI	DMF			240–241 (dec)	−48	DMF	357
S-Bzl-N-tos-Cys-p-me-Phe-Ile-Gln-Asn-S-bzl-Cys-Pro-Leu-Gly Amide	2+7 A	DMF	88	DMF-Aq	238–243	−33	DMF	778
S-Bzl-Z-Cys-Phe-Ile-Gln-Asn-S-bzl-Cys-Pro-N^δ-tos-Orn-Gly Amide	3+6 ONP	DMF	87		241–243	−40	DMF	254
S-Bzl-Z-Cys-Phe-Ile-Glu-Asp-S-bzl-Cys-Pro-N^G-tos-Arg-Gly Amide	3+6 ONP	DMF	66	Me	238–240			257
S-Bzl-N-tos-Cys-Phe-Ile-Glu-Asp-S-bzl-Cys-Pro-Leu-Gly Amide	2+7 A	DMF	74	Aq-DMF	232–236			294
S-Bzl-Z-Cys-Phe-Ile-Glu-Asp-S-bzl-Cys-Pro-N^δ-tos-Orn-Gly Amide	3+6 ONP	DMF	87		241–243	−40	DMF	254
S-Bzl-Z-Cys-Phe-Phe-Gln-Asn-S-bzl-Cys-Pro-Leu-Gly					246	−50	DMF	68
S-Bzl-Z-Cys-Phe-Phe-Gln-Asn-S-bzl-Cys-Pro-N^ϵ-tos-Lys-Gly	3+6 A	DMF	61		222	−50	DMF	68
S-Bzl-Z-Cys-Phe-Phe-Gln-Asn-S-bzl-Cys-Pro-tos-N^ϵ-Lys-Gly Amide	1+8 ONP	DMF	88	Ac-Alc	222–223			413

Table 9 Nonapeptides (continued)

Compound	Method	Solvent	% Yield	Solvent Crystallization	M.P.(°C)	[α]D	Solvent Rotation	Ref.
S-Bzl-Z-Cys-Phe-Phe-Gln-Asn-S-bzl-Cys-Pro-Orn-Gly Amide	3+6 ONP	DMF			222–224	–39	DMF	254
S-Bzl-Z-Cys-Phe-Phe-Glu-Asp-S-bzl-Cys-Pro-N^G-tos-Arg-Gly Amide	3+6 ONP	DMF	56					257
S-Bzl-Z-Cys-Phe-Tyr-Gln-Asn-S-bzl-Cys-Pro-Leu-Gly	3+6 A	DMF	43		218	–44	DMF	68
S-Bzl-Z-Cys-Phe-Tyr-Gln-Asn-S-bzl-Cys-Pro-N^ε-tos-Lys-Gly Amide	3+6 A	DMF	49		200	–34	DMF	68
S-Bzl-Z-Cys-Trp-Phe-Gln-Asn-S-bzl-Cys-Pro-Cit-Gly Amide	1+8 ONP		8	Me	201–210			61
S-Bzl-N-tos-Cys-Try-di-et-Ala-Gln-Asn-S-bzl-Cys-Pro-Leu-Gly Amide	1+8 A	DMF	75	DMF-Aq	238–242	–31	DMF	128
S-Bzl-N-tos-Cys-Tyr-cyclo-hexyl-Gly-Gln-Asp-S-bzl-Cys-Pro-Leu-Gly Amide	3+6 A	DMF	76	DMF-Aq	232–235	–21	DMF	128
S-Bzl-N-tos-Cys-Tyr-D-cyclo-hexyl-Gly-Gln-Asp-S-bzl-Cys-Pro-Leu-Gly Amide	3+6 A	DMF	42	DMF-Aq	212–217			128
S-Bzl-N-tos-Cys-Tyr-cyclo-pentyl-Gly-Gln-Asp-S-bzl-Cys-Pro-Leu-Gly Amide	3+6 A	DMF	60	DMF-Aq	232–240	–32	DMF	128
S-Bzl-Z-Cys-Tyr-Gly-Glu-Asp-S-bzl-Cys-Pro-Leu-Gly Amide	2+7 A	DMF	90		210–212	–50	DMF	126
Cys-Tyr-Gly-Glu-Asp-Cys-Pro-Leu-Gly Amide						–62	1 N Ac	126
S-Bzl-Z-Cys-Tyr-Ile-β-Ala-Asn-S-bzl-Cys-Pro-Leu-Gly Amide	1+8 ONP	DMF	63		230.5–232	–52	DMF	397
S-Bzl-N-tos-Cys-Tyr-Ile-Ala-Asp-S-bzl-Cys-Pro-Leu-Gly Amide	3+6 ONP	DMF	62		239–242			191
S-Bzl-N-tos-Cys-Tyr-Ile-Gln-Asn-S-bzl-Cys-Pro-Ala-Gly Amide	3+6 ONP	DMF			265	–69 / –23	Ac-Aq / DMF	275

Compound	Method	Solvent	Yield (%)	Cryst.	M.p. (°C)	[α]	Solvent	Ref.
S-Bzl-N-tos-Cys-Tyr-Ile-Gln-Asn-S-bzl-Cys-Pro-Gly-Gly Amide	3+6 ONP	DMF	55		262	−57; −20	Ac-Aq; DMF	275
S-Bzl-N-tos-Cys-Tyr-Ile-Gln-Asn-S-bzl-Cys-Pro-Ile-Gly Amide	3+6 A		59		268–270 (dec)	−28	DMF	277
S-Bzl-Z-Cys-N-me-Tyr-Ile-Gln-Asn-S-bzl-Cys-Pro-Leu-Gly Amide	3+6 DCCI	DMF	25		140	−64; −83	DMF; Me	258
S-Bzl-Z-Cys-O-tos-Tyr-Ile-Gln-Asn-S-bzl-Cys-Pro-Leu-Gly Amide	2+7 ONP	DMF	81	Ac-Alc	237–238	−50	DMF	628
S-Bzl-Z-Cys-Tyr-Ile-Gln-Asn-S-bzl-Cys-Pro-Leu-Gly	2+7 ONP	Ac-DMF	67	Ac-Alc	240.5–241.5	−64	Ac	628
S-Bzl-Z-Cys-Tyr-Ile-Gln-Asn-S-bzl-Cys-Pro-D-Leu-Gly Amide	4+5 DCCI	DMF		Aq-DMF	237–239 (dec)	−27	DMF	546
S-Bzl-Z-Cys-Tyr-Ile-Gln-Asn-S-bzl-Cys-Pro-Leu-Gly Amide	3+6 A	DMF	34		245	−35	DMF	517
	1+8 ONP	DMF	82		233–236	−43; −60	DMF; Ac	289
S-Bzl-Z-Cys-Tyr-Ile-Gln-Asn-se-bzl-Cys-Pro-Leu-Gly Amide	1+8 ONP	DMF	67		242–245 (dec)	−51	DMF	687
S-Bzl-Cys-Tyr-Ile-Gln-Asn-bz-Cys-Pro-Leu-Gly Amide				DMF-Aq	220			192
S-Bzl-N-tos-Cys-OEt-Tyr-Ile-Gln-Asn-S-bzl-Cys-Pro-Leu-Gly Amide	2+7 A	DMF	67		216–218	−30	DMF	778
S-Bzl-N-tos-Cys-Tyr-Ile-Gln-Asn-S-bzl-Cys-Pro-Leu-Gly Amide	5+4 DCCI	DMF			238–241 (dec)	−33	DMF	84
S-Eac-Z-Cys-Tyr-Ile-Gln-Asn-S-Eac-Cys-Pro-Leu-Gly Amide	1+8 OTCP	DMF	70		237–240	−64	DMF	188

Table 9 Nonapeptides (continued)

Compound	Method	Solvent	% Yield	Solvent Crystallization	M.P.(°C)	$[\alpha]_D$	Solvent Rotation	Ref.
S-Eac-Cys-Tyr-Ile-Gln-Asn-S-Eac-Cys-Pro-Leu-Gly Amide	1+8 DCCI	DMF			90(dec)	-34	DMF	188
Se-Bzl-Z-Cys-Tyr-Ile-Gln-Asn-S-bzl-Cys-Pro-Leu-Gly Amide					246-248 (dec)	-60	F	687
Oxytocin								
Oxytocin								271
								265
								84
AOC-Oxytocin					100-120	-70	Ac-Aq	750
N-Z-S,S'-di-bzl-Oxytocin						-48	DMF	265
Deamino-Oxytocin								46
Desamino-Phe^2-Orn^8-Oxytocin						-118	1N Ac	657
Deamino-dicarba-Oxytocin								253
Leu-Oxytocin						+12	0.5N Ac	546
Pro-Oxytocin								167
D-Cys-Oxytocin								251
D-Penicillamine'-Oxytocin						-28	1N Ac	568
Penicillamine'-Oxytocin						+18	1N Ac	568
Deaminopenicillamine'-Oxytocin						-53	1N Ac	568
Se'-Oxytocin						-13	1N Ac	687
Deamino-Se'-Oxytocin						-46	Ac	687
Phe^2-Orn^8-Oxytocin								254
Phe(p-OEt)^2-Oxytocin						-24	Ac	778
Phe(p-Et)^2-Oxytocin						-22	Ac	778
Phe(p-Me)^2-Oxytocin						-23	Ac	778
(N-me-Tyr)^2-Oxytocin								258

Compound			mp	$[\alpha]$	Solvent	Ref.
Tyr(Me)^2-Oxytocin				−31	Ac	294
Di-et-Ala^3-Oxytocin				−3.7	Ac	128
Cyclopentyl-Gly^3-Oxytocin				−26	Ac	128
Cyclohexyl-Gly^3-Oxytocin				−8.9	Ac	128
D-Cyclohexyl-Gly^3-Oxytocin						128
Thr(Me)^3-Oxytocin						91
Tyr^3-Oxytocin						68
βAla^4-Oxytocin			168	+120	1N Ac	397
D-Asn^5-Oxytocin				+30	DMF	127
Deamino^1-Val^5-Oxytocin				−46	Ac	688
Val^5-Oxytocin				−48	Ac	688
Penicillamine^6-Oxytocin						567
Se^6-Oxytocin				−10	1N Ac	687
Deamino-Se^6-Oxytocin				−54	1N Ac	687
Pro^7-Oxytocin						276
Abu^8-Oxytocin				−53	Aq	275
Ala^8-Oxytocin						275
Arg^8-Oxytocin				−5	1N Ac	63
Cit^8-Oxytocin						61
Gly^8-Oxytocin				−28	Aq	275
Ile^8-Oxytocin						277
Leu^8-Oxytocin						276
Orn^8-Oxytocin				−7	1N Ac	63
Val^8-Oxytocin						277
Decarboxamide^9-Oxytocin				−24	1N Ac	72
Gly^9-Oxytocin						276
Sar^9-Oxytocin				−21	1N Ac	84
Cysteine (cont'd.)						
S-Bzl-Z-Cys-Tyr-Ile-D-Gln-D-Asn-S-bzl-Cys-Pro-Leu-Lys Amide	3+6 A	DMF	22	245	−30	DMF	127
S-Bzl-Z-Cys-Tyr-Ile-Gln-Asn-S-bzl-Cys-Pro-N$^\delta$-Pht-Orn-Gly Amide	1+8 ONP		93	257–261	−49	Ac	63

353

Table 9 Nonapeptides (continued)

Compound	Method	Solvent	% Yield	Solvent Crystallization	M.P.(°C)	$[\alpha]_D$	Solvent Rotation	Ref.
S-Bzl-N-tos-Cys-Tyr-Ile-Gln-Asn-S-bzl-Cys-Pro-Val-Gly Amide	3+6 A		35		260(dec)	−27 −64	DMF Ac-Aq	277
S-Bzl-Z-Cys-Tyr-Ile-Gln-Asp-S-bzl-Cys-Pro-Ala-Gly Amide	1+8	DMF			244–247 (dec)	−46	DMF	690
S-Bzl-Z-Cys-Tyr-Ile-Gln-Asp-S-bzl-Cys-Pro-Leu-Gly Amide	DCCI CDI WRK		80 70.5 85		225–230	−44	DMF	141
S-Bzl-Z-Cys-Tyr-Ile-Gln-Val-S-bzl-Cys-Pro-Leu-Gly Amide	1+8 ONP	DMF			235–239 (dec)	−74	Fm	688
S-Bzl-N-tos-Cys-Tyr-Ile-Glu-Asp-S-bzl-Cys-Pro-tos-Arg-Gly Amide	3+6 ONP	DMF	53		236–238	−32	DMF	257
S-Bzl-Z-D-Cys-Tyr-Ile-Glu-Asp-S-bzl-Cys-Pro-Leu-Gly Amide	1+8 ONP	DMF	80		237–238			251
S-Bzl-Z-Cys-Tyr-Ile-Glu-Asp-Cys-Pro-Leu-Gly Amide	3+6 DCCI	DMF	56		234–235	−57 −46	Ac DMF	51
S-Bzl-N-tos-Cys-Tyr-Allo-Ile-Glu-Asp-Cys-S-bzl-Pro-Leu-Gly Amide	3+6 A	DMF						437
S-Bzl-N-tos-Cys-Tyr-Ile-Glu-Asp-Cys-S-bzl-Pro-tos-Orn-Gly Amide	3+6 ONP	DMF	62		222–226			256
S-Bzl-Z-Cys-Tyr-Ile-Gly-Asp-S-bzl-Cys-Pro-Leu-Gly Amide	5+4 DCCI 5+4 WRK		39 89		204–215	−54	DMF	141
S-Bzl-Z-Cys-Tyr-Ile-Gly-Asp-S-bzl-Cys-Pro-Leu-Gly Amide	1+8 ONP	DMF			225–227	−60	DMF	126

354

Compound	Method	Solvent	MP (°C)	Recryst. solvent	Range (°C)	$[\alpha]$	Solvent	Ref
S-Bzl-N-tos-Cys-Tyr-Ile-Ser-Asn-S-bzl-Cys-Pro-Ile-Gly Amide								189
S-Bzl-N-tos-Cys-Tyr-Ile-Ser-Asp-S-bzl-Cys-Pro-Leu-Gly Amide	3+6 ONP							191
S-Bzl-N-tos-Cys-Tyr-Leu-Glu-Asp-S-bzl-Cys-Pro-Leu-Gly Amide	3+6 A		47		230–234			437
S-Bzl-N-tos-Cys-Tyr-Phe-Asn-Asn-S-bzl-Cys-Pro-N$^\epsilon$-tos-Lys-Gly Amide	6+3 A	DMF	53–60	DMF-Alc	223–225	−18	DMF	765
S-Bzl-N-tos-Cys-Tyr-Phe-Gln-Asn-S-bzl-Cys-Gly-N$^\epsilon$-tos-Lys-Gly Amide	6+3 A	DMF	78.5	DMF-Aq	244–247	−17	DMF	336
S-Bzl-Z-Cys-Tyr-Phe-Gln-Asn-S-bzl-Cys-Pro-N^G-tos-Arg-Gly Amide	3+6 A	DMF	70	DMF-Aq	208–209		DMF	640
S-Bzl-N-tos-Cys-Tyr-Phe-Gln-Asn-S-bzl-Cys-Pro-N^G-tos-D-Arg-Gly Amide				DMF-Aq	213–215	−9.0	DMF	769
Cys-Tyr-Phe-Gln-Asn-Cys-Pro-Arg-Gly Amide	A	DMF	67					640

Vasopressins

Compound	$[\alpha]$	Solvent	Ref
Deamino'-D-γ-Aminobutyrine[8]-Vasopressin	−109	0.1N Ac	768
Deamino-Phe[2]-Arg[8]-Vasopressin	−119	0.1N Ac	255
Deamino-Phe[2]-Ile[3]-Orn[8]-Vasopressin			253
Phe[2]-Lys[8]-Vasopressin			413
			68
Phe[2]-[14C]-Lys[8]-Vasopressin			671
Phe[2]-Orn[8]-Vasopressin			254
Phe[2]-Tyr[3]-Lys[8]-Vasopressin			68
Tyr(Et)[2]-Lys[8]-Vasopressin Diacetate	−42	1M Ac	766
Tyr(Me)[2]-Lys-Vasopressin Hydrated Acetate	−32	1M Ac	766
Deamino-Ile[3]-Orn[8]-Vasopressin	−84	0.1N Ac	253
Tyr[3]-Lys[8]-Vasopressin			68
Asn[4]-Lys-Vasopressin Diacetate Hydrate	−37		765
Gly[7]-Lys[8]-Vasopressin Diacetate Monohydrate	−19		336
D-Pro[7]-Lys-Vasopressin Diacetate	+26		336
Arg-Vasopressin	−21	1N Ac	63

Table 9 Nonapeptides (continued)

Compound	Method	Solvent	% Yield	Solvent Crystallization	M.P.(°C)	[α]D	Solvent Rotation	Ref.
Arg^8-Vasopressin								643
D-Arg^8-Vasopressin						-18		769
Deamino-Arg^8-Vasopressin						-103	0.1N Ac	255
Deamino-D-Arg^8-Vasopressin						-82		768
Dab^8-Vasopressin Monohydrate Diacetate								771
D-Dab^8-Vasopressin Diacetate						-31		770
Lys^8-Vasopressin								62
								604
D-Lys^8-Vasopressin						-31	1M Ac	765
								414
Lys-Vasopressin						-25		769
Deamino'-D-Lys^8-Vasopressin						-70		412a
Thia-Lys^8-Vasopressin Diacetate Monohydrate						-46		768
Orn^8-Vasopressin						-28		215
								63
Deamino-Orn^8-Vasopressin						-111	0.1N Ac	253
Ala^9-Lys-Vasopressin						-35	1M Ac	767
D-Ala^9-Lys-Vasopressin						-23	1M Ac	767
Ethylene-diamine^9-Lys^8-Vasopressin								767
Cysteine (cont'd.)								
S-Bzl-Z-Cys-Tyr-Phe-Gln-Asn-S-bzl-Cys-Pro-Cit-Glu Amide	5+4 DCCI	DMF	27	Ac-Alc	210–220			61
S-Bzl-N-tos-Cys-Tyr-Phe-Gln-Asn-S-bzl-Cys-Pro-N^ϵ-tos-Lys-Ala Amide	6+3 A	DMF	73	DMF-Aq	238–242	-11	DMF	767
S-Bzl-N-tos-Cys-Tyr-Phe-Gln-Asn-S-bzl-Cys-Pro-N^ϵ-tos-Lys-D-Ala Amide	6+3 A	DMF	61	DMF-Aq	244–248	-13	DMF	767
S-Bzl-Z-Cys-OMe-Tyr-Phe-Gln-Asn-S-bzl-Cys-Pro-N^ϵ-tos-Lys-Gly Amide	3+6 A	DMF	36		211–213			604

Compound	Method	Solvent	Yield (%)	Recryst.	mp (°C)	[α]	Solvent	Ref.
S-Bzl-Z-Cys-Tyr-Phe-Gln-Asn-S-bzl-Cys-Pro-N$^\epsilon$-tos-Lys-Gly Amide	1+8 ONP	DMF		Ac-Alc	217-221	-43	DMF	62
S-Bzl-Cys-Tyr-Phe-Gln-Asn-S-bzl-Cys-Pro-N$^\epsilon$-tos-Lys-Gly Amide Hydrobromide				Me-Alc-Eth	180			192
Z-S-bzl-Cys-Tyr-Phe-Gln-Asn-S-bzl-Cys-Pro-N$^\epsilon$-tos-Lys-Gly Amide	1+8 ONP	DMF	59	Aq-DMF	195-200	-35	DMF	289
S-Bzl-N-tos-Cys-OBzl-Tyr-Phe-[14C]-Gln-Asn-S-bzl-Cys-Pro-N$^\epsilon$-tos-Lys-Gly Amide	2+7 ONP	DMF	84	DMF-Aq	190-200	-26	DMF	671
S-Bzl-N-tos-Cys-OEt-Tyr-Phe-Gln-Asn-S-bzl-Cys-Pro-N$^\epsilon$-tos-Lys-Gly Amide	2+7 A	DMF	75	DMF-Aq	188-190	-18	DMF	766
S-Bzl-N-tos-Cys-OMe-Tyr-Phe-Gln-Asn-S-bzl-Cys-Pro-N$^\epsilon$-tos-Lys-Gly Amide	2+7 A	DMF	56	DMF-Aq	216-218	-17	DMF	766
S-Bzl-N-tos-Cys-O-tos-Tyr-Phe-Gln-Asn-S-bzl-Cys-Pro-N$^\epsilon$-tos-Lys-Gly Amide Dihydrate	2+7 ONP	DMF	84	DMF-Aq	180-192	-29	DMF	671
S-Bzl-N-tos-Cys-Tyr-Phe-Gln-Asn-S-bzl-Cys-Pro-N$^\epsilon$-tos-Lys-Gly Amide	4+5 DCCI	THF-Aq	63.5	DMF-Fm	231-232	-24	DMF	414
	6+3 A	DMF	65	DMF-Aq	218-220	-27	DMF	215
	6+3 A	DMF	63-71	Aq-DMF	225-230	-27		765
	2+7 A	DMF	64-73	Aq-DMF	225-230			
S-Bzl-N-tos-Cys-Tyr-Phe-Gln-Asn-S-bzl-Cys-Pro-N$^\epsilon$-tos-Lys-D-Lys Amide				DMF-Aq	215-217	-3.8	DMF	769
S-Bzl-N-tos-Cys-Tyr-Phe-Gln-Asn-S-bzl-Cys-D-Pro-N$^\epsilon$-tos-Lys-Gly Amide	6+3 A		75	DMF-Aq	209-213	-7.1	DMF	336
S-Bzl-N-tos-Cys-Tyr-Phe[14C]-Gln-Asn-S-bzl-Cys-Pro-N$^\epsilon$-tos-Lys-Gly Amide	1+8 A	DMF	63.5	DMF-Aq	187-195			671
S-Bzl-Z-Cys-Tyr-Phe-Gln-Asn-S-bzl-Cys-Pro-Orn-Gly Amide						-28	1N Ac	63
S-Bzl-Z-Cys-Tyr-Phe-Gln-Asn-S-bzl-Cys-Pro-N$^\delta$-Pht-Orn-Gly Amide	1+8 ONP	DMF	96		222-234	-44	Ac	63
S-Bzl-Z-Cys-Tyr-Phe-Glu-Asp-S-bzl-Cys-Pro-Ala-Gly Amide	1+8 ONP	DMF			251-253 (dec)	-47	DMF	690

357

Table 9 Nonapeptides (continued)

Compound	Method	Solvent	% Yield	Solvent Crystallization	M.P.(°C)	$[\alpha]_D$	Solvent Rotation	Ref.
S-Bzl-N-tos-Cys-Tyr-Phe-Glu-Asp-S-bzl-Cys-Pro-tos-Arg-Gly Amide	3+6 A	DMF	37		198-199			257
S-Bzl-N-tos-Cys-Tyr-OMe-Thr-Gln-Asn-S-bzl-Cys-Pro-Leu-Gly Amide	3+6 A	DMF	78	Aq-DMF	210-214			91
S-Bzl-Z-Cys-Tyr-Tyr-Gln-Asn-S-bzl-Cys-Pro-Leu-Gly Amide	3+6 A	DMF	47		210	-50	DMF	68
S-Bzl-Z-Cys-Tyr-Tyr-Gln-Asn-S-bzl-Cys-Pro-N$^\epsilon$-tos-Lys-Gly Amide	3+6 A	DMF	62		206	-40	DMF	68
Glutamine								
γ-OBzl-Z-Gln-N^G-tos-Arg-Gly-Phe-Phe-Thr-Pro-N$^\epsilon$-tos-Lys-Ala	2+7 MCA ONP	THF-DMF DMF	61 17.5	Me-Aq DMF-EtAc	178-181	-24	DMF	539
γ-OBu^t-Z-Glu-N^G-tos-Arg-Phe-Phe-Tyr-Thr-Pro-N$^\epsilon$-tos-Lys-Ala-OBu^t	2+7 ONP	DMF	75		168-171	-35	DMF	542
Z-Octa-γ-OMe-Glu-di-et-Glu						-32	DCA	175
Z-Glu-Ile-Val-γ-OBu^t-Glu-Gln-S-bzl-Cys-S-bzl-Cys-Ala-Gly-OMe	4+5 A		73		274(dec)	-29	DMSO	314
Z-Glu-Ile-Val-Glu-Gln-S-bzl-Cys-S-bzl-Cys-Ala-Gly Hydrazide								314
Z-Pyro-Glu-Pro-Ser-N$^\epsilon$-boc-Lys-β-OBu^t-Asp-Ala-Phe-Ile-Gly	2+7 ONP	DMF	92		183-185			25
Pyro-Glu-Pro-Ser-N$^\epsilon$-boc-Lys-β-OBu^t-Asp-Ala-Phe-Ile-Gly-OBu^t	4+5 A	DMF			215-217 (dec)	-62	Ac	85
Pyro-Glu-Pro-Ser-Lys-Asp-Ala-Phe-Ile-Gly Trifluoroacetate					190(dec)	-66	Ac-Aq	85

Glycine

Compound	Method	Solvent	Yield (%)	Recryst. solvent	M.p. (°C)	[α]	Solvent	Ref.
Z(NO$_2$)-Gly-Ile-Val-γ-OBu^t-Glu-Gln-S-bzl-Cys-S-bzl-Cys-Ala-Gly					254–259			305
Z(NO$_2$)-Gly-Ile-Val-γ-Bu^t-Glu-Gln-S-bzl-Cys-S-bzl-Cys-Ala-Gly					254–259 (dec)			305
Z(NO$_2$)-Gly-Ile-Val-γ-Bu^t-Glu-Gln-S-bzl-Cys-S-bzl-Cys-Ala-Gly-OEt	4+5 DCCI	DMF	52	DMSO-Di	270–272	−27	DMSO	305
Z(NO$_2$)-Gly-Ile-Val-γ-OBu^t-Glu-Gln-S-bzl-Cys-S-bzl-Cys-Ala-Gly-OEt	4+5 DCCI	DMF	52	DMSO-Di	270–272	−27	DMSO	305
Z-Gly-Ile-Val-γ-OBu^t-Glu-Gln-S-bzl-Cys-S-bzl-Cys-Thr-Ser Hydrazide				HMPA-Aq	258 (dec)	−20	HMPA	317
Z-Gly-Ile-Val-γ-OBu^t-Glu-Gln-S-bzl-Cys-S-bzl-Cys-Thr-Ser-OMe	4+5 A		60	DMF-Aq	263–264 (dec)	−30	DMF	317

Leucine

Compound	Method	Solvent	Yield (%)	Recryst. solvent	M.p. (°C)	[α]	Solvent	Ref.
Z-Leu-Gln-nitro-Arg-Leu-Leu-Gln-Gly-Leu-Val Amide	1+8 ONP	DMF	99		267–269 (dec)	−41	Ac	66
Z-Leu-γ-OBu^t-Glu-γ-OBu^t-Glu-γ-OBu^t-Glu-γ-OBu^t-Glu-Ala-Tyr-Gly-OMe Hydrate	1+8 ONP	DMF	100		260–261	−17	DMF	423
Leu-γ-OBu^t-Glu-γ-OBu^t-Glu-γ-OBu^t-Glu-γ-OBu^t-Glu-Ala-Tyr-Gly-OMe Acetate Hydrate			92		259–260 (dec)	−11	DMF	423
Z-Leu-Tyr-Gln-Leu-Glu-Asp-Tyr-S-bzl-Cys-Asp-ONBzl	4+5 A		73		242–243	−46	DMF	315
Z-Leu-Val-γ-OBzl-Glu-Ala-Leu-Tyr-Leu-Val-S-bzl-Cys Amide	2+7 ONP	DMF	91	DMF-Aq	262–266			307

Table 9 Nonapeptides (continued)

Compound	Method	Solvent	% Yield	Solvent Crystallization	M.P.(°C)	$[\alpha]_D$	Solvent Rotation	Ref.
Lysine								
N^ϵ,N^α-di-Z-Lys-N^G-nitro-Arg-Pro-Pro-Phe-Gly-Pro-Phe-N^G-nitro-Arg-OMe	1+8 ONP	DMF	59		135–150			65
Lys-Arg-Pro-Pro-Phe-Gly-Pro-Phe-Arg								65
N^ϵ,N^α-diBoc-Lys-γ-OBu^t-Glu-Thr-Ala-Ala-N^ϵ-For-Lys-Phe-γ-OBu^t-Glu-OMe	3+6 A		50		217.5–218.5	−23	DMF	535
Lys-Pro-Pro-Gly-Phe-Ser-Pro-Phe-Lys					145–149	−66	Me	722
N^ϵ-Boc-Z-Lys-Pro-Val-Gly-N^ϵ-boc-Lys-N^ϵ-boc-Lys-N^G-tos-Arg-N^G-tos-Arg-Pro	4+5 WRK		86		129–131	−43	Me	455
N^ϵ-Boc-Z-Lys-Pro-Val-Gly-N^ϵ-boc-Lys-N^ϵ-boc-Lys-N^G-tos-Arg-N^G-tos-Arg-Pro Amide	4+5 WRK		66		128–134	−44	Me	492
N^ϵ-Boc-Z-Lys-Pro-Val-Gly-N^ϵ-boc-Lys-N^ϵ-boc-Lys-N^G-tos-Arg-N^G-tos-Arg-Pro-OBu^t	4+5 DCCI		78		123–125	−48	Me	368
N^ϵ-Boc-N^α-Z-Lys-Pro-Val-Gly-N^ϵ-boc-Lys-N^ϵ-boc-Lys-N^G-tos-Arg-N^G-tos-Arg-Pro-OBu^t	DCCI	EtAc-DMF	78	Me	123–125	−48	Me	368
N^ϵ-Boc-Lys-Pro-Val-Gly-N^ϵ-boc-Lys-N^ϵ-boc-Lys-Arg-Arg-Pro-OBu^t-tri-p-toluenesulfonate		DMF-An	52					503
N^ϵ-Boc-Lys-Pro-Val-Gly-N^ϵ-boc-Lys-N^ϵ-boc-Lys-N^G-nitro-Arg-N^G-nitro-Arg-Pro-OBu^t					173–182			503
N^ϵ-Boc-Lys-Pro-Val-Gly-N^ϵ-boc-Lys-N^ϵ-boc-Lys-N^G-tos-Arg-N^G-tos-Arg-Pro					131–133	−36	Me	455
N^ϵ-Boc-Lys-Pro-Val-Gly-N^ϵ-boc-Lys-N^ϵ-boc-Lys-N^G-tos-Arg-N^G-tos-Arg-Pro Amide					165–167	−19	DMF	492

Compound	Method	Solvent	Yield	Recryst. solvent	m.p.	[α]	Solvent	No.
N^ε-Boc-Lys-Pro-Val-Gly-N^ε-boc-Lys-N^ε-boc-Lys-N^G-tos-Arg-N^G-tos-Arg-Pro-OBu^t					120–130	−42	Me	368
N^ε-Boc-N^α-Pz-Lys-Pro-Val-Gly-N^ε-boc-Lys-N^ε-boc-Lys-N^G-nitro-Arg-N^G-nitro-Arg-Pro								298
N^ε-Boc-Pz-Lys-Pro-Val-Gly-N^ε-boc-Lys-N^ε-boc-Lys-N^G-nitro-Arg-N^G-nitro-Arg-Pro-OBu^t	4+5 MCA	THF-DMF	58		143–148			503
N^ε-Boc-N^α-Pz-Lys-Pro-Val-Gly-N^ε-boc-Lys-N^ε-boc-Lys-N^G-nitro-Arg-N^G-nitro-Arg-Pro-OMe	4+5 A							298
N^ε-Boc-Pz-Lys-Pro-Val-Gly-N^ε-boc-Lys-N^ε-boc-Lys-N^G-nitro-Arg-N^G-nitro-Arg-Pro-OMe	4+5 A	DMF	75	Acn	136–138			574
N^ε-Boc-N^α-trt-Lys-Pro-Val-Gly-N^ε-boc-Lys-N^ε-boc-Lys-N^G-nitro-Arg-N^G-nitro-Arg-Pro-OBu^t	4+5 MCA	THF						503
Lys-Pro-Val-Gly-Lys-Lys-Arg-Arg-Pro-OBu^t tri-toluenesulfonate					130–150			503
N^G-Tos-Z-Lys-Pro-Val-Gly-N^ε-tos-Lys-N^ε-tos-Lys-N^G-tos-Arg-Pro	4+5 ONP	Acn	91	An-Eth	126–132	−27	DMF	493
N^ε-Tos-N^α-Z-Lys-Pro-Val-Gly-N^ε-tos-Lys-N^ε-tos-Lys-N^G-tos-Arg-Pro	5+4 WRK	Acn	71.5	Me-Eth	135–137			371
N^ε-Tos-N^α-Z-Lys-Pro-Val-Gly-N^ε-tos-Lys-N^ε-tos-Lys-N^G-tos-Arg-Pro-OBu^t					115–120	−45	Me	368
N^ε-Tos-Lys-Pro-Val-Gly-N^ε-tos-Lys-N^ε-tos-Lys-N^G-tos-Arg-N^G-tos-Arg-Pro-OBu^t					120–130	−37	Me	368

Table 9 Nonapeptides (continued)

Compound	Method	Solvent	% Yield	Solvent Crystallization	M.P.(°C)	$[\alpha]_D$	Solvent Rotation	Ref.
Phenylalanine								
N,N'-Bis[Phe-Val-Asn-Gln-His-Leu]-Cystine-di-Gly					177-183	-71	Aq	763
Proline								
Z-Pro-N^G-nitro-Arg-Pro-Gly-Phe-Ser-Pro-Phe-N^G-nitro-Arg-ONBzl	2+7 DCCI		65		160-165	-40	DMF	565
Pro-Arg-Pro-Gly-Phe-Ser-Pro-Phe-Arg-ONBzl Acetate Pentahydrate						-67	Aq	565
Serine								
Boc-Ser-N$^\epsilon$-boc-Lys-Asn-Ala-Phe-Ile-Gly-Leu-Met Amide Hydrate	5+4 DCCI				245(dec)	-38	Ac	392
Ser-Lys-Asn-Ala-Phe-Ile-Gly-Leu-Met Amide					242(dec)	-62	Aq	392
Z-Ser-Tyr-Ser-Met-Gln-His-Phe-Ala-Arg Tetrahydrate*	5+4 A	DMF	35		198-202 (dec)	-22	Ac	240
Z-Ser-Tyr-Ser-Met-Glu-His-Phe-Arg-Tyr Hydrazide								407
Z-Ser-Tyr-Ser-Met-Glu-His-Phe-Arg-Tyr-OMe	7+2 A		76		160(dec)			407
Threonine								
OBu^t-Z-Thr-OBu^t-Ser-β-OBu^t-Asp-OBu^t-Tyr-OBu^t-Ser-N$^\epsilon$-boc-Lys-OBu^t-Tyr-Leu-β-OBu^t-Asp	1+8 OSU	DMF	82	Me-Eth-Pe	207-209	-5.6	DMF	735
	1+8 2,4-DNPO	DMF	70		208-209	-5.5	DMF	

*Azide explodes when heated in a capillary tube.

362

Compound								
OBu^t-Nps-Thr-OBu^t-Ser-Asp-β-OBu^t-OBu^t-Tyr-OBu^t-Ser-N^ε-boc-Lys-OBu^t-Tyr-Leu-β-OBu^t-Asp	1+8 OSU 1+8 ONP	DMF DMF	89 75			-20 -20	DMF DMF	735
Tyrosine								
Z-Se-bzl-selenocystein-Tyr-Ile-Gln-Asn-Se-bzl-selenocystein-Pro-Leu-Gly Amide	3+6 ONP		74		229–231	-42	DMF	143
Valine								
Z(OMe)-Val-N^δ-Z-Orn-Leu-D-Phe-Gly-Val-N^δ-Z-Orn-Leu-D-Phe-Gly	A	DMF	82	DMF-EtAc-Eth	253–257	-48	Ac	18
β-Bzl-mercapto-iso-Val-Tyr-Ile-Gln-Asn-S-bzl-Cys-Pro-Leu-Gly Amide				THF-Aq	234–237	-48	DMF	568
Z-Val-D-Val-Trp-D-Leu-Trp-D-Leu-Trp-D-Leu-Trp 2-Hydroxy-et Amide								527
Val-D-Val-Trp-D-Leu-Trp-D-Leu-Trp-D-Leu-Trp 2-Hydroxy-et Amide								527

363

10

Decapeptides

With two exceptions (OTCP and 2,4-DNPO) the decapeptides of Table 10 were obtained by ONP, A, MCA or DCCI coupling procedures. In Table 10 and elsewhere in Parts 1-3, these reagents were generally used in the presence of triethylamine; in more recent work with mixed carbonic anhydrides, either N-ethylmorpholine, N-ethylpiperidine or diethylglycine was substituted. One example[451] of washing (0.5M citric acid-3% sodium bicarbonate-water) a crude reaction product appears among the protected decapeptides of Table 10. Two groups of investigators[28,451] employed thin layer chromatography and two others[575,571] employed electrophoresis for assessing purity. Some of the decapeptides were purified by column chromatography using Sephadex G-25,[28] aminoethylcellulose,[28] carboxymethylcellulose[747,162,644] or Dowex 50 W-X 2.[527] Application of countercurrent distribution techniques appears in references 190, 392 and 403.

A few of the protected decapeptides were successfully crystallized and recrystallized. The solvent systems found successful were dimethylformamide-water,[772] dioxane-ether,[337] methanol-ligroin,[431] dioxane-ether-ligroin,[338] and ethyl acetate-ether-ligroin.[338] Persistent application of the solvents similarly mentioned in the introductions to Tables 5-8 should simplify final purification of peptides in these molecular weight ranges.

Two recent advances in synthesis of decapeptides involve preparation of Gly[5]-Gly[10]-gramicidin-S[463a] and a decapeptide (Leu-Ala-Ala-Gly-Lys-Val-Glu-Asp-Ser-Asp) component of human gastric juice.[4a]

Table 10 Decapeptides

Compound	Method	Solvent	% Yield	Solvent Crystallization	M.P.(°C)	$[\alpha]_D$	Solvent Rotation	Ref.
Alanine								
Z(OMe)-Ala-N^δ-Z-Orn-Leu-D-Phe-Pro-Ala-N^δ-Z-Orn-Leu-D-Phe-Pro	A		87	Di-Eth-Pe	115–118	–41	DMF	338
Arginine								
N^G-Nitro-Z-Arg-Leu-Gln-N^G-nitro-Arg-Leu-Leu-Gln-Gly-Leu-Val Amide	1+9 2,4-DNPO	DMF		Alc-EtAc	255–264 (dec)	–36	Ac	66
Tri-Z-Arg-Pro-Pro-Gly-Phe-Ser-Pro-Phe-Ala-N^G-nitro-Arg-OBzl	1+9 ONP	DMF	61	EtAc-Eth	115–118	–44	DMF	518
Arg-Pro-Pro-Gly-Phe-Ser-Pro-Phe-Ala-Orn						–86	Aq	565
N^G-Nitro-Z-Arg-Pro-Pro-Gly-Phe-Ser-Pro-Phe-Ala-N^δ-boc-Orn						–51	DMF	565
N^G-Nitro-Z-Arg-Pro-Pro-Gly-Phe-Ser-Pro-Phe-Ala-N^δ-boc-Orn-OMe	4+6 A		49			–52	DMF	565
Asparagine								
Asp-Arg-Val-Tyr-Ile-His-Pro-Phe-His-Leu								15
β-OBzl-Z-Asp-N^G-nitro-Arg-Val-Tyr-Ile-N^{im}-bzl-His-Pro-Pro-N^{im}-bzl-His-Leu-ONBzl	1+9 MA		79		138–144	–30	Ac	15
Val^5-Angiotensin-I					285–290 (dec)	–74	Ac	190
Val^5-D-Phe^8-Angiotensin-I					285–290 (dec)	–74	0.05N Ac	190
Asp-Arg-Val-Tyr-Val-His-Pro-Phe-His-Leu								190
Asp-Arg-Val-Tyr-Val-His-Pro-D-Phe-His-Leu	4+6 A		62		235 (dec)	–64	Ac	190
β-OBzl-Z-Asp-Arg-Val-Tyr-Val-His-Pro-Phe-His-Leu-ONBzl			56		235	–52	Me	190

365

Table 10 Decapeptides (continued)

Compound	Method	Solvent	% Yield	Solvent Crystallization	M.P.(°C)	$[\alpha]_D$	Solvent Rotation	Ref.
β-OBzl-Z-Asp-Arg-Val-Tyr-Val-His-Pro-D-Phe-His-Leu-ONBzl	A		46		180-200 (dec)	-27	Me	190
β-OBzl-Z-Asp-Arg-Val-Tyr-Val-His-Pro-Phe-His-Leu-ONBzl Hydrochloride	4+6 A	EtAc			180-200 (dec)	-27	Me	190
β-OBzl-Z-Asp-Arg-Val-Tyr-Val-His-Pro-Phe-His-Leu-ONBzl Trihydrochloride	4+6 A	EtAc	56		235	-52	Me	190
Cysteine								
S,S'-N-Z-hemi-Cystine-S-Bzh-Cys-Gly-Phe-Gly-Phe-Gly-hemi-Cystine-Phe-Gly				DMF-Eth	240-241.5	+32	DMF	226
Z-S-bzl-Cys-Phe-Ala-Glu-Asp-S-bzl-Cys-Pro-N^δ-tos-Orn-Gln	3+7 ONP	DMF	54		220-224			256
Oxytocin								
Phe^2-Phe^3-Oxytocin								68
Phe^2-Tyr-^{3}-Oxytocin								68
Phe^3-Cit^8-Oxytocin								61
4-D-Gln-5-D-Asn-Oxytocin				Alc	155	+24	DMF	127
Vasopressin								
Gly-Cys^1-Lys-Vasopressin Trihydrate Diacetate						-63		772
N^α-Trp-8-Lys-Vasopressin								300
Gly-Cys^1-$Tyr(Me)^2$-Lys-Vasopressin Dihydrate Diacetate						-70		772
Cysteine (cont'd.)								
S-Bzl-Z-Cys-Tyr-Tyr-Tyr-Gln-Ans-S-bzl-Cys-Pro-N^ϵ-tos-Lys-Gly Amide	6+4 DCCI		57		190-194	-38	DMF	50

Compound	Ref.	Solvent	$[\alpha]$	m.p.	Recryst.	Yield %	Method	Solvent
S-Bzl-Z-Cys-Tyr-Tyr-Glu-Asp-S-bzl-Cys-Pro-N$^\epsilon$-tos-Lys-Gly Amide	50			194		40	6+4 DCCI	Aq-THF-DMF
Glutamine								
γ-OBzl-Z-Glu-N^G-tos-Arg-Gly-Phe-Tyr-Thr-Pro-N$^\epsilon$-tos-Lys-Ala-OMe	306			197–200	Me	70	1+9 ONP	DMF
γ-OBu^t-Z-Glu-N^G-nitro-Arg-Gly-Phe-Phe-OBu^t-Tyr-OBu^t-Thr-Pro-Lys-N$^\epsilon$-boc-Ala-OBu^t	403	DMSO	−19	203–205	DMF-Aq	20	DCCI	DMF
γ-OBu^t-Z-Glu-N^G-nitro-Arg-Gly-Phe-Phe-Tyr-Thr-Pro-N$^\epsilon$-boc-Lys-Ala-OBu^t	536	DMSO	−16	214–216		65	3+7 DCCI	THF
γ-OBu^t-Z-Glu-N^G-tos-Arg-Gly-Phe-Phe-OBu^t-Tyr-OBu^t-Thr-Pro-Lys-N$^\epsilon$-boc-Ala-OBu^t	403			182–186		65	3+7 MCA	DMF
γ-OBu^t-Z-Glu-N^G-tos-Arg-Gly-Phe-Phe-OBu^t-Tyr-OBu^t-Thr-Pro-N$^\epsilon$-tos-Lys-Ala-OBu^t	403	DMF	−19	182–184	DMF-Eth	50	3+7 DCCI	DMF
γ-OMe-Z-Glu-Arg-Gly-Phe-Tyr-Thr-Pro-N$^\epsilon$-tos-Lys-Ala-OMe Hydrochloride Hydrate	306			161–163	Me-Eth	60.5	1+9 ONP	
γ-OMe-Z-Glu-N^G-nitro-Arg-Gly-Phe-Phe-Tyr-Thr-Pro-N$^\epsilon$-tos-Lys-Ala-OMe	351	DMF	−30	187–189	Alc-Ac	58	3+7 DCCI	DMF-THF
γ-OMe-Glu-Arg-Gly-Phe-Phe-Tyr-Thr-Pro-N$^\epsilon$-tos-Lys-Ala-OMe Trihydrate	306							
γ-OBu^t-Z-Glu-N^G-tos-Arg-Gly-Phe-Phe-Tyr-Thr-Pro-N$^\epsilon$-tos-Lys-OBu^t-Thr-OBu^t	408	Ac	−24	208–209		66	3+7 DCCI	
Pyro-Glu-Glu-Ala-Tyr-Gly-Trp-Met-Asp-Phe Amide	28					43	6+4 MCA	DMF
Glycine								
Z-Gly-S-bzl-Cys-Tyr-Phe-Gln-Asp-S-bzl-Cys-Pro-N$^\epsilon$-tos-Lys-Gly Amide Hydrate	772	DMF	−37	214–216	DMF-Aq	46	3+7 A	
Z-Gly-S-bzl-Cys-OMe-Tyr-Phe-Glu-Asp-S-bzl-Cys-Pro-N$^\epsilon$-tos-Lys-Gly Amide	772	DMF	−34	218–220	DMF-Aq	73	3+7 A	
Z(OMe)-Gly-N$^\delta$-Z-Orn-Leu-D-Phe-Gly-Gly-N$^\delta$-Z-Orn-Leu-D-Phe-Gly	337	DMF	−0.6	239–242	Di-Eth	70	A	EtAc

367

Table 10 Decapeptides (continued)

Compound	Method	Solvent	% Yield	Solvent Crystallization	M.P.(°C)	$[\alpha]_D$	Solvent Rotation	Ref.
Z(OMe)-Gly-N$^\delta$-Z-Orn-Leu-D-Phe-Gly-Gly-N$^\delta$-Z-Orn-Leu-Phe-Gly-ONp								337
Z(OMe)-Gly-N$^\delta$-Z-Orn-Leu-D-Phe-Pro-Gly-N$^\delta$-Z-Orn-Leu-D-Phe-Pro	A	EtAc	48	EtAc-Eth	104-109	-37	DMF	338
Z(OMe)-Gly-N$^\delta$-Z-Orn-Leu-D-Phe-Pro-Gly-N$^\delta$-Z-Orn-Leu-D-Phe-Pro-OEt	MCA	Chf-THF	71	EtAc-Eth-Pe	108-110	-35	DMF	338
Boc-Gly-Tyr-Ser-Met-γ-OBu^t-Glu-His-Phe-Arg-Trp-Gly Hydrate	4+6 A		63	DMF-Me	213-216	-10	DMF	463
Gly-Tyr-Ser-Met-Glu-His-Phe-Arg-Trp-Gly						-32	1N Ac	463
Histidine								
His-Phe-Arg-Trp-Gly-Ser-Pro-N$^\epsilon$-For-Lys-Asp	5+5 MCA	DMF	31.2			-65	Aq	747
His-Phe-Arg-Trp-Gly-Ser-Pro-Lys-Asp						-62	Aq	747
Leucine								
Tos-Leu-S-bzl-Cys-Trp-Ile-Glu-Asp-Cys-S-bzl-Pro-Leu-Gly Amide	3+7 A	EtAc	87	Aq-DMF	239-242			293
Lysine								
Di-Z-Lys-N^G-nitro-Arg-Pro-Pro-Gly-Phe-Ser-Pro-Phe-N^G-nitro-Arg	3+7 DCCI	DMF	62	Alc-Eth		-46	DMF	558
Di-Z-Lys-N^G-nitro-Arg-Pro-Pro-Gly-Phe-Ser-Pro-Phe-N^G-nitro-Arg-OMe						-44	DMF	558
Lys-Arg-Pro-Pro-Gly-Phe-Ser-Pro-Phe-Arg Acetate						-88	1N Ac	558
N$^\epsilon$-Boc-Z-Lys-N$^\epsilon$-boc-Lys-Pro-Pro-Gly-Phe-Ser-Pro-Phe-Lys-OBzl	5+5 DCCI					-83	Aq	722

Compound	Method	Solvent	Yield (%)	Recryst. solvent	M.p.	[α]	Rot. solvent	No.
Lys-Lys-Pro-Pro-Gly-Phe-Ser-Pro-Phe-Lys	5+5 A					−77	Me	722
N$^\epsilon$-Boc-Lys-Lys-Pro-Val-Gly-N$^\epsilon$-boc-Lys-Arg-Arg-Pro-Val-N$^\epsilon$-boc-Lys Amide Trihydrochloride						−67	Aq	644
N$^\epsilon$-Boc-Lys-Pro-Val-Gly-boc-Lys-N$^\epsilon$-boc-Lys-Arg-Arg-Pro-Val-OBu^t Trihydrochloride	6+4 A		36			−76	Aq	644
N$^\epsilon$-Boc-Lys-Pro-Val-Gly-N$^\epsilon$-boc-Lys-N$^\epsilon$-boc-Lys-N$^\epsilon$-boc-Lys-Arg-Arg-Pro-Val Trihydrochloride	6+4 DCCI		35			−67	Aq	644
Methionine								
Met-Lys-Arg-Pro-Gly-Phe-Ser-Pro-Arg						−86	Aq	557
Ornithine								
Di-Z-Orn-N^G-nitro-Arg-Pro-Pro-Gly-Phe-Ser-Pro-Phe-N^G-nitro-Arg	3+7 DCCI	THF	66.5	Alc-Eth		−43	DMF	558
Di-Z-Orn-N^G-nitro-Arg-Pro-Pro-Gly-Phe-Ser-Pro-Phe-N^G-nitro-Arg-OMe						−46	DMF	558
Orn-Arg-Pro-Pro-Gly-Phe-Ser-Pro-Phe-Arg-Triacetate						−86	Aq	558
Z(OMe)-N$^\delta$-Z-Orn-Leu-D-Phe-Gly-Gly-N$^\delta$-Z-Orn-Leu-D-Phe-Gly-Gly	A	DMF	66	Di-Eth	235 (dec)	−91	1N Ac	337
Z(OMe)-N$^\delta$-Z-Orn-Leu-D-Phe-Gly-Gly-N$^\delta$-Z-Orn-Leu-D-Phe-Gly-Gly-ONp						+0.4	DMF	337
Phenylalanine								
Z-Phe-Gly-Pro-Phe-N^G-tos-Arg-N$^\epsilon$-tos-Lys-N^G-tos-Arg-Pro-Gly-OBu^t	6+4 A		63		124–128	−49	DMF	409
Z-(OMe)-Phe-D-Phe-Asn-Gln-Tyr-Val-δ-Z-Orn-Leu-D-Phe-Pro	A	DMF	75	DMF-Eth	233–236 (dec)	−31	DMF	451
Z(OMe)-Phe-D-Phe-Asn-Gln-Tyr-Val-N$^\delta$-Z-Orn-Leu-D-Phe-Pro-OEt	A	DMF	70	DMF-Me-Eth	242–243 (dec)	−27	DMF	451

Table 10   Decapeptides (continued)

Compound	Method	Solvent	% Yield	Solvent Crystallization	M.P.(°C)	[α]D	Solvent Rotation	Ref.
Z(OMe)-Phe-D-Phe-Asn-Gln-Tyr-Val-δ-Z-Orn-Leu-D-Phe-Pro-ONp								451
Phe-Phe-Asn-Gln-Tyr-Val-Nδ-Z-Orn-Leu-D-Phe-Pro-ONp Trifluoroacetate								451
Proline								
Z-Pro-S-bzl-Cys-Tyr-Ile-Gln-Asn-S-bzl-Cys-Pro-Leu-Gly Amide	3+7 A			DMF-Aq	222–235			299
Boc-Pro-Ser-Nε-boc-Lys-Asn-Ala-Phe-Ile-Gly-Leu-Met Amide	6+4 DCCI							392
Pro-Ser-Lys-Asn-Ala-Phe-Ile-Gly-Leu-Met Amide								392
Pyro-Pro-Ser-Nε-boc-Lys-β-OBut-Asp-Ala-Phe-Ile-Gly-Leu-Met Amide	8+2 DCCI / 8+2 MA		92 / 92					25
Serine								
Z-Ser-Leu-Tyr-Gln-Leu-γ-OBzl-Glu-Asn-Tyr-S-NBzl-Cys-Asn-ONBzl Tetrahydrate	5+5 A		40	DMF-Aq	231–233			311
OAc-Ser-Tyr-Ser-Met-Gln-His-Phe-Arg-Trp-Gly Dihydrochloride Octahydrate	3+7 A	DMF	70	DMF-EtAc	202			245
Boc-Ser-Tyr-Ser-Met-Gln-His-Phe-Arg-Trp-Gly Acetate Trihydrate	4+6 A		40					575
Ser-Tyr-Ser-Met-Gln-His-Phe-Arg-Trp-Gly Acetate Hydrate				Me-Acn	192–194			162 575
OAc-Ser-Tyr-Met-γ-OBut-Glu-His-Phe-Arg-Trp-Gly	4+6 A		76.8		220			571

Compound			Yield (%)		M.p. (°C)	[α]		Ref.
Z-Ser-Tyr-Ser-Met-Glu-His-Phe-N^G-tos-Arg-Trp-Gly	4+6 A			DMF-Aq	214–216			369
Boc-Ser-Tyr-Ser-Met-γ-OBu^t-Glu-His-Phe-Arg-Trp-Gly	4+6 A				206			298
Boc-Ser-Ser-Met-γ-OBu^t-Gly-His-Phe-Arg-Trp-Gly Acetate Tetrahydrate	4+6 A	THF	89	DMF	196–197			575
	4+6 A	DMF	72.6	Me	201–204			162
Boc-Ser-Tyr-Ser-Met-γ-OBu^t-Glu-His-Phe-Arg-Trp-Gly Methanol Solvate	4+6 A			Me	203			575
N-Boc-Ser-Tyr-Ser-Met-γ-OBu^t-Glu-His-Phe-Arg-Trp-Gly-OMe Acetate Hydrate	4+6 A	DMF	80	Me	202			575
Ser-Tyr-Ser-Met-Glu-His-Phe-Arg-Trp-Gly					210	−30	1N Ac	575, 463
Boc-Ser-Tyr-Ser-Met-γ-OBu^t-Glu-His-Phe-Arg-Tyr-Glu Dihydrate	4+6 A		80.2		202 (dec)	−13	DMF	463
Z-Ser-Tyr-Ser-Met-γ-OBzl-Glu-His-Phe-N^G-tos-Arg-Tyr-Gly	4+6 A		78		214–216	−22	DMF	373
Z-Ser-Tyr-Ser-Met-γ-OBzl-Glu-His-Phe-N^ε-tos-Lys-Trp-Gly	4+6 A	DMF	83	DMF-Aq	174–176	−7.7	DMF	94

Tryptophan

Compound			Yield (%)		M.p. (°C)			Ref.
Z-Trp-Leu-γ-OBu^t-Glu-γ-OBu^t-Glu-γ-OBu^t-Glu-γ-OBu^t-Glu-γ-OBu^t-Glu-Ala-Tyr-Gly-OMe Hydrate	1+9 OTCP	DMF	86		248–250 (dec)			423
Trp-Leu-γ-OBu^t-Glu-γ-OBu^t-Glu-γ-OBu^t-Glu-γ-OBu^t-Glu-γ-OBu^t-Glu-Ala-Tyr-Gly-OMe Acetate Hydrate					249–251 (dec)			423

Valine

Compound					M.p. (°C)			Ref.
Z-Val-N^ε-tos-Lys-Leu-D-Phe-Pro-Val-N^ε-tos-Lys-Leu-D-Phe-Pro-OMe	4+6 A			Aq-Alc	194–196			130
Val-Lys-Leu-D-Phe-Pro-Val-Lys-Leu-D-Phe-Pro Trihydrochloride								130

Table 10 Decapeptides (continued)

Compound	Method	Solvent	% Yield	Solvent Crystallization	M.P. (°C)	$[\alpha]_D$	Solvent Rotation	Ref.
Z(OMe)-Val-N$^\delta$-Z-Orn-Leu-Gly-Pro-Val-N$^\delta$- Z-Orn-Leu-Gly-Pro	A	DMF	45	Me-Pe	223–225	−76	Ac	431
Z(OMe)-Val-N$^\delta$-Z-Orn-Leu-D-Phe-Sar-Val-δ- Z-Orn-Leu-D-Phe-Sar	A	DMF	73	Di-Eth	208–209	−45	Ac	16
Z-D-Val-Val-D-Val-Trp-D-Leu-Trp-D-Leu- Trp-D-Leu-Trp 2-Hydroxyethylamide								527
D-Val-Val-D-Val-Trp-D-Leu-Trp-D-Leu-Trp- D-Leu-Trp-D-Leu-Trp 2-Hydroxyethylamide								527

Part 3

Undecapeptides to Nucleopeptides

Introduction

The first part of this review dealt with amino acid derivatives and dipeptides and the second part with tripeptides to decapeptides. The present part has been devoted to more specialized, but potentially the most biologically significant aspects of peptide syntheses. Because of the relatively small number of chromo-, glyco- and phospho- peptides encountered, these fields were not given separate treatment in Part 3. Instead, such compounds can be located, for the most part, among the amino acid derivatives and dipeptides of Part 1. Two of the most recent advances in these areas pertain to amino acid derivatives of the antitumor antibiotics daunomycin[71a] and actinomycin.[77a]

Except for using a composite summary to introduce the undecapeptide to insulin tables, the general style of Part 2 has been continued. That is, introduction to the tables has been primarily devoted to a brief outline of pertinent experimental methods.

11

Undecapeptides to Insulin

Introductions to the tripeptide to decapeptide summaries of Part 2 were mainly used to mention pertinent experimental and purification procedures. The availability of such information becomes increasingly more limited and/or specific with increasing chain length. Thus, in this part, it was considered advisable to group the undecapeptide to insulin entries under one introduction. Separate tables have been used for each of the 11- to 19-unit peptides, but peptides comprising 20 to 48 amino acids have been grouped into one table.

The final coupling reaction used in the peptide syntheses generally involved an A, ONP or DCCI method. The MCA, WRK, NHS-DCCI and OTCP procedures were used to a lesser extent. A few examples involving the use of CDI, 2,4-DNPO and MA are also available. Only a paucity of studies concerned with comparison of coupling methods have been reported for relatively large peptides. Three such comparisons have been made among the undecapeptides and encompass MCA (2+9, 92%) *vs* DCCI (2+9, 93%),[25] MCA (6+5, 73%) *vs* A (4+7, 62%)[560] and DCCI (9+2, 92%) *vs* MCA (9+2, 92%).[25] One such example pertains to a dodecapeptide (A, 8+4, 56% *vs* A, 5+7, 39%),[329] and one each among the 14-unit (ONP, 4+10, 78% *vs* DCCI, 7+7, 30%),[351] 15-unit (MA and OTCP, 11+4)[423] and 17-unit (OSu, 2+15, 70% *vs* DCCI, 9+8, 71%)[735] peptides. As with smaller peptides, the peptide bond-forming method and position of coupling determine optical integrity (and yield) and systematic investigations of these matters with larger peptides should yield much valuable information.

Only two examples of recrystallized peptides were noted when preparing Tables 11 to 20; namely, an 11 (from methanol)[226] and 14 (from ethanol)[549] unit peptide. Thin layer chromatography was used to assess the purity of undeca-,[28] dodeca-,[323,28] and pentadecapeptides.[527] Thin layer assessment of

376

synthetic ACTH was also reported.[579] Applications of column chromatography, electrophoresis, and countercurrent distribution techniques for isolation were encountered as summarized below in tabular form. Appropriate reference(s) has been placed in the columns to the right of each peptide unit.

Recent developments in the field of relatively large synthetic peptides include syntheses of ribonuclease A units,[509,508,303,425,505] ribonuclease S-peptide$_{1-20}$,[242] Orn^8- and Orn^{8,17,18}-β-corticotropin (1-24),[663] 17-unit peptides related to human[5] and canine[281b] gastrin, insulin analogs,[676,420,229a] and the C-terminal 14-unit sequence of straphylococcal nuclease.[449b] A particularly exciting new development pertains to syntheses of the 104-unit S-protein of ribonuclease using, in part, the N-carboxyanhydride method (NCA)[187a] and a 123-unit ribonuclease by the Merrifield solid phase technique.[217a] Both approaches to ribonuclease constitute the first syntheses of an enzyme, albeit in crude form. While both preparations gave enzymatic activity of 20% or better in a qualitative study, neither were active toward DNA as a substitute. Eventual refinement of the ribonuclease syntheses will no doubt provide relatively pure enzyme.

Isolation Procedures

PEPTIDE UNIT	COLUMN CHROMATOGRAPHY					ELECTROPHORESIS	COUNTERCURRENT DISTRIBUTION
	Cellulose	Aminoethyl Cellulose	Carboxymethyl Cellulose	Sephedex G-25	Alumina		
11			244,247	28	423		71,192,246
12	246	28		28, 323		28, 644	194, 246
13						246, 571	66
14			372, 645				371, 372, 374, 527
15				423			493, 577
16		28	247, 577				369, 492
17			94, 373	28			492
18			492				
19			244, 368, 458, 492			244	368, 371, 492
20				549, 582, 583		549	
23			245				458
25			493				493
27							458

378

Table 11 Undecapeptides

Compound	Method	Solvent	% Yield	Solvent Crystallization	M.P. (°C)	[α] D	Solvent Rotation	Ref.
Alanine								
Z-Ala-N^G-nitro-Arg-Leu-Gln-N^G-nitro-Arg-Leu-Leu-Gln-Gly-Leu-Val	1+10 ONP	DMF	95		258–264 (dec)	–38	Ac-Aq	66
Ala-S-bzl-Cys-Asp-S-Tyr-Thr-S-bzl-Cys-Gly-Ser-Asp-S-bzl-Cys-Tyr								452
Z-Ala-S-bzl-Cys-Asp-Tyr-Thr-S-bzl-Cys-Gly-Ser-Asp-S-bzl-Cys-Tyr				DMF	150–155	–23	DMF	452
Z-Ala-S-bzl-Cys-Asp-Tyr-Thr-S-bzl-Cys-Gly-Ser-Asp-bzl-Cys-Tyr-OEt	A	DMF	66	DMF-Eth	246–247 (dec)	–27	DMF	452
Asparagine								
[5-Asn] Eledoisin-(4-11)-Octapeptide								443
[5-Asn, 7-α-Hydrazino-β-phenyl-propion] Eledoisin-(4-11)-Octapeptide (Bis-Tfa)								185
β-OBu^t-Asp-Gln-Leu-Ala-γ-OBu^t-Glu-Ala-Phe-Pro-Leu-γ-OBu^t-Glu-Phe-OBu^t								579
β-OBu^t-Z-Asp-Gln-Leu-Ala-γ-OBu^t-Glu-Ala-Phe-Pro-Leu-γ-OBu^t-Glu-Phe-OBu^t								579
Cysteine								
S,S'-N-Z-hemicystine-S-bzh-Cys-Gly-Phe-Gly-Hemicystine-Phe-Gly-S-trt-Cys-Gly-Val-OBu^t					228	+17	DMF	226
S,S'-Z-hemicystine-S-bzh-Cys-Gly-Phe-Gly-hemicystine-Phe-Gly-S-trt-Cys-Gly-Val-OMe				Me	232–236	–80	DMF	226
Di-Z-Cystine-(Gly-Gly-Gly-S-bzh-Cys-Gly)$_2$					197–198 (dec)			220

Table 11 Undecapeptides (continued)

Compound	Method	Solvent	% Yield	Solvent Crystallization	M.P. (°C)	$[\alpha]_D$	Solvent Rotation	Ref.
Di-Z-Cystine-(Gly-Lys-Gly-S-bzh-Cys-Gly-OBu^t)$_2$					192–202	−60	DMF	220
Glutamine								
Z-Gln-Pro-Ser-N$^\epsilon$-Z-Lys-Asp-Ala-Phe-Ile-Gly-Leu-Met	4+7 A							89
Boc-Gln-Pro-Ser-N$^\epsilon$-boc-Lys-β-OBu^t-Asp-Ala-Phe-Ile-Gly-Leu-Met Amide	5+6 DCCI		50		210 (dec)	−22	DMF	90
Gln-Pro-Ser-Lys-Asp-Ala-Phe-Ile-Gly-Leu-Met Amide					250 (dec)	−54 −52	Ac Ac	90 89
Glu-Glu-Glu-Ala-Tyr-Gly-Trp-Met-Asp-Phe Amide Ammonium Salt	7+4 MA		20			−40	NH$_4$OH	28
γ-OBu^t-Z-Glu-His-Phe-Arg-Trp-Gly-Ser-Pro-Pro-N$^\epsilon$-boc-Lys-Asp-di-OBu^t Acetate	6+5 DCCI	DMF	57					573
Pyroglu-Pro-Ser-N$^\epsilon$-boc-Lys-Asp-Ala-Phe-Ile-Gly-Leu-Met Amide	4+7 A							395
Pyroglu-Pro-Ser-N$^\epsilon$-boc-Lys-β-OBu^t-Asp-Ala-Phe-Ile-Gly-Leu-Met Amide	2+9 MCA 2+9 DCCI	DMF DMF	92 93		233 (dec) 208–210			25
Pyroglu-Pro-Ser-Lys-Asp-Ala-Phe-Ile-Gly-Leu-Met Amide						−42	Ac	90
Pyroglu-Pro-Ser-N$^\epsilon$-boc-Lys-γ-OBu^t-Glu-Ala-Phe-Ile-Gly-Leu-Met Amide	7+4 DCCI							395
Pyroglu-Pro-Ser-Lys-Glu-Ala-Phe-Ile-Gly-Leu-Met Amide								395
Pyroglu-Pro-Ser-N$^\epsilon$-boc-Lys-Gly-Ala-Phe-Ile-Gly-Leu-Met Amide	4+7 DCCI		75					394

Compound	Method	Solvent	Yield	M.p.	Recryst.	$[\alpha]$		Ref.
Pyroglu-Pro-Ser-Lys-Gly-Ala-Phe-Ile-Gly-Leu-Met Amide								394
Pyroglu-Pro-Ser-N^ϵ-boc-Lys-Gly-Ala-Phe-Leu-Gly-Leu-Met Amide	4+7 DCCI					-60	Ac	394
Pyroglu-Pro-Ser-Lys-Gly-Ala-Phe-Leu-Gly-Leu-Met Amide								394
Pyroglu-Pro-Ser-N^ϵ-boc-Lys-Gly-Ala-Phe-Val-Leu-Met Amide	4+7 DCCI					-66	Ac	394
Pyroglu-Pro-Ser-Lys-Gly-Ala-Phe-Val-Gly-Leu-Met Amide						-41	Ac	394
Glycine								
Z-Gly-Gly-S-bzl-Cys-Tyr-Phe-Gln-Asp-S-bzl-Cys-Pro-N^ϵ-tos-Lys-Gly Amide	4+7 A	EtAc	77	207–213	DMF-Aq	-36		300
N^α-Gly-Gly-8 Lys-vasopressin								300
N-Tri-Gly-N^ϵ-Z-Lys-Pro-Val-Gly-N^ϵ-Z-Lys-N^ϵ-Z-Lys-Arg-Arg-Pro-Val-OMe Dihydrochloride	4+7 DCCI	DMF-Acn	52	190 (dec)	Me-Eth			71
Histidine								
His-Phe-Arg-Trp-Gly-N^ϵ-for-Lys-Pro-Val-Gly-N^ϵ-For-Lys-N^ϵ-for-Lys Amide Diacetate Tetraacetate	5+6 CDI	DMF						247
His-Phe-Arg-Trp-Gly-N^ϵ-for-Lys-Pro-Val-Gly-N^ϵ-for-Lys-N^ϵ-for-Lys Amide Diacetate Tetrahydrate	DCCI	DMF	42					247
N^{im}-Bzl-Z-His-Ser-Cys-Tyr-Ile-Gln-Asn-Cys-Pro-Leu-Gly Amide	2+9 A	DMF	69	229				192
His-Ser-Cys-Tyr-Ile-Gln-Asn-Cys-Pro-Leu-Gly Amide								192
N^{im}-Bzl-Z-His-Ser-S-bzl-Cys-Tyr-Phe-Gln-Asn-S-bzl-Cys-Pro-Lys-Gly Amide	2+9 A		65	206				192
N^{im}-Bzl-Z-His-Ser-S-bzl-Cys-Tyr-Phe-Gln-Asn-S-bzl-Cys-Pro-N^ϵ-tos-Lys-Gly Amide	5+6 A		50					192

Table 11 Undecapeptides (continued)

Compound	Method	Solvent	% Yield	Solvent Crystallization	M.P.(°C)	$[\alpha]_D$	Solvent Rotation	Ref.
His-Ser-Cys-Tyr-Phe-Gln-Asn-Cys-Pro-Lys-Gly								192
Leucine								
N,N'-(Leu-Val)$_2$-Cystine-(Gly-Glu-Arg)$_2$								674
Lysine								
N^ϵ-For-Z-Lys-Pro-Val-Gly-Gly-N^ϵ-for-Lys-N^ϵ-for-Lys-Arg-Arg-Pro-Val Amide Diacetate Hexahydrate	6+5 A	DMF-THF	80					244
N^ϵ-For-Lys-Pro-Val-Gly-Gly-N^ϵ-for-Lys-N^ϵ-for-Lys-Arg-Arg-Pro-Val Amide Triacetate Octahydrate								244
Methionine								
Boc-Met-N^ϵ-boc-Lys-Arg-Pro-Pro-Gly-Phe-Ser-Pro-Phe-Arg Hydrochloride Trihydrate	3+8 A	DMF	85		170-174	-49	DMF	20
Proline								
Z-Pro-Trp-Leu-γ-OBu^t-Glu-γ-OBu^t-Glu-γ-OBu^t-Glu-γ-OBu^t-Glu-Ala-Tyr-Gly Hydrate					237-239 (dec)	-17 / +54	DMF / 0.1N NaOH-Aq	423
Z-Pro-Trp-Leu-γ-OBu^t-Glu-γ-OBu^t-Glu-γ-OBu^t-Glu-γ-OBu^t-Glu-Ala-Tyr-Gly-OMe Hydrate	1+10 ONP	DMF	86		250-251 (dec)	-17	DMF	423

Compound	Method	Solvent	Yield (%)	Recryst.	mp (°C)	[α]	Solvent	Ref.
Boc-Pro-Trp-Leu-γ-OBu^t-Glu-γ-OBu^t-Glu-γ-OBu^t-Glu-γ-OBu^t-Glu-γ-OBu^t-Glu-Ala-Tyr-Gly Hydrate	OTCP	Aq-Ac			231–232 (dec)			423
Boc-Pro-Trp-Leu-γ-OBu^t-Glu-γ-OBu^t-Glu-γ-OBu^t-Glu-γ-OBu^t-Glu-Ala-Tyr-Gly-OMe Hydrate	1+10 OTCP				237–239 (dec)			423
Pro-Trp-Leu-γ-OBu^t-Glu-γ-OBu^t-Glu-γ-OBu^t-Glu-γ-OBu^t-Glu-γ-OBu^t-Glu-Ala-Tyr-Gly					245–247 (dec)			423
Pro-Trp-Leu-γ-OBu^t-Glu-γ-OBu^t-Glu-γ-OBu^t-Glu-γ-OBu^t-Glu-Ala-Tyr-Gly-OMe-Ac Hydrate					243–245 (dec)	−7	DMF	423
Z-Pro-Val-Gly-N^ϵ-tos-Lys-N^ϵ-tos-Lys-N^G-nitro-Arg-N^G-nitro-Arg-Pro-Val-N^ϵ-tos-Lys-Val-OMe	4+7 A	DMF	62	Ac-Eth		−46	Ac	560
	6+5 MCA	THF-DMF	73	Ac-Eth		−47	Ac	560
Pro-Val-Gly-N^ϵ-tos-Lys-Arg-Arg-Pro-Val-N^ϵ-tos-Lys-Val-OMe Trihydrochloride						−30	DMF	560
Pro-Val-Gly-N^ϵ-tos-Lys-N^ϵ-tos-Lys-N^G-nitro-Arg-Pro-Val-N^ϵ-tos-Lys-Val-OMe Hydrobromide				Alc-Eth		−34	Ac	560

Serine

Compound	Method	Solvent	Yield (%)	Recryst.	mp (°C)	[α]	Solvent	Ref.
Z-Ser-N^{im}-bzl-His-S-bzl-Cys-Tyr-Ile-Gln-Asn-S-bzl-Cys-Pro-Leu-Gly Amide	2+9 A	DMF	50		238			192
Ser-His-Cys-Tyr-Ile-Gln-Asn-Cys-Pro-Leu-Gly Amide								192
Z-Ser-N^{im}-bzl-His-S-bzl-Cys-Tyr-Phe-Gln-Asn-S-bzl-Cys-Pro-N^ϵ-tos-Lys-Gly Amide	2+9 A	DMF	53		220			192
Ser-His-Cys-Tyr-Phe-Gln-Asn-Cys-Pro-Lys-Gly Amide								192

Table 12 Dodecapeptides

Compound	Method	Solvent	% Yield	Solvent Crystallization	M.P. (°C)	$[\alpha]$ D	Solvent Rotation	Ref.
Glutamine								
γ-OBu^t-Z-Glu-β-OBu^t-Asp-Gln-Leu-Ala-γ-OBu^t-Glu-Ala-Phe-Pro-Leu-γ-OBu^t-Glu-Phe-OBu^t								579
H-γ-OBu^t-Glu-β-OBu^t-Asp-Gln-Leu-Ala-γ-OBu^t-Glu-Ala-Phe-Pro-Leu-γ-OBu^t-Glu-Phe-OBu^t-Acetate								579
Penta-(Glu)-Ala-Tyr-Gly-Trp-Leu-Asp-Phe-Amide Ammonium Salt	8+4 MA	DMF	43					323
Glu-Glu-Glu-Glu-Glu-Ala-Tyr-Gly-Trp-Met-Asp-Phe Amide	8+4 MA		21					28
Glycine								
Z-Gly-Pro-Ala-Gly-Pro-Ala-Gly-Pro-Ala-Gly-Pro-Ala				Aq	252–254 (dec)			59
Z-Gly-Pro-Ala-Gly-Pro-Ala-Gly-Pro-Ala-Gly-Pro-Ala-OMe	6+6 WRK	Acn		Me-Aq	263–264 (dec)			59
Gly-Pro-Ala-Gly-Pro-Ala-Gly-Pro-Ala-Gly-Pro-Ala								59
Z-Gly-Pro-Gly-Gly-Pro-Gly-Gly-Pro-Gly-Gly-Pro-Gly				Alc-Aq	262–263 (dec)			59
Z-Gly-Pro-Gly-Gly-Pro-Gly-Gly-Pro-Gly-Gly-Pro-Gly-OEt	6+6 WRK	Acn	42.4	Alc-Aq	274–276 (dec)			59
Gly-Pro-Gly-Gly-Pro-Gly-Gly-Pro-Gly-Gly-Pro-Gly								59

Compound	Method	Solvent	Yield	Recryst.	m.p.	$[\alpha]$	Solvent	Ref.
Isoleucine								
Z-Ile-S-bzl-Cys-Ser-Leu-Tyr-Gln-Leu-Glu-Asn-Tyr-S-bzl-Cys-Asn-ONBzl	3+9 A	DMF	89	DMF-Aq	263–265 (dec)	−28	DMSO	317
Leucine								
Z-Leu-Gly-Gly-Leu-Gly-Gly-Gly-Leu-Gly-Gly-Gly					260			29
Z-Leu-(Gly)$_3$-[Leu-(Gly)$_3$]$_2$ Anhydride								29
Lysine								
N^α, N^ϵ-Di-boc-Lys-γ-OBu^t-Glu-Thr-Ala-Ala-Ala-N^ϵ-boc-Lys-Ala-γ-OBu^t-Glu-N$^\delta$-boc-Orn-Gln-His Hydrazide					242–244 (dec)	−23	Ac	583
N^α, N^ϵ-Di-boc-Lys-γ-OBu^t-Glu-Thr-Ala-Ala-Ala-N^ϵ-boc-Lys-Ala-γ-OBu^t-Glu-N$^\delta$-boc-Orn-Glu-His-OMe					230–233 (dec)	−24	DMF	583
N^α, N^ϵ-Di-boc-Lys-γ-OBu^t-Glu-Thr-Ala-Ala-Ala-N^ϵ-boc-Lys-Ile-γ-OBu^t-Glu-N$^\delta$-boc-Orn-Gly-His Hydrazide				DMF-Aq	255–257 (dec)	−29	Ac	583
N^γ, N^ϵ-Di-boc-Lys-γ-OBu^t-Glu-Thr-Ala-Ala-Ala-N^ϵ-boc-Lys-Ile-γ-OBu^t-Glu-N$^\delta$-boc-Orn-Glu-His-OMe	6+6 A	DMF	62	DMF-Eth	250–253 (dec)	−21	DMF	583
N^ϵ, N^α-boc-Lys-γ-OBu^t-Glu-Thr-Ala-Ala-Ala-N^ϵ-boc-Lys-Phe-Glu-Arg-Glu-β-(pyrazoyl-1)-Ala Amide	7+5 A	DMF	80			−23	DMF	232
Lys-Glu-Thr-Ala-Ala-Ala-Lys-Phe-Glu-Arg-Glu-β-(pyrazoyl-1)-Ala Amide						−66	Ac-Aq	232

385

Table 12 Dodecapeptides (continued)

Compound	Method	Solvent	% Yield	Solvent Crystallization	M.P. (°C)	[α]_D	Solvent Rotation	Ref.
Lys-Glu-Thr-Ala-Ala-Lys-Phe-Glu-Arg-Glu-β-(pyrazoyl-3)-Ala Amide	7+5 A					-63	Aq	232
Nα, Nε-Di-boc-Lys-γ-OBut-Glu-Thr-Ala-Ala-Ala-Nε-boc-Lys-Phe-γ-OBut-Glu-Nδ-Orn-γ-OBut-Glu-His Hydrazide					237-239 (dec)	-12	DMF	582
						-23	Ac	582
Nα, Nε-Di-boc-Lys-γ-OBut-Glu-Thr-Ala-Ala-Ala-Nε-boc-Lys-Phe-γ-OBut-Glu-Nδ-boc-Orn-γ-OBut-Glu-His-OMe	6+6 A	DMF	60	DMF-Eth	236-237	-15	DMF	582
Nα, Nε-Di-boc-Lys-γ-OBut-Glu-Thr-Ala-Ala-Ala-Nε-boc-Lys-Phe-γ-OBut-Glu-Nδ-boc-Orn-Glu-His Hydrazide				DMF-Aq	238-239 (dec)	-23	Ac	582
Nα, Nε-Di-boc-Lys-γ-OBut-Glu-Thr-Ala-Ala-Ala-Nε-boc-Lys-Phe-γ-OBut-Glu-Nδ-boc-Orn-Glu-His-OMe	6+6 A		73	DMF	234-235 (dec)	-13	DMF	506
Lys-Di-Gly-Glu-Di-Gly-Lys-Di-Gly-Gly-Glu-Gly-Gly					192-194	+7	Ac	422
Nε-Tfa-Nα-Z-Lys-Di-Gly-γ-OMe-Glu-Di-Gly-Nε-Tfa-Lys-Di-Gly-γ-OMe-Glu-Gly-Gly-OBut	6+6 DCCI	Py	38	DMF-Eth	171-173	-11	Ac	422
Nε-Boc-Lys-Pro-Val-Gly-Nε-boc-Lys-Nε-boc-Lys-Arg-Arg-Pro-Val-Nε-boc-Lys-Val-OBut- Hydrochloride	6+6 A	DMF	36			-80	Aq	644
Serine								
OBzl-N-boc-Ser-Ala-NG-nitro-Arg-Leu-Gln-NG-nitro-Arg-Leu-Gln-Gly-Leu-Val	1+11 ONP	DMF	93		300 (dec)	-33	Ac-Aq	66

Compound								
Z-Ser-His-Leu-Val-γ-OBu^t-Glu-Ala-Leu-Tyr-Leu-Val-S-bzl-Cys-Gly	6+6 A	HMPA	54			-34		411
OBu^t-N-trt-Ser-His-Leu-Val-Glu-γ-OBu^t-Ala-Leu-OBu^t-Tyr-Leu-Val-S-bzl-Cys-Gly	8+4 A 5+7 A	THF THF	56 39	DMF-Eth DMF-Eth	267-273 280 (Dec)	-28 -29	HMPA HMPA	329

Valine

Z-Val-S-bzl-Cys-Ser-Leu-Tyr-Gln-Leu-Gln-Asp-Tyr-S-bzl-Cys-Asp-ONBzl	3+9 A		84		265 (dec)	-27	DMSO	315

Table 13 Tridecapeptides

Alanine

Compound								
Ala-γ-OBu^t-Glu-β-OBu^t-Asp-Gln-Leu-Ala-γ-OBu^t-Glu-Ala-Phe-Pro-Leu-γ-OBu^t-Glu-Phe-OBu^t Acetate	1+12 ONP	DMF		Alc				579
Z-Ala-γ-OBu^t-Glu-β-OBu^t-Asp-Gln-Leu-Ala-γ-OBu^t-Glu-Ala-Phe-Pro-Leu-γ-OBu^t-Glu-Phe-OBu^t								579

Asparagine

Boc-β-bzl-Asp-OBzl-Ser-Ala-nitro-Arg-Leu-Glu-N^G-nitro-Arg-Leu-Leu-Gln-Gly-Leu-Val		Alc		315 (dec)	-27	Ac	66

Glutamine

Pyro-Glu-Gly-Pro-Trp-Leu-γ-OBu^t-Glu-γ-OBu^t-Glu-γ-OBu^t-Glu-γ-OBu^t-Glu-Ala-Tyr-Gly	2+11 OTCP	DMF	83	Alc	234-236 (dec)	-10	DMF	423

Table 13 Tridecapeptides (continued)

Compound	Method	Solvent	% Yield	Solvent Crystallization	M.P.(°C)	[α]D	Solvent Rotation	Ref.
Pyro-Glu-Gly-Pro-Trp-Leu-γ-OBu^t-Glu-γ-OBu^t-Glu-γ-OBu^t-Glu-γ-OBu^t-Glu-Ala-Tyr-Gly-OMe	2+11 OTCP	DMF	90		246-247 (dec)	-23	DMF	423
Lysine								
N^ε-Boc-Lys-Pro-Val-Gly-N^ε-boc-Lys-N^ε-boc-Lys-Arg-Arg-Pro-Val-N^ε-boc-Lys-Val-Tyr Trihydrochloride	5+8 A	DMF	36			-77	Ac-Aq	644
N^ε-For-Lys-Pro-Val-Gly-N^ε-for-Lys-N^ε-for-Lys-Arg-Arg-Pro-Val-N^ε-for-Lys-Val-Tyr Amide Trihydrochloride Trihydrate								245
N^ε-Boc-Z-Lys-Pro-Val-N^ε-boc-Lys-N^ε-boc-Lys-N^δ-boc-Orn-N^δ-boc-Orn-Pro-Val-N^ε-boc-Lys-Val-Tyr-Pro-OBu^t	5+8 A				192-194	-37	DMF	664
N^ε-Boc-Lys-Pro-Val-N^ε-boc-Lys-N^ε-boc-Lys-N^δ-boc-Orn-N^δ-boc-Orn-Pro-Val-N^ε-boc-Lys-Val-Tyr-Pro-OBu^t Toluenesulfonate					179-181	-65	Py	664
Phenylalanine								
Boc-Phe-γ-OBu^t-Glu-Arg-Gln-His-Met-(sulfoxide)-Asp-Ser-Thr-Ser-Ala-Ala	4+9 A							238
Phe-Glu-Arg-Gln-His-Met-(sulfoxide)-Asp-Ser-Thr-Ser-Ala-Ala						-38	Ac-Aq	238
Z-Phe-Gly-N^ε-boc-Lys-γ-OBu^t-Glu-Phe-Thr-Pro-Pro-Val-Gln-Ala-Ala-Tyr-OMe	A	DMF			194-196 (dec)	-52	Ac	98

Serine

Compound	Method	Solvent	Yield	M.p.	Ref.
OAc-Ser-Tyr-Ser-Met-Gln-His-Phe-Arg-Trp-Gly-N^ϵ-for-Lys-Pro-Val Amide	5+8 A	DMF			246
OAc-Ser-Tyr-Ser-Met-Gln-His-Phe-Arg-Trp-Gly-N^ϵ-tos-Lys-Pro-Val Amide	5+8 A	DMF			246
Z-Ser-Tyr-Ser-Met-Gln-His-Phe-Arg-Trp-Gly-N^ϵ-tos-Lys-Pro-Val Amide	5+8 A	DMF			246
OAc-Ser-Tyr-Ser-Met-Glu-His-Phe-Arg-Trp-Gly-Lys-Pro-Val Amide	5+8 A	DMF			571
Ac-Ser-Tyr-Ser-Met-γ-OBzl-Glu-His-Phe-Arg-Trp-Gly-N^ϵ-Z-Lys-Pro-Val Amide Hydrochloride	5+8 DCCI	Acn	86.6	180 (dec)	194
Ac-Ser-Tyr-Ser-Met-γ-OBu^t-Glu-His-Phe-Arg-Trp-Gly-N^ϵ-boc-Lys-Pro-Val Amide Toluenesulfonate	10+3 DCCI				571
Ac-Ser-Tyr-Ser-Met-Glu-His-Phe-Arg-Trp-Gly-Lys-Pro-Val					194
Ac-Ser-Tyr-Ser-Met-Glu-His-Phe-Arg-Trp-Gly-Lys-Pro-Val Amide Acetate					571
Boc-Ser-Tyr-Ser-Met-γ-OBu^t-Glu-His-Phe-Arg-Trp-Gly-N^ϵ-pht-Lys-Pro-Val Amide	10+3 DCCI	Py	85		571
Ser-Tyr-Ser-Met-Glu-His-Phe-Arg-Trp-Gly-N^ϵ-pht-Lys-Pro-Val Amide Trifluoroacetate					571

Table 14 Tetradecapeptides

Compound	Method	Solvent	% Yield	Solvent Crystallization	M.P. (°C)	$[\alpha]_D$	Solvent Rotation	Ref.
Arganine								
N^G-Nitro-boc-Arg-β-OBzl-Asp-OBzl-Ser-Ala-N^G-nitro-Arg-Leu-Glu-N^G-nitro-Arg-Leu-Glu-Gly-Leu-Val	1+13 2,4-DNPO	DMF				−39	Ac	66
Glycine								
Z-Gly-Ala-γ-OBu^t-Glu-β-OBu^t-Asp-Gln-Leu-Ala-γ-OBu^t-Glu-Ala-Phe-Pro-Leu-γ-OBu^t-Glu-Phe-OBu^t								579
Gly-Ala-γ-OBu^t-Glu-β-OBu^t-Asp-Gln-Leu-Ala-γ-OBu^t-Glu-Ala-Phe-Pro-Leu-γ-OBu^t-Glu-Phe-OBu^t Acetate								579
Leucine								
Z-Leu-Val-S-bzl-Cys-Gly-γ-OMe-Glu-N^G-nitro-Arg-Gly-Phe-Phe-Tyr-Thr-Pro-N$^\epsilon$-tos-Lys-Ala-OMe	4+10 ONP 7+7 DCCI	DMF DMF	78 30	DMF-Aq DMF-Alc	260-262 (dec) 258-260	−30 −30	DMF DMF	351
Lysine								
N$^\epsilon$-Boc-Lys-Pro-Val-Gly-N$^\epsilon$-boc-Lys-N$^\epsilon$-boc-Lys-Arg-Arg-Pro-Val-N$^\epsilon$-boc-Lys-Val-Tyr-Pro-OBu^t-Tri-toluene-sulfonate								574
N$^\epsilon$-Boc-Lys-Pro-Val-Gly-N$^\epsilon$-boc-Lys-N$^\epsilon$-boc-Lys-Arg-Arg-Pro-Val-N$^\epsilon$-boc-Lys-Val-Tyr-Pro Trihydrochloride tetrahydrate	6+8 A	THF	31					645

Compound	Method	Solvent	Yield	Recryst.	m.p.	[α]	Solvent	Ref.
N$^\epsilon$, N$^\alpha$-Boc-Pz-Lys-Pro-Val-Gly-N$^\epsilon$-boc-Lys-N$^\epsilon$-boc-Lys-N^G-nitro-Arg-N^G-nitro-Arg-Pro-Val-N$^\epsilon$-boc-Lys-Val-Tyr-Pro-OBu^t	9+5 MCA	THF	80	Acn	160–165			574
N$^\epsilon$-Boc-Z-Lys-Val-Leu-Thr-Gly-Leu-Pro-Ala-Leu-Ile-Ser-Trp-Ile-OBu^t				Alc	193–195	−37	DMF	549
N$^\epsilon$-Boc-Lys-Val-Leu-Thr-Thr-Gly-Leu-Pro-Ala-Leu-Ile-Ser-Trp-Ile-OBu^t				Alc-Eth	170–174	−34	DMF	549
N$^\epsilon$, N$^\alpha$-Boc-Lys-Val-Leu-Thr-Thr-Thr-Gly-Leu-Pro-Ala-Leu-Ile-Ser-Trp-Ile-OBu^t								549
Lys-Val-Leu-Thr-Thr-Gly-Leu-Pro-Ala-Leu-Ile-Ser-Trp-Ile Diacetate Dihydrate						−94	Aq	549

Serine

Compound	Method	Solvent	Yield	Recryst.	m.p.	[α]	Solvent	Ref.
OBu^t-N-Nps-Ser-Arg-Arg-Ala-Gln-β-OBu^t-Asp-Phe-Val-Gln-Trp-Leu-Met-Asn-OBu^t-Thr-OBu^t Dihydrobromide	6+8 NHS-DCCI	DMF		DMF-EtAc-Aq	230–232 (dec)	−18	DMF	725
OBu^t-Ser-Arg-Arg-Ala-Gln-β-OBu^t-Asp-Phe-Val-Gln-Trp-Leu-Met-Asn-OBu^t-Thr-OBu^t Trihydrobromide				Me-OAc	212–213	−32	Ac-Aq	725
OBu^t-N-pht-Ser-Arg-Arg-Ala-Gln-β-OBu^t-Asp-Phe-Val-Gln-Trp-Leu-Met-Asp-OBu^t-Thr-OBu^t Dihydrobromide	5+9 NHS-DCCI	DMF	77.5		224 (dec)	−31	Ac-Aq	726
Z-Ser-Tyr-Ser-γ-OBzl-Glu-His-Phe-N^G-Tos-Arg-Tyr-Gly-N$^\epsilon$-boc-Lys-N$^\epsilon$-boc-Lys-N^G-tos-Arg-N^G-tos-Arg-Pro-OBu^t						−51	DMF	372
Ser-Tyr-Ser-Glu-His-Phe-Arg-Tyr-Gly-Lys-Lys-Arg-Arg-Pro	9+5 WRK					−56	0.1M Ac	372

Table 15 Pentadecapeptides

Compound	Method	Solvent	% Yield	Solvent Crystallization	M.P. (°C)	$[\alpha]_D$	Solvent Rotation	Ref.
Asparagine								
β-OBu^t-Asp-Gly-Ala-γ-OBu^t-Glu-β-OBu^t-Asp-Gln-Leu-Ala-γ-OBu^t-Glu-Ala-Phe-Pro-Leu-γ-OBu^t-Glu-Phe-OBu^t Acetate								579
β-OBu^t-Z-Asp-Gly-Ala-γ-OBu^t-Glu-β-OBu^t-Asp-Gln-Leu-Ala-γ-OBu^t-Glu-Ala-Phe-Pro-Leu-γ-OBu^t-Glu-Phe-OBu^t								579
β-OBu^t-Asp-OBu^t-Tyr-OBu^t-Ser-N$^\epsilon$-boc-Lys-OBu^t-Tyr-Leu-β-OBu^t-Asp-OBu^t-Ser-Arg-Arg-Ala-Gln-β-OBu^t-Asp-Phe-Val-OBu^t Trihydrobromide	7+8 NHS-DCCI				207	−22	Ac-Aq	737
β-OBu^t-Z-Asp-OBu^t-Tyr-OBu^t-Ser-N$^\epsilon$-boc-Lys-OBu^t-Tyr-Leu-β-OBu^t-Asp-OBu^t-Ser-Arg-Arg-Ala-Gln-β-OBu^t-Asp-Phe-Val-OBu^t	7+8 NHS-DCCI	DMF		DMF-Aq	237 (dec)	−24	Ac-Aq	737
β-OBu^t-Z-Asp-OBu^t-Tyr-OBu^t-Ser-N$^\epsilon$-boc-Lys-Tyr-Leu-β-OBu^t-Asp-OBu^t-Ser-Arg-Arg-Ala-Gln-β-OBu^t-Asp-Phe-Val-Bu^t Dihydrobromide	7+8 NHS-DCCI	DMF	88	DMF-Aq	230			737
Glutamine								
γ-OBzl-Z-Glu-N^{im}-bzl-His-Phe-N^G-tos-Arg-Tyr-Gly-N$^\epsilon$-tos-Lys-Pro-Val-Gly-N$^\epsilon$-tos-Lys-N$^\epsilon$-tos-Lys-N^G-tos-Arg-N^G-tos-Arg-Pro	9+6 MCA	DMF	35		135–140			371
Isoleucine								
For-Ile-Gly-Ala-Leu-Ala-Val-Val-Val-Trp-Leu-Trp-Leu-Trp-Leu-Trp 2-Hydroxyethylamide	5+10 DCCI		62					527

Compound								
Leucine								
Boc-Leu-N^G-nitro-Arg-β-OBzl-Asp-OBzl-Ser-Ala-N^G-nitro-Arg-Leu-Gln-N^G-nitro-Arg-Leu-Leu-Gln-Gly-Leu-Val Amide	1+14 ONP	DMF	98		245 (dec)	-32	Ac	64
Proline								
Boc-Pro-Trp-Leu-γ-OBu^t-Glu-γ-OBu^t-Glu-γ-OBu^t-Glu-γ-OBu^t-Glu-γ-OBu^t-Glu-Ala-Tyr-Gly-Trp-Met-Asp-Phe Amide	11+4 OTCP		63					423
Boc-Pro-Trp-Leu-γ-OBu^t-Glu-γ-OBu^t-Glu-γ-OBu^t-Glu-γ-OBu^t-Glu-Ala-Tyr-Gly-Trp-Met-β-OBu^t-Asp-Phe Amide	11+4 MA	DMF	78		239-244			423
	11+4 OTCP	DMF		Ac	240-244			423
Pro-Trp-Leu-Glu-Glu-Glu-Ala-Tyr-Gly-Trp-Met-Asp-Phe Amide					243-245			423
Serine								
N-Z-Ser-Tyr-Ser-Met-γ-OBzl-Glu-His-Phe-N^G-tos-Arg-Trp-Gly-N^ε-boc-Lys-N^ε-boc-Lys-N^G-tos-Arg-N^G-tos-Arg-Pro-OBu^t	10+5 WRK					-51	DMF	372
Ser-Tyr-Ser-Met-Glu-His-Phe-Arg-Trp-Gly-Lys-Lys-Arg-Arg-Pro						-56	0.1M Ac	374
								372
Valine								
Z-Val-Gly-Ala-D-Leu-Ala-D-Val-Val-D-Val-Trp-D-Leu-Trp-D-Leu-Trp 2-Hydroxyethylamide	8+7 A	DMF	30					527
	5+10 DCCI	DMF						
For-Val-Gly-Ala-D-Leu-Ala-D-Val-Val-D-Val-Trp-D-Leu-Trp-D-Leu-Trp 2-Hydroxyethylamide								527

Table 16 Hexadecapeptides

Compound	Method	Solvent	% Yield	Solvent Crystallization	M.P.(°C)	$[\alpha]_D$	Solvent Rotation	Ref.
Glutamine								
Pyro-Glu-Gly-Pro-Trp-Leu-Glu-Glu-Glu-Glu-Ala-Tyr-Gly-Trp-Met-Asp-Phe Amide Ammonium Salt	5+11 A	DMF	85					28
Lysine								
Nε-Tos-Z-Lys-Pro-Val-Gly-Nε-tos-Lys-Nε-tos-Lys-NG-tos-Arg-NG-tos-Arg-Pro-Val-Nε-tos-Lys-Val-Tyr-Pro-γ-OBut-Asp-Gly-OBut					132–136	−30	DMF	493
Nε-Tos-Lys-Pro-Val-Gly-Nε-tos-Lys-Nε-tos-Lys-NG-tos-Arg-NG-tos-Arg-Pro-Val-Nε-tos-Lys-Val-Tyr-Pro-γ-OBut-Asp-Gly-OBut					128–132			493
Serine								
OAc-Ser-Tyr-Ser-Met-Gln-His-Phe-Arg-Tyr-Gly-Nε-for-Lys-Pro-Val-Gly-Nε-for-Lys-Nε-for-Lys Amide Acetate Octahydrate	5+11 A	DMF	90					247
Ser-Tyr-Ser-Met-Gln-His-Phe-Arg-Tyr-Gly-Lys-Pro-Val-Gly-Lys-Lys Acetate								247
N-Boc-Ser-Tyr-Ser-Met-γ-OBut-Glu-His-Phe-Arg-Trp-Gly-Nε-boc-Lys-Pro-Val-Gly-Nε-boc-Lys-Nε-boc-Lys-OMe Acetate	10+6 DCCI	Py						577
Ser-Tyr-Ser-Met-Glu-His-Phe-Arg-Trp-Gly-Lys-Pro-Val-Gly-Lys-Lys-OMe Tetraacetate								577

Table 17 Heptadecapeptides

			Yield		mp			
Alanine								
Z-Ala-Leu-Tyr-Leu-Val-S-bzl-Cys-Gly-γ-OBzl-Glu-N^G-tos-Arg-Gly-Phe-Phe-Tyr-Thr-Pro-N^ε-tos-Lys-Ala-OMe	7+10 WRK	DMF	38		265–268	−33	DMF	310
Glutamine								
Z-Gln-S-bzl-Cys-S-bzl-Cys-Ala-Gly-Val-S-bzl-Cys-Ser-Leu-Tyr-Gln-Leu-Glu-Asp-Tyr-S-bzl-Cys-Asp-ONBzl	5+12 A		75		270–271 (dec)	−31	DMSO	314
γ-OBzl-Z-Glu-Ala-Leu-Tyr-Leu-Val-S-bzl-Cys-Gly-Glu-N^G-tos-Arg-Gly-Phe-Tyr-Thr-Pro-N^ε-tos-Lys-Ala	MCA	DMF	25	Fm	271–273 (dec)	−43	Fm	539
Z-Glu-S-bzl-Cys-S-bzl-Cys-Thr-Ser-Ile-bzl-Cys-Ser-Leu-Tyr-Glu-Leu-Glu-Asp-Tyr-S-bzl-Cys-Asp-ONBzl	5+12 A	DMF	70	DMF-Aq	274–276 (dec)	−29	DMSO	313
Pyro-Glu-Gly-Pro-Trp-Leu-(penta-Glu)-Ala-Tyr-Gly-Trp-Leu-Asp-Phe Amide Ammonium Salt	5+12 A	DMF	92					323
Pyro-Glu-Gly-Pro-Trp-Leu-Glu-Glu-Glu-Glu-Ala-Tyr-Gly-Trp-Met-Asp-Phe-Amide Ammonium Salt	5+12 A	DMF	82					28
Pyro-Glu-Gly-Pro-Trp-Met-(penta-Glu)-Ala-Tyr-Gly-Trp-Leu-Asp-Phe Amide Ammonium Salt	5+12 A	DMF	74					323

Table 17 Heptadecapeptides (continued)

Compound	Method	Solvent	% Yield	Solvent Crystallization	M.P. (°C)	$[\alpha]_D$	Solvent Rotation	Ref.
Serine								
Z-Ser-Tyr-Ser-Met-Glu-His-Phe-N^G-tos-Arg-Trp-Gly-N$^\epsilon$-tos-Lys-Pro-Val-Gly-N$^\epsilon$-tos-Lys-N$^\epsilon$-tos-Lys-N^G-tos-Arg	7+10 WRK 7+10 DCCI							369
Ser-Tyr-Ser-Met-Glu-His-Phe-Arg-Trp-Gly-Lys-Pro-Val-Gly-Lys-Lys-Arg								369
Z-Ser-Tyr-Ser-Met-γ-OBzl-Glu-His-Phe-N^G-tos-Arg-Tyr-Gly-Lys-Lys-N^G-tos-Arg Amide	10+7 DCCI		37					492
Ser-Tyr-Ser-Met-Glu-His-Phe-Arg-Tyr-Gly-Lys-Pro-Val-Gly-Lys-Lys-Arg	10+7 DCCI					−97	0.1M Ac	373
Ser-Tyr-Ser-Met-Glu-His-Phe-Arg-Tyr-Gly-Lys-Pro-Val-Gly-Lys-Lys-Arg Amide	DCCI					−77	0.1N Ac	492
Ser-Tyr-Ser-Met-Glu-His-Phe-Lys-Trp-Gly-Lys-Pro-Val-Gly-Lys-Lys-Arg Amide						−84	0.1N Ac	94
Threonine								
Z-OBu^t-Thr-OBu^t-Ser-β-OBu^t-Asp-OBu^t-Tyr-OBu^t-Ser-N$^\epsilon$-boc-Lys-OBu^t-Tyr-Leu-β-OBu^t-Asp-OBu^t-Ser-Arg-Arg-Ala-Gln-β-OBu^t-Asp-Phe-Val-OBu^t Dihydrobromide	2+15 NHS-DCCI	DMF	70	Alc-Aq	230–230.5 (dec)	−12	Ac-Aq	735
	9+8 NHS-DCCI	DMF			242(dec)	−12	Ac-Aq	

396

Sequence	Method	Solvent	m.p.	[α]		Ref.
OBu^t-N-Nps-Thr-OBu^t-Ser-β-OBu^t-Asp-OBu^t-Tyr-OBu^t-Ser-N^ε-boc-Lys-OBu^t-Tyr-Leu-β-OBu^t-Asp-OBu^t-Ser-Arg-Arg-Ala-Gln-β-OBu^t-Asp-Phe-Val-OBu^t Dihydrobromide	9+8 NHS-DCCI	Me-EtAc-Eth	238(dec)	−4	Me	735
OBu^t-Thr-OBu^t-Ser-β-OBu^t-Asp-OBu^t-Tyr-OBu^t-Ser-N^ε-boc-Lys-OBu^t-Tyr-Leu-β-OBu^t-Asp-OBu^t-Ser-Arg-Arg-Ala-Gln-β-OBu^t-Asp-Phe-Val-OBu^t			223(dec)	−16	Ac-Aq	735

Table 18 Octadecapeptides

Sequence	Method		[α]	Solvent	Ref.
Arginine					
Arg-Pro-Gly-Phe-Ser-Pro-Phe-Arg-Arg-Pro-Pro-Gly-Phe-Ser-Pro-Phe-Arg (Bradykininyl bradykinin)					433
Asparagine					
Asp-Glu-Gly-Pro-Tyr-Arg-Met-Glu-His-Phe-Arg-Trp-Gly-Ser-Pro-Pro-Lys-Asp					746a
Serine					
Z-Ser-Tyr-Ser-Met-γ-OBzl-Glu-His-Phe-N^G-tos-Arg-Trp-Gly-Lys-Pro-Val-Gly-Lys-Lys-N^G-tos-Arg-N^G-tos-Arg Amide	DCCI	36			492
Ser-Tyr-Ser-Met-Glu-His-Phe-Arg-Trp-Gly-Lys-Pro-Val-Gly-Lys-Lys-Arg-Arg					462
Ser-Tyr-Ser-Met-Glu-His-Phe-Arg-Trp-Gly-Lys-Pro-Val-Gly-Lys-Lys-Arg-Arg Amide			−92	0.1 N Ac	492

Table 19 Nonadecapeptides

Compound	Method	Solvent	% Yield	Solvent Crystallization	M.P.(°C)	$[\alpha]_D$	Solvent Rotation	Ref.
Asparagine								
Asp-Ser-Gly-Pro-Tyr-Lys-Met-Glu-Glu-His-Phe-Arg-Trp-Gly-Ser-Pro-Pro-Lys-Asp β-OBu^t-boc-Asp-Ser-Gly-Pro-Tyr-N$^\epsilon$-boc-Lys-Met-γ-OBu^t-Gly-Glu-His-Phe-Arg-Trp-Gly-Ser-Pro-Pro-N$^\epsilon$-boc-Lys-Asp-di-OBu^t Acetate	7+12 A	DMF	55		220–225 (dec)			573
Glutamine								
γ-OBzl-boc-Glu-Leu-OBzl-Ser-N^G-nitro-Arg-Leu-N^G-nitro-Arg-β-OBzl-Asp-OBzl-Ser-Ala-N^G-nitro-Arg-Leu-Gln-N^G-nitro-Arg-Leu-Leu-Gln-Gly-Leu-Val Amide	1+18 ONP	DMF	92		315(dec)	−22	Ac	64
γ-OBzl-Glu-Leu-OBzl-Ser-N^G-nitro-Arg-Leu-N^G-nitro-Arg-β-OBzl-Asp-OBzl-Ser-Ala-N^G-nitro-Arg-Leu-Gln-N^G-nitro-Arg-Leu-Leu-Gln-Gly-Leu-Val Amide Trifluoroacetate					312(dec)			64
Glu-Leu-Ser-Arg-Leu-Arg-Asp-Ser-Ala-Arg-Leu-Gln-Arg-Leu-Leu-Gln-Gly-Leu-Val Amide						−56	1N Ac	458
Glu-Leu-Ser-Arg-Leu-N^G-nitro-Arg-β-OBzl-Asp-OBzl-Ser-Ala-N^G-nitro-Arg-Leu-Gln-N^G-nitro-Arg-Leu-Gln-Gly-Leu-Val Amide Trifluoroacetate	5+14 A	DMF	80					458

Serine								
Ac-Ser-Tyr-Met-Gln-His-Phe-Arg-Trp-Gly-N$^\epsilon$-for-Lys-Pro-Val-Gly-N$^\epsilon$-for-Lys-N$^\epsilon$-for-Lys-Arg-Arg-Pro-Val Amide Triacetate Decahydrate	9+10 DCCI	DMF	59					244
Ser-Tyr-Met-Gln-His-Phe-Arg-Trp-Gly-Lys-Pro-Val-Gly-Lys-Arg-Arg-Pro-Val Amide Acetate								244
Z-Ser-Tyr-Ser-Met-γ-OBzl-Glu-His-Phe-Arg-Trp-Gly-N$^\epsilon$-tos-Lys-Pro-Val-Gly-N^G-tos-Lys-N$^\epsilon$-tos-Lys-N^G-tos-Arg-N^G-tos-Arg-Pro				Me-EtAc	167–170			371
Z-Ser-Tyr-Ser-Met-γ-OBzl-Glu-His-Phe-N$^\epsilon$-tos-Arg-Trp-Gly-N$^\epsilon$-boc-Lys-Pro-Val-Gly-N$^\epsilon$-boc-Lys-N$^\epsilon$-boc-Lys-N^G-tos-Arg-N^G-tos-Arg-Pro-OBu^t	9+10 DCCI	DMF	38					368
Ser-Tyr-Ser-Met-Glu-His-Phe-Arg-Trp-Gly-Lys-Pro-Val-Gly-Lys-Lys-Arg-Arg-Pro						−76 / −84	0.1 M Ac / 0.1 M Ac	371 / 455 / 368
Z-Ser-Tyr-Ser-Met-γ-OBzl-Glu-His-Phe-N^G-tos-Arg-Tyr-Gly-N$^\epsilon$-boc-Lys-Pro-Val-Gly-N$^\epsilon$-boc-Lys-N$^\epsilon$-boc-Lys-N^G-tos-Arg-N^G-tos-Arg-Pro-OBu^t	10+9 DCCI		38					368
Z-Ser-Tyr-Ser-Met-γ-OBzl-Glu-His-Phe-N^G-tos-Arg-Tyr-Gly-Lys-Lys-N^G-tos-Arg-Arg-Pro Amide	10+9 DCCI		44					492
Ser-Tyr-Ser-Met-Glu-His-Phe-Arg-Tyr-Gly-Lys-Pro-Val-Gly-Lys-Lys-Arg-Arg-Pro						−84	1 M Ac	368
Ser-Tyr-Ser-Met-Glu-His-Phe-Arg-Tyr-Gly-Lys-Pro-Val-Gly-Lys-Lys-Arg-Arg-Pro Amide						−102	0.1 N Ac	492

Table 20 20-48 Unit Peptides

Compound	Method	Solvent	% Yield	Solvent Crystallization	M.P.(°C)	$[\alpha]_D$	Solvent Rotation	Ref.
20-Unit Peptides								
Glycine								
Gly-Ile-Gly-Ala-Val-Leu-Lys-Val-Leu-Thr-Thr-Gly-Leu-Pro-Ala-Leu-Ile-Ser-Trp-Ile	A					−95	2N Ac	549
Lycine								
Lys-Glu-Thr-Ala-Ala-Ala-Lys-Ala-Glu-Orn-Glu-His-Met-Asp-Ser-Ser-Thr-Ser-Ala-Ala						−79	Aq	583
Lys-Glu-Thr-Ala-Ala-Ala-Lys-Ile-Glu-Orn-Glu-His-Met-Asp-Ser-Ser-Thr-Ser-Ala-Ala						−72	Aq	583
Lys-Glu-Thr-Ala-Ala-Ala-Lys-Phe-Glu-Orn-Glu-His-Met-Asp-Ser-Ser-Thr-Ser-Ala-Ala	12+8 A					−57 −57	Aq Aq	582 581
21-Unit Peptides								
Glycine								
Z-Gly-Ile-Val-γ-OBu^t-Glu-Gln-S-bzl-Cys-S-bzl-Cys-Thr-Ser-Ile-S-bzl-Cys-Ser-Leu-Tyr-Gln-Leu-Glu-Asn-Tyr-S-bzl-Cys-Asn-ONBzl	4+17 A	DMF		DMSO-Aq	281–283 (dec)	−27	DMSO	313
Gly-Ile-Val-Glu-Gln-S-sulfo-Cys-S-sulfo-Cys-Thr-Ser-Ile-sulfo-Cys-Ser-Leu-Tyr-Gln-Leu-Glu-Asn-Tyr-S-sulfo-Cys-Asn	9+12 A	DMF						313

400

Compound	Coupling	Solvent	Yield	M.p.	$[\alpha]$	Solvent	Ref.
Gly-Ile-Val-Glu-Glu-S-sulfo-Cys-S-sulfo-Cys-Ala-Gly-Val-S-sulfo-Cys-Ser-Leu-Tyr-Glu-Leu-Glu-Asp-Tyr-S-sulfo-Cys-Asp	9+12 CDI						314
Z-Gly-Ile-Val-Glu-Glu-S-bzl-Cys-S-bzl-Cys-Thr-Ser-Ile-S-bzl-Cys-Ser-Leu-Tyr-Gln-Leu-Gln-Asn-Tyr-S-bzl-Cys-Asn-ONBzl				279–282 (dec)	−38	DMSO	313

Threonine

Compound	Coupling	Solvent	Yield	M.p.	$[\alpha]$	Solvent	Ref.
Boc-Thr-OBzl-Ser-γ-OBzl-Glu-Leu-OBzl-Ser-N^G-nitro-Arg-Leu-N^G-nitro-Arg-β-OBzl-Asp-OBzl-Ser-Ala-N^G-nitro-Arg-Leu-Gln-N^G-nitro-Arg-Leu-Leu-Gln-Gly-Leu-Val Amide	1+20 2,4-DNPO	DMF	95	315 (dec)	−17	Ac	64

23-Unit Peptides

Arginine

Compound	Coupling	Solvent	Yield	M.p.	$[\alpha]$	Solvent	Ref.
Arg-Arg-Pro-Val-N^ϵ-boc-Lys-Val-Tyr-Pro-β-OBu^t-Asp-Gly-Ala-γ-OBu^t-Glu-β-OBu^t-Asp-Gln-Leu-Ala-γ-OBu^t-Glu-Ala-Phe-Pro-Leu-γ-OBu^t-Glu-Phe-OBu^t							579
Z-Arg-Arg-Pro-Val-N^ϵ-boc-Lys-Val-Tyr-Pro-β-OBu^t-Asp-Gly-Ala-γ-OBu^t-Glu-β-OBu^t-Asp-Gln-Leu-Ala-γ-OBu^t-Glu-Ala-Phe-Pro-Leu-γ-OBu^t-Glu-Phe-OBu^t Diacetate							579

Serine

Compound	Coupling	Solvent	Yield	M.p.	$[\alpha]$	Solvent	Ref.
Ser-Tyr-Met-γ-OBu^t-Glu-His-Phe-Arg-Trp-Gly-N^ϵ-boc-Lys-Pro-Val-Gly-N^ϵ-boc-Lys-N^ϵ-boc-Lys-N^δ-boc-Orn-N^δ-boc-Orn-Pro-Val-N^ϵ-boc-Lys-Val-Tyr-Pro-OBu^t Acetate	9+14 DCCI			195–200	−55	Me	664
Ser-Tyr-Met-Glu-His-Phe-Arg-Trp-Gly-Lys-Pro-Val-Gly-Lys-Lys-Orn-Orn-Pro-Val-Lys-Val-Tyr-Pro Hexaacetate							664

401

Table 20 20-48 Unit Peptides (continued)

Compound	Method	Solvent	% Yield	Solvent Crystallization	M.P.(°C)	$[\alpha]_D$	Solvent Rotation	Ref.
Ac-Ser-Tyr-Ser-Met-Gln-His-Phe-Arg-Trp-Gly-N^ϵ-for-Lys-Pro-Val-Gly-N^ϵ-for-Lys-N^ϵ-for-Lys-Arg-Arg-Pro-Val-N^ϵ-for-Lys-Val-Tyr Amide	10+13 DCCI	DMF	49					245
N-Boc-Ser-Tyr-Ser-Met-γ-OBu^t-Glu-His-Phe-Arg-Trp-Gly-N^ϵ-boc-Lys-Pro-Val-Gly-N^ϵ-boc-Lys-N^ϵ-boc-Lys-Arg-Arg-Pro-Val-N^ϵ-boc-Lys-Val-Tyr Amide	10+13 ONP	Py						161
Ser-Tyr-Ser-Met-Glu-His-Phe-Arg-Trp-Gly-Lys-Pro-Val-Gly-Lys-Lys-Arg-Arg-Pro-Val-Lys-Val-Tyr Amide								161
Threonine								
Thr-Phe-Thr-Ser-Glu-Leu-Ser-Arg-Leu-Arg-Asp-Ser-Ala-Arg-Leu-Gln-Arg-Leu-Leu-Gln-Gly-Leu-Val Amide	4+19 A	DMF				-48	1N Ac	458
OBu^t-N-Nps-Thr-OBu^t-Ser-β-OBu^t-Asp-OBu^t-Tyr-OBu^t-Ser-N^ϵ-boc-Lys-OBu^t-Tyr-Leu-β-OBu^t-Asp-OBu^t-Ser-Arg-Arg-Ala-Gln-β-OBu^t-Asp-Phe-Val-Gln-Trp-Leu-Met-Asn-OBu^t-Thr-OBu^t Dihydrobromide	9+4 NHS-DCCI	DMF	68	DMA-Eth	250(dec)			725
OBu^t-Thr-OBu^t-Ser-β-OBu^t-Asp-OBu^t-Tyr-OBu^t-Ser-N^ϵ-boc-Lys-OBu^t-Tyr-Leu-β-OBu^t-Asp-OBu^t-Ser-Arg-Arg-Ala-Gln-β-OBu^t-Asp-Phe-Val-Gln-Trp-Leu-Met-Asn-OBu^t-Thr-OBu^t Trihydrobromide						+15	DMA-HMPA	725

24 Unit Peptides

Serine

Peptide	Method	Solvent	Yield (%)	M.p.	[α]		No.
Boc-Ser-Tyr-Ser-Met-Glu-His-Phe-Arg-Trp-Gly-N$^\epsilon$-boc-Lys-Pro-Val-Gly-N$^\epsilon$-boc-Lys-N$^\epsilon$-boc-Lys-Arg-Arg-Pro-Val-N$^\epsilon$-boc-Lys-Val-Tyr-Pro-OBu^t	10+14 DCCI						298
Ser-Tyr-Ser-Met-Glu-His-Phe-Arg-Trp-Gly-Lys-Pro-Val-Gly-Lys-Lys-Arg-Arg-Pro-Val-Lys-Val-Tyr-Pro							298
Boc-Ser-Tyr-Ser-Met-γ-OBu^t-Glu-His-Phe-Arg-Tyr-Gly-N$^\epsilon$-boc-Lys-Pro-Val-Gly-N$^\epsilon$-boc-Lys-N$^\epsilon$-boc-Lys-Arg-Arg-Pro-Val-N$^\epsilon$-boc-Lys-Val-Tyr-Pro-OBu^t Tritoluene sulfonate	10+14 DCCI	Py	55				574

26-Unit Peptides

Serine

Peptide	Method	Solvent	Yield (%)	M.p.	[α]		No.
Z-Ser-Tyr-Ser-Met-γ-OBu^t-Glu-His-Phe-N^G-tos-Arg-Trp-Gly-N$^\epsilon$-tos-Lys-Pro-Val-Gly-N$^\epsilon$-tos-Lys-N$^\epsilon$-tos-Lys-N^G-tos-Arg-N^G-tos-Arg-Pro-Val-N^G-tos-Lys-Val-Tyr-Pro-β-OBu^t-Asp-Gly-OBu^t	DCCI		70				493
Ser-Tyr-Ser-Met-Glu-His-Phe-Arg-Trp-Gly-Lys-Pro-Val-Gly-Lys-Lys-Arg-Arg-Pro-Val-Lys-Val-Tyr-Pro-Asp-Gly			20				493

27-Unit Peptides

Histidine

Peptide	Method	Solvent	Yield (%)	M.p.	[α]		No.
Z-His-OBzl-Ser-β-OBzl-Asp-Gly-Thr-Phe-Thr-OBzl-Ser-γ-OBzl-Glu-Leu-OBzl-Ser-N^G-nitro-Arg-Leu-N^G-nitro-Arg-β-OBzl-Asp-OBzl-Ser-Ala-N^G-nitro-Arg-Leu-Gln-N^G-nitro-Arg-Leu-Leu-Gln-Gly-Leu-Val Amide	1+26 A	DMF		312(dec)	−11	Ac	64

403

Table 20 20-48 Unit Peptides (continued)

Compound	Method	Solvent	% Yield	Solvent Crystallization	M.P.(°C)	[α] D	Solvent Rotation	Ref.
Bis-Z-His-OBzl-Ser-β-OBzl-Asp-Gly-Thr-Phe-Thr-OBzl-Ser-γ-OBzl-Glu-Leu-CBzl-Ser-N^G-nitro-Arg-Leu-N^G-nitro-Arg-β-OBzl-Asp-OBzl-Ser-Ala-N^G-nitro-Arg-Leu-Gln-N^G-nitro-Arg-Leu-Leu-Gln-Gly-Leu-Val Amide	4+23 A	DMF	33					64
His-Ser-Asp-Gly-Thr-Phe-Thr-Ser-Glu-Leu-Ser-Arg-Leu-Arg-Asp-Ser-Ala-Arg-Leu-Gln-Arg-Leu-Leu-Gln-Gly-Leu-Val Amide						-61	1N Ac	458 64
29-Unit Peptides								
N$^\epsilon$-Boc-Lys-Pro-Val-Gly-N$^\epsilon$-boc-Lys-N$^\epsilon$-boc-Lys-Arg-Arg-Pro-Val-N$^\epsilon$-boc-Lys-Val-Tyr-Pro-β-OBu^t-Asp-Gly-Ala-γ-OBu^t-Glu-β-OBu^t-Asp-Gln-Leu-Ala-γ-OBu^t-Glu-Ala-Phe-Pro-Leu-γ-OBu^t-Glu-Phe-OBu^t Sesquisulfate								579
N$^\epsilon$-Boc-N$^\alpha$-Z-Lys-Pro-Val-Gly-N$^\epsilon$-boc-Lys-N$^\epsilon$-boc-Lys-Arg-Arg-Pro-Val-N$^\epsilon$-boc-Lys-Val-Tyr-Pro-β-OBu^t-Asp-Gly-Ala-γ-OBu^t-Glu-β-OBu^t-Asp-Glu-Leu-Ala-γ-OBu^t-Glu-Ala-Phe-Pro-Leu-γ-OBu^t-Glu-Phe-OBu^t Diacetate	6+23 A	DMF	35.2					579
39-Unit Peptides								
Serine								
Boc-Ser-Tyr-Ser-Met-γ-OBu^t-Glu-His-Phe-Arg-Trp-Gly-N$^\epsilon$-boc-Lys-Pro-Val-Gly-N$^\epsilon$-boc-Lys-								

	10+29 DCCI	Py	
N$^\epsilon$-boc-Lys-Arg-Arg-Pro-Val-N$^\epsilon$-boc-Lys-Val-Tyr-Pro-β-OBu^t-Asp-Gly-Ala-γ-OBu^t-Glu-β-OBu^t-Asp-Gln-Leu-Ala-γ-OBu^t-Glu-Ala-Phe-Pro-Leu-γ-OBu^t-Glu-Phe-OBu^t Triacetate	10+29 DCCI	Py	579

48-Unit Peptides

Insulin

Des-Phe^{B1}-Insulin	73
Des-Asn^{A21}-des-Ala^{B30}-Insulin	490
Des-Gly^{A1}-des-Phe^{B1}-Insulin	490
Trimethionyl-Insulin	490
Triaminoacyl-Insulins	367a
Insulin	754a, 311a, 316c, 316b, 401a, 316a

12

Polypeptides

Because of obvious experimental difficulties, most of the polypeptides included in Table 21 are nebulously defined substances. Increasing use of the more sophisticated peptide reagents suggests that better progress will be forthcoming. Among the many interesting reasons for synthesizing the polypeptides included in Table 21 may be cited the attempted resolution of D,L-Met using poly[S]-(ar-vinyl-bzl)-D-Cys.[504] The racemic methionine in water was passed through a column of the polymer and partial resolution was realized.

The recent syntheses of poly-γ-D- and L-Glu, using an OPCP procedure,[348] and preparation of poly(Glu-Gln-Ala-Gly)[1–14C]-Gly-OEt[280] illustrate current work in this area.

Table 21 Polypeptides

Compound	Method	Solvent	% Yield	Solvent Crystallization	M.P. (°C)	$[\alpha]_D$	Solvent Rotation	Ref.
Poly-α-Ala								284
Poly-Arg Hydrochloride						−21	Aq	212
Poly-nitro-Arg								212
Poly[S-(ar-vinyl-bzl)-Cys]								504
Poly[S-(ar-vinyl-bzl)-D-Cys]								504
Poly-Gln-RNase	Anhydride	Di						705
Poly-Gln Rabbit Serum Albumin								705
Co-Poly-γ-bzl-Glu-DL-p-Sarcolysin								426
Poly-Glu								705
Poly-oc-Glu-melphalan OEt	Anhydride	Di-Chf				−73	N NaOH	656
Co-Poly-Glu-DL-Sarcolysin								426
Poly-γ-pht-me-Glu	Anhydride	Di	70			+12	DMF	705
Poly-Gly								460
Poly-N$^\epsilon$-Z-Lys								132
Poly-Lys								665
Poly-oc-Lys-amino-l-cyclopentane Carboxylic Acid	Anhydride	Di	65					447
Poly-oc-Lys-amino-l-cyclopentane Carboxylic (amido-^{14}C) Acid								447
Poly-Lys Hydrochloride								132
Poly-N$^\delta$-Z-Orn						+20	DMF	112
Poly-Orn Hydrobromide								112
Poly-Phe	WRK	DMF						57
Poly-DL-p-Sarcolysin								426
Poly-OAc-Ser								67
Poly-OBzl-Ser	Anhydride							67
Poly-OBzl-D-Ser						+27	DCA	655
Poly-OBzl-DL-Ser						−26	DCA	655

407

Table 21 Polypeptides (continued)

Compound	Method	Solvent	% Yield	Solvent Crystallization	M.P.(°C)	$[\alpha]_D$	Solvent Rotation	Ref.
Poly-O,O'-(N,N-bis-β-chloro-et-amido)-phosphoryl-Ser								655
Poly-O,O'-(N,N-bis-β-chloro-et-amido)-phosphoryl-D-Ser								655
Poly-O,O'-(N,N-bis-β-chloro-et-amido)-phosphoryl-DL-Ser								655
Poly-OMe-DL-Ser								655
Poly-Ser								67
								655
Poly-D-Ser								655
Poly-DL-Ser								655
Poly-(β-Asp-oc-Glu)								383
Poly-oc-Bu^t-D-Glu-β-Ala	PCP	DMF	71.5					346
Poly-oc-Bu^t-γ-Glu-β-Ala	PCP	DMF	88					346
Poly-γ-Glu-β-Ala								346
Poly-γ-D-Glu-β-Ala	ONP	DMSO	84			−30	6N HCl	346
Poly-γ-OMe-Asp-Ser-Gly	ONP	DMSO	33			−206	Aq	118
Poly(Gly-Pro-Ala)								59
								459a
Poly(Gly-Pro-Gly)	ONP	DMSO	31			−120	Fm-Aq	459a
						−198	Me	59
Poly-(Gly-Ser-Ala)	A	DMA	50					711
Poly-Ala-Gly-Ala-Gly-Ser-Gly								632
N-Poly-OAc-Ser-Val-Tyr-Ile-His-Pro-Phe								20
N-Poly-OAc-Ser-Asp-Arg-Val-Tyr-Ile-His-Pro-Phe								20

408

13

Solid Phase Synthesis

Introduction of a practical solid phase peptide synthesis by R. B. Merrifield represents one of the most significant advances in peptide chemistry over the past decade. Directly after the first publication by Merrifield, the general procedure was adopted in our laboratory and has given good results. Doubtlessly, further refinement in the experimental methods and automation will allow even more rapid progress in peptide syntheses. Because of the importance of the solid phase synthesis, it was planned to include here an extensive survey of the method. However, the recent appearance of a book on this subject by Stewart and Young[638] has made such a review at present unnecessary. The solid phase text reviews the general chemistry, laboratory techniques, and apparatus in a very useful manner. Thus, only an abbreviated selection of amino acid and peptide resin attachments has been listed with corresponding reference. The term polymer used in the table refers to the polystyrene resin applied by Merrifield. Presumably enough examples have been included to serve as a ready reference to the literature in this area. The substantial number of synthetic peptides prepared by solid phase synthesis have been listed in the other tables of Parts 1-3.

Among recent advances appear solid phase syntheses of Phe[8]-oxytocin[26] (see also ref. 52a), the antibiotic valinomycin (a cyclic dodecadepsipeptide),[166a] a tetradepsipeptide, Lys peptides,[179a] human fibrinopeptide A,[281b] ribonuclease,[217a] and the coupling (with WRK or DCCI-NHS) of a solid phase peptide unit with a di-, tri-, or tetrapeptide.[455a] Other contributions[349a,486b] received too late to enter in Table 22 include use of an enamine N-protecting group with a benzhydryl resin,[613] the role of steric hindrance,[607a] a method for determining completeness of reaction with the Merrifield solid phase synthesis,[125b] total synthesis of ferredoxin by the solid phase method,[27] and syntheses of certain hexapeptides containing an Asp-Gly sequence.[457] Related work pertaining to a new automated apparatus,[397a] bromoacylpolystyrene,[421a] (a new polymer), and syntheses of Gly-Gly-Leu-Gly[436b] and Ala-Ile-N^G-nitro-Arg-Ser-Ala[180a] using a polymeric carrier in solution is also of interest. One of the most promising recent advances in overall method entails use of a resin-*t*-alkyloxycarbonylhydrazide.[691a] The peptide sequence is then begun from the hydrazide using a 2-(4'-diphenyl)isopropyloxycarbonyl protecting group. Very mild acid treatment cleaves the protecting group and somewhat stronger acid removes the resin leaving the peptide hydrazide.

Table 22 Solid Phase (Resin)

Compound	Ref.
Boc-Ala-Polymer	468
Boc-N^G-nitro-Arg-Polymer	547
N^G-Nitro-Arg-Polymer	416
N^G-Nitro-Nps-Arg-Resin	416
Boc-Gly Nitrated Resin	433
Boc-Gly-Polymer	657
Z-Phe-Polymer	46
Boc-Phe-Polymer	137
Z-Val-Nitro-Polymer	325
Val-Nitro-Polymer	415
Z-Gly-Val-Nitro-Polymer	415
N$^\epsilon$-Boc-Lys-Gly-Polymer	415
N$^\epsilon$-Boc-N$^\alpha$-Nps-Lys-Gly-Polymer	324
Boc-Phe-N^G-nitro-Arg-Polymer	324
Nps-Phe-N^G-nitro-Arg-Resin	416
Poly-β-OMe-Asp-OAc-Ser-Gly	433
Z-Phe-N$^\epsilon$-boc-Lys-Gly-Polymer	118
Z-Leu-Ala-Gly-Val-nitro-Polymer	324
Leu-Ala-Gly-Val-nitro-Polymer	415
Boc-Leu-Gly-Pro-N^G-nitro-Arg-Polymer	415
Dansyl-Pro-Leu-Gly-Pro-nitro-Arg-Polymer	547
Boc-Gln-Asn-S-bzl-Cys-Pro-Leu-Gly-nitro-Polymer	547
Boc-Ile-Gln-Asn-S-bzl-Cys-Pro-Leu-Gly-nitro-Polymer	657
Boc-β-bzl-Asp-nitro-Arg-Ala-OBzl-Tyr-Ile-N^{im}-bzl-His-Pro-Phe-Polymer	657
β-OBzl-Z-Asp-N^G-nitro-Arg-Val-OBzl-Tyr-Ile-N^{im}-bzl-His-Pro-Ala-Polymer	325
S-Bzl-β-mercaptopropionyl-OBzl-Tyr-Ile-Gln-Asn-S-bzl-Cys-Pro-Leu-Gly Nitrated Resin	468
S-Bzl-Z-Cys-OBzl-Tyr-Ile-Gln-Asn-S-bzl-Cys-Pro-Leu-Gly-Polymer	657
N^G-Nitro-boc-Arg-Pro-Pro-Gly-Phe-OBzl-Ser-Pro-Phe-N^G-nitro-Arg-Polymer	416
Aoc-Cys-Tyr-Ile-γ-et-Glu-β-me-Asp-Cys-Pro-Leu-Gly-Polymer	46
S-Et-mercapto-Aoc-Cys-Tyr-Ile-γ-et-Glu-β-me-Asp-S-et-mercapto-Cys-Pro-Leu-Gly-Polymer	265
	265

14

Cyclopeptides

The cyclopeptides of Table 23 have been arranged using current IUPAC nomenclature. For example, cyclo-(Ala-Orn-Leu-D-Phe-Pro) hydrochloride[338] refers to a cyclic pentapeptide and cyclo-(Gly-D-Phe-Leu)$_2^{57}$ indicates a cyclic hexapeptide. The general approach to cyclopeptide synthesis involves intramolecular condensation at high dilution. Unfortunately, only one comparison of coupling methods appears in Table 23.[337] The study was made with cyclo-(Gly-N$^\delta$-Z-Orn-Leu-D-Phe-Gly) as product and significant differences in yield were obtained by changing solvent and/or peptide bond-forming method. Cyclization of peptides usually results in yields near 30%. Improvement in synthetic methods for the cyclization of peptides should be warmly received. By way of illustration, it has been reported that the CTCI method proved successful where the azide and several others were unsuccessful in analogous reactions.[593]

A few of the cyclopeptides have been purified by column chromatography on carboxymethylcellulose[337,338,593] or Sephadex G-25.[338] A few applications of countercurrent distribution have also been described.[202,580]

Recent advances in the chemistry of cyclopeptides include syntheses of cyclo-(Val-Tyr-Ile-His-Pro-Phe)[287] and cyclopeptides containing sarcosine.[110] Application of NPS protected 4-nitrophenylthio esters and cyclization catalyzed by imidazole has been employed to prepared cyclic peptides in 28-32% yields.[132a]

Table 23 Cyclopeptides

Compound	Method	Solvent	% Yield	Solvent Crystallization	M.P. (°C)	[α]D	Solvent Rotation	Ref.
Cyclo(β-Ala-4-aminobutyryl)				Alc	119–120			11
Cyclo(β-Ala-6-aminohexanoyl)				Alc	259			11
Gramicidin-S-3-OBzl-4-me-2-bz(NO$_2$) Derivative								404
N-[2-Nitro-3-OBzl-4-me-bz]-cyclo-[Thr-D-allo-Ile-Pro-sarkosyl-N-me-Val-O$_{thr}$]						+8	Me	76
Cyclo[N$^\gamma$-tos-Dbu-Thr-N$^\gamma$-tos-Dbu-Thr-N$^\gamma$-tos-Dbu-D-Leu-Ile-N$^\gamma$-tos-Dbu-N$^\gamma$-pelargonyl-Dbu]				Me-Pe				486
N-[2-Nitro-3-OBzl-4-me-bz]-cyclo-[Thr-D-Val-Pro-sarkosyl-N-me-Val-O$_{thr}$]					106–108	−14	Me	76
Cyclo-[Ala-N$^\delta$-Z-Orn-Leu-D-Phe-Pro]					243–244 (dec)	−134	Ac	338
Cyclo-(Ala-Orn-Leu-D-Phe-Pro)$_2$ Dihydrochloride					194–196 (dec)	−252	Ac	338
Cyclo-(Ala-Orn-Leu-D-Phe-Pro) Hydrochloride	DCCI	Aq-Me	12.7		300–328 (dec)	−163	Ac	338
Cyclo-(Gly-Leu-Leu-Gly-Gly)					310–330 (dec)			202
Cyclo-(Gly-Leu-D-Leu-Gly-Gly)	ONP	DMF	21	Me-EtAc-Eth	274–275 (dec)	−5	DMF	202
Cyclo-(Gly-N$^\delta$-Z-Orn-Leu-D-Phe-Gly)	ONP	Py	36	Me-EtAc-Eth	274–276 (dec)	−4	DMF	337
Cyclo-(Gly-Orn-Leu-D-Phe-Gly) Hydrochloride	ONP	DMF	32	Me-Eth	282–283 (dec)	−49	DMF	337
	A	Aq	8	Me-Eth	281–282 (dec)	−50	DMF	337
	ONP	Py	37		270–272 (dec)	−54	Ac	337

413

Table 23 Cyclopeptides (continued)

Compound	Method	Solvent	% Yield	Solvent Crystallization	M.P. (°C)	$[\alpha]_D$	Solvent Rotation	Ref.
Cyclo-(Gly-N$^{\delta}$-Z-Orn-Leu-D-Phe-Pro)	ONP	Py	45	Me-Eth-Pe	165–168	−84	Ac	338
Cyclo-(Gly-Orn-Leu-D-Phe-Pro) Hydrochloride					190–192 (dec)	−96	Ac	338
Cyclo-(Gly-Sar-Lys-Val-Pro) Hydrochloride	ONP		46			+48	Chf	75
Cyclo-[O-(Gly)-N-Z-Ser-D-allo-Ile-Pro-Sar]				Me-Eth	224–227	+80	Ac	74
Cyclo-(Val-N$^{\delta}$-Z-Orn-Leu-D-Phe-Sar)						+0.7	Ac	74
Cyclo-(Val-Orn-Leu-D-Phe-Sar) Hydrochloride					198	−26	Alc	16
Cyclo-(Gly-Gly-β-Ala-Gly-Gly-β-Ala)	SPh	Py	47					719
Cyclo-[Gly-Gly-DL-Ala-Gly-Gly-DL-Ala]	SPh	Py	37					719
Cyclo-(Digly-ONp-Ala-digly-Phe)	SPh	Py	46	Me-Aq	334	−89	DMF	548
Cyclo-(Gly-Gly-Gly-Gly-Gly-Gly)	A	Aq			350			719
Cyclo-(Digly-N$^{\epsilon}$-Z-Lys)$_2$				Di-Eth	263–265	−13	DMF	1
Cyclo-(Digly-Lys)$_2$ Dihydrochloride	EDCI	DMF	58					1
Cyclo-(Gly-N^{im}-bzl-His-Gly-Tyr-Gly-Gly)				Ac-Aq	360	−105	DMF	341
Cyclo-(Gly-His-Gly-Tyr-Gly-Gly)								341
Cyclo-(Gly-p-nitro-Phe-Gly)$_2$								548
Cyclo-(Gly-Phe-Leu-Gly-Phe-Leu)	WRK	DMF	30	Ac-Aq	312–314	−38	Ch-Alc	57
Cyclo-(Gly-D-Phe-Leu-Gly-Phe-Leu)	A	DMF	39	Ac-Aq	347–351	−40	Ch-Alc	87
Cyclo-(Gly-D-Phe-Leu)$_2$	WRK	DMF	15		316–319			57
Cyclo-(Gly-D-Phe-Leu-Gly-D-Phe-Leu)	WRK	DMF	45	Ac-Aq / Ac-Aq	324–326 / 322–324 (dec)	+12 / +13	Ch-Alc / Ch-Alc	87
Cyclo-(Gly-Phe-Leu-Gly-Phe-Leu) Dihydrate	A		22	Aq-Ac	315–318	−43 / −77	Ch-Alc / DCA	87
Cyclo-(Gly-Pro-Digly-Pro-Gly) Hydrate	A			Aq				496
Cyclo-(Gly-Pro-Digly-pro-Gly) ONp Complex	ONP	DMF	35	Aq		+45	Aq	496
Cyclo-(Gly-Tyr-Gly-N^{im}-bzl-His-Gly)								278

Compound	Method	Solvent	Yield (%)	Recryst.	m.p. (°C)	[α]	Solvent	Ref.
Cyclo-(D-Phe-D-Leu-δ-Z-D-Orn-Val-δ-Z-D-Orn-Pro)	ONP	DMF	48	EtAc-Eth-Pe	184	+7	Ac	301
Cyclo-(D-Phe-D-Leu-Orn-Val-D-Orn-Pro) Hydrobromide					242–244 (dec)	+6	Ac	301
Cyclo-(D-Phe-D-Leu-Orn-Val-D-Orn-Pro) Dihydrochloride					173–180 (dec)		Ac	301
Cyclo-(Ser-Gly-His-Ser-Gly-His)	CTCl			i-Pr-An				593
Cyclo-(Val-N$^\delta$-Z-Orn-Leu-D-Phe-Pro-Gly)	ONP	DMF	32	EtAc-Eth	224–226	−22	DMF	302
Cyclo-(Val-Orn-Leu-D-Phe-Pro-Gly) Hydrochloride					283 (dec)	−125	Me-Aq	302, 641
Cyclo-OAc-Ser-Phe-Leu-Pro-Val-Asn-Leu)					250–252			641
Cyclo-(Ser-Phe-Leu-Pro-Val-Asn-Leu)	ONP	DMF	23	Di-Me-Eth	255–258 (dec)	−254	Ac	338
Cyclo-[Ala-N$^\delta$-Orn-Leu-D-Phe-Pro]$_2$								
Cyclo-(Gly-Orn-Leu-D-Phe-Gly)$_2$ Dihydrochloride	ONP	DMF	28	Me-Eth	239–242 (dec)	−42	Ac	337
Cyclo-[Gly-N$^\delta$-Z-Orn-Leu-D-Phe-Pro]$_2$					137–138 (dec)	−102	Ac	338
Cyclo-(Gly-Orn-Leu-D-Phe-Pro)$_2$ Dihydrochloride					192–195 (dec)	−108	Ac	338
Cyclo-(Lys-Arg-Pro-Gly-Phe-Gly-Pro-Phe-Arg)	DCCI		34					409
Cyclo-(Phe-Phe-Asn-Gln-Tyr-Val-δ-Z-Orn-Leu-D-Phe-Pro)				Di-Eth-Pe	263–265 (dec)	−111	DMF	451
Cyclo-(Phe-D-Phe-Asn-Gln-Tyr-Val-Orn-Leu-D-Phe-Pro) Hydrochloride				Me-Eth	239–240 (dec)			451
Cyclo(Phe-Pro-Pro-Phe-Phe-Val-Pro-Pro-Ala-Phe)								703a
Cyclo-[Val-N$^\epsilon$-Z(OMe)-Lys-Leu-D-Phe-Pro]$_2$	ONP	DMF-Py	29	Me-Aq	246–248			580

Table 23 Cyclopeptides (continued)

Compound	Method	Solvent	% Yield	Solvent Crystallization	M.P. (°C)	[α]_D	Solvent Rotation	Ref.
Cyclo-(Val-Lys-Leu-D-Phe-Pro)₂								580
Cyclo-(Val-Lys-Leu-D-Phe-Pro)₂ Dihydrobromide Hydrate				Me	284–285			580
Cyclo-(Val-Lys-Leu-D-Phe-Pro)₂ Dihydrochloride Hydrate				Alc	298–299			580
Cyclo-(Val-Nᵉ-tos-Lys-Leu-D-Phe-Pro)₂				Me-Aq	302–303			580
					266–268			580
Cyclo-(Val-δ-Z-Orn-Leu-Gly-Pro)₂	ONP		43	Me-Eth-Pe	159–161	−195	Ac	431
Cyclo-(Val-Orn-Leu-Gly-Pro)₂ Dihydrochloride					239–240	−203	Alc	431
Cyclo-(Val-Nᵈ-Z-Orn-Leu-D-Phe-Gly)₂	ONP	DMF	38	Me-Eth	248–250	−127	Ac	18
Cyclo-(Val-Orn-Leu-D-Phe-Gly)₂ Dihydrochloride				Me-Eth-Pe	227–230	−190	Alc	18
Cyclo-(Val-δ-Z-Orn-Leu-D-Phe-Sar)₂					165	−139	Ac	16
Cyclo-(Val-Orn-Leu-D-Phe-Sar)₂ Dihydrochloride				Me-Eth-Pe	212–214	−157	Alc	16

15

Depsipeptides and Cyclodepsipeptides

Included among the depsipeptide and cyclodepsipeptide tables appear derivatives of hydroxy-proline and simple esters such as those derived from glycolic and hydroxy-isovaleric acid. Generally, the depsipeptide ester linkage was achieved using an acid chloride procedure. In this regard, the recent contributions (see for example ref. 621) of Stewart using an accelerated active ester coupling with imidazole is particularly noteworthy. Otherwise, as will be seen in Table 24, the peptide bonds were formed using one of the common coupling procedures. The cyclodepsipeptides of Table 24 were generally obtained in similar fashion.

New advances (see also Chapter 5) in this field entails synthesis of several 14-membered cyclodepsipeptides[206] and a study of the conformation of *cyclo*-(D-Hyv-N-Me-Ile-D-Hyv-N-Me-Leu) by X-ray crystallography.[339] The increasing potential importance of depsipeptides and cyclodepsipeptides as medicinal agents emphasizes the need for even better synthetic methods in this branch of peptide chemistry.

Table 24 Depsipeptides

Compound	Method	Solvent	% Yield	Solvent Crystallization	M.P. (°C)	[α]D	Solvent Rotation	Ref.
Ala-glycolyl-ONp Hydrobromide				Me-Eth	173.5-174.5	-13	Alc	622
Z-Ala-glycolyl-OPmb				EtAc-Cy-Alc	120-120.5	-35	Alc	621
				EtAc-Cy	119-120	-36	Alc	621
Z-Ala-glycolyl-ONp				Alc-Cy	109-109.5	-56	Alc	621
				Alc-Cy	100.5-101	-53	Alc	622
Z-β-Ala-DL-mandelic Acid				EtAc-Cy	108.5-109.5			621
Z-β-Ala Mandelyl-OPmb				EtAc-Cy	98.5-99			621
Z-Gly-glycolyl-O-p-bromophenacyl				Alc	141.5-142			621
Boc-Gly-glycolic Acid DCHA Salt								164
Boc-Gly-glycolyl-OBzl								164
Boc-Gly-glycolyl-Pmb				Alc	136-136.5			621
Gly-Glycolamide Ester Hydrobromide				Me-Eth	192-193 (dec)			636
Gly-glycolyl-O-p-Bromophenacyl Hydrobromide				Alc-Eth	205.5-206.5			621
Gly-glycolyl-OBzl Hydrobromide								164
Gly-glycolyl-OBzl Hydrochloride								164
Gly-glycolyl-OEt Hydrochloride								164
Pht-Gly-glycolic Acid				Pe	133-133.5			622
Trt-Gly-glycolic Acid								164
Trt-Gly-glycolyl-OBzl								164
Z-N-me-Ile-D-α-hyv-OBu^t	BSC	Py	51		oil	-57		489
N-Nitroso-N-me-Ile-D-α-hyv-ONBzl	MA	Eth	53		oil	-37	Be	488
Z-Leu-glycolyl-OPmb				Me	105.105.5	-36	Alc	621
Bu^t-Z-Leu-α-hyv acid					oil	-27	Be	464

Compound	Method	Solvent	Yield (%)	Cryst. solvent	M.p./B.p. (°C)	[α]	Recryst. solvent	Ref.
Bu^t-Leu-α-hyv acid					B.p. 102–104 (0.5 mm)	–2	Be	464
Z-Hyp-D-Phe	WRK	Acn			148–150	–16	DMF	440a
N-Nps-Hyp DCHA Salt	WRK	Acn			169–171	–39		774
Z-Hyp-D-Val					62–68	–10	DMF	440a
[N-Z-N-me-Val]-α-Hyv Acid								387
[N-Z-N-me-Val]-α-Hyv Acid OBu^t				EtAc-Pe	117–117.5	–17	Alc	387
Z-Val-glycolic Acid DCHA Salt					92–93	–9	Be	622
Z-Val-D-α-Hyv Acid					oil	+4	Be	642
Boc-D-Val-α-D-Hyv-OBzl				Eth-Pe	92–93	–9	Be	566
Z-Val-α-D-Hyv-OBu^t					127–129	+4		642
Z-D-Val-α-D-Hyv-boc-hydrazide					oil	+34		566
Z-Val-D-α-Hyv Acid					78–80	–6		642
Z-Val-D-α-Hyv-OBu^t				Eth-Pe	44–46	+52	Bz	642
Boc-D-Val-α-D-Hyv Acid								566
Boc-D-Val-α-D-Hyv-OBzl								566
D-α-Hyv-Val-OBzl	A	THF	59		62–64	+15	Ac	396
α-D-Hyv-D-Val-OBzl	A		62					566
α-Hyv-Val Hydrazide					210–212	+9	Ac	396
α-Hyv-D-Val Hydrazide				Me-Eth	210–212	–15	Ac	396
α-Hyv-D-Val-OMe	A		67					396
DL-α-Hyv Anilide								564
δ-D-Hyv-OBzl								566
α-Hyv-OCH$_2$CN					b.p. 81–83 (0.5 mm)	–7	EtAc	564
D-α-Hyv-OCH$_2$CN				Eth-Pe	94–96	+7		564
D-α-Hydroxy-Val Bzl-amide					93–101			564
[N-Me-Val]-α-Hyv-OBu^t								387
D-MeVal-D-Hyv-OBu^t			66			+34		387
L-MeVal-L-Hyv-OBu^t			73			–39		387
D-MeVal-L-Hyv-OBu^t			69			–20		387
L-MeVal-D-Hyv-OBu^t			74			+22		387

Table 24 Depsipeptides (continued)

Compound	Method	Solvent	% Yield	Solvent Crystallization	M.P. (°C)	[α]D	Solvent Rotation	Ref.
α-D-THP-isovaleryl-D-Val					115	+66		566
α-D-THP-isovaleryl-D-Val-OBzl				EtAc-Pe	oil	+21		566
D-Val-α-D-isovaleric Acid Hydrochloride					oil			566
D-Val-α-D-isovaleryl Boc-hydrazide					116–116.5	+40	Be	642
Val-D-α-oxy-isovaleryl-OBu^t	MCA	Acn	74	Alc	191.5–	−67	Alc	622
Z-Ala-Ala-glycolyl-ONp				Me-EtAc	192.5			622
Ala-Gly-glycolyl-OPmb Hydrochloride						+3	Me	621
N-Z-Ala-Gly-glycolyl Amide Ester	ONP		51	Alc-Cy	159–160	−5	DMF	636
Z-Ala-glycolyl-OPmb	ONP		79	Alc	178–178.5	−3	DMF	621
Z-Ala-glycolyl-Gly-2,4,6-tri-me-OBzl	ONP	DMF	96	EtAc-Pe	86.5–87	−18	Alc	622
Z-β-Ala-DL-mandelyl-Gly-2,4,6-tri-me-OBzl	DCCI	Acn	87	EtAc-Eth	147–147.5			622
Nps-Ala-glycolyl-OPmb	ONP		89	Alc	170–170.5	−29	DMF	621
Boc-Ala-Hyp			40–50		161			704
Z-Asn-Gly-glycolyl Amide Ester	ONP	DMF	72	Aq	198.5–200	−8	DMF	636
Z-Gly-Gly-glycolyl-O-β-Bromophenacyl	ONP	DMF	98	EtAc	175–176			621
Z-Gly-Gly-glycolyl-OEt					103–104			164
Boc-Gly-glycolyl-Gly				Pe-Ac	102.5–			570
Boc-Gly-glycolyl-Gly-ONBzl					103.5			570
Boc-Gly-glycolyl-Gly-ONp					156–158			570
Gly-glycolyl-Gly-ONBzl					148–149			570
Pht-Gly-glycolyl-Gly-OEt	2+2 MCA		75					164
Pht-Gly-glycolyl-glycolyl-Gly-OEt								164
Pht-Tauryl-Gly-Gly				Alc-Aq	274–275			614
Pht-Tauryl-Gly-OEt				THF	102–103			614
Trt-Gly-Gly-glycolyl-OCH₂CN								164
Pht-Tauryl-Gly-DL-Met				Alc-Aq	300 (dec)			614
Pht-Tauryl-Gly-DL-Met-OEt				Alc	123–124			614

Z-N-me-Ile-D-α-Hyv-N-me-Ile-D-α-Hyv-OBu^t						-85		489
N-Me-Ile-D-α-Hyv-N-me-Ile-D-α-Hyv-OBu^t	2+2 MA				149	-57	Alc	489
N-Me-Ile-D-α-Hyv-N-me-Ile-D-α-Hyv-ONp					92-94	-37	Be	488
D-Leu-α-Hyv-OBu^t					b.p. 90-92 (0.15 mm)	-33	Be	596
N-Me-Leu-α-Hyv-OBu^t					oil	-28	Be	596
Z(NO2)-D-Leu-α-Hyv-OBu^t	BSC	Py	80	He	46-47	+7	Be	596
Z(NO2)-N-me-Leu-α-Hyv-OBu^t						-30	Be	596
D-α-Hyv-Gly Bzl-amide				EtAc-Pe	109-110	-38	Alc	564
DL-α-Hyv-Gly Bzl-amide				MeCl-Eth-Alc	183-184	+34	Me	564
N-(2-Hydroxy-1-naphthal)-Val-Gly-OEt	DCCI	MeCl	70		oil	+15	Be	592
Z-D-Val-D-Leu-α-hydroxyisocaproic Acid					oil	-26	Be	464
Z-D-Val-D-Leu-α-hydroxyisocaproyl-OBu^t	MCA	THF	85		oil		Be	464
Z-D-Val-D-Leu-α-Hyv acid								596
Z-D-Val-D-Leu-α-Hyv-OBu^t	1+2 MCA	THF	90	He	78-79	+26	Be	596
D-α-Hyv-Val-Leu	1+2 A		35		184-187	-56	Ac	396
α-Hyv-D-Val-D-Leu	1+2 A		95		196-199	+60	Ac	396
D-α-Hyv-Val-Leu-OBzl	1+2 A		62		156-157	-59	Ac	396
D-α-Hyv-Val-Leu-OBu^t	2+1 MCA		52		177-178	-27	Alc	396
α-Hyv-Val-Leu-OMe	2+1 A		70	EtAc-Eth	154-156	+64	Ac	396
α-Hyv-D-Val-D-Leu-OMe	2+1 A		70	EtAc-Pe	154-156			396
D-α-Hyv-Val-Leu-OMe	1+2 A	EtAc-DMF	74		153-155	-65	Ac	396
Z(NO2)-Val-N-me-Leu-α-Hyv-OBu^t	1+2 AC	Eth	85		oil	-42	Be	596
Nps-Val-Leu-α-Hyv-OBu^t	1+2 DCCI	THF	98		oil	-74	Be	464
Val-Leu-α-Hyv-OBu^t Hydrochloride						-28	Alc	464
Val-N-me-Leu-α-Hyv-OBu^t Hydrochloride				PrEth	143-146	-24	Alc	596
Z-(L-MeVal-D-Hyv-)2-OBu^t			92		121-123	-99		387
Z-(D-MeVal-D-Hyv-)2-OBu^t			89		80-81	+87		387
Z-(L-MeVal-L-Hyv-)2-OBu^t			94		81-82	-90		387
Z-(D-MeVal-L-Hyv-)2-OBu^t			92		123-123.5	+101		387
Z-Val-D-α-Hyv-Val-D-Hyv-OBu^t				Eth-Pe	78-79	+11	Be	642
Z-D-Val-Lac-Val-D-α-Hyv Acid	AC		80			-12	Alc	595

Table 24 Depsipeptides (continued)

Compound	Method	Solvent	% Yield	Solvent Crystallization	M.P. (°C)	[α]D	Solvent Rotation	Ref.
Z-D-Val-Lac-Val-D-α-Hyv-OBu^t	1+2 AC	Be	92		oil	-1	Alc	595
Z-D-Val-Lac-Val-lactic Acid						-21	Alc	595
Z-D-Val-Lac-Val-Lac-OBu^t						-47	Alc	595
For-D-Val-D-Val-glycolyl-OBzl				Ac-Aq	154-160	+73	Ac	164
D-α-Hyv-D-Val-Val								564
D-α-Hyv-D-Val-D-Val-OBu^t								564
(D-MeVal-D-Hyv-)$_2$-OBu^t			80			+87		387
(MeVal-Hyv-)$_2$-OBu^t			86			-92		387
(D-MeVal-Hyv-)$_2$-OBu^t			83			+55		387
(MeVal-D-Hyv-)$_2$-OBu^t			85			-58		387
Z(NO$_2$)-N-me-Val-D-2-hydroxy-3-me-butyryl-N-me-Val-D-2-hydroxy-3-me-butyric Acid						-110	Be	597
Val-D-α-Hyv-Val-D-α-Hyv-OBu^t	2+3 ONP	DMF-Ac		Eth	97-98	+38	Be	642
D-Val-Lac-Val-D-α-Hyv-OBu^t	1+2 DCCI	THF	80-90	Alc	193-193.5	-32	Alc	595
Z-Ala-glycolyl-Ala-Gly-glycolyl-OPmb						-16	DMF	621
S-Bzl-Z-Cys-Ala-Hyp-OMe								704
S-Bzl-Cys-Ala-Hyp-OMe								704
Z-Gly-Gly-glycolyl-Gly-OEt								164
Trt-Gly-Gly-glycolyl-Gly-OBzl	2+2 MCA		90	EtAc-Pe				164
Z-His-Hyp-Phe-OMe	1+2 A		66.2	EtAc-Eth	92-95	-23	Alc	606
Z-N-me-Ile-D-α-Hyv-N-me-Ile-D-α-Hyv-N-me-Ile-D-α-Hyv-OBu^t	2+4 AC		86			-107		489
N-Me-Ile-D-α-Hyv-N-me-Ile-D-α-Hyv-N-me-Ile-D-α-Hyv-acid Hydrobromide						-48	Alc	489
N-Me-Ile-D-α-Hyv-N-me-Ile-D-α-Hyv-N-me-Ile-D-α-Hyv-acid Hydrochloride						-50	Alc	488

Compound	Yield (%)	Solvent	M.p. (°C)	$[\alpha]$	Solvent	Ref.
N-Me-Ile-D-α-Hyv-N-me-Ile-D-α-Hyv-N-me-Ile-D-α-Hyv-N-me-Ile-D-α-Hyv-ONBzl				−103	Be	488
Z(NO$_2$)-N-me-Ile-D-2-hydroxy-3-me-butyryl-N-me-Ile-D-2-hydroxy-3-me-butyryl-N-me-Ile-D-2-hydroxy-3-me-butyryl-OBu^t			oil	−100	Be	597
Z(NO$_2$)-N-me-Ile-D-2-hydroxy-3-me-butyryl-N-me-Ile-D-2-hydroxy-3-me-butyryl-N-me-Val-D-2-hydroxy-3-me-butyryl-OBu^t			oil	−106	Be	597
Z-Hyp-Gly-Gly-OEt			145–146	−15	DMF	712
Z-Hyp-Gly-Phe-OMe		Chf				22
Z-(D-MeVal-D-Hyv-)$_3$-OBu^t	93	ONP	102–104	+115		387
Z-(MeVal-Hyv-)$_3$-OBu^t	83		105–106	−116		387
Z-(D-MeVal-Hyv-)$_3$-OBu^t	94			+108		387
Z-(MeVal-D-Hyv-)$_3$-OBu^t	86			−104		387
Z-N-me-Val-D-α-Hyv-Val-D-α-Hyv-Val-D-α-Hyv-OBu^t	46	Eth	oil	+13	Be	642
Z-Val-D-α-Hyv-N-me-Val-D-α-Hyv-N-me-Val-D-α-Hyv-OBu^t	93	Eth		−90		642
Z-Val-D-α-Hyv-Val-D-α-Hyv-Val-D-α-Hyv-OBu^t	79	Eth	oil	+33	Be	642
Z-D-Val-Lac-Val-Lac-Val-D-α-Hyv Acid				−34	Alc	595
Z-D-Val-Lac-Val-Lac-Val-D-α-Hyv-OBu^t				+27	Alc	595
(D-MeVal-D-Hyv-)$_3$ Hydrobromide	80			+91		387
(MeVal-Hyv-)$_3$ Hydrobromide	95			−92		387
(D-MeVal-Hyv-)$_3$ Hydrobromide	90			+65		387
(MeVal-D-Hyv-)$_3$ Hydrobromide	65			−67		387
N-Me-Val-D-α-Hyv-Val-D-α-Hyv-Val-D-α-Hyv Acid Hydrobromide				−4	Alc	642
Z(NO$_2$)-N-me-Val-D-2-hydroxy-3-me-butyryl-N-me-Val-D-2-hydroxy-3-me-butyryl-N-me-Val-D-2-hydroxy-3-me-butyric Acid				−120	Be	597

Table 24 Depsipeptides (continued)

Compound	Method	Solvent	% Yield	Solvent Crystallization	M.P. (°C)	[α]D	Solvent Rotation	Ref.
Z(NO$_2$)-N-me-Val-D-2-hydroxy-3-me-butyryl-N-me-Val-D-2-hydroxy-3-me-butyryl-N-me-Val-D-2-hydroxy-3-me-butyryl-OBu^t					oil	-120	Be	597
Val-D-α-Hyv-N-me-Val-D-α-Hyv-N-me-Val-D-α-Hyv Acid Hydrobromide				EtAc-Pe		-70	Alc	642
Val-D-α-Hyv-Val-D-α-Hyv-Val-D-α-Hyv Acid Hydrobromide				EtAc-Pe		-7	Alc	642
Z-Ala-Ala-glycolyl-Val-Gly-2,4,6-tri-me-OBzl	3+2 ONP		93	Me	198.5-199	-22	DMF	622
Boc-Gly-glycolyl-Gly-glycolyl-Gly-OCH$_2$CN					oil			164
Boc-Gly-glycolyl-Gly-glycolyl-Gly-ONBzl	WRK	Acn	86		127.5-128.5			570
Z-Ile-His-Hyp-Phe-ONBzl	2+2 A	EtAc-DMF	62.7	EtAc-Eth	108-110	-47	Alc	606
Ile-His-Hyp-Phe-ONBzl Dihydrobromide				Alc-Eth	169-171	+30	DMF	606
Z-Hyp-Gly-Gly-Pro-OMe	1+3 MCA	THF-Di	65		119.5-120.5			716
Z-D-Val-D-Leu-α-Hyv-D-Val-Leu-α-Hyv-OBu^t				Me-Aq	203-204	-20	DMF	464
Z-D-Val-D-Leu-α-Hyv-Val-N-me-Leu-α-Hyv-OBu^t				He	122-124	-28	Be	596
Bu^t-Z-D-Val-D-Leu-α-hydroxyisocaproyl-Val-N-me-Leu-α-Hyv				He	112-113	-22	Be	464
D-Val-D-Leu-α-hydroxyisocaproyl-Val-N-me-Leu-α-Hyv Acid Hydrobromide					213 (dec)	-47	Alc	464
D-Val-D-Leu-α-Hyv-Val-N-me-Leu-α-Hyv Acid Hydrobromide						-55	Alc	596
Z-D-Val-Lac-Val-D-α-Hyv-D-Val-Lac-Val-D-α-Hyv Acid						0	Alc	595
Z-D-Val-Lac-Val-D-α-Hyv-D-Val-Lac-Val-D-α-Hyv Acid						-3	Alc	595

Compound	Method	Solvent	Yield (%)	Recryst. solvent	M.p.	$[\alpha]$	Rotation solvent	Ref.
Z-D-Val-Lac-Val-D-α-Hyv-D-Val-D-α-Hyv Acid	AC					−1	Alc	595
Boc-D-Val-D-Hyv-D-Val-D-Hyv-OBzl	MCA	THF	95			+64		566
Boc-D-Val-D-Hyv-D-Val-D-Hyv Boc-hydrazide	CDI	THF	83			+25		566
Hyv-D-Val-D-Hyv-D-Val	CDI	THF	90					566
$Z(NO_2)$-N-me-Val-D-2-hydroxy-3-me-butyryl-N-me-Val-D-2-hydroxy-3-me-butyryl-N-me-Val-D-2-hydroxy-3-me-butyryl-OBu^t			52	Eth-Pe	75–77	−125	Be	597
D-Val-D-Hyv-D-Val-D-Hyv Hydrazide					195–198	+30		566
D-Val-D-Hyv-D-Val-D-Hyv Hydrochloride						+35		566
D-Val-Lac-Val-D-α-Hyv-D-Val-D-α-Hyv Acid Hydrobromine						−26	Alc	595
Boc-Leu-Ala-Thr-S-bzl-Cys-Ala-Hyp-OMe	MCA	THF						704
Boc-Leu-Ala-Thr-Cys-Ala-Hyp-OMe	DCCI							704
Z-D-Val-Lac-Val-D-α-Hyv-D-Val-Lac-Val-D-α-Hyv-OBu^t						+1	Alc	595
D-Val-Lac-Val-D-α-Hyv-D-Val-Lac-Val-D-α-Hyv Acid Hydrobromide						−16	Alc	595
N^G-Nitro-Arg-Val-Tyr-Ile-His-Hyp-Phe Dihydrobromide				Alc-Eth	175–181			606
N^G-Nitro-Arg-Val-Tyr-Ile-His-Hyp-Phe-ONBzl				Alc	180–182	−24	DMF	606
N^G-Nitro-Z-Arg-Val-Tyr-Ile-His-Hyp-Phe ONBzl	1+6 MCA	DMF	63.5	Me	199–205			606
Asp-Arg-Val-Tyr-Ile-His-Hyp-Phe Acetate					243–248 (dec)	−60	1N Ac	606
β-OBzl-Z-Asp-N^G-nitro-Arg-Val-Tyr-Ile-His-Hyp-Phe-ONBzl	1+7 MCA	DMF	74		176–181	−19	DMF	606

CYCLODEPSIPEPTIDES

Compound	Method	Solvent	% Yield	Solvent Crystallization	M.P. (°C)	$[\alpha]_D$	Solvent Rotation	Ref.
Cyclo(hydracryloyl-Ala-hydracryloyl-Ala)				Aq-Me	250-251	-120	Fm	12
Cyclo(β-Ala-5-amino-Val)				Aq	258-259			11
Cyclo(hydracryloyl-Gly-hydracryloyl-Gly)								12
Cyclo(hydracryloyl-glycoloyl-Gly-hydracryloyl-glycoloyl-Gly)				Cte-Be	147-149			12
Cyclo(hydracryloyl-hydracryloyl-Gly-hydracryloyl-hydracryloyl-Gly)				Me	229-231			12
Cyclo(DL-3-hydroxybutyryl-Gly-DL-3-hydroxybutyryl-Gly)				DMF	231-232			12
Cyclo(β-Leu-oxy-propionyl)2					220-224	-108	DMF	205
Cyclo[β-(OBu^t-seryloxy)propionyl]2					256-258			205
Cyclo(hydracryloyl-OAc-Ser-hydracryloyl-OAc-Ser)					242	-47	Fm	12
Cyclo(hydracryloyl-OFor-Ser-hydracryloyl-OFor-Ser)				DMF-Alc	231-232			12
Cyclo(hydracryloyl-Ser-hydracryloyl-Ser)				Me	237 (dec)			12
Cyclo(L-Ser-D-β-HyDec-L-Ser-D-β-HyDec)				Aq-Alc	241-243			598
Cyclo(β-seryloxy-propionyl)2				Me	265-266			205
Cyclo(hydracryloyl-Val-hydracryloyl-D-Val)								12
Cyclo(L-N-MeVal-D-Hyv)2								598
Cyclo(D-Val-D-Hyv-D-Val-D-Hyv)								598
Cyclo(L-Val-L-Hyv-L-Val-L-Hyv)				Alc	252	-51	Chf	598
Cyclo(D-Val-L-Lac-L-Val-L-Hyv)				Alc	246	-73	Chf	598
Cyclo(D-Val-L-Lac-L-Val-L-Lac)								598
Cyclo-(N-me-Ile-D-2-hydroxy-3-me-butyryl-N-me-Ile-D-2-hydroxy-3-me-butyryl-N-me-Ile-D-2-hydroxy-3-me-butyryl)				Aq-Alc	120-121	-87	Chf	597

Compound	No.	Solvent	mp (°C)	$[\alpha]$	Solvent	Ref.
Cyclo-(N-me-Ile-D-2-hydroxyl-3-me-butyryl-N-me-Ile-D-2-hydroxy-3-me-butyryl-N-me-Val-D-2-hydroxy-3-me-butyryl)		Aq-Me	116–117	−94	Chf	597
Cyclo(L-N-MeIle-D-Hyv)$_3$						598
Cyclo(L-N-MeLeu-D-Hyv)$_3$						598
Enniatin A						489
Enniatine A						488
Cyclo L-N-MeVal-D-Hyv-(L-N-MeIle-D-Hyv)$_2$		Aq-Me	117	−94	Chf	598
Cyclo-(L-N-MeVal-D-Hyv)$_3$						598
Cyclo(L-MeVal-L-Hyv)$_3$	22		182–184	−71	Benzol	387
Cyclo-(D-MeVal-D-Hyv-)$_3$	28		183–185	+73	Benzol	387
Cyclo-(D-MeVal-L-Hyv-)$_3$ (Enantio-Enniatin B)	28		173–175	+100	Chf	387
Cyclo-(N-me-Val-D-2-hydroxy-3-me-butyryl-N-me-Val-D-2-hydroxy-3-me-butyryl-N-me-Val-D-2-hydroxy-3-me-butyryl) (Enniatin B)	25	He	168–169	−110	Chf	597
Enniatin B			172–174	−107	Benzol	387
Cyclo-D-Val-D-Leu-L-Hyv-L-Val-L-N-MeLeu-L-Hyv						598
Cyclo-(N-me-Val-D-2-hydroxy-3-me-butyryl-N-me-Val-D-2-hydroxy-3-me-butyryl-N-me-Val-D-2-hydroxy-3-me-butyryl)		He	177–179	−106	Chf	597
Cyclo-(L-N-MeVal-D-Hyv)$_4$						598
Cyclo-(D-Val-D-Hyv)$_4$			245–246	+143	Chf	566
Cyclo-(D-Val-D-Hyv-D-Val-D-Hyv)$_2$		Pe	241	0	Chf	598
Cyclo-(D-Val-L-Hyv-L-Val-D-Hyv)$_2$						598
Cyclo-(D-Val-L-Lac-L-Val-D-Hyv)$_2$						598
Cyclo-(D-Val-Lac-Val-Lac-Val-D-α-Hyv-D-Val-D-α-Hyv)		Be-Eth	221–222	+2	Chf	595

Cyclodepsipeptides (continued)

Compound	Method	Solvent	% Yield	Solvent Crystallization	M.P. (°C)	[α]D	Solvent Rotation	Ref.
Cyclo-(D-Val-L-Lac-L-Val-L-Lac-L-Val-D-Hyv-D-Val-D-Hyv				Be-Eth	222	+2	Chf	598
Cyclo-(L-Val-L-Hyv-L-Val-L-Hyv)$_2$				Alc	232	-37	Chf	598
Cyclo-(L-Val-L-Lac-L-Val-D-Hyv)$_2$				Pe	173	+34	Be	598
Cyclo-D-Ala-L-Lac-L-Ala-D-Hyv-(D-Val-L-Lac-L-Val-D-Hyv)$_2$				Alc	70; 173	+36	Be	598
Cyclo-D-Ala-L-Lac-L-Val-D-Hyv-(D-Val-L-Lac-L-Val-D-Hyv)$_2$				Eth	164	+28	Be	598
Cyclo-(D-Ile-L-Lac-L-Val-D-Hyv)$_3$				Pe	165	+25	Alc	598
Cyclo-D-Ile-L-Lac-L-Val-D-Hyv-(D-Val-L-Lac-L-Val-D-Hyv)$_2$				Pe	167	+45	Be	598
Cyclo-D-Leu-L-Lac-L-Leu-D-Hyv-(D-Val-L-Lac-L-Val-D-Hyv)$_2$				Pe	176	+40	Be	598
Cyclo-D-Leu-L-Lac-L-Val-D-Hyv-(D-Val-L-Lac-L-Val-D-Hyv)$_2$				Dipropyl Ether	274	+33	Be	598
Cyclo-D-Val-L-Lac-L-Ile-D-Hyv-(D-Val-L-Lac-L-Val-D-Hyv)$_2$				Alc	210	0	Be	598
Cyclo-D-Val-L-Hyv-L-Val-D-Hyv)$_3$				He	122; 155	+25	Chf	598
Cyclo-D-Val-L-Hyv-L-Val-D-Hyv-(D-Val-L-Lac-L-Val-D-Hyv)$_2$						+44	Be	598
Cyclo-D-Val-D-Lac-L-Val-D-Hyv-(D-Val-L-Lac-L-Val-D-Hyv)$_2$								
Cyclo-(D-Val-L-Lac-L-Val-D-α-Hyv)$_3$ (Valinomycin)				Dibutyl Ether	187-188	+32	Be	595
Cyclo-(D-Val-L-Lac-D-Val-D-Hyv)$_3$						+60	Be	598
Cyclo-D-Val-L-Lac-D-Val-D-Hyv-(D-Val-L-Lac-L-Val-D-Hyv)$_2$				Pe	96; 187	+29	Alc	598
Cyclo-(D-Val-L-Lac-L-Val-D-Hyv)$_2$							Be	598
Cyclo-(D-Val-L-Lac-L-Val-L-Hyv)$_3$				Hep	223	-35	Chf	598

Cyclo-D-Val-L-Lac-L-Val-L-Hyv-(D-Val-L-Lac-L-Val-D-Hyv)$_2$	He	180	+2	Be	598
Cyclo-(D-Val-L-Lac-L-Val-D-Lac)$_3$	Dipropyl Ether	210	0	Chf	598
Cyclo-(D-Val-L-Lac-L-Val-L-Lac)$_3$	Dibutyl Ether	222	−23	Chf	598
Cyclo-(L-Val-L-Lac-L-Val-D-Hyv)$_3$	Dipropyl Ether	130	−36	Alc	598
Cyclo-(L-Val-L-Lac-L-Val-D-Hyv-(D-Val-L-Lac-L-Val-D-Hyv)$_2$	Dipropyl Ether	219	+24	Be	598
Cyclo-D-Val-L-Ala-L-Val-D-Hyv-(D-Val-L-Lac-L-Val-D-Hyv)$_2$	Pe	192	+40	Alc	598
Cyclo-(D-Val-L-Lac-L-Val-D-Hyv)$_4$	Alc	236	−23	Chf	598

429

16

Alkaloidal and
Steroidal Peptides

For purposes of convenience, all steroids appearing in Parts 1–3 (whether simple amino acid derivatives or attached to polypeptides) have been collected in Table 25.

Assuming that steroidal peptides might interfere with *in vivo* hormone production, provide leads to treatment of hormone-based medical problems and/or prove useful in future steroid-protein binding or immunicological studies, our group set out in 1959 to synthesize such compounds. Initial studies were concentrated on the Arg-Arg segment of ACTH and a majority of the entries in Table 25 reflect this early approach, which led to the first examples of synthetic steroidal peptides. Procedures were initially developed for stepwise construction of the peptide from a steroidal amine. Meanwhile, as part of yet unpublished syntheses, we have coupled preformed, for example, tetrapeptides with amino steroids. By this means and employing segments of TMV virus protein, we have prepared relatively large steroidal peptides. Deployment of column (silica gel or activated alumina), preparative, and thin layer chromatography has proved especially valuable in this work. Analogous comments apply to the alkaloidal peptides in Table 25. The latter class of substances is being encountered with increasing frequency in phytochemical investigations. The small number of known synthetic alkaloidal peptides have been prepared in the writer's laboratory and Table 25 reflects current status.

Some additional steroid examples[113b,138,274,702] were received too late for inclusion in Table 25. Only a minor beginning has been made in the synthesis of alkaloidal and steroidal peptides and much remains to be undertaken.

Table 25 Alkaloidal and Steroidal Peptides

Compound	Method	Solvent	% Yield	Solvent Crystallization	M.P. (°C)	[α]D	Solvent Rotation	Ref.
Alkaloidal Peptides								
2'-[N-Bis(2-chloro-et)Gly]emetine Diperchlorate	MCA	THF		Me-Eth	193-195			475
2'-(Nα-Boc-Gly)emetine	MCA	THF		An-Pe	106-108			475
2'-(Gly)emetine Ditrifluoroacetate	DCCI	THF-Acn		Chf-Eth	159.5-160.5			475
2'-(Boc-Phe)emetine	MCA	THF		EtAc-Pe	102-103			475
2'-(Phe)emetine Diperchlorate Monohydrate				Me-Eth	196-198			475
2'-(Nα-Z-Pro)emetine	DCCI	THF-Chf	85	Be-Eth	121-122			474
2'-(Nα-Boc-Pro)emetine	EDCI	MeCl		Pe	133-135	-50	Chf	474
2'-(Pro)emetine Dihydrochloride				Me-Eth	215-216	-46	Chf	474
2'-(Boc-Trp)emetine	EDCI	MeCl		Be-Pen	115-116			475
2'-(Trp)emetine Ditrifluoroacetate				Chf-Eth	156-157			475
2'-[N-Bis(2-chloro-et)Gly-Phe]emetine Hydrochloride Hydrate	EDCI	MeCl	55	MeCl-Eth	140-142			475
2'-[N-Bis(2-chloro-et)Gly-Trp]emetine Hydrochloride Hydrate	EDCI	MeCl		Chf-Eth	168-170			475
2'-(Nα-Boc-Pro-Pro)emetine	MCA	THF		Be-He	133-135			474
	EDCI	MeCl	93	Eth-Pe	131-133			474
2'-(Pro-Pro)emetine Dihydrate				Eth-Pen	133-135			476
9-(Z-Thr-Ser)amino-(9-deoxy)quinidine	A	THF		An-Eth	135-136			476
9-(Z-Val-Trp)amino-(9-deoxy)quinidine	MCA	THF		EtAc	220-222			476
2'-[N-Bis(2-chloro-et)Gly-Pro-Pro]-emetine Dihydrochloride	MCA	THF	95	Me-Eth	165-166.5			475

431

Table 25 Alkaloidal and Steroidal Peptides (continued)

Compound	Method	Solvent	% Yield	Solvent Crystallization	M.P. (°C)	[α]D	Solvent Rotation	Ref.
Steroidal Peptides								
3β-Hydroxy-17β-(N^G-tos-Arg)amino-5α-androstane				Me	145–152	−43	Me	472
3β-Hydroxy-17β-(N^G-tos-Arg)amino-androst-5-ene				Me	194–195			472
3β-Hydroxy-17β-(N^G-tos-N^α-Z-Arg)-amino-5α-androstane	WRK	Acn		Me	215–216	−17	DMF	472
3β-Hydroxy-17β-(N^G-tos-N^α-Z-Arg) amino-androst-5-ene	WRK	Acn		Me	192–194	0.0	DMF	472
Glu-γ-O-sitosteryl				Alc	184–186			124
Glu-γ-O-cholesteryl N-carboxyanhydride				EtAc-Pe	140–142 (dec)	−85	Chf	124
Glu-γ-O-cholesteryl Pht-hydrazide Salt					216–218	−50	Chf	124
N-Pht-Glu-γ-O-cholesteryl				Alc	201–203	+40	Chf	124
N-Pht-Glu-γ-O-sitosteryl				Alc				
3β-Hydroxy-17β-(N^α-Z-Gly)amino-androst-5-ene	WRK	Acn		Chf-EtAc	201–202	−66	Chf	477
N^ϵ-3,6-Dichloroformyl-cholic-acidamido-Lys-N-carboxyAnhydride					155–157 (dec)	+47	Chf	3
N^ϵ-3-Chloroformyl Deoxycholic Acidamido-Lys-N-carboxyanhydride					169–173 (dec)	+50	Chf	3
N^ϵ-Cholic Acidamido-N^α-Z-Lys-OBzl				Chf-He	75–76	+10	Chf	3
N^ϵ-Cholic Acidamido-Lys				Me-Eth	68–70	+25	Me	3
N^ϵ-Deoxycholic Acidamido-N^α-Z-Lys-OBzl					72–73	+35	Chf	3
N^ϵ-Deoxycholic Acidamido-Lys					120–122	+45	Me	3
3β-Acetoxy-17β-(N^α-Z-Pro)amino-5α-androstane				Me-Aq	166–169	−69	Chf	478

Table 25 Alkaloidal and Steroidal Peptides (continued)

Compound	Method	Solvent	% Yield	Solvent Crystallization	M.P. (°C)	[α]D	Solvent Rotation	Ref.
3β-Acetoxy-17β-(Pro)amino-5α-androstane				EtAc	212-214	-63	Me	478
3β-Hydroxy-17β-(Nα-Z-Pro)amino-5α-androstane				Chf-EtAc	196.5-198	-76	Chf	473
3β-Hydroxy-17β-Pro-amino-5α-androstane					230-238 (dec)	-52	Chf	473
3β-Hydroxy-17β-Pro-amino-5α-androstane-Hydrochloride				Me-Eth	256 (dec)			473
3β-Hydroxy-17β-(Nα-Z-Pro)amino-androst-5-ene	WRK	Acn		Chf-He	194-198.5	-113	Chf	477
3β-Hydroxy-17β-(Pro)amino-androst-5-ene				Me	225-228	-118	Chf	477
3β-Hydroxy-17β-(Nα-Z-Trp)amino-androst-5-ene	WRK	NMe-Acn		Me-Chf	130-133	-39	Chf	477
3β-Hydroxy-17β-(NG-tos-Nα-Z-Arg-NG-tos-Arg)amino-5α-androstane	WRK	Acn		Me-Eth	136-143	-38	Me	472
3β-Hydroxy-17β-(NG-tos-Nα-Z-Arg-NG-tos-Arg)amino-androst-5-ene	WRK	Acn				-25	Chf	472
3β-Acetoxy-17β-(Nα-Z-NG-tos-Arg-Pro)amino-5α-androstane	WRK			Me-Eth	125-130	-68	Chf	472
3β-Acetoxy-17β-(NG-nitro-Arg-Pro)amino-5α-androstane Hydrochloride				Me-Eth	193-194	-65	Me	478
3β-Acetoxy-17β-(NG-nitro-Nα-Z-Arg-Pro)-amino-5α-androstane	WRK	Acn				-105	Me	478
3β-Hydroxy-17β-(NG-nitro-Nα-Z-Arg-Pro)-amino-5α-androstane	WRK	Acn		Me-Aq	141.5-148	-49	Chf	478
3β-Hydroxy-17β-(NG-tos-Nα-Z-Arg-Pro)amino-androst-5-ene	WRK	Acn		Me-Eth	126-130	-80	Chf	472
3β-Hydroxy-17β-(Nα-Z-Pro-Pro)amino-5α-androstane	WRK	Acn		Me-Eth-Pen	120-123	-142	Me	473

433

Table 25 Alkaloidal and Steroidal Peptides (continued)

Compound	Method	Solvent	% Yield	Solvent Crystallization	M.P. (°C)	$[\alpha]_D$	Solvent Rotation	Ref.
3β-Hydroxy-17β-(Pro-Pro)amino-5α-androstane				Me-Eth	213–217 (dec)	−134	Me	473
3β-Acetoxy-17β-(Arg-Arg-Pro)amino-5α-androstane Triacetate				Me-Eth	154	−58	Me	478
3β-Acetoxy-17β-(N^G-nitro-N$^\alpha$-Z-Arg-N^G-nitro-Arg-Pro)amino-5α-androstane	1+2 WRK	Acn-DMF	72	Me-Aq	147–149	−62 −66	Me	478
3β-Hydroxy-17β-(N^G-tos-N$^\alpha$-Z-Arg-N^G-tos-Arg-Pro)amino-androst-5-ene	1+2 WRK	Acn-DMF		Me-Eth	174–176	−82	Chf	472
Steroidal Polypeptides								
α-Poly-γ-cholesteryl-Glu						−52	Chf	124
α-Poly-γ-β-sitosteryl-Glu						−41	Chf	124
α-Poly-N$^\epsilon$-Z-Lys Cholesteryl Ester								4
α-Poly-N$^\epsilon$-Z-Lys Testosteryl Ester								4
α-Poly-N$^\epsilon$-cholic Acidamido-Lys								3
α-Poly-N$^\epsilon$-deoxycholic Acidamido-Lys								3
α-Poly-Lys Cholesteryl Ester Hydrochloride								4
α-Poly-Lys Estryl Ester Hydrochloride								4
α-Poly-Lys Testosteryl Ester Hydrochloride								4
α-Poly-N$^\epsilon$-Z-Tyr Estryl Ester								4
α-Poly-N$^\epsilon$-Z-Tyr 19-nortestosteryl Ester								4

17

Nucleopeptides

Doubtlessly, one of the most important but so far among the most neglected branches of peptide chemistry is that of the nucleopeptides. The relatively small number of such peptides available for Table 26 emphasizes the current situation. The experimental difficulties characteristic of nucleoside and nucleotide chemistry are probably in no small way responsible for the paucity of examples. Inspection of experiments recorded in this field suggest that purification is generally difficult and very few physical constants have been reported.

Recent progress[470a] encompasses dipeptide derivatives of adenosine,[92] Boc-Ala derivatives of several nucleotides,[349] adenine derivative of alanine[125a] and condensation of poly-Lys and poly-Orn with 6-chloropurine and 6-chloropurine-riboside.[38]

Table 26 Nucleopeptides

Compound	Method	Solvent	% Yield	Solvent Crystallization	M.P. (°C)	[α]D	Solvent Rotation	Ref.
Cytidine								
2'-(3')-O-(N-Z-Gly)cytidine								773
2'-(3')-O-Gly-cytidine								773
Thymidine								
N-Thymidyl-Gly				Aq				418
5'-Thymidilyl-(P→N)-Phe								22a
Thymidylyl-(3'→5')-uridino-(P→N)-Phe								608b
Uracil and Uridine								
1-(3-Ala-amido-3-deoxy-β-glucopyranosyl) uracil						-2.5	Aq	148
1-(3-N-Z-Ala-amido-3-deoxy-tri-OAc-β-D-glucopyranosyl) uracil					135–155			148
1-(3-N-Z-Ala-amido-3-deoxy-β-D-glucopyranosyl)uracil								148
1-(3-Deoxy-3-Gly-amido-α-D-glucopyranosyl) uracil						0	Aq	148
1-(3-N-Z-Gly-amido-3-deoxy-tri-OAc-β-D-glucopyranosyl)uracil					171–191			148
1-(3-N-Z-Gly-amido-3-deoxy-β-D-glucopyranosyl)-uracil								148
2'(3')-O-(N-Z-Gly)uridine					90–100			148
Uridylyl-(3'→5')-2'(3')-(N-Z) Gly-uridine								773
Uridylyl-(3'→5')-2'(3')-O-Gly-uridine								773
2'(3')-O-Gly-uridine								93
								93
1-(3-N-Z-D-Phe-amido-3-deoxy-tri-OAc-β-D-glucopyranosyl) uracil					246–247			148

436

Compound				Ref.
1-(3-N-Z-D-Phe-amido-3-deoxy-β-D-glucopyranosyl) uracil	Aq	+24	222–226	148
1-(3-Deoxy-3-D-Phe-amido-β-D-glucopyranosyl) uracil				148
1-(3-N-Z-Sar-amido-3-deoxy-tri-OAc-β-D-glucopyranosyl) uracil				148
1-(3-N-Z-Sar-amido-3-deoxy-β-D-glucopyranosyl) uracil				148
Uridylyl-(5'-N)-Phe-Gly				608a
Deoxyuridylyl-(5'-N)-Phe-deoxy-adenylyl-(5'-N)-Phe				608a
Uridylyl-(5'-N)-Phe-Val				608a
Arg-Ala-Arg-Ala-5'-uridylic acid				203

Adenine and Adenosine

Compound				Ref.
Pht-Glu-adenine			204–207	131
Pht-Gly-adenine			310	131
Adenylyl-(5'→N)-Phe-Val-Gly				514a
2'(3')-O-(N-Z-Gly)adenosine				773
2'(3')-O-(N-Z-Gly)adenosine 5'-Phosphate				773
2'(3')-O-Gly-adenosine				773
2'-(3')-O-Gly-adenosine-5'-Phosphate				773

Guanosine

Compound				Ref.
Guanylyl-(5'-N)-Phe-Gly				608a
Guanylyl-(5'-N)-Phe-Val				440a
Guanylyl-(5'-N)-Phe-Val-Ala				608a

Dinucleopeptides

Compound				Ref.
Cytidylyl-(3'→5')-2'(3')-O-(N-Z)-Gly adenosine				93
Cytidylyl-(3'→5')-2'(3')-O-Gly-adenosine				93, 514b

437

Table 26 Nucleopeptides (continued)

Compound	Method	Solvent	% Yield	Solvent Crystallization	M.P. [°C]	$[\alpha]_D$	Solvent Rotation	Ref.
Uridylyl-(3'→5')-2'(3')-(N-Z)-Gly-adenosine								93
Uridylyl-(3'→5')-2'(3')-O-Gly-adenosine								93
Miscellaneous								
1-(3',4',6'-Tri-OAc-2'-deoxy-2'-carbomethoxyamino-β-D-glucopyranosyl)-4-[p-(Z-Gly-amino)benzamido]-2(1H)-pyrimidinone				Alc	203–204	+3.5	Chf	617
1-(Tetra-OAc-β-D-glucopyranosyl)-4-[p-(ac-Gly-amino)benzamido]-2(1H)-pyrimidinone				Alc	265	–6.2	Alc	617
1-(Tetra-OAc-β-D-glucopyranosyl)-4-[p-(Z-Gly-amino)benzamido]-2(1H)-pyrimidinone				Alc	246–248	–24	Chf	617
3-Phenyl-N-[(purin-6-ylthio)ac]-β-Ala-Ala-OEt					223–224 (dec)			318
3-Phenyl-N-[(purin-6-ylthio)ac]-β-Ala-Gly				Alc	223–225			318
3-Phenyl-N-[(purin-6-ylthio)ac]-β-Ala-Gly-OEt				Alc	192–194			318
N-[(purin-6-ylthio)ac]-Ala-Gly-OEt				Alc	171–173			318
N-[(Purine-6-ylthio)ac]-Val-Ala-OEt				Alc	171–173			318
N-[(Purine-6-ylthio)ac]-Val-Gly-OEt								318

Bibliography

The references cited in Parts 1-3 were combined and alphabetized in order to eliminate any possibility of duplication. The first alphabetical reference was then numbered 1, the second 2, etc. Appendix 1 contains a list of journals reviewed for the preparation of Parts 1-3.

1. O. Abe, H. Takiguchi, M. Ohno, S. Makisumi and N. Izumiya, *Bull. Chem. Soc. Japan*, **40**, 1945 (1967).
2. A. J. Adler, G. D. Fasman and E. R. Blout, *J. Am. Chem. Soc.*, **85**, 90 (1963).
3. K. L. Agarwal and M. M. Dhar, *Steroids*, **6**, 105 (1965).
4. K. L. Agarwal and M. M. Dhar, *Steroids*, **4**, 495 (1964).
4a. K. L. Agarwal, G. W. Kenner and R. C. Sheppard, *J. Chem. Soc.*, 2213 (1969).
5. K. L. Agarwal, G. W. Kenner and R. C. Sheppard, *J. Chem. Soc.*, 1384 (1968).
6. G. W. Anderson and F. M. Callahan, *J. Am. Chem. Soc.*, **82**, 3359 (1960).
7. G. W. Anderson, J. E. Zimmerman and F. M. Callahan, *J. Am. Chem. Soc.*, **86**, 1839 (1964).
8. G. W. Anderson, J. E. Zimmerman and F. M. Callahan, *J. Am. Chem. Soc.*, **89**, 5012 (1967).
9. J. C. Anderson, M. A. Barton, P. M. Hardy, G. W. Kenner, J. Preston and R. C. Sheppard, *J. Chem. Soc.*, 108 (1967).
10. R. Andreatta and K. Hofmann, *J. Am. Chem. Soc.*, **90**, 7334 (1968).
11. V. K. Antonov, T. E. Agadzhanyan, T. R. Telesnina and M. M. Shemyakin, *J. Gen. Chem. USSR*, **35**, 2221 (1965).
12. V. K. Antonov, V. I. Shchelokev and M. M. Shemyakin, *J. Gen. Chem. USSR*, **35**, 2228 (1965).
13. V. K. Antonov, V. I. Shchelokov and M. M. Shemyakin, *J. Gen. Chem. USSR*, **35**, 2239 (1965).

14. I. Antonovics and G. T. Young, *J. Chem. Soc.*, 595 (1967).
15. H. Aoyagi, K. Arakawa and N. Izumiya, *Bull. Chem. Soc. Japan*, **41**, 433 (1968).
16. H. Aoyagi and N. Izumiya, *Bull. Chem. Soc. Japan,* **39**, 1747 (1966).
17. H. Aoyagi, T. Kato, M. Ohno, M. Kondo and N. Izumiya, *J. Am. Chem. Soc.*, **86**, 5700 (1964).
18. H. Aoyagi, T. Kato, M. Ohno, M. Kondo, M. Waki, S. Makisumi and N. Izumiya, *Bull. Chem. Soc. Japan*, **38**, 2139 (1965).
19. K. Arakawa and F. M. Bumpus, *J. Am. Chem. Soc.*, **83**, 728 (1961).
20. K. Arakawa, R. P. Smeby and F. M. Bumpus, *J. Am. Chem. Soc.*, **84**, 1424 (1962).
21. M. Augustin, *Chem. Ber.*, **99**, 1039 (1966).
22. R. Badiello, G. Vidali and A. Marzotto, *Gazz. Chim. Ital.*, **94**, 322 (1964).
22a. V. A. Bakanova, Z. A. Shabarova and M. A. Prokof'ev, *Khim. Prir. Soedin.*, *Akad. Nauk Uz. SSR*, **2**, 35 (1966); *Chem. Abstr.*, **65**, 5521 (1966).
22b. R. K. Barclay, M. A. Phillipps, G. C. Perri and K. Sugiura, *Cancer Res.*, **24**, 1324 (1964).
23. A. Barth, *Ann. Chem.*, **683**, 216 (1965).
24. A. Barth, *Ann. Chem.*, **686**, 221 (1965).
25. S. Batusz, *Acta. Chim. Acad. Sci. Hung.*, **42**, 383 (1964).
26. J. W. M. Baxter, M. Manning and W. H. Sawyer, *Biochemistry*, **8**, 3592 (1969).
26a. E. Bayer and H. Hagenmaier, *Tetrahedron Letters*, **17**, 2037 (1968).
27. E. Bayer, G. Jung and H. Hagenmaier, *Tetrahedron*, **24**, 4853 (1968).
28. J. Beacham, P. H. Bentley, G. W. Kenner, J. K. MacLeod, J. J. Mendive and R. C. Sheppard, *J. Chem. Soc.*, 2520 (1967).
29. A. F. Beecham, *Australian J. Chem.*, **16**, 160 (1963).
30. A. F. Beecham, *Australian J. Chem.*, **20**, 1983 (1967).
31. B. Belleau and G. Malek, *J. Am. Chem. Soc.*, **90**, 1651 (1968).
32. L. Benoiton, *Can. J. Chem. Soc.*, **41**, 1718 (1963).
33. L. Benoiton, R. W. Hanson and H. N. Rydon, *J. Chem. Soc.*, 824 (1964).
34. L. Benoiton and H. N. Rydon, *J. Chem. Soc.*, 3328 (1960).
35. F. Bergel, J. M. Johnson and R. Wade, *J. Chem. Soc.*, 3802 (1962).
36. F. Bergel and J. A. Stock, *J. Chem. Soc.*, 3658 (1960).
37. A. Y. Berlin and V. P. Bronovitskaya, *J. Gen. Chem. USSR*, **30**, 347 (1960).
38. L. Berlinquet and J. Gautier, *Can. J. Chem.*, **47**, 3641 (1969).
39. S. A. Bernhard, A. Berger, J. H. Carter, E. Katchalski, M. Sela and Y. Shalitin, *J. Am. Chem. Soc.*, **84**, 2421 (1962).
40. C. Berse and K. Jankowski, *Can. J. Chem.*, **44**, 1513 (1966).
41. C. Berse, T. Massiah and L. Piché, *Can. J. Chem.*, **41**, 2767 (1963).
42. C. Berse, T. Massiah and L. Piché, *J. Org. Chem.*, **26**, 4514 (1961).
43. C. Berse, L. Piché, L. Lachance and G. Laflamme, *J. Org. Chem.*, **27**, 3489 (1962).
44. C. Berse, L. Piché and A. Uchiyama, *Can. J. Chem.*, **38**, 1946 (1960).

45. W. S. Bertaud, M. C. Probine, J. S. Shannon and A. Taylor, *Tetrahedron*, **21**, 677 (1965).

46. H. C. Beyerman, C. A. M. Boers-Boonekamp and H. Maasen van den Brink-Zimmermannova, *Rec. Trav. Chim.*, **87**, 257 (1968).

47. H. C. Beyerman and J. S. Bontekoe, *Rec. Trav. Chim.*, **83**, 255 (1964).

48. H. C. Beyerman and J. S. Bontekoe, *Rec. Trav. Chim.*, **81**, 699 (1962).

49. H. C. Beyerman and J. S. Bontekoe, *Rec. Trav. Chim.*, **81**, 691 (1962).

50. H. C. Beyerman and J. S. Bontekoe, *Rec. Trav. Chim.*, **79**, 1165 (1960).

51. H. C. Beyerman and J. S. Bontekoe and A. C. Koch, *Rec. Trav. Chim.*, **78**, 935 (1959).

52. H. C. Beyerman and W. M. van den Brink, *Rec. Trav. Chim.*, **84**, 213 (1965).

52a. H. C. Beyerman and H. Maassen van den Brink-Zimmermannova, *Rec. Trav. Chim.*, **87**, 1196 (1968).

53. B. Bezas and L. Zervas, *J. Am. Chem. Soc.*, **83**, 719 (1961).

54. L. Birkofer, E. Bierwirth and A. Ritter, *Chem. Ber.*, **94**, 821 (1961).

55. L. Birkofer, A. Ritter and P. Neuhausen, *Ann. Chem.*, **659**, 190 (1962).

56. K. Blaha and J. Rudinger, *Collection Czech. Chem. Commun.*, **32**, 2365 (1967).

57. K. Blaha and J. Rudinger, *Collection Czech. Chem. Commun.*, **30**, 3325 (1965).

58. A. T. Blomquist, B. F. Hiscock and D. N. Harpp, *J. Org. Chem.*, **31**, 4121 (1966).

59. S. M. Bloom, S. K. Das Gupta, R. P. Patel and E. R. Blout, *J. Am. Chem. Soc.*, **88**, 2035 (1966).

60. M. Bodanszky and R.J. Bath, *Chem. Comm.*, 766 (1968).

61. M. Bodanszky and C. Birkhimer, *J. Am. Chem. Soc.*, **84**, 4943 (1962).

61a. M. Bodanszky and A. Bodanszky, *Chem. Commun.*, 591 (1967).

62. M. Bodanszky, J. Meienhofer and V. duVigneaud, *J. Am. Chem. Soc.*, **82**, 3195 (1960).

63. M. Bodanszky, M. A. Ondetti, C. A. Birkhimer and P. L. Thomas, *J. Am. Chem. Soc.*, **86**, 4452 (1964).

64. M. Bodanszky, M. A. Ondetti, S. D. Levine and N. J. Williams, *J. Am. Chem. Soc.*, **89**, 6753 (1967).

64a. M. Bodanszky and J. T. Sheehan, *Chem. Ind. (London)*, 1597 (1966).

65. M. Bodanszky, J. T. Sheehan, M. A. Ondetti and S. Lande, *J. Am. Chem. Soc.*, **85**, 991 (1963).

66. M. Bodanszky and N. J. Williams, *J. Am. Chem. Soc.*, **89**, 685 (1967).

67. Z. Bohak and E. Katchalski, *Biochemistry*, **2**, 228 (1963).

68. R. A. Boissonnas and St. Guttmann, *Helv. Chim. Acta*, **43**, 190 (1960).

69. R. A. Boissonas, St. Guttmann, R. L. Huguenin, P. A. Jaquenoud and E. Sandrin, *Helv. Chim. Acta*, **46**, 2347 (1963).

70. R. A. Boissonnas, St. Guttmann and P. A. Jaquenoud, *Helv. Chim. Acta*, **43**, 1349 (1960).

71. R. A. Boissonnas, St. Guttmann, P. A. Jaquenoud, E. Sandrin and J. P. Waller, *Helv. Chim. Acta*, **44**, 123 (1961).

71a. J. Bouchaudon and G. Jolles, Ger., Offen. 1, 811, 518, July 10, 1969; *Chem. Abstr.*, **71**, No. 10, 440 (1969).

72. L. A. Branda and V. duVigneaud, *J. Med. Chem.*, **9**, 169 (1966).

73. D. Brandenburg, *Z. Physiol. Chem.*, Bd. **350**, S. 741 (1969).

73a. E. Bricas, Editor, "Peptides 1968," North-Holland Publishing Co., Amsterdam, 1968.

74. H. Brockman and H. Bujard, *Naturwissenschaften*, **49**, 515 (1962).

75. H. Brockmann and V. Graef, *Naturwissenschaften*, **49**, 540 (1962); *Chem. Abstr.*, **59**, No. 1, 755 (1963).

76. H. Brockmann and H. Lackner, *Chem. Ber.*, **101**, 2231 (1968).

77. H. Brockmann and H. Lackner, *Chem. Ber.*, **100**, 353 (1967).

77a. H. Brockmann and E. Schulze, *Chem. Ber.*, **102**, 3205 (1969).

78. P. Brown and G. R. Pettit, *J. Org. Mass Spec.*, (in press).

79. D. L. Buchanan, E. E. Haley, F. E. Dorer and B. J. Corcoran, *Biochemistry*, **5**, 3240 (1966).

80. H. J. Burkhardt and H. K. Mitchell, *Arch. Biochem. Biophys.*, **94**, 32 (1961).

81. F. M. Callahan, G. W. Anderson, R. Paul and J. E. Zimmerman, *J. Am. Chem. Soc.*, **85**, 201 (1963).

81a. R. Camble, R. Garner and G. T. Young, *J. Chem. Soc.*, 1911 (1969).

82. W. D. Cash, *J. Org. Chem.*, **27**, 3329 (1962).

83. W. D. Cash, *J. Org. Chem.*, **26**, 2136 (1961).

84. W. D. Cash, L. M. Mahaffey, A. S. Buck, D. E. Nettleton, Jr., C. Romas and V. du Vigneaud, *J. Med. Pharm. Chem.*, **5**, 413 (1962).

85. R. De Castiglione, F. Chillemi, L. Bernardi and O. Goffredo, *Gazz. Chim. Ital.*, **94**, 875 (1964).

86. N. C. Chaturvedi, M. C. Khosla and N. Anand, *J. Med. Chem.*, **9**, 971 (1966).

87. Y. Chen-su, K. Bláha and J. Rudinger, *Collection Czech. Chem. Commun.*, **29**, 2633 (1964).

88. H. T. Cheung, T. S. Murty and E. R. Blout, *J. Am. Chem. Soc.*, **86**, 4200 (1964).

89. F. Chillemi, *Gazz. Chim. Ital.*, **93**, 1079 (1963).

90. F. Chillemi, L. Bernardi and G. Bosisio, *Gazz. Chim. Ital.*, **94**, 891 (1964).

91. A. Chimiak and J. Rudinger, *Collection Czech. Chem. Commun.*, **30**, 2592 (1965).

92. S. Chládek and J. Žemlička, *Collection Czech. Chem. Commun.*, **33**, 4299 (1968).

93. S. Chládek and J. Žemlička, *Collection Czech. Chem. Commun.*, **32**, 1776 (1967).

94. D. Chung and C. H. Li, *J. Am. Chem. Soc.*, **89**, 4208 (1967).

95. Patent–CiBA Ltd., Brit. 880, 245, Oct. 18, 1961; *Chem. Abstr.*, **58**, 12, 12672 (1963).

96. J. P. Collman and E. Kimura, *J. Am. Chem. Soc.*, **89**, 6096 (1967).

97. T. A. Connors, A. B. Mauger, M. A. Peutherer and W. C. J. Ross, *J. Chem. Soc.*, 4601 (1962).

98. A. Corbellini, F. Chillemi and P. G. Pietta, *Gazz. Chim. Ital.*, **97**, 514 (1967).

99. A. Cosmatos, I. Photaki and L. Zervas, *Chem. Ber.*, **94**, 2644 (1961).

100. A. A. Costopanagiotis, B. O. Handford and B. Weinstein, *J. Org. Chem.*, **33**, 1261 (1968).

101. A. A. Costopanagiotis, J. Preston and B. Weinstein, *J. Org. Chem.*, **31**, 3398 (1966).

102. A. A. Costopanagiotis, J. Preston and B. Weinstein, *Can. J. Chem.*, **45**, 759 (1967).

103. M. E. Cox, H. G. Garg, J. Hollowood, J. M. Hugo, P. M. Scopes and G. T. Young, *J. Chem. Soc.*, 6806 (1965).

104. F. Cramer, E. Scheiffele and A. Vollmar, *Chem. Ber.*, **95**, 1670 (1962).

105. D. H. G. Crout, *J. Chem. Soc.*, 1579 (1969).

106. P. Cruickshank and J. C. Sheehan, *J. Am. Chem. Soc.*, **86**, 2070 (1964).

107. J. C. Craig, S. R. Johns and M. Moyle, *J. Org. Chem.*, **28**, 2779 (1963).

108. M. Dagiene, L. Rasteikiene, O. V. Kil'disheva and I. L. Knunyants, *Izv. Akad. Nauk SSSR, Ser. Khim.*, 917 (1965).

109. K. Daigo, W. T. Brady and L. J. Reed, *J. Am. Chem. Soc.*, **84**, 662 (1962).

110. J. Dale and K. Titlestad, *Chem. Commun.*, 656 (1969).

111. J. M. Davey, A. H. Laird and J. S. Morley, *J. Chem. Soc.*, 555 (1966).

112. V. G. Debabov, V. D. Davydov and A. A. Morozkin, *Bull. Acad. Sci. USSR*, 2084 (1967).

113. V. G. Debabov and V. A. Shibnev, *Izv. Akad. Nauk SSSR, Otd. Khim. Nauk*, 870 (1963); *Chem. Abstr.*, **59**, 7, 7644 (1963).

113a. A. Deer. *Angew. Chem.*, **5**, 1041 (1966).

113b. G. Defaye and M. Fetizon, *Bull. Soc. Chim. France*, 2835 (1969).

114. P. O. Dennis and P. A. Lorkin, *J. Chem. Soc.*, 4968 (1965).

115. V. A. Derevitskaya, L. M. Likhosherstov, S. G. Kara-Murza and N. K. Kochetkev, *J. Gen. Chem. USSR*, **32**, 2134 (1962).

116. V. A. Derevitskaya, N. M. Molodtsov and N. N. Kochetkov, *Izv. Akad. Nauk SSSR, Ser. Khim.*, 1143 (1966).

117. V. A. Derevitskaya, N. V. Molodtsov and N. K. Kochetkov, *Izv. Akad. Nauk SSSR, Ser. Khim.*, 677 (1964).

118. D. F. DeTar, F. F. Rogers, Jr. and H. Bach, *J. Am. Chem. Soc.*, **89**, 3039 (1967).

119. D. F. DeTar, R. Silverstein and F. F. Rogers, Jr., *J. Am. Chem. Soc.*, **88**, 1024 (1966).

120. H. Determann, H. J. Torff and O. Zipp, *Ann. Chem.*, **670**, 141 (1963).

121. H. Determann and T. Wieland, *Ann. Chem.*, **670**, 136 (1963).

122. H. Determann, O. Zipp and T. Wieland, *Ann. Chem.*, **651**, 173 (1962).

123. H. A. DeWald and E. D. Nicolaides, *J. Med. Pharm. Chem.*, **7**, 50 (1964).

123a. R. Dewey, E. Schoenwaldt, H. Joshua, W. Paleveda, Jr., H. Schwam, H. Barkemeyer, B. Arison, D. Veber, R. Denkewalter and R. Hirschmann, *J. Am. Chem. Soc.*, **90**, 3254 (1968).

124. M. M. Dhar and K. L. Agarwal, *Steroids*, **3**, 139 (1964).

125. J. F. Diehl and E. A. Young, *J. Med. Chem.*, **7**, 820 (1964).

125a. M. T. Doel, A. S. Jones and N. Taylor, *Tetrahedron Letters*, 2285 (1969).

125b. L. C. Dorman, *Tetrahedron Letters*, 2319 (1969).

126. S. Drabarek, *J. Am. Chem. Soc.*, **86**, 4477 (1964).

127. A. S. Dutta, N. Anand and K. Kar, *J. Med. Chem.*, **9**, 497 (1966).

128. K. Eisler, J. Rudinger and F. Šorm, *Collection Czech. Chem. Commun.*, **31**, 4563 (1966).

129. B. F. Erlanger, W. V. Curran and N. Kokowsky, *J. Am. Chem. Soc.*, **81**, 3055 (1959).

130. B. F. Erlanger, W. V. Curran and N. Kokowsky, *J. Am. Chem. Soc.*, **81**, 3051 (1959).

131. H. von Euler and H. Hasselquist, *Arkiv. Kemi*, **20**, 129 (1962); *Chem. Abstr.*, **59**, 1, 755 (1963).

132. G. D. Fasman, M. Iderson and E. R. Blout, *J. Am. Chem. Soc.*, **83**, 709 (1961).

132a. H. Faulstich, H. Trischmann and Th. Wieland, *Tetrahedron Letters*, 4131 (1969).

133. N. V. Fedoseeva, T. R. Telesnina and A. B. Silaev, *J. Gen. Chem. USSR*, **33**, 2689 (1963).

134. A. M. Felix, J. Unowsky, J. Bontempo and R. I. Fryer, *J. Med. Chem.*, **11**, 929 (1968).

135. M. Fell and E. Schnabel, *Z. Physiol. Chem.*, **333**, 218 (1963).

136. J. J. Ferraro and V. Vigneaud, *J. Am. Chem. Soc.*, **88**, 3847 (1966).

137. M. Firdkin, A. Patchornik and E. Katchalski, *J. Am. Chem. Soc.*, **90**, 2953 (1968).

138. G. Flouret and W. Cole, *J. Med. Chem.*, **11**, 880 (1968).

139. G. Flouret and V. du Vigneaud, *J. Am. Chem. Soc.*, **87**, 3775 (1965).

140. G. Folsch, *Acta Chem. Scand.*, **20**, 459 (1966).

141. A. P. Fosker and H. D. Law, *J. Chem. Soc.*, 4922 (1965).

142. S. W. Fox, T. Hayakawa and K. Harada, *Bull. Chem. Soc. Japan*, **36**, 1050 (1963).

143. W. Frank, *Z. Physiol. Chem.*, **339**, 222 (1964).

144. W. Frank, *Z. Physiol. Chem.*, **339**, 214 (1964).

145. W. Frank, *Z. Physiol. Chem.*, **339**, 202 (1964).

146. M. Frankel, D. Gertner, A. Shenhar and A. Zilkha, *J. Chem. Soc.*, 1334 (1967).

147. R. D. B. Fraser, B. S. Harrap, T. P. MacRae, F. H. C. Stewart and E. Suzuki, *J. Mol. Biol.*, **12**, 482 (1965).

147a. M. Fridkin, A. Patchornik and E. Katchalski, *J. Am. Chem. Soc.*, **87**, 4646 (1965).

148. H. A. Friedman, K. A. Watanabe and J. J. Fox, *J. Org. Chem.*, **32**, 3775 (1967).

149. O. M. Friedman and R. Chatterji, *J. Am. Chem. Soc.*, **81**, 3750 (1959).

150. S. C. J. Fu, H. Terzian, C. L. Maddock and V. M. Binns, *J. Med. Chem.*, **9**, 214 (1966).

151. M. Fujino and C. Hatanaka, *Chem. Pharm. Bull. (Tokyo)*, **15**, 2015 (1967).

152. M. Fujino and C. Hatanaka, *J. Chem. Soc.*, 2638 (1967).

153. Y. Fujita, J. Kollonitsch and B. Witkop, *J. Am. Chem. Soc.*, 87, 2030 (1965).

154. J. Gante, *Fortschr. Chem. Forsch.*, 6, 358 (1966).

155. J. Gante, *Chem. Ber.*, 99, 2521 (1966).

156. J. Gante, *Chem. Ber.*, 99, 1576 (1966).

157. J. Gante, *Chem. Ber.*, 98, 3334 (1965).

158. N. I. Gavrilov, I. P. Grigor'eva, L. N. Akimova and V. K. Erokin, *J. Gen. Chem. USSR*, 31, 678 (1961).

159. G. Gawne, G. W. Kenner and R. C. Sheppard, *J. Am. Chem. Soc.*, 91, 5669 (1969).

160. R. Geiger, G. Jager, A. Volk and W. Siedel, *Chem. Ber.*, 101, 2189 (1968).

161. R. Geiger, K. Sturm and W. Siedel, *Chem. Ber.*, 97, 1207 (1964).

162. R. Geiger, K. Sturm and W. Siedel, *Chem. Ber.*, 96, 1080 (1963).

163. H. Gibian and E. Klieger, *Ann. Chem.*, 640, 145 (1961).

164. H. Gibian and K. Lübke, *Ann. Chem.*, 644, 130 (1961).

165. H. Gibian and E. Schröder, *Ann. Chem.*, 642, 145 (1961).

166. D. Gillessen, E. Schnabel and J. Meienhofer, *Ann. Chem.*, 667, 164 (1963).

166a. B. F. Gisin, R. B. Merrifield and D. C. Tosteson, *J. Am. Chem. Soc.*, 91, 2691 (1969).

167. J. A. Glasel, S. M. Vratsanos, N. Wassermann and B. F. Erlanger, *Arch. Biochem. Biophys.*, 115, 237 (1966).

168. O. Goffredo, L. Bernardi, G. Bosisio and F. Chillemi, *Gazz. Chim. Ital.*, 95, 172 (1965).

169. S. Goldschmidt and K. K. Gupta, *Chem. Ber.*, 98, 2831 (1965).

170. L. Goodman, R. R. Spencer, G. Casini, O. P. Crews and E. J. Reist, *J. Med. Chem.*, 8, 251 (1965).

171. M. Goodman and C. B. Glaser, *Tetrahedron Letters*, 3473 (1969).

172. M. Goodman, I. Listowsky and E. E. Schmitt, *J. Am. Chem. Soc.*, 84, 1296 (1962).

173. M. Goodman and W. J. McGahren, *Tetrahedron*, 23, 2031 (1967).

174. M. Goodman and W. J. McGahren, *J. Am. Chem. Soc.*, 88, 3887 (1966).

175. M. Goodman, E. E. Schmitt and D. A. Yphantis, *J. Am. Chem. Soc.*, 84, 1283 (1962).

176. M. Goodman and K. C. Stueben, *J. Org. Chem.*, 27, 3409 (1962).

177. M. Goodman and K. C. Stueben, *J. Am. Chem. Soc.*, 84, 1279 (1962).

178. T. R. Govindachari, K. Nagarajan, S. Rajappa, A. S. Akerkar and V. S. Iyer, *Tetrahedron*, 22, 3367 (1966).

179. T. R. Govindachari, S. Rajappa, A. S. Akerkar and V. S. Iyer, *Tetrahedron*, 23, 4811 (1967).

179a. O. Grahl-Nielsen and G. L. Tritsch, *Biochemistry*, 8, 187 (1969).

180. C. J. Gray and A. M. Khoujah, *Tetrahedron Letters*, 2647 (1969).

180a. B. Green and L. R. Garson, *J. Chem. Soc.*, 401 (1969).

181. H. Gregory, J. S. Morley, J. M. Smith and J. J. Smithers, *J. Chem. Soc.*, 715 (1968).

182. J. Grimshaw, *J. Chem. Soc.*, 7136 (1965).

183. C. Gros, M. P. de Garilhe, A. Costopanagiotis and R. Schwyzer, *Helv. Chim. Acta*, **44**, 2042 (1961).

184. H. Gross and L. Bilk, *Tetrahedron*, **24**, 6935 (1968).

185. R. Grupe and H. Niedrich, *Chem. Ber.*, **100**, 3283 (1967).

186. S. C. J. Gu, H. Terzian and S. Craven, *J. Am. Chem. Soc.*, **7**, 759 (1964).

187. E. L. Gustus, *J. Org. Chem.*, **32**, 3425 (1967).

187a. B. Gutte and R. B. Merrifield, *J. Am. Chem. Soc.*, **91**, 501 (1969).

188. St. Guttmann, *Helv. Chim. Acta*, **49**, 83 (1966).

189. St. Guttmann, *Helv. Chim. Acta*, **45**, 2622 (1962).

190. St. Guttmann, *Helv. Chim. Acta*, **44**, 721 (1961).

191. St. Guttmann and R. A. Boissonnas, *Helv. Chim. Acta*, **46**, 1626 (1963).

192. St. Guttmann and R. A. Boissonnas, *Helv. Chim. Acta*, **45**, 2517 (1962).

193. St. Guttmann and R. A. Boissonnas, *Helv. Chim. Acta*, **44**, 1713 (1961).

194. St. Guttmann and R. A. Boissonnas, *Helv. Chim. Acta*, **42**, 1257 (1959).

195. W. L. Haas, E. V. Krumkalns and K. Gerzon, *J. Am. Chem. Soc.*, **88**, 1988 (1966).

196. B. Halpern, *Australian J. Chem.*, **18**, 417 (1965).

197. B. Halpern and L. B. James, *Australian J. Chem.*, **17**, 1282 (1964).

197a. B. Halpern and D. E. Nitecki, *Tetrahedron Letters*, 3031 (1967).

198. B. O. Handford, T. A. Hylton, K. T. Wang and B. Weinstein, *J. Org. Chem.*, **33**, 4251 (1968).

199. B. O. Handford, T. A. Hylton, J. Preston and B. Weinstein, *J. Org. Chem.*, **32**, 1243 (1967).

200. R. W. Hanson and H. D. Law, *J. Chem. Soc.*, 7285 (1965).

201. R. W. Hanson and H. N. Rydon, *J. Chem. Soc.*, 836 (1964).

202. P. M. Hardy, G. W. Kenner and R. C. Sheppard, *Tetrahedron*, **19**, 95 (1963).

203. G. Harris and I. C. MacWilliam, *J. Chem. Soc.*, 2053 (1961).

204. G. Harris and I. C. MacWilliam, *J. Chem. Soc.*, 1054 (1963).

205. C. H. Hassall, T. G. Martin, J. A. Schofield and J. O. Thomas, *J. Chem. Soc.*, 997 (1967).

206. C. H. Hassall and J. O. Thomas, *J. Chem. Soc.*, 1495 (1968).

207. E. Havinga and C. Schattenkerk, *Tetrahedron*, Suppl. 8, Part I, 313 (1967).

208. E. Havinga, C. Schattenkerk, G. M. Visser and K. E. T. Kerling, *Rec. Trav. Chim.*, **83**, 672 (1964).

209. R. T. Havran, I. L. Schwartz and R. Walter, *J. Am. Chem. Soc.*, **91**, 1836 (1969).

210. R. T. Havran and V. du Vigneaud, *J. Am. Chem. Soc.*, **91**, 3626 (1969).

211. R. T. Havran and V. du Vigneaud, *J. Am. Chem. Soc.*, **91**, 2696 (1969).

212. T. Hayakawa, Y. Fujiwara and J. Noguchi, *Bull. Chem. Soc. Japan*, **40**, 1205 (1967).

213. T. Hayakawa, K. Harada and S. W. Fox, *Bull. Chem. Soc. Japan*, **39**, 391 (1966).

215. P. Hermann and M. Zaoral, *Collection Czech. Chem. Commun.*, **30**, 2817 (1965).

216. H. J. Hess and J. W. Constantine, *J. Med. Chem.*, **7**, 602 (1964).

217. J. T. Hill and F. W. Dunn, *J. Med. Chem.*, **12**, 737 (1969).

217a. R. Hirschmann, R. F. Nutt, D. F. Veber, R. A. Vitali, S. L. Varga, T. A. Jacob, F. W. Holly and R. G. Denkewalter, *J. Am. Chem. Soc.*, **91**, 507 (1969).

218. R. Hirschmann, R. G. Strachan, H. Schwam, E. F. Schoenewaldt, H. Joshua, B. Barkemeyer, D. F. Veber, W. J. Paleveda, Jr., T. A. Jacob, T. E. Beesley and R. G. Denkewalter, *J. Org. Chem.*, **32**, 3415 (1967).

219. R. G. Hiskey and J. B. Adams, Jr., *J. Am. Chem. Soc.*, **87**, 3969 (1965).

220. R. G. Hiskey and J. B. Adams, Jr., *J. Org. Chem.*, **31**, 2178 (1966).

221. R. G. Hiskey and J. B. Adams, Jr., *J. Org. Chem.*, **30**, 1340 (1965).

222. R. G. Hiskey and M. A. Harpold, *J. Org. Chem.*, **33**, 559 (1968).

223. R. G. Hiskey, T. Mizoguchi and H. Igeta, *J. Org. Chem.*, **31**, 1188 (1966).

224. R. G. Hiskey, T. Mizoguchi and T. Inue, *J. Org. Chem.*, **31**, 1192 (1966).

225. R. G. Hiskey, T. Mizoguchi and E. L. Smithwick, Jr., *J. Org. Chem.*, **32**, 97 (1967).

226. R. G. Hiskey and R. L. Smith, *J. Am. Chem. Soc.*, **90**, 2677 (1968).

227. R. G. Hiskey and E. L. Smithwick, Jr., *J. Am. Chem. Soc.*, **89**, 437 (1967).

228. R. G. Hiskey and G. L. Southard, *J. Org. Chem.*, **31**, 3582 (1966).

229. R. G. Hiskey, J. T. Staples and R. L. Smith, *J. Org. Chem.*, **32**, 2772 (1967).

229a. R. G. Hiskey, A. M. Thomas, R. L. Smith and W. C. Jones, Jr., *J. Am. Chem. Soc.*, **91**, 7525 (1969).

230. R. G. Hiskey and W. P. Tucker, *J. Am. Chem. Soc.*, **84**, 4794 (1962).

231. R. G. Hiskey and W. P. Tucker, *J. Am. Chem. Soc.*, **84**, 4789 (1962).

232. K. Hofmann and H. Bohn, *J. Am. Chem. Soc.*, **88**, 5914 (1966).

233. E. Hoffmann and I. Faiferman, *J. Org. Chem.*, **29**, 748 (1964).

234. K. Hofmann, F. Finn, W. Haas, M. J. Smithers, Y. Wolman and N. Yanaihara, *J. Am. Chem. Soc.*, **85**, 833 (1963).

235. K. Hofmann and S. Lande, *J. Am. Chem. Soc.*, **83**, 2286 (1961).

236. K. Hofmann, J. Rosenthaler, R. D. Wells and H. Yajima, *J. Am. Chem. Soc.*, **86**, 4991 (1964).

237. K. Hofmann, R. Schmiechen, R. D. Wells, Y. Wolman and N. Yanaihara, *J. Am. Chem. Soc.*, **87**, 611 (1965).

238. K. Hofmann, M. J. Smithers and F. M. Finn, *J. Am. Chem. Soc.*, **88**, 4107 (1966).

239. K. Hofmann, E. Stutz, G. Spuhler, H. Yajima and E. T. Schwartz, *J. Am. Chem. Soc.*, **82**, 3727 (1960).

240. K. Hofmann, T. A. Thompson, M. E. Woolner, G. Spuhler, H. Yajima, J. D. Cipera and E. T. Schwartz, *J. Am. Chem. Soc.*, **82**, 3721 (1960).

241. K. Hofmann, T. A. Thompson, H. Yajima, E. T. Schwartz and H. Inouye, *J. Am. Chem. Soc.*, **82**, 3715 (1960).

242. K. Hofmann, J. P. Visser and F. M. Finn, *J. Am. Chem. Soc.*, **91**, 4883 (1969).

243. K. Hofmann, R. D. Wells, H. Yajima and J. Rosenthaler, *J. Am. Chem. Soc.*, **85**, 1546 (1963).

244. K. Hofmann, H. Yajima, T. Liu and N. Yanaihara, *J. Am. Chem. Soc.*, **84**, 4481 (1962).

245. K. Hofmann, H. Yajima, T. Liu and N. Yanaihara, *J. Am. Chem. Soc.*, **84**, 4475 (1962).

246. K. Hofmann, H. Yajima and E. T. Schwartz, *J. Am. Chem. Soc.*, **82**, 3732 (1960).

247. K. Hofmann, N. Yanaihara, S. Lande and H. Yajima, *J. Am. Chem. Soc.*, **84**, 4470 (1962).

248. I. Honda, Y. Shimonishi and S. Sakakibara, *Bull. Chem. Soc. Japan*, **40**, 2415 (1967).

249. J. Honzl and J. Rudinger, *Collection Czech. Chem. Commun.*, **26**, 2332 (1961).

250. D. B. Hope and K. C. Horncastle, *J. Chem. Soc.* (**C**), 1098 (1966).

251. D. B. Hope, V. V. S. Murti and V. du Vigneaud, *J. Am. Chem. Soc.*, **85**, 3686 (1963).

251a. V. S. Hörnle, *Z. Physiol. Chem.*, **348**, 1355 (1967).

252. V. J. Hruby and V. du Vigneaud, *J. Med. Chem.*, **12**, 731 (1969).

253. R. L. Huguenin, *Helv. Chim. Acta*, **49**, 711 (1965).

254. R. L. Huguenin, *Helv. Chim. Acta*, **47**, 1934 (1964).

255. R. L. Huguenin and R. A. Boissonnas, *Helv. Chim. Acta*, **49**, 695 (1965).

256. R. L. Huguenin and R. A. Boissonnas, *Helv. Chim. Acta*, **46**, 1669 (1963).

257. R. L. Huguenin and R. A. Boissonnas, *Helv. Chim. Acta*, **45**, 1629 (1962).

258. R. L. Huguenin and R. A. Boissonnas, *Helv. Chim. Acta*, **44**, 213 (1961).

259. R. L. Huguenin and St. Guttmann, *Helv. Chim. Acta*, **48**, 1885 (1965).

260. T. A. Hylton, J. Preston and B. Weinstein, *J. Org. Chem.*, **31**, 3400 (1966).

261. K. Inouye and H. Otsuka, *J. Org. Chem.*, **27**, 4236 (1962).

262. K. Inouye, I. M. Voynick, G. R. Delpierre and J. S. Fruton, *Biochemistry*, **5**, 2473 (1966).

263. S. Inouye, S. Kakakibara and S. Akabori, *Bull. Chem. Soc. Japan*, **37**, 713 (1963).

264. K. Inouye and H. Otsuka, *J. Org. Chem.*, **26**, 2613 (1961).

265. N. Inukai, D. Nakano and M. Murakami, *Bull. Chem. Soc. Japan*, **41**, 182 (1968).

266. L. V. Ionova and E. A. Morozova, *J. Gen. Chem. USSR*, **34**, 407 (1964).

267. L. V. Ionova, D. D. Mosshukhin and E. A. Morozova, *J. Gen. Chem. USSR*, **34**, 768 (1964).

268. B. Iselin, *Helv. Chim. Acta*, **44**, 61, (1961).

269. B. Iselin and R. Schwyzer, *Helv. Chim. Acta*, **45**, 1499 (1962).

270. B. Iselin and R. Schwyzer, *Helv. Chim. Acta*, **44**, 169 (1961).

270a. "IUPAC-IUB Commission on Biochemical Nomenclature. Amino Acid Derivatives and Peptides. Tentative Rules." *Biochemistry*, **5**, 2485 (1966).

271. D. A. J. Ives, *Can. J. Chem.*, **46**, 2318 (1968).

272. N. Izumiya and M. Muraoka, *J. Am. Chem. Soc.*, **91**, 2391 (1969).
273. H. Jakubke, *Chem. Ber.*, **97**, 2816 (1964).
274. K. Janowski and C. Berse, *Can. J. Chem.*, **46**, 1835 (1968).
275. P. A. Jaquenoud, *Helv. Chim. Acta*, **48**, 1899 (1965).
276. P. A. Jaquenoud and R. A. Boisonnas, *Helv. Chim. Acta*, **45**, 1462 (1962).
277. P. A. Jaquenoud and R. A. Boisonnas, *Helv. Chim. Acta*, **44**, 113 (1961).
278. R. R. Jarabak, P. L. Bhatia and K. D. Kopple, *Biochemistry*, **2**, 958 (1963).
279. D. Jarvis, H. N. Rydon and J. A. Schofield, *J. Chem. Soc.*, 1752 (1961).
280. B. J. Johnson, *J. Chem. Soc.*, 1412 (1969).
281. B. J. Johnson and P. M. Jacobs, *J. Org. Chem.*, **33**, 4524 (1968).
281a. B. J. Johnson and D. E. Tracey, *J. Pharm. Sci.*, **58**, 1299 (1969).
281b. B. Johnson and W. P. May, *J. Pharm. Sci.*, **58**, 1568 (1969).
282. B. J. Johnson and E. G. Trask, *J. Org. Chem.*, **33**, 4521 (1968).
283. J. M. Johnson and J. A. Stock, *J. Chem. Soc.*, 3806 (1962).
284. D. S. Jones, G. W. Kenner, J. Preston and R. C. Sheppard, *J. Chem. Soc.*, 6227 (1965).
285. D. S. Jones, G. W. Kenner and R. C. Sheppard, *J. Chem. Soc.*, 4393 (1965).
286. J. H. Jones, B. Liberek and G. T. Young, *J. Chem. Soc.*, 2371 (1967).
287. E. C. Jorgensen and W. Patton, *J. Med. Chem.*, **12**, 935 (1969).
288. E. C. Jorgensen, G. C. Windridge, W. Patton and T. C. Lee, *J. Med. Chem.*, **12**, 733 (1969).
289. K. Jost, *Collection Czech. Chem. Commun.*, **31**, 2784 (1966).
290. K. Jost and J. Rudinger, *Collection Czech. Chem. Commun.*, **33**, 109 (1968).
291. K. Jost and J. Rudinger, *Collection Czech. Chem. Commun.*, **32**, 1229 (1967).
292. K. Jost and J. Rudinger, *Collection Czech. Chem. Commun.*, **26**, 2345 (1961).
293. K. Jost, J. Rudinger and F. Šorm, *Collection Czech. Chem. Commun.*, **28**, 2021 (1963).
294. K. Jost, J. Rudinger and F. Šorm, *Collection Czech. Chem. Commun.*, **28**, 1706 (1963).
295. K. Jost, J. Rudinger and F. Šorm, *Collection Czech. Chem. Commun.*, **26**, 2496 (1961).
295a. B. Kamber and W. Rittel, *Helv. Chim. Acta*, **51**, 2061 (1968).
296. T. Kaneko, I. Takeuchi and T. Inui, *Bull. Chem. Soc. Japan*, **41**, 974 (1968).
297. H. Kappeler, *Helv. Chim. Acta*, **44**, 476 (1961).
298. H. Kappeler and R. Schwyzer, *Helv. Chim. Acta*, **44**, 1136 (1961).
299. E. Kasafirek, K. Jost, J. Rudinger and F. Šorm, *Collection Czech. Chem. Commun.*, **30**, 2600 (1965).
300. E. Kasafirek, V. Rabek, J. Rudinger and F. Šorm, *Collection Czech. Chem. Commun.*, **31**, 4581 (1966).

301. T. Kato and N. Izumiya, *Bull. Chem. Soc. Japan*, **39**, 2242 (1966).
302. T. Kato, M. Kondo, M. Ohno and N. Izumiya, *Bull. Chem. Soc. Japan*, **38**, 1202 (1965).
303. T. Kato, N. Mitsuyasu, M. Waki, S. Makisumi and N. Izumiya, *Bull. Chem. Soc. Japan*, **41**, 2480 (1968).
304. P. G. Katsoyannis, *J. Am. Chem. Soc.*, **83**, 4053 (1961).
305. P. G. Katsoyannis, K. Fukuda and A. Tometsko, *J. Am. Chem. Soc.*, **85**, 1681 (1963).
306. P. G. Katsoyannis and (in part) K. Suzuki, *J. Am. Chem. Soc.*, **85**, 2659 (1963).
307. P. G. Katsoyannis and K. Suzuki, *J. Am. Chem. Soc.*, **85**, 1679 (1963).
308. P. G. Katsoyannis and K. Suzuki, *J. Am. Chem. Soc.*, **84**, 1420 (1962).
309. P. G. Katsoyannis and K. Suzuki, *J. Am. Chem. Soc.*, **83**, 4956 (1961).
310. P. G. Katsoyannis and M. Tilak, *J. Am. Chem. Soc.*, **85**, 4028 (1963).
311. P. G. Katsoyannis, K. Suzuki and A. Tometsko, *J. Am. Chem. Soc.*, **85**, 1139 (1963).
311a. P. G. Katsoyannis and A. Tometsko, *Proc. Nat. Acad. Sci.*, **55**, 1554 (1966).
312. P. G. Katsoyannis and A. Tometsko, *Biochemistry*, **55**, 1554 (1966).
313. P. G. Katsoyannis, A. M. Tometsko and C. Zalut, *J. Am. Chem. Soc.*, **89**, 4505 (1967).
314. P. G. Katsoyannis, A. M. Tometsko and C. Zalut, *J. Am. Chem. Soc.*, **88**, 5622 (1966).
315. P. G. Katsoyannis, A. M. Tometsko and C. Zalut, *J. Am. Chem. Soc.*, **88**, 5618 (1966).
316. P. G. Katsoyannis, A. M. Tometsko, C. Zalut and K. Fukuda, *J. Am. Chem. Soc.*, **88**, 5625 (1966).
316a. P. G. Katsoyannis, A. Tometsko, C. Zalut, S. Johnson and A. C. Trakatellis, *Biochemistry*, **6**, 2635, (1967).
316b. P. G. Katsoyannis, A. C. Trakatellis, S. Johnson, C. Zalut and G. Schwartz, *Biochemistry*, **6**, 2642 (1967).
316c. P. G. Katsoyannis, A. C. Trakatellis, C. Zalut, S. Johnson, A. Tometsko, G. Schwartz and J. Ginos, *Biochemistry*, **6**, 2656 (1967).
317. P. G. Katsoyannis, C. Zalut and A. M. Tometsko, *J. Am. Chem. Soc.*, **89**, 4502 (1967).
318. E. D. Kaverzneva, V. K. Zvorykina, V. V. Kiseleva and T. A. Gorokhova, *Bull. Acad. Sci. USSR*, 2079 (1967).
319. L. T. Ke, Y. T. Kung, K. Z. Wang and C. I. Niu, *Sci. Sinica (Peking)*, **13**, 1435 (1964).
320. B. Keil, J. Moravek, V. Klouha and J. Filip, *Collection Czech. Chem. Commun.*, **27**, 1687 (1962).
321. B. Keil and F. Šorm, *Collection Czech. Chem. Commun.*, **27**, 1673 (1962).
322. B. Keil, J. Zikan. L. Rexova and F. Šorm, *Collection Czech. Chem. Commun.*, **27**, 1678 (1962).
323. G. W. Kenner, J. J. Mendive and R. C. Sheppard, *J. Chem. Soc.*, 761 (1968).

324. W. Kessler and B. Iselin, *Helv. Chim. Acta*, **49**, 1330 (1966).
325. M. C. Khosla, R. R. Smeby and F. M. Bumpus, *Biochemistry*, **6**, 754 (1967).
326. H. Kienhuis, J. P. J. van der Holst and A. Verweij, *Rec. Trav. Chim.*, **88**, 592 (1969).
327. H. Kienhuis, A. Van de Linde, J. P. J. vander Holst and A. Verweij, *Rec. Trav. Chim.*, **80**, 1278 (1961).
328. M. Kinoshita and H. Klostermeyer, *Ann. Chem.*, **696**, 226 (1966).
329. M. Kinoshita and H. Zahn, *Ann. Chem.*, **696**, 234 (1966).
330. E. Klieger and H. Gibian, *Ann. Chem.*, **649**, 183 (1961).
331. E. Klieger and H. Gibian, *Ann. Chem.*, **655**, 195 (1962).
332. E. Klieger and E. Schröder, *Ann. Chem.*, **661**, 193 (1963).
333. E. Klieger, E. Schröder and H. Gibian, *Ann. Chem.*, **640**, 157 (1961).
334. D. G. Knorre and T. N. Shubina, *J. Gen. Chem. USSR*, **36**, 671 (1966).
335. P. V. Koehn and C. A. Kind, *Arch. Biochem. Biophys.*, **111**, 614 (1965).
336. J. Kolc, M. Zaoral and F. Šorm, *Collection Czech. Chem. Commun.*, **32**, 2667 (1967).
337. M. Kondo, H. Aoyagi, T. Kato and N. Izumiya, *Bull. Chem. Soc. Japan*, **39**, 2234 (1966).
338. M. Kondo and N. Izumiya, *Bull. Chem. Soc. Japan*, **40**, 1975 (1967).
339. J. Konnert and I. L. Karle, *J. Am. Chem. Soc.*, **91**, 4888 (1969).
340. H. C. Koppel, I. L. Honigberg, R. H. Springer and C. C. Cheng, *J. Org. Chem.*, **28**, 1119 (1963).
341. K. D. Kopple and D. E. Nitecki, *J. Am. Chem. Soc.*, **84**, 4457 (1962).
342. K. D. Kopple, T. Saito and M. Ohnishi, *J. Org. Chem.*, **34**, 1631 (1969).
343. J. Kovacs, M. Q. Ceprini, C. A. Dupraz and G. N. Schmit, *J. Org. Chem.*, **32**, 3696 (1967).
344. J. Kovacs and U. R. Ghatak, *J. Org. Chem.*, **31**, 119 (1966).
345. J. Kovacs, R. Giannotti and A. Kapoor, *J. Am. Chem. Soc.*, **88**, 2282 (1966).
346. J. Kovacs and B. J. Johnson, *J. Chem. Soc.*, 6777 (1965).
347. J. Kovacs, G. L. Mayers, R. H. Johnson and U. R. Ghatak, *Chem. Commun.*, 1066 (1968).
348. J. Kovacs, G. H. Schmit and B. J. Johnson, *Can. J. Chem.*, **47**, 3690 (1969).
349. A. A. Kraevskii, P. P. Purygin, L. Rudzite, Z. S. Belova and B. P. Gottikh, *Izv. Akad. Nauk SSSR, Ser. Khim.*, 378 (1968); *Chem. Abstr.*, **69**, 2596 (1968).
349a. C. L. Krumdieck and C. M. Baugh, *Biochemistry*, **8**, 1568 (1969).
350. J. Kunde and H. Zahn, *Ann. Chem.*, **646**, 137 (1961).
351. Y. T. Kung, L. T. Ke, C. T. Niu and S. C. Hu, *Sci. Sinica (Peking)*, **13**, 1245 (1964).
352. A. N. Kurtz and C. Niemann, *J. Am. Chem. Soc.*, **83**, 3309 (1961).
353. S. Kuwata and H. Watanabe, *Bull. Chem. Soc. Japan*, **38**, 676 (1965).
354. S. Lande, *J. Org. Chem.*, **27**, 4558 (1962).
355. S. Lande and R. A. Landowne, *Tetrahedron*, **22**, 3085 (1966).
356. D. A. Laufer and E. R. Blout, *J. Am. Chem. Soc.*, **89**, 1246 (1967).

356a. D. A. Laufer, T. M. Chapman, D. I. Marlborough, V. M. Vaidya and E. R. Blout, *J. Am. Chem. Soc.*, **90**, 2696 (1968).

357. H. D. Law and V. duVigneaud, *J. Am. Chem. Soc.*, **82**, 4579 (1960).

358. W. B. Lawson, E. Gross, C. M. Foltz and B. Witkop, *J. Am. Chem. Soc.*, **84**, 1715 (1962).

359. J. Leclerc and L. Benoiton, *Can. J. Chem.*, **46**, 1047 (1968).

360. R. Ledger and F. H. C. Stewart, *Australian J. Chem.*, **20**, 787 (1967).

361. R. Ledger and F. H. C. Stewart, *Australian J. Chem.*, **19**, 1729 (1966).

362. R. Ledger and F. H. C. Stewart, *Australian J. Chem.*, **18**, 1477 (1965).

363. R. Ledger and F. H. C. Stewart, *Australian J. Chem.*, **18**, 933 (1965).

364. J. Lenard and A. B. Robinson, *J. Am. Chem. Soc.*, **89**, 181 (1967).

365. M. T. Leplawy, D. S. Jones, G. W. Kenner and R. C. Sheppard, *Tetrahedron*, **11**, 39 (1960).

366. I. Levi, H. Blondal, J. W. R. Weed, A. C. Frosst, H. C. Reilly, F. A. Schmid, K. Sugiura, G. S. Tarnowski and C. C. Stock, *J. Med. Chem.*, **8**, 715 (1965).

367. S. D. Levine and M. Bodanszky, *Biochemistry*, **5**, 3441 (1966).

367a. D. Levy and F. H. Carpenter, *Biochemistry*, **6**, 3559 (1967).

368. C. H. Li, D. Chung and J. Ramachandran, *J. Am. Chem. Soc.*, **86**, 2715 (1964).

369. C. H. Li, D. Chung, J. Ramachandran and B. Gorup, *J. Am. Chem. Soc.*, **84**, 2460 (1962).

370. C. H. Li, B. Gorup, D. Chung and J. Ramachandran, *J. Org. Chem.*, **28**, 178 (1963).

371. C. H. Li, J. Meienhofer, E. Schnabel, D. Chung, T. Lo and J. Ramachandran, *J. Am. Chem. Soc.*, **83**, 4449 (1961).

372. C. H. Li, J. Ramachandran and D. Chung, *J. Am. Chem. Soc.*, **86**, 2711 (1964).

373. C. H. Li, J. Ramachandran, D. Chung and B. Gorup, *J. Am. Chem. Soc.*, **86**, 2703 (1964).

374. C. H. Li, J. Ramachandran and D. Craig, *J. Am. Chem. Soc.*, **85**, 1895 (1963).

375. C. H. Li, E. Schnabel and D. Chung, *J. Am. Chem. Soc.*, **82**, 2062 (1960).

376. B. Liberek and Z. Grzonka, *Bull. Acad. Polon. Sci.*, **12**, 367 (1964).

377. M. Liefländer, *Z. Physiol. Chem.*, **320**, 35 (1960).

378. M. A. Lipson and E. Sondheimer, *J. Org. Chem.*, **29**, 2392 (1964).

379. Y. Liwschitz, E. Nemes and E. Levi, *J. Org. Chem.*, **27**, 3555 (1962).

380. Y. Liwschitz, A. Singerman and S. Sokoloff, *J. Chem. Soc.*, 1843 (1968).

381. G. Losse and G. Bachmann, *Chem. Ber.*, **97**, 2671 (1964).

381a. G. Losse, W. Grenzer and K. Neubert, *Z. Chem.*, **8**, 21 (1968).

382. G. Losse, H. Jeschkeit and R. Hohn, *Ann. Chem.*, **676**, 222 (1964).

383. G. Losse, H. Jeschkeit and D. Knopf, *Chem. Ber.*, **97**, 1789 (1964).

384. G. Losse, H. Jeschkeit and W. Langenbeck, *Chem. Ber.*, **96**, 204 (1963).

385. V. G. Losse, H. Jeschkeit and H. Zaschke, *Ann. Chem.*, **676**, 232 (1964).

386. G. Losse and G. Müller, *Chem. Ber.*, **94**, 2768 (1961).

387. G. Losse and H. Raue, *Chem. Ber.*, **101**, 1532 (1968).

388. G. Losse and H. Weddige, *Ann. Chem.*, **636**, 144 (1960).
389. G. Losse and W. Zönnchen, *Ann. Chem.*, **636**, 140 (1960).
390. J. H. Loudfoot and Y. M. Chan, *Can. J. Chem.*, **45**, 1505 (1967).
391. J. H. Loudfoot and J. E. Kruger, *Can. J. Chem.*, **41**, 2462 (1963).
392. K. Lübke, R. Hempel and E. Schröder, *Experientia*, **21**, 84 (1965).
393. K. Lübke and E. Schroder, *Ann. Chem.*, **692**, 237 (1966).
394. V. K. Lübke and E. Schroder, *Ann. Chem.*, **681**, 250, (1965).
395. K. Lübke, E. Schröder, R. Schmiechen and H. Gibian, *Ann. Chem.*, **679**, 195 (1964).
396. K. Lübke and E. Schröder, *Ann. Chem.*, **665**, 205 (1963).
396a. M. Manning, *J. Am. Chem. Soc.*, **90**, 1348 (1968).
397. M. Manning and V. duVigneaud, *Biochemistry*, **4**, 1884 (1965).
397a. G. W. H. A. Mansveld, H. Hindriks and H. C. Beyerman, *Colloq. Inst. Centre Nat. Rech. Sci.*, No. 175, 197 (1968); *Chem. Abstr.*, No. 11, 391 (1969).
398. F. Marchiori, R. Rocchi, L. Morader, G. Vidali and E. Scoffone, *J. Chem. Soc.*, 89 (1967).
399. F. Marchiori, R. Rocchi and E. Scoffone, *Gazz. Chim. Ital.*, **93**, 834 (1963).
400. F. Marchiori, R. Rocchi, G. Vidali, A. Tamburro and E. Scoffone *J. Chem. Soc.*, 81 (1967).
401. F. Marcus and J. F. Morrison, *Biochem. J.*, **92**, 429 (1964).
401a. A. Marglin and R. B. Merrifield, *J. Am. Chem. Soc.*, **88**, 5051 (1966).
402. J. P. Marsh, Jr. and L. Goodman, *Can. J. Chem.*, **44**, 799 (1966).
403. K. B. Mathur, H. Klostermeyer and H. Zahn, *Z. Physiol. Chem.*, **346**, 60 (1966).
404. A. B. Mauger and R. Wade, *J. Chem. Soc.*, (**C**), 1406 (1966).
405. R. H. Mazur, *Can. J. Chem.*, **40**, 1098 (1962).
406. R. H. Mazur and J. M. Schlatter, *J. Org. Chem.*, **28**, 1025 (1963).
407. K. Medzihradszky, V. Bruckner, M. Kajtar, M. Low, S. Bajusz and L. Kisfaludy, *Acta Chim. Acad. Sci. Hung.*, **30**, 105 (1962).
408. J. Meienhofer, *Ann. Chem.*, **692**, 231 (1966).
409. J. Meienhofer, *Ann. Chem.*, **691**, 218 (1966).
410. J. Meienhofer, *J. Org. Chem.*, **32**, 1143 (1967).
411. J. Meienhofer, *Z. Naturforsch.*, **19b**, 114 (1964).
412. J. Meienhofer and C. H. Li, *J. Am. Chem. Soc.*, **84**, 2434 (1962).
412a. J. Meienhofer and Y. Sano, *J. Am. Chem. Soc.*, **90**, 2996 (1968).
413. J. Meienhofer and V. duVigneaud, *J. Am. Chem. Soc.*, **82**, 6336 (1960).
414. J. Meienhofer and V. duVigneaud, *J. Am. Chem. Soc.*, **82**, 2279 (1960).
415. R. B. Merrifield, *J. Am. Chem. Soc.*, **85**, 2149 (1963).
416. R. B. Merrifield, *Biochemistry*, **3**, 1385 (1964).
417. R. B. Merrifield, *J. Org. Chem.*, **29**, 3100 (1964).
417a. R. Merrifield, J. Steward and N. Jernberg, *Anal. Chem.*, **38**, 1905 (1966).
418. M. P. Mertes and Q. Gilman, *J. Med. Chem.*, **10**, 965 (1967).
419. F. Michael and H. Haneke, *Chem. Ber.*, **95**, 1009 (1962).
420. H. B. Milne and F. H. Carpenter, *J. Org. Chem.*, **33**, 4476 (1968).

421. H. B. Milne, S. L. Razniak, R. P. Bayer and D. W. Fish, *J. Am. Chem. Soc.*, **82**, 4582 (1960).

421a. T. Mizoguchi, K. Shigezane and N. Takamura, *Chem. Pharm. Bull.* (Tokyo), **17**, 411 (1969).

422. A. T. Moore, H. N. Rydon and M. J. Smithers, *J. Chem. Soc.*, 2349 (1966).

423. J. S. Morley, *J. Chem. Soc.*, 2410 (1967).

424. J. S. Morley and J. M. Smith, *J. Chem. Soc.*, 726 (1968).

425. L. Moroder, F. Marchiori, R. Rocchi, A. Fontana and E. Scoffone, *J. Am. Chem. Soc.*, **91**, 3921 (1969).

426. C. W. Mosher, R. H. Iwamoto, E. M. Acton and L. Goodman, *J. Med. Chem.*, **7**, 650 (1964).

427. T. MuKaiyama, M. Ueki, H. Maruyama and R. Matsueda, *J. Am. Chem. Soc.*, **90**, 4490 (1968).

428. E. Muñoz, J. M. Ghuysen, H. Leyh-Bouille, J. F. Petit, H. Heymann, E. Bricas and P. Lefrancier, *Biochemistry*, **5**, 3748 (1966).

429. W. J. McGahren and M. Goodman, *Tetrahedron*, **23**, 2017 (1967).

430. W. M. McGregor and F. H. Carpenter, *J. Org. Chem.*, **26**, 1849 (1961).

431. R. Nagata, M. Waki, M. Kondo, H. Agoyagi, T. Kato, S. Makisumi and N. Izumiya, *Bull. Chem. Soc. Japan*, **40**, 963 (1967).

432. A. M. el Naggar and N. A. Poddubnaya, *J. Gen. Chem. USSR*, **36**, 1606 (1966).

433. V. A. Najjar and R. B. Merrifield, *Biochemistry*, **5**, 3765 (1966).

434. G. H. L. Nefkens, G. I. Tesser and R. J. F. Nivard, *Rec. Trav. Chim.*, **82**, 941 (1963).

435. W. J. P. Neish and A. Rylett, *Tetrahedron*, **19**, 2031 (1963).

436. H. Nesvadba, H. Bachmayer and H. Michl, *Monatsh. Chem.*, **96**, 1125 (1965).

437. H. Nesvadba, J. Honzl and J. Rudinger, *Collection Czech. Chem. Commun.*, **28**, 1691 (1963).

438. E. D. Nicolaides, M. K. Craft and H. A. DeWald, *J. Med. Chem.*, **6**, 525 (1963).

439. E. D. Nicolaides and H. A. DeWald, *J. Org. Chem.*, **26**, 3872 (1961).

440. E. D. Nicolaides and H. A. DeWald, *J. Org. Chem.*, **28**, 1926 (1963).

440a. E. Nicolaides, H. DeWald, R. Westland, M. Lipnik and J. Posler, *J. Med. Chem.*, **11**, 74 (1968).

441. E. Nicolaides and M. Lipnik, *J. Med. Chem.*, **9**, 958 (1966).

442. C. Nicot, J. van Heijenoort, P. Lefrancier and E. Bricas, *J. Org. Chem.*, **30**, 3746 (1965).

443. H. Niedrich, *Chem. Ber.*, **100**, 3273 (1967).

444. H. Niedrich, *Chem. Ber.*, **97**, 2527 (1964).

445. H. Niedrich, *Chem. Ber.*, **96**, 2774 (1963).

446. K. Noda, H. Okai, T. Dato and N. Izumiya, *Bull. Chem. Soc. Japan*, **41**, 401 (1968).

447. A. Normand and L. Berlinguet, *Can. J. Chem.*, **45**, 1551 (1967).

448. S. J. Norton, C. G. Skinner and W. Shive, *J. Org. Chem.*, **26**, 1495 (1961).

449. Y. Obata and R. Kitasawa, *Agr. Biol. Chem. (Tokyo)*, **28**, 624 (1964).
449a. M. Ohno and C. B. Anfinsen, *J. Am. Chem. Soc.*, **89**, 5994 (1967).
449b. M. Ohno, À. Eastlake, D. A. Ontjes and C. B. Anfinsen, *J. Am. Chem. Soc.*, **91**, 6842 (1969).
450. M. Ohno and N. Izumiya, *J. Am. Chem. Soc.*, **88**, 376 (1966).
451. M. Ohno, T. Kato, S. Makisumi and N. Izumiya, *Bull. Chem. Soc. Japan*, **39**, 1738 (1966).
452. M. Ohno, T. Kato, N. Mitsuyasu, M. Waki, S. Makisumi and N. Izumiya, *Bull. Chem. Soc. Japan*, **40**, 204 (1967).
453. M. Okamoto, S. Kimoto, T. Oshima, Y. Kinomura, K. Kawasaki and H. K. Yajima, *Chem. Pharm. Bull. (Tokyo)*, **15**, 1618 (1967).
454. W. Oelofsen and C. H. Li, *J. Org. Chem.*, **33**, 1581 (1968).
455. W. Oelofsen and C. H. Li, *J. Am. Chem. Soc.*, **88**, 4254 (1966).
455a. G. S. Omenn and C. B. Anfinsen, *J. Am. Chem. Soc.*, **90**, 6571 (1968).
456. M. A. Ondetti, *J. Med. Chem.*, **6**, 10 (1963).
457. M. A. Ondetti, A. Deer, J. T. Sheehan, J. Plušcec and O. Kocy, *Biochemistry*, **7**, 4069 (1968).
458. M. A. Ondetti, V. L. Narayanan, M. vonSaltza, J. T. Sheehan, E. F. Sabo and M. Bodanszky, *J. Am. Chem. Soc.*, **90**, 4711 (1968).
459. M. A. Ondetti and P. L. Thomas, *J. Am. Chem. Soc.*, **87**, 4373 (1965).
459a. P. J. Oriel and E. R. Blout, *J. Am. Chem. Soc.*, **88**, 2041 (1966).
460. J. Oró and C. L. Guidry, *Arch. Biochem. Biophys.*, **93**, 166 (1961).
461. H. Otsuka, K. Inouye, M. Kanayama and F. Shinozaki, *Bull. Chem. Soc. Japan*, **39**, 882 (1966).
462. H. Otsuka, K. Inouye, F. Shinozake and M. Kanayama, *J. Biochem. (Tokyo)*, **58**, 512 (1965).
463. H. Otsuka, K. Inouye, F. Shinozaki and M. Kanayama, *Bull. Chem. Soc. Japan*, **39**, 1171 (1966).
463a. Y. A. Ovchinnikov, A. A. Kiryushkin and I. V. Kozhevnikova, *J. Gen. Chem. USSR*, **38**, 2551 (1968).
463b. Y. A. Ovchinnikov, A. A. Kiryushkin and I. V. Kozhevnikova, *J. Gen. Chem. USSR*, **38**, 2546 (1968).
464. Y. A. Ovchinnikov, A. A. Kiryushkin and M. M. Shemyakin, *J. Gen. Chem. USSR*, **36**, 637 (1966).
465. R. Paul and G. W. Anderson, *J. Am. Chem. Soc.*, **82**, 4596 (1960).
466. R. Paul and G. W. Anderson, *J. Org. Chem.*, **27**, 2094 (1962).
467. R. Paul, G. W. Anderson and F. M. Callahan, *J. Org. Chem.*, **26**, 3347 (1961).
468. W. K. Park, R. R. Smeby and F. M. Bumpus, *Biochemistry*, **6**, 3458 (1967).
469. A. Patchornik and M. Sokolovsky, *J. Am. Chem. Soc.*, **86**, 1206 (1964).
470. R. A. Payne and C. H. Stammer, *J. Org. Chem.*, **33**, 2421 (1968).
470a. M. E. Perel'son, G. P. Syrova, Y. N. Sheinker and A. P. Prokopenki, *Chem. Nat. Compds. (USSR)*, **3**, 290 (1967).
471. H. Peter, M. Brugger, J. Schreiber and A. Eschenmoser, *Helv. Chim. Acta*, **46**, 577 (1963).

472. G. R. Pettit and A. K. Das Gupta, *Can. J. Chem.*, **45**, 567 (1967).
473. G. R. Pettit, A. K. Das Gupta and R. L. Smith, *Can. J. Chem.*, **44**, 2023 (1966).
474. G. R. Pettit and S. K. Das Gupta, *Can. J. Chem.*, **45**, 1600 (1967).
475. G. R. Pettit and S. K. Das Gupta, *Can. J. Chem.*, **45**, 1561 (1967).
476. G. R. Pettit and S. K. Das Gupta, *J. Chem. Soc.* (**C**), 1208 (1968).
477. G. R. Pettit, R. L. Smith, A. K. Das Gupta and J. L. Occolowitz, *Can. J. Chem.*, **45**, 501 (1967).
478. G. R. Pettit, R. L. Smith and H. Klinger, *J. Med. Chem.*, **10**, 145 (1967).
479. I. Phocas, C. Yovanidis, I. Photaki and L. Zervas, *J. Chem. Soc.*, 1506 (1967).
480. I. Photaki, *J. Am. Chem. Soc.*, **88**, 2292 (1966).
481. I. Photaki and V. Bardakos, *J. Am. Chem. Soc.*, **87**, 3489 (1965).
482. I. Photaki, V. Bardakos, A. W. Lake and G. Lowe, *J. Chem. Soc.*, 1860 (1968).
483. I. Photaki and V. duVigneaud, *J. Am. Chem. Soc.*, **87**, 908 (1965).
484. R. E. Plapinger, M. M. Nachlas, M. L. Seligman and A. M. Seligman, *J. Org. Chem.*, **30**, 1781 (1965).
485. K. Poduška, *Collection Czech. Chem. Commun.*, **31**, 2955 (1966).
486. K. Poduška and J. Rudinger, *Collection Czech. Chem. Commun.*, **31**, 2938 (1966).
486a. K. P. Polzhofer, *Tetrahedron Letters*, 2305 (1969).
486b. K. P. Polzhofer, *Tetrahedron*, **25**, 4127 (1969).
487. Z. Pravda, K. Poduska and K. Bláha, *Collection Czech. Chem. Commun.*, **29**, 2626 (1964).
488. P. Quitt, R. O. Studer and K. Vogler, *Helv. Chim. Acta*, **47**, 166 (1963).
489. P. Quitt, R. O. Studer and K. Vogler, *Helv. Chim. Acta*, **46**, 1715 (1963).
490. K. Rager, W. Kemmler and P. Schauder, *Z. Physiol. Chem.*, **350**, 717 (1969).
491. S. Rajappa, K. Nagarajan and V. S. Iyer, *Tetrahedron*, **23**, 4805 (1967).
492. J. Ramachandran, D. Chung and C. H. Li, *J. Am. Chem. Soc.*, **87**, 2696 (1965).
493. J. Ramachandran and C. H. Li, *J. Am. Chem. Soc.*, **87**, 2691 (1965).
494. J. Ramachandran and C. H. Li, *J. Org. Chem.*, **28**, 173 (1963).
495. J. Ramachandran and C. H. Li, *J. Org. Chem.*, **27**, 4006 (1962).
496. J. A. Reader and P. W. G. Smith, *J. Chem. Soc.*, 3479 (1965).
497. C. Ressler, *J. Am. Chem. Soc.*, **82**, 1641 (1960).
498. C. Ressler and D. V. Kashelikar, *J. Am. Chem. Soc.*, **88**, 2025 (1966).
499. B. Riniker and R. Schwyzer, *Helv. Chim. Acta*, **44**, 677 (1961).
500. B. Riniker and R. Schwyzer, *Helv. Chim. Acta*, **44**, 674 (1961).
501. B. Riniker and R. Schwyzer, *Helv. Chim. Acta*, **44**, 658 (1961).
502. B. Riniker and R. Schwyzer, *Helv. Chim. Acta*, **44**, 685 (1961).
503. W. Rittel, *Helv. Chim. Acta*, **45**, 2464 (1962).
504. C. W. Roberts and D. H. Haigh, *J. Org. Chem.*, **27**, 3375 (1962).
505. R. Rocchi, F. Marchiori, L. Moroder, G. Borin and E. Scoffone, *J. Am. Chem. Soc.*, **91**, 3927 (1969).

506. R. Rocchi, F. Marchiori, A. Scatturin and E. Scoffone, *J. Chem. Soc.*, 86 (1967).

507. R. Rocchi, F. Marchiori and E. Scoffone, *Gazz. Chim. Ital.*, **93**, 823 (1963); [*Chem. Abstr.*, **60**, 4246 (1964)]; *Gazz. Chim. Ital.*, **93**, 834 (1963); [*Chem. Abstr.*, **60**, 4246 (1964)].

508. R. Rocchi, L. Moroder, F. Marchiori, E. Ferrarese and E. Scoffone, *J. Am. Chem. Soc.*, **90**, 5885 (1968).

509. R. Rocchi, A. Scatturin, L. Moroder, F. Marchiori, A. M. Tamburro and E. Scoffone, *J. Am. Chem. Soc.*, **91**, 492 (1969).

510. R. Roeske, *J. Org. Chem.*, **28**, 1251 (1963).

511. M. Rothe, K. D. Steffen and I. Rothe, *Angew. Chem.*, **4**, 356 (1965).

512. J. Rudinger, O. V. Kesarev, P. Poduška, B. T. Pickering, R. E. J. Dyball, D. R. Ferguson and W. R. Ward, *Experientia*, **25**, 680 (1969).

513. J. Rudinger, K. Poduška and M. Zaoral, *Collection Czech. Chem. Commun.*, **25**, 2202 (1960).

514. D. W. Russell, *J. Chem. Soc.*, 4664 (1965).

514a. T. S. Ryabova, Z. A. Shabarova and M. A. Prokof'ev, *Vestn. Mosk. Univ.*, Ser. 11, Khim., **20**, 89 (1965); *Chem. Abstr.*, **63**, 11696 (1965).

514b. J. Rychlik, S. Chlader and J. Zemlicka, *Biochim. Biophys. Acta*, **138**, 640 (1967).

515. H. N. Rydon and J. Šavrda, *J. Chem. Soc.*, 4246 (1965).

516. T. S. Safonova and S. I. Sergrievskaya, *J. Gen. Chem. USSR*, **34**, 919 (1964).

517. S. Sakakibara and M. Fujino, *Bull. Chem. Soc. Japan*, **39**, 947 (1966).

518. S. Sakakibara and N. Inukai, *Bull. Chem. Soc. Japan*, **39**, 1567 (1966).

519. S. Sakakibara and M. Itoh, *Bull. Chem. Soc. Japan*, **40**, 656 (1967).

520. S. Sakakibara, Y. Kishida, R. Nishizawa and Y. Shimonishi, *Bull. Chem. Soc. Japan*, **41**, 438 (1968).

521. S. Sakakibara, N. Nakamizo, Y. Kishida and S. Yoshimura, *Bull. Chem. Soc. Japan*, **41**, 1477 (1968).

522. F. Sakiyama, *Bull. Chem. Soc. Japan*, **35**, 1943 (1962).

523. Y. Sakurai and M. Aoshima, *Chem. Pharm. Bull.* (Tokyo), **10**, 979 (1962).

524. E. Sandrin and R. A. Boissonnas, *Helv. Chim. Acta*, **47**, 417 (1964).

525. E. Sandrin and R. A. Boissonnas, *Helv. Chim. Acta*, **46**, 1637 (1963).

526. R. Sarges and B. Witkop, *J. Am. Chem. Soc.*, **87**, 2027 (1965).

527. R. Sarges and B. Witkop, *J. Am. Chem. Soc.*, **87**, 2020 (1965).

528. R. Sarges and B. Witkop, *J. Am. Chem. Soc.*, **87**, 2011 (1965).

529. C. Schattenkerk and E. Havinga, *Rec. Trav. Chim.*, **84**, 653 (1965).

530. C. Schattenkerk, G. H. Visser, K. E. T. Kerling and E. Havinga, *Rec. Trav. Chim.*, **83**, 679 (1964).

531. C. Schattenkerk, G. H. Visser, K. E. T. Kerling and E. Havinga, *Rec. Trav. Chim.*, **83**, 677 (1964).

532. I. Schechter and A. Berger, *Biochemistry*, **5**, 3362 (1966).

533. K. A. Schellenberg, *J. Org. Chem.*, **28**, 3259 (1963).

534. E. Schnabel, *Ann. Chem.*, **696**, 220 (1966).

535. E. Schnabel, *Ann. Chem.*, **688**, 238 (1965).
536. E. Schnabel, *Ann. Chem.*, **674**, 218 (1964).
537. E. Schnabel, *Ann. Chem.*, **673**, 171 (1964).
538. E. Schnabel, *Ann. Chem.*, **667**, 179 (1963).
539. E. Schnabel, *Ann. Chem.*, **667**, 171 (1963).
540. E. Schnabel, *Ann. Chem.*, **622**, 181 (1959).
541. E. Schnabel, *Peptides*, 71 (1965).
542. E. Schnabel, *Z. Naturforsch.*, **19b**, 120 (1964).
542a. E. Schnabel, H. Herzog, P. Hoffmann, E. Klauke and I. Ugi, *Angew. Chem.*, **7**, 380 (1968).
543. E. Schnabel, H. Klostermeyer, J. Dahlmans and H. Zahn, *Ann. Chem.*, **707**, 227 (1967).
544. E. Schnabel and C. H. Li, *J. Am. Chem. Soc.*, **82**, 4576 (1960).
545. F. Schneider, *Z. Physiol. Chem.*, **332**, 38 (1963).
546. C. H. Schneider and V. duVigneaud, *J. Am. Chem. Soc.*, **84**, 3005 (1962).
547. G. Schollmann, *Z. Physiol. Chem.*, **348**, 1629 (1967).
548. G. Schreiber, W. Schreiber and W. Lautsch, *Chem. Ber.*, **98**, 2765 (1965).
549. E. Schröder, *Ann. Chem.*, **711**, 227 (1968).
550. E. Schröder, *Ann. Chem.*, **692**, 241 (1966).
551. E. Schröder, *Ann. Chem.*, **691**, 232 (1966).
552. E. Schröder, *Ann. Chem.*, **680**, 132 (1964).
553. E. Schröder, *Ann. Chem.*, **679**, 207 (1964).
554. E. Schröder, *Ann. Chem.*, **673**, 220 (1964).
555. E. Schröder, *Ann. Chem.*, **673**, 186 (1964).
556. E. Schröder, *Ann. Chem.*, **670**, 127 (1963).
557. E. Schröder, *Experientia*, **20**, 39 (1964).
558. E. Schröder and H. Gibian, *Ann. Chem.*, **673**, 176 (1964).
559. E. Schröder and H. Gibian, *Ann. Chem.*, **656**, 190 (1962).
560. E. Schröder and H. Gibian, *Ann. Chem.*, **649**, 168 (1961).
560a. E. Schröder and R. Hempel, *Experientia*, **20**, 1 (1964).
561. E. Schröder and E. Klieger, *Ann. Chem.*, **673**, 208 (1964).
562. E. Schröder and E. Klieger, *Ann. Chem.*, **673**, 196 (1964).
563. E. Schröder and K. Lubke, *Experientia*, **20**, 19 (1964).
564. E. Schröder and K. Lubke, *Ann. Chem.*, **655**, 211 (1962).
565. E. Schröder, H. S. Petras and E. Klieger, *Ann. Chem.*, **679**, 221 (1964).
566. H. Schulz, *Chem. Ber.*, **99**, 3425 (1966).
567. H. Schulz and V. du Vigneaud, *J. Med. Chem.*, **10**, 1037 (1967).
568. H. Schulz and V. du Vigneaud, *J. Med. Chem.*, **9**, 647 (1966).
569. H. Schwarz and F. M. Bumpus, *J. Am. Chem. Soc.*, **81**, 890 (1959).
570. R. Schwyzer, J. P. Carrion, B. Gorup, H. Nolting and A. T. Kyl, *Helv. Chim. Acta*, **47**, 441 (1964).
571. R. Schwyzer, A. Costopanagiotis and P. Sieber, *Helv. Chim. Acta*, **46**, 870 (1963).
572. R. Schwyzer and H. Dietrich, *Helv. Chim. Acta*, **44**, 2003 (1961).
573. R. Schwyzer, B. Iselin, H. Kappeler, B. Riniker, W. Rittel and H. Zuber, *Helv. Chim. Acta*, **46**, 1975 (1963).

574. R. Schwyzer and H. Kappeler, *Helv. Chim. Acta*, **46**, 1550 (1963).

575. R. Schwyzer and H. Kappeler, *Helv. Chim. Acta*, **44**, 1991 (1961).

576. R. Schwyzer and W. Rittel, *Helv. Chim. Acta*, **44**, 159 (1961).

577. R. Schwyzer, W. Rittel and A. Costopanagiotis, *Helv. Chim. Acta*, **45**, 2473 (1962).

578. R. Schwyzer, B. Riniker and H. Kappeler, *Helv. Chim. Acta*, **46**, 1541 (1963).

579. R. Schwyzer and P. Sieber, *Helv. Chim. Acta*, **49**, 134 (1966).

580. R. Schwyzer and P. Sieber, *Helv. Chim. Acta*, **43**, 1910 (1960).

581. E. Scoffone, F. Marchiori, R. Rocchi, G. Vidali, A. Tamburro, A. Scatturin and A. Marzotto, *Tetrahedron Letters*, 943 (1966).

582. E. Scoffone, R. Rocchi, F. Marchiori, A. Marzotto, A. Scatturin, A. Tamburro and G. Vidali, *J. Chem. Soc.*, 606 (1967).

583. E. Scoffone, R. Rocchi, F. Marchiori, L. Moroder, A. Marzotto and A. M. Tamburro, *J. Am. Chem. Soc.*, **89**, 5450 (1967).

584. E. Scoffone, R. Rocchi, G. Vidali, A. Scatturin and F. Marchiori, *Gazz. Chim. Ital.*, **94**, 743 (1964).

585. P. M. Scopes, K. B. Walshaw, M. Welford and G. T. Young, *J. Chem. Soc.*, 782 (1965).

586. T. Scott-Burden and A. O. Hawtrey, *Tetrahedron Letters*, 4831 (1967).

586a. E. P. Semkin, N. D. Gafurova and L. A. Shchukina, *Khim. Prir. Soedin*, **3**, 220 (1967); *Chem. Abstr.*, **68**, 4864 (1968).

586b. E. P. Semkin, A. P. Smirnova and L. A. Shchukina, *J. Gen. Chem. USSR*, **37**, 1169 (1967), *Chem. Abstr.*, **68**, 2928 (1968).

587. A. B. Sen and M. S. Yajnik, *J. Indian Chem. Soc.*, **42**, 145 (1965).

588. J. H. Seu, R. R. Semby and F. M. Bumpus, *J. Am. Chem. Soc.*, **84**, 4948 (1962).

589. Y. Shalitin and S. A. Bernhard, *J. Am. Chem. Soc.*, **88**, 4711 (1966).

590. S. Shankman, S. Makineni and V. Gold, *Arch. Biochem. Biophys.*, **100**, 431 (1963).

591. J. C. Sheehan and G. D. Daves, Jr., *J. Org. Chem.*, **29**, 2006 (1964).

592. J. C. Sheehan and V. J. Grenda, *J. Am. Chem. Soc.*, **84**, 2417 (1962).

593. J. C. Sheehan and D. N. McGregor, *J. Am. Chem. Soc.*, **84**, 3000 (1962).

594. J. C. Sheehan, J. Preston and P. A. Cruickshank, *J. Am. Chem. Soc.*, **87**, 2492 (1965).

595. M. M. Shemyakin, N. A. Aldanova, E. I. Vinogradova and M. Y. Feigina, *Bull. Acad. Sci. USSR*, 2074 (1967).

596. M. M. Shemyakin, Y. A. Ovchinnikov, V. T. Ivanov and A. A. Kiryushkin, *Tetrahedron*, **19**, 995 (1963).

597. M. M. Shemyakin, Y. A. Ovchinnikov, A. A. Kiryushkin and V. T. Ivanov, *Bull. Acad. Sci. USSR*, 1584 (1965).

598. M. M. Shemyakin, E. I. Vinogradova, M. Y. Feigina, N. A. Aldanova, N. F. Loginova, I. D. Ryabova and I. A. Pavlenko, *Experientia*, **21**, 548 (1965).

599. J. E. Shields, *Biochemistry*, **5**, 1041 (1966).

600. J. E. Shields and F. H. Carpenter, *J. Am. Chem. Soc.*, **83**, 3066 (1961).

601. J. E. Shields, W. H. McGregor and F. H. Carpenter, *J. Org. Chem.*, **26**, 1491 (1961).

602. J. E. Shields and H. Renner, *J. Am. Chem. Soc.*, **88**, 2304 (1966).

603. Y. Shimonishi, S. S. Sakakibara and S. Akabori, *Bull. Chem. Soc. Japan*, **35**, 1966 (1962).

604. W. Siedel, K. Sturm and R. Geiger, *Chem. Ber.*, **96**, 1436 (1963).

605. I. Z. Siemion, *Roczniki Chem.*, **38**, 811 (1964).

606. D. M. Sivanandaiah, R. R. Smeby and F. M. Bumpus, *Biochemistry*, **5**, 1224 (1966).

607. N. A. Smart, G. T. Young and M. W. Williams, *J. Chem. Soc.*, 3902 (1960).

607a. A. R. H. Smith, L. J. Goad and T. W. Goodwin, *Chem. Commun.*, 1259 (1969).

608. H. E. Smith and S. L. Cook, *J. Med. Chem.*, **7**, 680 (1964).

608a. N. I. Sokolova, R. K. Ledneva, P. P. Purygin and Z. A. Shabarova, *Khim. Prir. Soedin.*, **3**, 290 (1967); *Chem. Abstr.*, **68**, 7595 (1968).

608b. N. I. Sokolova, V. I. Mel'nikova, A. A. Shabarova and M. A. Prokof'ev, *Vestn. Mosk. Univ.*, Ser. 11, **21**, 119 (1966); *Chem. Abstr.*, **66**, 5276 (1967).

609. M. Sokolovsky, T. Sadeh and A. Parchornik, *J. Am. Chem. Soc.*, **86**, 1212 (1964).

610. M. Sokolovsky, M. Wilchek and A. Patchornik, *J. Am. Chem. Soc.*, **86**, 1202 (1964).

611. H. Z. Sommer, C. Scher, S. Bien, G. Olsen, J. K. Chakrabarti and O. M. Freidman, *J. Med. Chem.*, **9**, 84 (1966).

612. E. Sondheimer, *J. Org. Chem.*, **30**, 665 (1965).

613. G. L. Southard, G. S. Brooke and J. M. Pettee, *Tetrahedron Letters*, 3505 (1969).

614. A. W. Spears and H. Tieckelmann, *J. Org. Chem.*, **26**, 1498 (1961).

615. G. C. Stelakatos, *J. Am. Chem. Soc.*, **83**, 4222 (1961).

616. G. C. Stelakatos, A. Paganou and L. Zervas, *J. Chem. Soc.* (**C**), 1191 (1966).

617. C. L. Stevens, T. S. Sulkowski and M. E. Munk, *J. Org. Chem.*, **31**, 4014 (1966).

618. F. H. C. Stewart, *Australian J. Chem.*, **21**, 2831 (1968).

619. F. H. C. Stewart, *Australian J. Chem.*, **21**, 2543 (1968).

620. F. H. C. Stewart, *Australian J. Chem.*, **21**, 1935 (1968).

621. F. H. C. Stewart, *Australian J. Chem.*, **21**, 1639 (1968).

622. F. H. C. Stewart, *Australian J. Chem.*, **21**, 1327 (1968).

623. F. H. C. Stewart, *Australian J. Chem.*, **21**, 477 (1968).

624. F. H. C. Stewart, *Australian J. Chem.*, **20**, 2243 (1967).

625. F. H. C. Stewart, *Australian J. Chem.*, **20**, 1991 (1967).

626. F. H. C. Stewart, *Australian J. Chem.*, **20**, 365 (1967).

627. F. H. C. Stewart, *Australian J. Chem.*, **19**, 2373 (1966).

628. F. H. C. Stewart, *Australian J. Chem.*, **19**, 2361 (1966).

629. F. H. C. Stewart, *Australian J. Chem.*, **19**, 1503 (1966).

630. F. H. C. Stewart, *Australian J. Chem.*, **19**, 1511 (1966).
631. F. H. C. Stewart, *Australian J. Chem.*, **19**, 1067 (1966).
632. F. H. C. Stewart, *Australian J. Chem.*, **19**, 489 (1966).
633. F. H. C. Stewart, *Australian J. Chem.*, **18**, 1877 (1965).
634. F. H. C. Stewart, *Australian J. Chem.*, **18**, 1699 (1965).
635. F. H. C. Stewart, *Australian J. Chem.*, **18**, 1095 (1965).
636. F. H. C. Stewart, *Australian J. Chem.*, **18**, 1089 (1965).
637. F. H. C. Stewart, *Australian J. Chem.*, **18**, 887 (1965).
638. J. M. Stewart and J. D. Young, "Solid Phase Peptide Synthesis," W. H. Freeman and Co., San Francisco, Calif., 1969.
639. W. Stoffel and L. C. Craig, *J. Am. Chem. Soc.*, **83**, 145 (1961).
640. R. O. Studer, *Helv. Chim. Acta*, **46**, 421 (1963).
641. R. O. Studer and W. Lergier, *Helv. Chim. Acta*, **48**, 460 (1965).
642. R. O. Studer, P. Quitt, E. Böhni and K. Vogler, *Monatsh. Chem.*, **96**, 461 (1965).
643. R. O. Studer and V. du Vigneaud, *J. Am. Chem. Soc.*, **82**, 1499 (1960).
644. K. Sturm, R. Geiger and W. Siedel, *Chem. Ber.*, **97**, 1197 (1964).
645. K. Sturm, R. Geiger and W. Siedel, *Chem. Ber.*, **96**, 609 (1963).
646. K. Suzuki, *Chem. Pharm. Bull. (Tokyo)*, **14**, 909 (1966).
647. K. Suzuki and T. Abiko, *Chem. Pharm. Bull. (Tokyo)*, **16**, 1997 (1968).
648. K. Suzuki and T. Abiko, *Chem. Pharm. Bull. (Tokyo)*, **15**, 1508 (1967).
649. K. Suzuki and T. Abiko, *Chem. Pharm. Bull. (Tokyo)*, **15**, 1212 (1967).
650. K. Suzuki and T. Abiko, *Chem. Pharm. Bull. (Tokyo)*, **15**, 536 (1967).
651. K. Suzuki and T. Abiko, *Chem. Pharm. Bull. (Tokyo)*, **14**, 1017 (1966).
652. K. Suzuki, T. Abiko, and M. Asaka, *Chem. Pharm. Bull. (Tokyo)*, **14**, 217 (1966).
653. K. Suzuki, M. Asaka, and T. Abiko, *Chem. Pharm. Bull. (Tokyo)*, **14**, 211 (1966).
654. J. M. Swan, *Australian J. Chem.*, **18**, 411 (1965).
655. M. Szekerke, J. Császár and V. Bruckner, *Acta Chim. Acad. Sci. Hung.*, **46**, 379 (1965).
656. M. Szekerke, R. Wade and F. Bergel, *J. Chem. Soc.*, 1907 (1965).
656a. H. Takashima, W. Fraefel and V. du Vigneaud, *J. Am. Chem. Soc.*, **91**, 1682 (1969).
657. H. Takashima, V. du Vigneaud and R. B. Merrifield, *J. Am. Chem. Soc.*, **90**, 1323 (1968).
658. E. Taschner, A. Chimiak, J. F. Biernat, C. Wasielewski and T. Sokolowska, *Ann. Chem.*, **633**, 188 (1963).
659. E. Taschner, B. Rzeszotarska and L. Lubiewska, *Ann. Chem.*, **690**, 12 (1965).
660. E. Taschner, C. Wasielewski, T. Sokolowska and J. F. Biernat, *Ann. Chem.*, **646**, 127 (1961).
661. J. Taylor-Papadimitriou, C. Yovanidis, A. Paganou and L. Zervas, *J. Chem. Soc.*, 1830 (1967).
662. G. I. Tesser and R. J. F. Nivard, *Rec. Trav. Chim.*, **83**, 53 (1964).
663. G. I. Tesser and W. Rittel, *Rec. Trav. Chim.*, **88**, 553 (1969).

664. G. I. Tesser and R. Schwyzer, *Helv. Chim. Acta*, **49**, 1013 (1966).

665. D. A. Tewksbury and M. A. Stahmann, *Arch. Biochem. Biophys.*, **105**, 527 (1964).

666. D. M. Theodoropoulos and J. S. Fruton, *Biochemistry*, **1**, 933 (1962).

667. D. Theodoropoulos and J. Gazopoulos, *J. Org. Chem.*, **27**, 2091 (1962).

668. D. Theodoropoulos, I. L. Schwartz and R. Walter, *Biochemistry*, **6**, 3927 (1967).

669. D. Theodoropoulos and I. Souchleris, *J. Org. Chem.*, **31**, 4009 (1966).

670. D. Theodoropoulos and J. Tsangaris, *J. Org. Chem.*, **29**, 2272 (1964).

671. P. J. Thomas, M. Havranek and J. Rudinger, *Collection Czech. Chem. Commun.*, **32**, 1767 (1967).

672. M. A. Tilak and C. S. Hollinden, *Tetrahedron Letters*, 391 (1969).

673. K. Yueh-Ting, Du Yu-Cang, H. Wei-teh, C. Chan-chin, Ke Lin-Tsung, H. Shih-Chuan, J. Rong-Qing, C. Shang-Quan, N. Ching-I, H. Je-zen, C. Wei-Chun, C. Ling-Ling, L. Hong-Shueh, W. Yu, L. Teh-Pei, C. Ai-Hsech, L. Chung-Hsi, S. Pu-Tao, Y. Yuen-Hwa, T. Kar-Lo and H. Chi-Yi, *Sci. Sinica (Peking)*, **15**, 544 (1966).

674. G. T. Tritsch and D. W. Woolley, *J. Am. Chem. Soc.*, **82**, 2787 (1960).

675. M. Vafina, V. Derevitskaya and N. Kochetkov, *Bull. Acad. Sci. USSR*, 1777 (1965).

676. D. F. Veber, R. Hirschmann and R. G. Denkewalter, *J. Org. Chem.*, **34**, 753 (1969).

676a. S. I. Virovets, V. F. Martynov and M. I. Titov, *J. Gen. Chem. USSR*, **38**, 2264 (1968).

676b. V. du Vigneaud, *J. Med. Chem.*, **12**, 1035 (1969).

677. G. H. Visser, C. Schattenkerk, K. E. T. Kerling and E. Havinga, *Rec. Trav. Chim.*, **83**, 684 (1964).

678. G. Vita, L. Monti and R. Angelucci, *J. Med. Chem.*, **7**, 468 (1964).

679. G. P. Vlasov, Y. V. Mitin and M. M. Kroton, *Dokl. Aka. Nauk SSSR*, **168**, 1069 (1966), Engl. Transl., p. 594.

680. K. Vogler, P. Lanz and W. Lergier, *Helv. Chim. Acta*, **45**, 561 (1962).

681. K. Vogler, P. Lanz, W. Lergier and W. Haefely, *Helv. Chim. Acta*, **49**, 390 (1966).

682. K. Vogler, R. O. Studer, P. Lanz, W. Lergier and E. Bohni, *Experientia*, **20**, 365 (1964).

683. K. Vogler, R. O. Studer and W. Lergier, *Helv. Chim. Acta*, **44**, 1495 (1961).

684. K. Vogler, R. O. Studer, W. Lergier and P. Lanz, *Helv. Chim. Acta*, **48**, 1407 (1965).

685. O. Wacker and M. Lieflander, *Z. Physiol. Chem.*, **335**, 255 (1964).

686. K. B. Walshaw and G. T. Young, *J. Chem. Soc.*, 786 (1965).

687. R. Walter and W. Y. Chan, *J. Am. Chem. Soc.*, **89**, 3892 (1967).

688. R. Walter and I. L. Schwartz, *J. Biol. Chem.*, **24**, 5500 (1966).

689. R. Walter and V. du Vigneaud, *J. Am. Chem. Soc.*, **87**, 4192 (1965).

690. R. Walter and V. du Vigneaud, *Biochemistry*, **5**, 3720 (1966).

691. E. Walton, J. O. Rodin, C. H. Stammer and F. W. Holly, *J. Org. Chem.*, **26**, 1657 (1961).

691a. Su-sun Wang and R. B. Merrifield, *J. Am. Chem. Soc.*, **91**, 6488 (1969).

692. W. R. Waterfield, *J. Chem. Soc.*, 2731 (1963).

693. F. Weygand, D. Hoffmann and E. Wuensch, *Z. Naturforsch.*, **21**, 426 (1966).

694. F. Weygand and K. Hunger, *Chem. Ber.*, **95**, 7 (1962).

695. F. Weygand and K. Hunger, *Chem. Ber.*, **95**, 1 (1962).

696. F. Weygand, W. König, A. Prox and K. Burger, *Chem. Ber.*, **99**, 1443 (1966).

697. F. Weygand, A. Prox and W. König, *Chem. Ber.*, **99**, 1451 (1966).

698. F. Weygand, A. Prox and W. König, *Chem. Ber.*, **99**, 1446 (1966).

699. F. Weygand, A. Prox, M. A. Tilak, D. Hoffter and H. Fritz, *Chem. Ber.*, **97**, 1024 (1964).

700. F. Weygand and W. Steglich, *Chem. Ber.*, **93**, 2983 (1960).

701. F. Weygand, W. Steglich, F. Fraunberger, P. Pietta and J. Schmid, *Chem. Ber.*, **101**, 923 (1968).

702. O. H. Wheeler and C. Reyes-Zamora, *Can. J. Chem.*, **47**, 160 (1969).

703. T. Wieland and W. Kahle, *Ann. Chem.*, **691**, 212 (1966).

703a. T. Wieland, G. Luben, H. Ottenheym, J. Faesel, J. DeVries, A. Prox and J. Schmid, *Angew. Chem.*, **7**, 204 (1968). (Eng.)

703b. T. Wieland and I. Sangl, *Ann. Chem.*, **671**, 160 (1964).

704. T. Wieland and R. Sarges, *Ann. Chem.*, **658**, 181 (1962).

705. M. Wilchek, A. Frensdorff and M. Sela, *Arch. Biochem. Biophys.*, **113**, 742 (1966).

706. M. Wilchek and A. Parchornik, *J. Org. Chem.*, **29**, 1629 (1964).

707. M. Wilchek and A. Parchornik, *J. Org. Chem.*, **28**, 1874 (1963).

708. M. Wilchek, C. Zioudrou and A. Patchornik, *J. Org. Chem.*, **31**, 2865 (1966).

709. M. W. Williams and G. T. Young, *J. Chem. Soc.*, 881 (1963).

710. E. Winterberger, H. Tuppy and E. Stoklaska, *Monatsh. Chem.*, **91**, 577 (1960).

711. Y. Wolman, P. M. Gallop, A. Patchornik and A. Berger, *J. Am. Chem. Soc.*, **84**, 1889 (1962).

712. R. B. Woodward, R. A. Olofson and H. Mayer, *Tetrahedron*, Suppl. 8, Part I, 321 (1966).

713. R. B. Woodward and D. J. Woodman, *J. Org. Chem.*, **34**, 2742 (1969).

714. D. W. Woolley, *J. Am. Chem. Soc.*, **88**, 2309 (1966).

715. E. Wunsch, *Chem. Ber.*, **98**, 797 (1965).

716. E. Wunsch, *Z. Physiol. Chem.*, **332**, 295 (1963).

717. E. Wunsch, *Z. Physiol. Chem.*, **332**, 288 (1963).

718. E. Wunsch and F. Drees, *Chem. Ber.*, **100**, 816 (1967).

719. E. Wunsch and F. Drees, *Chem. Ber.*, **99**, 110 (1966).

720. E. Wunsch, F. Drees and J. Jentsch, *Chem. Ber.*, **98**, 803 (1965).

721. E. Wunsch and H-G. Heidrich, *Z. Physiol. Chem.*, **332**, 300 (1963).

722. E. Wunsch, H-G. Heidrich and W. Grassmann, *Chem. Ber.*, **97**, 1818 (1964).

723. E. Wunsch and J. Jentsch, *Chem. Ber.*, **97**, 2490 (1964).

724. E. Wunsch and A. Trinkl, *Z. Physiol. Chem.*, **345**, 193 (1966).

725. E. Wunsch and G. Wendlberger, *Chem. Ber.*, **101**, 326 (1968).

726. E. Wunsch and G. Wendlberger, *Chem. Ber.*, **100**, 820 (1967).

727. E. Wunsch and G. Wendlberger, *Chem. Ber.*, **100**, 160 (1967).

728. E. Wunsch and G. Wendlberger, *Chem. Ber.*, **97**, 2503 (1964).

729. E. Wunsch and A. Zwick, *Z. Physiol. Chem.*, **333**, 108 (1963).

730. E. Wunsch and A. Zwick, *Chem. Ber.*, **99**, 105 (1966).

731. E. Wunsch and A. Zwick, *Chem. Ber.*, **99**, 101 (1966).

732. E. Wunsch and A. Zwick, *Chem. Ber.*, **97**, 3312 (1964).

733. E. Wunsch and A. Zwick, *Chem. Ber.*, **97**, 3305 (1964).

734. E. Wunsch and A. Zwick, *Chem. Ber.*, **97**, 2497 (1964).

735. E. Wunsch, A. Zwick and A. Fontana, *Chem. Ber.*, **101**, 341 (1968).

736. E. Wunsch, A. Zwick and E. Jaeger, *Chem. Ber.*, **101**, 336 (1968).

737. E. Wunsch, A. Zwick and G. Wendlberger, *Chem. Ber.*, **100**, 173 (1967).

738. H. Yajima and K. Kawasaki, *Chem. Pharm. Bull.* (Tokyo), **16**, 1379 (1968).

739. H. Yajima, K. Kawasaki, Y. Kinomura, T. Oshima, S. Kimoto and M. Okamoto, *Chem. Pharm. Bull.* (Tokyo), **16**, 1342 (1968).

740. H. Yajima, K. Kawasaki, M. Koida and S. Lande, *Chem. Pharm. Bull.* (Tokyo), **14**, 884 (1966).

741. H. Yajima, Y. Kinomura, T. Oshima and Y. Okada, *Chem. Pharm. Bull.* (Tokyo), **15**, 1922 (1967).

742. H. Yajima and K. Kubo, *J. Am. Chem. Soc.*, **87**, 2039 (1965).

743. H. Yajima, K. Kubo and Y. Kinomure, *Chem. Pharm. Bull.* (Tokyo), **15**, 504 (1967).

744. H. Yajima, K. Kubo and Y. Okada, *Chem. Pharm. Bull.* (Tokyo), **13**, 1326 (1965).

745. H. Yajima, K. Kubo, T. Oshima, K. Hano and M. Koida, *Chem. Pharm. Bull.* (Tokyo), **14**, 775 (1966).

746. H. Yajima, O. Nishimura, K. Kawasaki and Y. Okada, *Chem. Pharm. Bull.* (Tokyo), **15**, 854 (1967).

746a. H. Yajima, Y. Okada, Y. Kinomura and H. Minami, *J. Am. Chem. Soc.*, **90**, 527 (1968).

747. H. Yajima, Y. Okada, Y. Kinomura and E. Seto, *Chem. Pharm. Bull.* (Tokyo), **15**, 270 (1967).

748. H. Yajima, Y. Okada, T. Oshima and S. Lande, *Chem. Pharm. Bull.* (Tokyo), **14**, 707 (1966).

749. D. Yamashiro, H. L. Aanning, L. A. Branda, W. D. Cash, V. V. S. Murti and V. du Vigneaud, *J. Am. Chem. Soc.*, **90**, 4141 (1968).

750. D. Yamashiro, D. Gillessen and V. du Vigneaud, *Biochemistry*, **5**, 3711 (1966).

751. D. Yamashiro, D. Gillessen and V. du Vigneaud, *J. Am. Chem. Soc.*, **88**, 1310 (1966).

752. N. Yanaihara, M. Sekiya, K. Takagi, H. Kato, M. Ichimura and T. Nagao, *Chem. Pharm. Bull.* (Tokyo), **15**, 110 (1966).

753. H. Zahn and D. Brandenburg, *Ann. Chem.*, **692**, 220 (1966).

754. H. Zahn and H. R. Falkenburg, *Ann. Chem.*, **636**, 117 (1960).

754a. H. Zahn, B. Gutte, E. F. Pfeiffer and J. Ammon, *Ann. Chem.*, **691**, 225 (1966).

755. H. Zahn, J. Kunde and R. Zabel, *Ann. Chem.*, **663**, 177 (1963).

756. H. Zahn and N. H. LaFrance, *Ann. Chem.*, **630**, 37 (1960).

757. H. Zahn and N. LaFrance, *Ann. Chem.*, **630**, 26 (1960).

758. V. H. Zahn, J. Meienhofer and H. Klostermeyer, *Z. Naturforsch.*, **19b**, 2 (1964).

759. H. Zahn and A. Meissner, *Ann. Chem.*, **636**, 132 (1960).

760. H. Zahn and H. G. Otten, *Ann. Chem.*, **653**, 139 (1962).

761. H. Zahn and W. Pätzold, *Chem. Ber.*, **96**, 2566 (1963).

761a. H. Zahn and H. Schussker, *Ann. Chem.*, **641**, 176 (1961).

762. H. Zahn, H. Schussker and R. Zabel, *Z. Physiol. Chem.*, **340**, 249 (1965).

763. H. Zahn and W. Sroka, *Ann. Chem.*, **706**, 230 (1967).

764. H. Zahn and R. Zabel, *Ann. Chem.*, **659**, 163 (1962).

765. M. Zaoral, *Collection Czech. Chem. Commun.*, **30**, 1853 (1965).

766. M. Zaoral, E. Kasafirek, J. Rudinger and F. Šorm, *Collection Czech. Chem. Commun.*, **30**, 1869 (1965).

767. M. Zaoral, J. Kolc, F. Korenczki, V. P. Černěckij and F. Šorm, *Collection Czech. Chem. Commun.*, **32**, 843 (1967).

768. M. Zaoral, J. Kolc and F. Šorm, *Collection Czech. Chem. Commun.*, **32**, 1250 (1967).

769. M. Zaoral, J. Kolc, and F. Šorm, *Collection Czech. Chem. Commun.*, **32**, 1242 (1967).

770. M. Zaoral and F. Šorm, *Collection Czech. Chem. Commun.*, **31**, 310 (1966).

771. M. Zaoral and F. Šorm, *Collection Czech. Chem. Commun.*, **31**, 90 (1966).

772. M. Zaoral and F. Šorm, *Collection Czech. Chem. Commun.*, **30**, 2812 (1965).

773. J. Zemlicka and S. Chladek, *Collection Czech. Chem. Commun.*, **31**, 3775 (1966).

774. L. Zervas, D. Borovas and E. Gazis, *J. Am. Chem. Soc.*, **85**, 3660 (1963).

775. L. Zervas and C. Hamalidis, *J. Am. Chem. Soc.*, **87**, 99 (1965).

776. L. Zervas, I. Photaki, A. Cosmatos and D. Borovas, *J. Am. Chem. Soc.*, **87**, 4922 (1965).

777. L. Zervas, I. Photaki and N. Ghelis, *J. Am. Chem. Soc.*, **85**, 1337 (1963).

777a. L. Zervas, I. Photaki and I. Phocas, *Chem. Ber.*, **101**, 3332 (1968).

778. A. Zhuze, K. Jošt, E. Kasafirek and J. Rudinger, *Collection Czech. Chem. Commun.*, **29**, 2648 (1964).

779. A. Zilkha and N. Lerman, *Can. J. Chem.*, **42**, 1226 (1964).

Appendix

The following journals were cited in the preparation of Parts 1-3.

Acta Chem. Scand.
Acta Chim. Acad. Sci. Hung.
Agr. Biol. Chem. (Tokyo)
Anal. Chem.
Angew. Chem.
Ann. Chem.
Arch. Biochem. Biophys.
Arkiv. Kemi
Australian J. Chem.
Biochemistry
Biochem. J.
Biochim. Biophys. Acta
Bull. Acad. Polon. Sci.
Bull. Acad. Sci. USSR
Bull. Chem. Soc. Japan
Bull. Soc. Chim. France
Can. J. Chem.
Cancer Res.
Chem. Abstr.
Chem. Ber.
Chem. Commun.
Chem. Ind. (London)
Chem. Nat. Compds. (USSR)
Chem. Pharm. Bull. (Tokyo)

Collection Czech. Chem. Commun.
Colloq. Inst. Centre Nat. Rech. Sci.
Dokl. Akad. Nauk SSSR
Experientia
Fortschr. Chem. Forsch.
Gazz. Chim. Ital.
Helv. Chim. Acta
Izv. Akad. Nauk SSSR
J. Am. Chem. Soc.
J. Biochem. (Tokyo)
J. Biol. Chem.
J. Chem. Soc.
J. Gen. Chem. USSR
J. Indian Chem. Soc.
J. Med. Chem.
J. Mol. Biol.
J. Org. Chem.
J. Org. Mass Spec.
J. Pharm. Sci.
Khim. Prir. Soedin.
Monatsh. Chem.
Naturwissenschaften
Rec. Trav. Chim.
Roczniki Chem.

Sci. Sinica (Peking)
Steroids
Tetrahedron
Tetrahedron Letters

Vestn. Mosk. Univ.
Z. Naturforsch.
Z. Chem.
Z. Physiol. Chem.